STRUCTURAL ANALYSIS
OF METAMORPHIC
TECTONITES

STRUCTURAL ANALYSIS
OF METAMORPHIC
TECTONITES

FRANCIS J. TURNER AND LIONEL E. WEISS

University of California, Berkeley

McGRAW-HILL BOOK COMPANY, INC.

New York   San Francisco   Toronto   London

STRUCTURAL ANALYSIS OF METAMORPHIC TECTONITES

PREFACE

In 1930 Bruno Sander, in his now classic *Gefügekunde der Gesteine*, presented a comprehensive account of the fabric of deformed rocks, new geometric methods for its analysis, and a broad philosophy for its kinematic interpretation. Since then, and especially since the Second World War, Sander's methods have been applied with varying degrees of success in attempts to elucidate the structure of metamorphic rocks in many countries. Outstandingly successful among such attempts are studies, still in progress, on the nature and geometry of repeated folding in the Highlands of Scotland. New possibilities have been opened in the United States by extensive programs of experimental deformation of rocks and minerals, stimulated initially by a committee of the National Science Foundation under the chairmanship of Mrs. E. B. Knopf. The time is now ripe to take stock anew of concepts and methods relating to the nature and significance of the structure or fabric of naturally deformed rocks and the procedures best suited to its analysis. This is the subject of this book. Following a general introduction it falls into three parts: the first describes the tectonite fabric and the methods devised for its analysis on all scales; the second provides a background of relevant stress-strain theory and experimental data; and the third part—necessarily tentative and especially open to subsequent revision—is concerned with the possible kinematic and dynamic interpretations to be placed upon the structural data.

The book is written for graduate students and geologists familiar with the broad concepts and methods of field geology, structural geology, and petrology. Structural analysis is supplementary to conventional field and microscopic study of deformed rocks. It can be expected to reveal the geometric properties of structures resulting from deformation, and thus to provide data for speculation on the dynamics and kinematics of the deformation process. But it is no substitute for stratigraphic and broad structural investigation. Much of the subject matter, especially that relating to interpretation of fabrics, is controversial. For clarity we have stated our opinions in the first person, even at the risk of appearing dogmatic; but all such opinions are tentative and open to future revision.

As in all works on structural analysis the geometric data are analyzed with the aid of equal-area projections. The technique and the use of the projection are fully described in Part I. Most of the projections and corresponding orientation diagrams throughout the book are of uniform size.

No comprehensive bibliography is appended. Instead we have made numerous references to works of the classic writers—especially Sander—and to recent publications with a preference for those written in English. These have been selected to illustrate and amplify the concepts and data summarized in this book.

Among the many who have stimulated and actively assisted us we gratefully thank the following: Professor Sander and Mrs. Knopf for continued encouragement and critical discussion over many years; D. T. Griggs, J. W. Handin, I. Y. Borg, and their associates for cooperation and criticism in the experimental field; M. S. Paterson for stimulus and help with respect to the significance of symmetry, and especially for critical reading of Chap. 7; D. B. McIntyre who introduced us to the possibilities of statistical study in the metamorphic terrane of the Scottish Highlands; various colleagues, notably I. Y. Borg, J. M. Christie, D. Flinn, H. C. Heard, and G. Oertel, for generous permission to cite unpublished data; the John Simon Guggenheim Memorial Foundation for financial aid enabling us to visit classic regions of metamorphism abroad; and the National Science Foundation (Projects G 3732, G 16316, G 10227) for continued support in studies of the fabrics of experimentally and naturally deformed rocks.

Francis J. Turner
Lionel E. Weiss

CONTENTS

INTRODUCTION

CHAPTER 1

SCOPE OF STRUCTURAL ANALYSIS

HISTORICAL BACKGROUND

For over a century geologists have mapped and recorded the more conspicuous structural features of naturally deformed rocks and discussed their possible dynamic significance. Attention has been focused especially on planar structures—variously termed *schistosity, cleavage,* or *foliation*—and on the obvious tendency for certain minerals of foliated rocks, such as micas and amphiboles, to show some degree of parallel alignment—in modern terminology a state of preferred orientation. Schistosity has been attributed by some writers[1] to the influence of a perpendicular compressive stress, by others[2] to shear on the schistosity surfaces. Geologists of the Wisconsin school[3] have identified "flow cleavage" with the plane of maximum strain in the deformed body. There has been a good deal of speculation as to the relative roles of such processes as recrystallization under pressure,[4] or rotation of tabular bodies in a plastically strained matrix[5] in the evolution of preferred orientation of micas and amphiboles in schistose rocks. During the decades spanning the turn of the century there was little unanimity of opinion and some controversy on such matters. But it had become clear that many metamorphic terranes are characterized by great regularity in orientation of foliation and linear structures. Some corresponding regularity in the deforming process was implied. Moreover widespread simple geometric relationships came to be recognized between foliation (cleavage) and bedding in foliated and folded rocks. These

---

[1] D. Sharpe, On slaty cleavage, *Geol. Soc. London Quart. Jour.*, vol. 5, pp. 111–115, 1849; H. C. Sorby, On the theory of slaty cleavage, *Philos. Mag.*, vol. 12, pp. 127–129, 1856; F. Becke, Über Mineralabstand und Struktur der kristallinischen Schiefer, *Akad. Wiss. Wien Denkschr.*, vol. 75, pp. 37–40, 1913; A. Harker, *Metamorphism*, pp. 153–155, 193–195, Methuen, London, 1932.

[2] G. Becker, Finite homogeneous strain, flow and rupture in rocks, *Geol. Soc. America Bull.*, vol. 4, pp. 13–90, 1893; Current theories of slaty cleavage, *Am. Jour. Sci.*, ser. 4, vol. 24, pp. 1–17, 1907.

[3] C. K. Leith, Rock cleavage, *U.S. Geol. Surv. Bull. 239*, pp. 112–116, 1905; C. K. Leith and W. J. Mead, *Metamorphic Geology*, pp. 117–179, Holt, New York, 1915.

[4] Becke, *op. cit.*

[5] Sorby, *op. cit.*

relationships have been explored, clarified, and successfully used to solve structural problems.[6]

Between 1911 and the Second World War, the study of deformed rocks was revolutionized by new methods and concepts developed in Austria, by B. Sander and W. Schmidt.[7] These were comprehensively set out in 1930 and revised and amplified after the war.[8] Sander's work is the basis of the modern science of structural petrology. It was introduced to English-speaking geologists in 1933 by E. B. Knopf.[9] Sander's method is essentially a statistical analysis of the orientation and mutual geometric relationships of all measurable structural elements of the rock in some particular domain. Some structural elements—bedding, cleavage, fold axes, lineations, etc.—are measured in the field; others, such as long axes of hornblende prisms, {001} cleavage of mica flakes, or optic axes of quartz grains, are measured in the laboratory. Many individual elements of each kind are measured; their attitudes are plotted on a suitable projection, and any tendency for regular orientation is apparent in the cumulative plot. Sander and his followers have demonstrated that a high degree of geometric order commonly pervades a body of deformed rock. This order has found expression in the concept of a tectonite fabric. More particularly the orientation patterns of the individual elements, whether macroscopic or microscopic, tend to conform to a common symmetry. Sander's emphasis on symmetry as the fundamental property of a naturally deformed rock is perhaps his most original and significant contribution to structural geology. His interpretation of rock structure—necessarily a speculative field—is based on the assumption that the symmetry of the structure is influenced by the respective symmetries of structural anisotropy in the parent rock and of the forces, stresses, and internal movements involved in deformation.

Many of the methods and ideas presented in this book are essentially those of Sander. Some of his ideas have here been modified in the light of recent experimental and field studies on rock deformation; others have been rejected. Illustrative examples include many new ones drawn from

[6] E.g., W. J. Mead, Studies for students: folding, rock flowage and foliate structures, *Jour. Geology*, vol. 48, pp. 1007–1021, 1940; G. Wilson, The relationship of slaty cleavage and kindred structures to tectonics, *Geologists' Assoc. Proc.*, vol. 62, pp. 263–302, 1946; M. P. Billings, *Structural Geology*, 2d ed., pp. 345–351, Prentice-Hall, Englewood Cliffs, N.J., 1958.

[7] If possible the student should read the classic introductory paper: B. Sander, Über Zusammenhänge zwischen Teilbewegungen und Gefüge in Gesteinen, *Tschermaks mineralog. petrog. Mitt.*, vol. 30, pp. 281–314, 1911.

[8] B. Sander, *Gefügekunde der Gesteine*, Springer, Berlin, Vienna, 1930; *Einführung in die Gefügekunde der geologischen Körper*, Springer, Berlin, Vienna, Pt. I, 1948, Pt. II, 1950.

[9] E. B. Knopf, Petrotectonics, *Am. Jour. Sci.*, vol. 25, pp. 433–470, 1933. See also E. B. Knopf and E. Ingerson, Structural petrology, *Geol. Soc. America Mem. 6*, 1938.

publications in English. While we do not claim to have mastered completely Sander's philosophy, his profound influence on this presentation will be obvious to any reader. However, for any views or concepts misinterpreted during translation from Sander's writings or erroneously attributed to Sander, we take full responsibility.

Of increasing importance in modern structural analysis of deformed rocks are concepts relating to the geometric properties of folds and to the persistence of structure in the direction of fold axes. These were developed especially by geologists of the Swiss school,[10] and were introduced to English-speaking geologists by D. B. McIntyre who used them to elucidate the structural relationship between contiguous Moinian and Dalradian rocks in a small sector of the Scottish Highlands.[11] Much earlier F. C. Phillips[12] had employed Sander's techniques to clarify the kinematic significance of lineation and accompanying orientation of mica and quartz in Moinian rocks over a much wider area. Stimulated by such studies and by the superb tradition of orthodox structural mapping long established by the Highland school of geologists under the Scottish Geological Survey, geologists of Imperial College, London, led first by H. H. Read and later by J. Sutton, have combined intensive mapping and statistical analysis in the Highlands with conspicuous success. From their work is emerging a uniquely comprehensive picture of deep-seated metamorphism and repeated deformation in a sedimentary pile and its underlying basement. For this reason in discussing analysis on the field scale we have drawn freely from studies published by the Imperial College school.[13] These emphasize the geometric properties of folds (both simple and complex), foliation, and lineation, rather than preferred orientation of mineral grains.

The interpretive side of structural analysis has been influenced to a growing degree by the results of experimental studies of rock deformation at temperatures and pressures consistent with natural environments of metamorphism. Most of these studies, initiated largely through the influence of E. B. Knopf,[14] have been pursued in the United States. A

[10] E.g., E. Argand, Les Nappes de recouvrement des Alpes pennines et leurs prolongements structuraux, *Matériaux Carte géol. Suisse*, n.s., 31, 1911; E. Wegmann, Beispiele tektonischer Analysen des Grundgebirges in Finnland, *Comm. géol. Finlande Bull.*, vol. 87, no. 8, 1929.

[11] D. B. McIntyre, The tectonics of the area between Grantown and Tomintoul (mid-Strathspey), *Geol. Soc. London Quart. Jour.*, vol. 107, pp. 1–22, 1951.

[12] F. C. Phillips, A fabric study of some Moine schists and associated rocks, *Geol. Soc. London Quart. Jour.*, vol. 93, pp. 581–620, 1937.

[13] E.g., J. G. Ramsay, Superimposed folding at Loch Monar, Inverness-shire and Ross-shire, *Geol. Soc. London Quart. Jour.*, vol. 113, pp. 221–308, 1958; J. Sutton and J. Watson, Structures in the Caledonides between Loch Duich and Glenelg, Northwest Highlands, *Geol. Soc. London Quart. Jour.*, vol. 114, pp. 231–257, 1959.

[14] E.g., E. B. Knopf, Study of experimentally deformed rocks, *Science*, vol. 103, pp. 99–103, 1946.

program of experimental deformation, concentrating at first upon marble, calcite, and quartz, was started by D. T. Griggs at Harvard and continued after the Second World War at the Institute of Geophysics of the University of California. For the past decade a parallel and complementary program, exploring the behavior of other rocks such as dolomite and quartz sand, has been carried on by J. Handin and associates at the Shell research laboratories at Houston, Texas. From these investigations has accrued a mass of information on such topics as strength, ductility, creep, and mechanisms of flow of minerals and rocks, evolution of preferred orientation patterns, and relations between stress, strain, and rock fabrics. Our picture of the genesis of tectonite fabrics has been clarified and broadened; and at the same time we have gained a clearer perception of how structural analysis of tectonites—especially on the microscopic scale—may be applied to problems of metamorphic deformation. Certain aspects of the interpretive philosophy of the Austrian school, such as the significance of fabric symmetry, have been confirmed and strengthened. Others, especially those relating to mechanisms responsible for preferred orientation of minerals in tectonites, have received no experimental confirmation and must be abandoned.

Structural analysis as developed by Sander has always combined field with microscopic investigation. Today there is a greater emphasis than thirty years ago on folds and related foliations and lineations as observed in the field. Analysis of preferred orientation of tectonite minerals is a further refinement which can clarify deductions based on field data and which makes it possible to correlate mineralogical and structural evolution of tectonites. The picture of progressive deformation that so emerges must be consistent with experimentally tested behavior of minerals and rocks under geologically significant conditions of high confining pressures and temperatures and slow rates of strain.

STRUCTURAL ANALYSIS

Definition and Purpose. The field of study with which this book is concerned is known in German as *Gefügekunde der Gesteine*. This has been variously translated into English as *petrofabrics*, *structural petrology*, and *structural analysis*. The first two of these terms now unfortunately carry a connotation of microscopic study. Such is not implied by Sander who views all rock bodies, regardless of size, as isotropic or anisotropic units whose internal structural elements commonly have a regular configuration in space. One aim of the structural geologist is to explore and interpret this regularity of structure within units ranging in size from an aggregate of a few hundred mineral grains to a major portion of an orogenic zone.

In this book *structural analysis* is synonymous with Sander's *Gefüge-*

kunde der Gesteine. It involves two philosophically distinct procedures. First is the study and description of a rock body in its present state—a study as free as possible from inference and extrapolation, except to the extent imposed by limitations of poor exposure in the field. Then comes genetic interpretation of the descriptive data, an attempt to reconstruct the structural evolution of the body in question.

It is emphasized that structural analysis of deformed rocks is complementary to stratigraphic investigation and other conventional geologic procedures. In the Highlands of Scotland, for example, orthodox mapping followed by the brilliant structural syntheses of Peach and Horne, Bailey, and others has revealed a broad picture of prolonged sedimentation and subsequent Caledonian deformation and metamorphism. Structural analysis in the same region is now filling in the details of a deformational history of hitherto unsuspected complexity. Ultimately the stratigraphic and structural history of the whole of this sector of the Caledonian orogen will be revised and modified in the light of this newer work.

Factors in Structural Analysis. The structural complexity of deformed rocks derives in part from the nature of the initial rock—igneous, sedimentary, or metamorphic—and in part from the deformation process. The principal factors concerned are as follows:

1. Internal structural order and correlated physical properties of the initial rock body
2. External forces and surface tractions acting upon the body during deformation
3. Internal stresses resulting from reaction of the body to external forces
4. Displacements, strains, rotations, and differential movements of different domains within the body, by which stresses become eliminated or reduced to some value below a flow threshold
5. Internal structural order and correlated physical properties of the rock body after deformation

Sander[15] emphasized the necessity of visualizing these contributing factors separately, and of drawing a clear distinction between the observed geometric and physical properties of a rock body (item 5 above) and their genetic interpretation in terms of factors 1 to 4. The geometric data of a deformed rock mass collectively constitute a property analogous to the symmetry and structure of a crystal. Different observers, working on the same body of rock, should obtain identical reproducible geometric data. Interpretation, for example, reconstruction of a picture of internal movements or of external forces concerned in deformation,

[15] Sander, *op. cit.*, p. 2, 1930.

necessarily is more speculative. Interpretations of the same geometric data by different geologists, even in the light of the same experimentally confirmed theories of flow and deformation, may be widely different.

Geometric, Kinematic, and Dynamic Analysis. *General Statement.* The geometric data of deformation may be interpreted either kinematically or dynamically. Physicists distinguish clearly between such interpretations. Thus Clerk Maxwell, referring to motion of a system, wrote as follows:[16]

> We have hitherto been considering the motion of a system in its purely geometrical aspect. We have shown how to study and describe the motion of such a system, however arbitrary, without taking into account any of the conditions of motion which arise from mutual action between bodies.
> The theory of motion treated in this way is called Kinematics. When mutual action between bodies is taken into account, the science of motion is called Kinetics, and when special attention is paid to force as the cause of motion, it is called Dynamics.

From geometric data the geologist can expect to learn a good deal about the relative movements of different domains within a deformed body. These may be expressed in terms of purely kinematic concepts— strains, rotations, translations, and so on—without taking account of physical factors operating between the domains concerned. Fortunately structural features inherited in distorted or modified form from the parent mass (folded beds, deformed oolites, etc.) commonly furnish markers from which much may be inferred as to the kinematics of deformation. Dynamic interpretation of geologic data is generally more uncertain. The physical state of a rock mass under conditions of flow during metamorphism is most imperfectly known, so that although a pattern of flow may be deduced kinematically, it is generally somewhat hazardous to attempt reconstruction of forces and stresses concerned.

Complete structural analysis of a body of deformed rock thus falls into three phases—geometric, kinematic, and dynamic. These are discussed below in order of decreasing certainty regarding the concepts on which they are based.

Geometric, or Descriptive, Analysis. Geometric analysis comprises direct measurement and observation of the geometric and physical properties of the deformed body. Only geometric properties are necessary if subsequent analysis is to be purely kinematic; but for later dynamic analysis other physical properties such as elasticity and ductility become significant. Ideally geometric analysis is descriptive and free from inference.

Kinematic Analysis. From the data of geometric analysis an attempt is made to reconstruct movements—strains, rotations, translations, and

---

[16] J. Clerk Maxwell, *Matter and Motion*, p. 26, Dover, New York.

so on—that took place within the body during deformation.   Such kinematic analyses can be made in two ways:[17]

1. The geometric features of a deformed body can be interpreted directly in terms of kinematic concepts on the empirical assumption that the nature of the geometric order of the body reflects the geometric order of the differential displacements, rotations, and strains that must be present during deformation of a real polycrystalline body.   These relative motions Sander collectively designates the *movement picture* of the deformation (page 367).   It is in the evaluation of the movement picture that symmetry principles are of greatest importance.
2. The observed final state of a deformed body is compared with some assumed initial state, and a path of kinematic development is proposed.   But even from the same observations and the same assumptions regarding parent states more than one kinematic reconstruction is possible.   For example, a plunging recumbent fold may develop along any of at least three alternative paths from sedimentary beds assumed to have been initially horizontal and planar:

   a. A fold forms about a horizontal axis which subsequently becomes tilted.
   b. The beds are first tilted and then folded about a plunging axis.
   c. The fold and the axial plunge develop simultaneously in a single deformation.

The validity of a kinematic analysis of this second kind depends on the soundness of assumptions regarding the initial state.   Strain may be estimated with confidence from the shape of deformed fossils of a well-known species.   It is reasonable to assume that strained oolites were once spherical, less so to assume that deformed pebbles were initially spherical, and so on.   Many kinds of layering and foliation in metamorphic rocks were almost certainly planar in the first instance; and inherited sedimentary bedding must once have been substantially horizontal.

Dynamic (Including Kinetic) Analysis.   The aim of dynamic analysis is to reconstruct stresses within a geologic body and "external" or "impressed" forces and surface tractions or body forces in reaction to which the internal stresses developed.   Analysis can profitably be applied only to a body with well-defined margins and with an internal structure differing from that of adjoining bodies in the earth's crust.   Such, for example, is the body, consisting of deformed Dalradian and Moinian rocks, lying between the Highland Boundary fault and the Moine Thrust in Scotland.   Or again it might ultimately be possible to attempt a kinetic analysis of the western foothill region of the Sierra Nevada of California.

[17] Sander, *op. cit.*, p. 170, 1948.

Where deformation of a body is the result of flow in the solid state, dynamic interpretation of strain depends on the rheologic condition of the body. Questions such as these must be answered: Was flow essentially elastic or "plastic" (irreversible)? Taking into account the extremely slow rate of much geologic strain, did the body perhaps behave more as a viscous liquid than as a plastic solid within familiar laboratory experience? And, remembering the possibility of "viscous" behavior, what magnitude of stress, applied over geologically long periods of time, is necessary to produce strain on the observed scale? Unambiguous answers to such questions are not yet forthcoming, so that dynamic analysis of rock structure remains correspondingly controversial and speculative.

SIGNIFICANCE OF SYMMETRY

Throughout his writings on *Gefügekunde der Gesteine* Sander has repeatedly stressed the prime significance of the overall symmetry of rock structures as a key to kinematic analysis. As structural analysis has progressed in many parts of the world, and as laboratory experiment has yielded information as to the symmetry relations of stress to strain and of strain to structure, the genetic significance of structural symmetry has become increasingly apparent. The concept has recently been revised and expanded by Paterson and Weiss[18] whose conclusions will be elaborated in later sections of this book. Sander's view that symmetry of strain and movement is reflected in symmetry of structure is a symmetry argument in the sense discussed by Paterson and Weiss as follows:

By a symmetry argument is meant a deduction concerning the symmetry of an unknown quantity from a knowledge of the symmetry of interrelated quantities. . . .

Such considerations of symmetry enable certain minimum deductions to be made in the study of phenomena for which insufficient information is available for a complete analysis to be made. For this reason, symmetry arguments have been invoked in geology where quantitative information on past physical influences is frequently unavailable and quantitative measurements on the physical properties of the rocks in question have not been made. On the other hand, in physics, where quantitative information on all aspects of a phenomenon can be obtained in the laboratory, symmetry relations are not usually discussed explicitly, although they arc implicit in a more complete quantitative description of the phenomenon.

An analogy may be drawn between symmetry arguments and dimensional analysis. Thus, in any equation relating the physical quantities concerned in a given phenomenon, the dimensions must be the same on both sides of the equation and use of this fact has frequently been made when more complete knowledge

[18] M. S. Paterson and L. E. Weiss, Symmetry concepts in the structural analysis of deformed rocks, *Geol. Soc. America Bull.*, vol. 72, pp. 841–882, 1961.

of the quantities is lacking. Similarly, there are general rules governing the symmetry of such quantities. . . . Sander's symmetry rule in structural analysis can therefore be viewed as an application of such symmetry considerations to geological phenomena in order to enable some conclusions to be drawn even though full details are not known.

How the symmetry principle may be applied and the restrictions it places upon kinematic and dynamic analysis of geologic bodies will become apparent in chapters dealing with interpretation of structural data. In the meantime we reemphasize the importance of symmetry of structure as one key to its interpretation.

SCOPE OF BOOK

This book is concerned with descriptive analysis and interpretation— on all scales from microscopic to that of a geologic map—of structure in rocks that have been deformed during metamorphism. With the aim of, as far as possible, separating fact from inference we have presented the material in three parts, as follows:

Part I deals principally with observations on the geometric properties of tectonite fabrics and with techniques of measurement, recording, and representation of these properties.

Part II is concerned largely with experimental data bearing upon problems of tectonites.

Part III is largely interpretive and outlines current theories of kinematic and dynamic significance of the special features of tectonite fabrics, with particular reference to published examples.

Our main aims are:

1. To demonstrate the use of statistical analysis of geometric data (by means of projections) in establishing the internal geometric and physical order that exists in bodies of deformed rock on any scale

2. To coordinate and summarize experimental data relating to strain of minerals and rocks

3. To demonstrate the possible use of geometric data, in the light of experiment and physical theory, in exploring the geometric properties and deformational history of rock bodies

The deformational history of a region is only one aspect of its total geologic history. This book, therefore, is concerned with only one phase of geologic investigation which, while complete in itself, gives information that must ultimately be supplemented by deductions drawn from more orthodox geologic study.

PART I

THE TECTONITE FABRIC AND ITS
GEOMETRIC ANALYSIS

CHAPTER 2

INTERNAL ORDER IN DEFORMED GEOLOGIC BODIES: THE TECTONITE FABRIC

GEOLOGIC BODIES AND SCALE

Geologic Bodies. In the title of his great two-volume treatise on structural analysis, Sander[1] uses the term *geologic body*. This has been employed widely in geology to denote somewhat loosely any volume of rock selected for study or comment, without restriction as to size. Thus, the great granite pluton of the Sierra Nevada in California, the volume of metamorphic rocks lying between the Moine Thrust and the Highland Boundary fault in the Scottish Highlands, a nodule of actinolite schist a few inches in diameter enclosed in serpentinite, and the aggregate of quartz grains comprising a thin section of any sandstone are all geologic bodies. Some geologic bodies, such as those cited, have structural or compositional unity and naturally defined bounding surfaces; others, such as the rocks exposed in any area covered by a single topographic quadrangle map, are outlined arbitrarily by nongeologic criteria.

Scale of Geologic Bodies. For convenience in observation, geologic bodies may be assigned to several "absolute" size ranges, which are termed *scales*. Each scale requires a different technique of investigation. The four scales adopted here are as follows:

1. Submicroscopic scale: covering bodies too small or too fine-grained to be studied by optical methods. Observation and analysis are by means of X rays. Although widely used in study of single crystals, this method of structural analysis hitherto has not been extensively applied to crystalline aggregates such as rocks.

2. Microscopic scale: covering bodies, such as thin sections or polished surfaces, that can be conveniently examined in their entirety with a microscope.

3. Mesoscopic scale: This term has been introduced[2] to cover bodies that can be effectively studied in three dimensions by direct observation

[1] B. Sander, *Einführung in die Gefügekunde der Geologischen Körper*, Springer, Berlin, Vienna, Pt. I, 1948, Pt. II, 1950.

[2] L. E. Weiss, Structural analysis of the Basement System at Turoka, Kenya, *Overseas Geology and Mineral Resources*, vol. 7, no. 1, p. 10, London, 1959.

(with or without a low-power hand lens).   They range from hand specimens to large but continuous exposures.

4. Macroscopic scale: covering bodies too large or too poorly exposed
to be examined directly in their entirety.   Such bodies are observed
indirectly by extrapolation from and synthesis of mesoscopic observations.   They range from groups of isolated exposures to the largest
mappable bodies.

Many complete geologic investigations involve observations made on
only the three larger scales.   Although techniques of investigation are
different, aims of geologic studies on the three scales are the same, namely,
to determine the structure, composition, and, if possible, the history of
development of the body concerned.

HOMOGENEOUS AND HETEROGENEOUS GEOLOGIC BODIES

The Notion of Homogeneity.   The geometric phase of structural
analysis is concerned with the internal geometric order of a geologic body,
as determined by observation of easily accessible parts and extrapolation
between these parts.   Before such extrapolation is significant, spatial
uniformity in internal constitution of the body must be established.
Such uniformity is best expressed by the notion of *homogeneity*.

Strictly Homogeneous Bodies.   A body is strictly homogeneous if any
two identically oriented equal-volume units or samples are identical.[3]
The nearest approach to strict homogeneity found in a natural body is
in a single crystal or in an unstrained glass of uniform chemical composition; and this homogeneity is reflected in uniformity of physical properties such as refractive index or density.

Statistically Homogeneous Bodies.   Strict homogeneity is not achieved
in nature because of the fundamental discontinuous character of matter.
A crystal can be considered homogeneous only where samples compared
are large in relation to the discontinuities in structure and composition
that are implicit in the periodicity of a crystal lattice: even a glass is
homogeneous only with respect to samples notably larger than the ionic
groups—imperfect crystal nuclei—that locally develop within it.   In
nature, therefore, a body can be homogeneous only in a statistical sense,
where samples compared are sufficiently large in relation to heterogeneities in structure so that each contains a representative distribution of
these heterogeneities.   Such samples are statistically identical and the
body concerned is *statistically homogeneous*.[4]   Such a body can appear

[3] Lord Kelvin and P. G. Tait, *A Treatise on Natural Philosophy*, 2d ed., Pt. II,
sec. 675, Cambridge, 1883: "A body is called 'homogeneous' when any two equal,
similar parts of it, with corresponding lines parallel and turned towards the same
parts, are indistinguishable from one another by any difference in quality."

[4] M. S. Paterson and L. E. Weiss (Symmetry concepts in the structural analysis of

heterogeneous on a smaller scale if subdivided into samples small enough for structural differences between them to be perceptible. To demonstrate that a body, which is heterogeneous on a small scale, is homogeneous on a large scale it is usually necessary to compare samples that are large fractions of the whole body.

These relations are clearly shown in crystalline aggregates such as rocks. Two equal-sized hand specimens of a fine-grained plutonic rock may have identical geometric and physical properties, because statistically the same number of grains of each mineral arranged in statistically the same fashion are present in each. However, a small volume of the same rock, such as a fragment a few millimeters in diameter, is not statistically homogeneous if subdivided into samples each containing only a few grains. The discontinuous nature of the aggregate becomes significant on this scale, as shown in Fig. 2-1.

Because of the absence of strict homogeneity in matter, the term *homogeneous* is used here to denote bodies that are statistically homogeneous on some particular stated scale. This usage implies that smaller parts of the body may be heterogeneous and also that the body may form part of a larger unit that may be either homogeneous or heterogeneous.

Structural Homogeneity. A body can be homogeneous or heterogeneous with respect to a variety of characteristics or physical properties. Most obvious in this respect are the related characteristics of composition and structure. Here we are concerned ultimately with structural homogeneity which implies identity with respect to all possible structural features in a rock body; but such identity is not easily established. Where structural homogeneity is established in a rock body it is generally with respect to specific geometric features of the body, and may disappear where additional geometric features are considered. For instance, a large body of horizontally bedded sedimentary rock can be considered structurally homogeneous with respect to the bedding when in any one portion the geometric properties of the bedding are statistically the same as in any other portion. The same body may be structurally heterogeneous with respect to linear structures such as groove or flute casts lying on bedding surfaces, because these linear structures may be impersistently developed and vary widely in orientation from one part of the body to another.

All bodies that are not homogeneous on a given scale are termed *heterogeneous*. Most large arbitrarily outlined bodies of rock are heterogeneous on the scale of the whole body, although they may be subdivisible into homogeneous portions. Even those large bodies that are effectively

deformed rocks, *Geol. Soc. America Bull.*, vol. 72, p. 854, 1961) define statistical homogeneity as follows: ". . . a body is statistically homogeneous on a certain scale when the average of the internal configuration in any volume element is the same for all volume elements with dimensions not smaller than the scale of consideration."

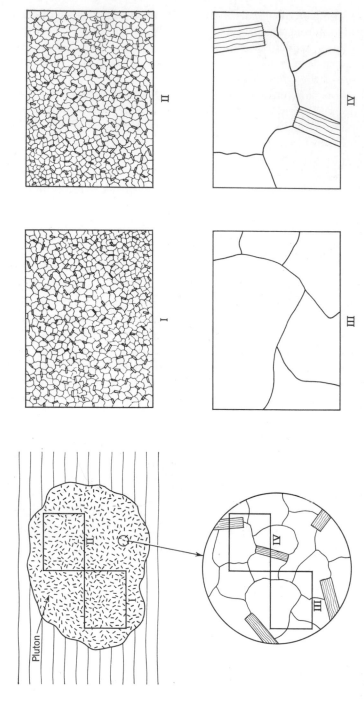

Fig. 2-1. Relation between statistical homogeneity and scale. Size of samples is exaggerated with respect to whole body. Samples I and II are statistically identical. On this scale the body is statistically homogeneous. Samples III and IV of a much smaller portion of the body are not statistically identical. On this scale the body is heterogeneous.

homogeneous in composition, such as some granite plutons, can be heterogeneous in structure; and those homogeneous in structure, such as certain bodies of sedimentary and metamorphic rock, can be heterogeneous in composition.

FABRIC OF GEOLOGIC BODIES

Fabric. The term *fabric* is the accepted English translation of the German word *Gefüge*, used by Sander[5] to denote the internal ordering of both geometric and physical spatial data in an aggregate. Paterson and Weiss[6] comment on the concept of fabric as follows:

. . . the "structure" of a noncrystal is the internal geometric configuration of its elementary parts and of any characteristic features to which the arrangement of these parts gives rise. Examples of such internal geometric configurations are seen in the preferred orientation of individual crystals in deformed metals or rocks, the slag stringers in wrought iron, the foliations and lineations in deformed rocks, and the fibrous character of wood and similar materials. This "structure" or configuration of particles (crystalline or otherwise) in an aggregate has been widely termed *texture* in physical and metallurgical literature. The geological term *fabric* (*Gefüge*) is synonymous with texture in this usage but is preferred in geology because texture has other meanings. . . . Sometimes the term "texture" or "fabric" is used for the body itself but it should be borne in mind that, strictly speaking, the fabric refers to the internal configuration of the body. Moreover, since no account is to be taken of any boundaries, a fabric can be considered to be of infinite extent.

The concept of a single crystal as a body with an ordered internal arrangement of invariant component parts (ions, atoms, or molecular configuration) is one familiar to all students of geology. The internal order in a crystal is primarily recognized by a similar ordering of physical properties. This order can be expressed in an abstract way in terms of its point-group or space-group symmetry. The concept of fabric extends the notion of internal spatial order to nonlattice bodies such as crystalline aggregates, geologically familiar as rocks. The component parts in aggregates are crystalline grains, and their spatial arrangement and mutual relations constitute the internal order of the fabric. In an aggregate the arrangement of components is not generally subject to the three-dimensional translational periodicity and the energy-dependent packing laws of the crystal lattice, so that the kinds of permissible order differ in some respects from those of crystals. But a close analogy can be pointed between the single crystal and the aggregate, because both possess abstract geometric properties or form and both possess physical properties that reflect in some fashion this form. For example, depending

[5] B. Sander, *Gefügekunde der Gesteine*, p. 1, Springer, Berlin, Vienna, 1930.
[6] Paterson and Weiss, *op. cit.*, p. 854.

upon its symmetry class, the elastic properties of a crystal are expressible by a fixed number of constants; likewise, upon the geometric order within a fabric depend its physical properties such as elasticity, thermal conductivity, and permeability.

The concept of a fabric, therefore, embodies not only a geometric or morphologic aspect expressible in terms of the geometric arrangement of components, but also a functional or behavioral aspect which is concerned with the directional physical properties that are a necessary correlate of geometrically regular organization of matter. To differentiate the two aspects of fabric, Sander[7] terms them respectively *formal* or *configurational (gestaltlich) fabric* and *functional* or *physical (funktional) fabric*. In this context form or configuration implies the abstract geometric order of a fabric divorced from the functional or physical properties that reflect it. The term *fabric* as used in this book covers aspects of both form and function. The term *geometry* can be used instead of form or configuration where a complete geometric abstraction is implied.

A fabric can be considered to be of infinite extent. Neither the bounding surfaces nor the shape of a body are part of its fabric. The geometric and symmetric properties of fabrics are therefore similar to those of other infinitely extended structures like crystal lattices. Implicit, therefore, in the concept of fabric is that of homogeneity.

Fabric Domains. The term *domain*[8] is here used to specify any finite three-dimensional portion of a rock body that is statistically homogeneous on the scale of the domain. Domains are usually outlined by boundaries that are natural surfaces of major discontinuity in structure or composition. A portion of a particular domain may be termed a *subdomain*.

Any homogeneous or heterogeneous body can be subdivided on some scale into homogeneous domains. These domains commonly differ in kind and degree of internal order, both amongst themselves and with respect to the body in which they occur. Each therefore has a fabric regardless of whether the whole body concerned is homogeneous and has a fabric, or is heterogeneous and does not. Such domains may be termed *fabric domains*. In rocks they are of two kinds, as follows:

1. Crystallographic domains: These are individual unstrained or weakly strained mineral grains. Strictly speaking, such domains have no fabric because their internal order is controlled by the laws of crystallography. The structure of all domains of the same composition is more or less the same in a given body.

---

[7] Sander, *op. cit.*, pp. 2, 3, 1948.

[8] The terms *area* (L. E. Weiss, A study of tectonic style, *Univ. California Geol. Sci. Pub.*, vol. 30, pp. 1–102, 1954) and *field* (L. E. Weiss, Geometry of superposed folding, *Geol. Soc. America Bull.*, vol. 70, pp. 91–106, 1959) have been used in the past in this sense. We now believe that *domain* is a preferable term and so have adopted it.

2. Noncrystallographic domains: These are homogeneous domains on some scale larger than that of a single crystal, and consist of aggregates of grains. The internal order of these domains is not directly subject to the laws of crystallography and is expressed by a fabric. This fabric may vary from domain to domain in a body of uniform composition.

Fabric as an Array of Discontinuities in Structure. For most purposes, such as determination of elastic, thermal, or electrical properties, a crystal can be treated as a homogeneous continuum. Understanding of the geometric and symmetric properties of crystals, however, is possible only where the crystal is viewed more rigorously as a periodic array of structural discontinuities.[9] Similarly, a homogeneous fabric, although in large domains conveniently treated as a structural continuum, must be examined in terms of small-scale discontinuities or local heterogeneities in its structure before the geometric and symmetric properties of its internal order can be expressed and the concept of a fabric becomes significant. A fabric can be treated, therefore, as a three-dimensionally ordered array of structural discontinuities: one aim of structural analysis is to establish this order and represent it in a graphic form.

Discontinuities in Crystallographic Domains. The planes and lines of structural discontinuity in crystals (that is, lattice planes and directions) are not directly observable because they occur on the atomic scale. Their orientation can be determined, however, either optically—on the basis of known relations between optical properties and crystallographic features—or, more directly, by observing related physical discontinuities on a much larger scale (cleavages, twin lamellae, partings, and so on). X-ray analysis gives a complete picture of the internal surfaces of discontinuity within crystals.

Because a crystal is a homogeneous domain on all but the smallest scales, one observation serves to define the orientation of a particular structural plane or line for the whole crystal. Such discontinuities in structure are here termed *penetrative* because they are repeated at distances so small, compared with the scale of the whole crystal, that they can be considered to pervade it uniformly and be present at every point.

Examples of planar and linear penetrative discontinuities in crystallographic domains commonly studied in structural analysis are as follows:

1. Planar discontinuities: any determinable crystallographic plane in a grain, for instance; {001} in mica (defined by visible cleavages); {01$\bar{1}$2} in calcite and {02$\bar{2}$1} in dolomite (defined by visible twin lamellae); {10$\bar{1}$1 }in calcite and dolomite (defined by visible cleavages).

2. Linear discontinuities: any determinable crystallographic line in a grain, for instance; [0001] in quartz (defined by optic axis); [0001] in

[9] P. Niggli, *Geometrische Kristallographie des Diskontinuums*, p. 1, Borntraeger, Berlin, 1919.

calcite and dolomite (defined by optic axis or known angular relation to $\{01\bar{1}2\}$ or $\{10\bar{1}1\}$).

Some discontinuities, for example, [0001] in quartz or X, Y, and Z of the olivine indicatrix, are unique for a given crystallographic domain. Others, such as $\{01\bar{1}2\}$ in calcite, are symmetrically repeated to conform to the particular symmetry class of the crystal. If the object of analysis is to determine the orientation of one kind of penetrative discontinuity, for example, $\{01\bar{1}2\}$ in the domain of a calcite crystal, all possible discontinuities of the same kind (three in calcite) must be recorded as of equal value, even though only one or two may be rendered visible by discrete discontinuities (twin lamellae in calcite). For some purposes it may be necessary to distinguish between lattice planes paralleled by visible discrete continuities and the latent invisible lattice planes of the same kind. Here the recorded visible discrete discontinuities (cleavage cracks, twin lamellae, and so on) fall into the nonpenetrative category on the scale of the grain (see below).

Discontinuities in Noncrystallographic Domains. *Penetrative and Non-penetrative Discontinuities.* Structural discontinuities that are not crystallographically controlled can occur in individual mineral grains, for example, the bounding surfaces of *kink bands*.[10] In one sense such surfaces make a crystal a noncrystallographic domain because they destroy homogeneity with respect to lattice orientation and convert the original crystal to an aggregate of crystals.

In noncrystallographic domains all surfaces of discontinuity are made up of grain boundaries. Where anhedral grains are in contact, these boundaries, even though they may be approximately planar, have no rational relation to the crystal lattice. But some common minerals tend to develop idioblastic outlines, and domain boundaries may then show the influence of crystallographic control. For instance, mica commonly crystallizes with a tabular habit parallel to $\{001\}$; hornblende prisms are habitually bounded by $\{110\}$. All larger-scale discontinuities are systematic arrays of grain boundaries. Even a nearly perfectly planar surface of discontinuity, such as a bedding surface separating a fine-grained limestone from a fine-grained mudstone, is defined statistically by a planar alignment of boundaries between microscopic grains.

The relations between grain boundaries and other noncrystallographic discontinuities are illustrated in Fig. 2-2. Fig. 2-2a shows part of an aggregate on a microscopic scale. Even on this scale the grain boundaries have a weak preferential orientation. On a larger scale (Fig. 2-2b) the arrangement of grain boundaries in planar parallel orientation imparts to the whole aggregate a penetrative planar structure parallel to S_1. On this scale the planar discontinuity S_1 is a penetrative family of statisti-

[10] See, for instance, C. S. Barrett, *Structure of Metals*, 2d ed., pp. 375, 376, McGraw-Hill, New York, 1952.

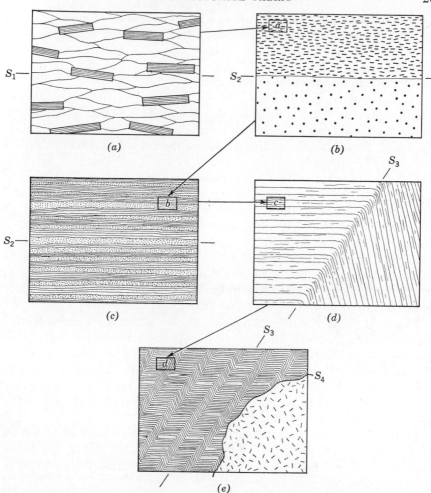

FIG. 2-2. Planar discontinuities in the same body on five different scales. (*a*) Micro-scopic scale; planar preferred orientation of grain boundaries defines a weakly penetra-tive planar structure S_1. (*b*) Mesoscopic scale; grain boundaries define a penetrative planar structure S_1 in the upper layer.   Discontinuity S_2 between layers of different composition is nonpenetrative on this scale. (*c*) Larger mesoscopic scale; alter-nating layers parallel to S_2 make this a penetrative planar structure. (*d*) Macro-scopic scale; kink surface S_3 divides the body into two homogeneous domains with different orientations of S and S_2. S_3 is nonpenetrative. (*e*) Larger macroscopic scale; S_3 becomes a series of closely spaced kink surfaces and is penetrative.   A new surface of discontinuity S_4 divides the body into unlike domains and is nonpenetrative on all scales.

cally defined parallel surfaces, present in every sample of moderate size. Because their attitude in the domain is not controlled crystallographically, homogeneity in nature and orientation of S_1 must be determined by comparison of measurements made on individual surfaces of discontinuity in different parts of the domain.

On the scale shown in Fig. 2-2b another kind of surface of discontinuity appears. This is the *nonpenetrative* surface S_2 that separates the fabric described from a different fabric below. On a yet larger scale, as shown in Fig. 2-2c, the aggregate takes on a finely laminated aspect owing to the rapid alternation of layers of the kind separated by S_2 in Fig. 2-2b. On this scale S_2 also becomes a penetrative discontinuity that is statistically present in every sample of the fabric. On a still larger scale (Fig. 2-2d) the aggregate is traversed by yet another surface of discontinuity—S_3, which divides the aggregate into noncrystallographic domains that are effectively internally homogeneous. Although this is a discrete surface of discontinuity on the scale shown, on a larger scale S_3 could become penetrative. On the other hand, surfaces such as S_4 divide the geologic body into completely unlike domains and are clearly nonpenetrative on all possible scales (Fig. 2-2e).

Noncrystallographic discontinuities are classified as nonpenetrative on a scale small enough for them to remain discrete surfaces separating domains of significant size. Those discontinuities classified as penetrative are generally so on macroscopic or mesoscopic scales (for example, bedding in most sediments and foliation in many kinds of metamorphic rock); but they can be penetrative also on a microscopic scale (for example, bedding in a shale and slaty cleavage).

In this book structural discontinuities of any kind occurring in rock bodies are termed *structures*. The various kinds of planar (including curviplanar[11]) and linear noncrystallographic discontinuities common in geologic bodies are summarized below.

1. *Nonpenetrative planar discontinuities.*
    a. Faults. Faults may separate like fabric domains without sensibly interrupting geometric continuity of penetrative structures (Fig. 2-3a), or they may separate unlike domains (Fig. 2-3b). Commonly—especially in the case of normal, reversed, or strike-slip faults—they are unrelated geometrically to the penetrative discontinuities that pervade the adjacent fabric domains. Thrust, glide, or slide surfaces, however, tend to be more closely related geometrically to the fabrics of the domains they separate (Fig. 2-3c). A glide or slide surface may be indistinguishable from a

---

[11] G. Oertel, Extrapolation in geologic fabrics, *Geol. Soc. America Bull.*, vol. 73, p. 326, 1962.

single surface in a family that collectively defines the penetrative discontinuity known as *foliation*.[12]

b. Igneous contacts.   Except where they separate igneous bodies of common origin, igneous contacts generally separate unlike fabrics. Geometrically they may be unrelated to either of the fabrics they separate (Fig. 2-4a).   But some intrusive contacts have a geometric

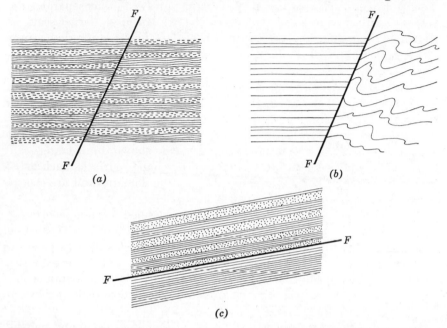

Fig. 2-3. Faults *F* as domain boundaries.   (*a*) Fault is transgressive to fabrics of wall rocks.   These fabrics are geometrically identical and are effectively uninterrupted by the fault.   (*b*) Fault is transgressive to fabrics of wall rocks.   The fault separates unlike domains and is a surface of discontinuity.   (*c*) Fault is not transgressive to fabrics of wall rocks.   These fabrics are geometrically identical and are effectively uninterrupted by the fault.

relation either to the country rock (foliation or bedding parallel to the margins of the sill shown in Fig. 2-4b), or to the igneous rock (flow structures parallel to the margins of the pluton shown in Fig. 2-4c), or to both (Fig. 2-4d).

c. Erosion surfaces and unconformities.   Most rock bodies studied by geologists have one bounding surface that is erosional and separates the body from the atmosphere or the hydrosphere.   The geometric properties of such a topographic surface may be unrelated

[12] E. Greenly, Foliation and its relation to folding in the Mona Complex at Rhoscolyn (Anglesey), *Geol. Soc. London Quart. Jour.*, vol. 86, pp. 185–187, 1930; E. B. Bailey, The structure of the south-west Highlands of Scotland, *Geol. Soc. London Quart. Jour.*, vol. 78, p. 86, 1922.

to those of the rock body they bound, or there may be recognizable geometric control of the surface by the fabric of the body.[13] Unconformities are former erosion surfaces. They can have a variety of geometric relations to the fabrics of the domains they separate. Figure 2-5a shows an unconformity geometrically unrelated to either fabric. A planar unconformity, on the other hand, is usually concordant with the stratification of the rocks above and

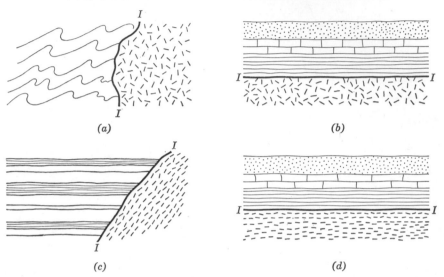

(a)   (b)

(c)   (d)

Fig. 2-4. Igneous contacts I as domain boundaries. (a) Contact surface is transgressive to unlike fabrics. (b) Contact surface is transgressive only to fabric of igneous rock. (c) Contact surface is transgressive only to fabric of country rock. (d) Contact surface is not transgressive to igneous and country rocks and geometrically is not a surface of discontinuity.

discordantly related to the rocks below (Fig. 2-5b). A disconformity has a strong geometric relation to both fabrics and, like some glide or slide surfaces, is not a visible surface of geometric discontinuity but a surface of stratigraphic discontinuity (Fig. 2-5c).

d. Metamorphic *fronts* and isograd surfaces. These are boundary surfaces either between metamorphosed and unmetamorphosed rocks (fronts) or between zones showing demonstrably different degrees of metamorphism (isograds). Such surfaces, along with fronts of migmatization and perhaps granitization, are thought by some geologists to migrate through a geologic body and partially

[13] F. J. Turner, "Gefügerelief" illustrated by "schist tor" topography in central Otago, New Zealand, *Am. Jour. Sci.*, vol. 250, pp. 802–807, 1952; G. Wilson, The influence of rock structures on coast-line and cliff development around Tintagel, North Cornwall, *Geologists' Assoc. Proc.*, vol. 63, pp. 20–58, 1952.

or completely to reconstruct the fabric of the rocks through which they pass. Fronts are sometimes depicted as discrete surfaces of discontinuity. More commonly they are thought to be finite domains with parallel boundaries, in which a mineralogic and thus a geometric gradient exists from one margin to the other. Such heterogeneous domains are not true surfaces of discontinuity.

e. *Joints.* Joints are only nonpenetrative on certain scales of observation. Where they are expressed as closely spaced microfractures they are more akin to penetrative discontinuities. They resemble penetrative discontinuities also in always separating like fabrics;

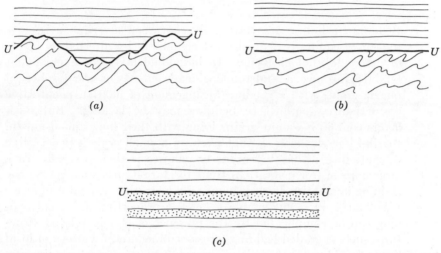

FIG. 2-5. Unconformities U as domain boundaries. (*a*) Unconformity transgressive to unlike fabrics. (*b*) Unconformity transgressive only to fabric of rocks below. (*c*) Disconformity is not transgressive to fabrics of rocks above or below and geometrically is not a surface of discontinuity.

but their geometric relation to penetrative discontinuities within these fabrics is commonly tenuous or inconsistent. Certain sets of joints, however, consistently have some fixed geometric relation to penetrative discontinuities. In unfolded sediments, joints are commonly developed normal to bedding. In deformed rocks, joints tend to develop subnormal to fold axes and lineations, or in conjugate sets symmetrically intersecting these structures. In structural analysis of deformed rocks, therefore, it is common practice to measure and consider joints that fall into one or other of these categories.

In the above discussion the nonpenetrative surfaces of discontinuity have been treated as discrete surfaces with no volume. In natural examples the surfaces are generally marked by a thin more or less parallel-sided domain whose fabric differs from the fabric on either side. Examples of such domains are slickenside films; thin layers of mylonite, crushed rock, or gouge paralleling fault surfaces; narrow zones of disordered and compositionally mixed material locally margining igneous contacts; and the conglomeratic or atypically coarse-grained layers developed above, and the weathered zones developed below, unconformities. Some of these thin local fabrics are of structural importance (for instance, a slickenside film on a fault may indicate the direction and sense of fault movement); but in the fabric of a large body of rock they are generally unimportant and can be neglected.

2. *Penetrative planar discontinuities.*

   a. Bedding (including gravitationally controlled layering in igneous rocks). Bedding is defined most commonly by alternating layers of different lithologic type. In individual layers of a particular kind (for instance, a sandstone bed made entirely of nearly spherical quartz grains with a random arrangement of [0001]), penetrative discontinuities parallel to bedding may be lacking. But most layers contain inequant grains lying with their long dimensions in the bedding surfaces, so that even on a small scale a penetrative discontinuity defined by grain boundaries is then present. In a large domain (for instance, a thick formation of bedded rocks) the bedding lamination itself becomes a penetrative discontinuity (see Fig. 2-2a, b, c). The simple geometric properties of normal bedding can be complicated by the presence of closely related structures such as graded bedding, cross-bedding, and a variety of local linear flow structures, such as groove and flute casts.

   b. Foliation. This is defined by the metamorphically produced penetrative surfaces of discontinuity in deformed rocks, including structures known as schistosity, cleavage, and so on. Structurally they resemble bedding in that they are defined by arrangements of grain boundaries or by lithologic lamination. All, like bedding, are present on most scales of observation as penetrative statistically defined parallel families. Some bodies contain more than one foliation. A common type is subparallel to the axial planes (page 108) of folds affecting an earlier set of surfaces. In a large body of rock the axial planes of folds themselves may be considered penetrative surfaces of discontinuity.

   Sander[14] has proposed the term "*s*-surface" to denote any kind of penetrative planar structure in rocks. The term covers bedding, foliation, and some kinds of joints. Strictly one should speak of a set or family of *s*-surfaces where all the surfaces in the family are

---

[14] B. Sander, Über Zusammenhänge zwischen Teilbewegung und Gefüge in Gesteinen, *Tschermaks mineralog. petrog. Mitt.*, vol. 30, p. 286, 1911.

to be specified; but such a family is sometimes more conveniently designated an *s*-surface.

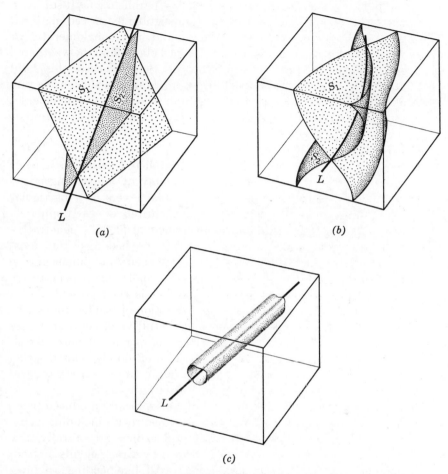

FIG. 2-6. Nonpenetrative linear discontinuities L. (*a*) Rectilinear intersection of two planar nonpenetrative discontinuities S_1 and S_2. (*b*) Curvilinear intersection of two curviplanar nonpenetrative discontinuities S_1 and S_2. (*c*) Bounding surface of small cylindrical or prismatic domain.

3. *Nonpenetrative linear discontinuities.*   Linear discontinuities in fabrics arise as modifications of planar discontinuities, as follows:

   a. The line of intersection of two nonparallel, nonpenetrative surfaces of discontinuity is a nonpenetrative linear discontinuity. Where both surfaces are planar the linear discontinuity is rectilinear (Fig. 2-6*a*); where one or both are curviplanar the linear discontinuity is in general curvilinear (Fig. 2-6*b*). An example of a discontinuity of this kind is the line of intersection of one contact of an igneous

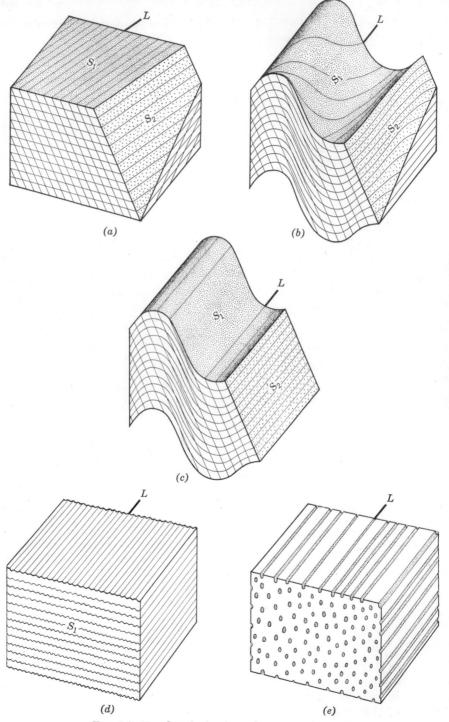

FIG. 2-7. For descriptive legend see opposite page.

dike with a thin planar vein.   Such nonpenetrative linear discontinuities are widely used in graphic solution of fault problems in structural geology.

b. A two-dimensionally penetrative linear discontinuity arises by the intersection of a set of penetrative surfaces with a nonpenetrative surface.   Examples of such structures are lines of intersection (traces) of bedding on a fault or a topographic surface.   These linear structures are not truly penetrative in three dimensions and are not true lineations.

c. Where individual prismatic or cylindrical domains can be outlined in a fabric, a nonpenetrative linear discontinuity is present (Fig. 2-6c).   On a microscopic scale a single prismatic grain is such a domain; on a mesoscopic or larger scale a *rod* of one lithologic type enclosed in a matrix of another, *mullion* structures defined by cylindrically curving surfaces of discontinuity, and the hinges of large folds in a particular surface are linear discontinuities of this kind.[15]

4. *Penetrative linear discontinuities.*

a. The three-dimensional array of lines of intersection of two sets of penetrative planar discontinuities is a penetrative linear discontinuity (Fig. 2-7a).   Examples are the lines of intersection of bedding and cleavage in a slate, or of two foliations in a schist.   Where the surfaces are planar the linear discontinuity is rectilinear. Where one set or both sets are curviplanar the linear discontinuity is curvilinear (Fig. 2-7b); an exception is the geologically common condition in which the line of intersection of the surfaces is also the axis of curvature in one or both sets (for instance, the lines of intersection of axial-plane foliation with folded bedding, as in Fig. 2-7c). Many *lineations* in deformed rocks are expressions of these geometric relations.   All true lineations are penetrative discontinuities.

b. Regular crenulations of a set of penetrative surfaces define a direction that is unique in the penetrative surface (Fig. 2-7d).   On a microscopic scale a lineation arises in this way; on larger scales, a fold axis.

c. Elongated prismatic or cylindrical domains of small size by alignment of their long axes define a penetrative linear discontinuity

[15] G. Wilson, Mullion and rodding structures in the Moine Series of Scotland, *Geologists' Assoc. Proc.*, vol. 64, pp. 118–151, 1953.

FIG. 2-7. Penetrative linear discontinuities L.   (a) Rectilinear intersection of two planar penetrative discontinuities S_1 and S_2.   (b) Curvilinear intersection of a curviplanar penetrative discontinuity S_1 with a planar penetrative discontinuity S_2. (c) Rectilinear intersection of a folded penetrative discontinuity S_1 with a penetrative planar discontinuity S_2 containing the axis of folding.   (d) Regular crenulations of a set of penetrative surfaces S_1.   (e) Preferred orientation of cylindrical or prismatic domains.

in a large domain of fabric (Fig. 2-7e). Such elongated domains may be individual grains such as hornblende prisms, or noncrystallographic domains of a particular composition (for example, trains of quartz or feldspar grains in a gneiss, elongated pebbles in a deformed conglomerate).

Fabric Elements and Fabric Data. Within a homogeneous domain—be it a thin section, a hand specimen, or a mountain range—only structures that are penetrative on the scale of the domain contribute to the fabric. Structures in aggregates falling into this category are defined by the following features:

1. Lattice planes and lines within individual grains
2. Shapes of inequant grains
3. Arrangements of grains of particular kinds in layers, linear bodies, and other inequant configurations

Such structures are termed *fabric elements* of the fabrics defined by their three-dimensional configuration, where this is statistically homogeneous. This term has been used by Sander[16] to denote the actual equivalent domains of which a body is composed, whereas Fairbairn[17] defines a fabric element as " . . . a single crystal or group of crystals which act as a unit with respect to the forces applied to it." Neither of these definitions embraces statistically pervasive features such as foliations and lineations since such features are not domains of a body but are surfaces and lines of structural discontinuity within or between domains of the body. All fabric elements as here defined can be viewed on some scale as surfaces and lines of structural discontinuity. For example, features defined by planar and linear preferred orientations of inequant grains are, in detail, also penetrative families of surfaces of discontinuity defined by the grain boundaries. Likewise, lattice planes and lines in individual crystals are planes and lines of discontinuity on the ionic or molecular scale.

In tectonite fabrics, therefore, we recognize two kinds of fabric element:

1. *Crystallographic fabric elements.* These are lattice planes or lines in individual grains, e.g., {001} planes in mica (determined from visible cleavages), {01$\bar{1}$2} planes in calcite and {02$\bar{2}$1} planes in dolomite (determined from visible twin lamellae), [0001] directions in quartz (determined as the optic axes), and [0001] directions in calcite and dolomite (determined as the optic axes or from known angular relations to cleavages and twin lamellae). Each element, according to the demands of

[16] Sander, *op. cit.*, p. 5, 1948.

[17] H. W. Fairbairn, *Structural Petrology of Deformed Rocks*, 2d ed., p. 3, Addison-Wesley, Reading, 1949.

crystal symmetry, must be accompanied by all other elements of the same crystallographic form. Thus in calcite $(10\bar{1}1)$ is necessarily accompanied by $(\bar{1}101)$ and $(0\bar{1}11)$. The attitude of a crystallographic element commonly is determined by measuring some individual visible structure such as a $(10\bar{1}1)$ cleavage or a twin lamella $(01\bar{1}2)$ in calcite. If these visible elements only are recorded they should be treated as noncrystallographic elements; a twin lamella may even be regarded as a distinct fabric domain.

2. *Noncrystallographic fabric elements.* These are visible structural discontinuities or heterogeneities in an aggregate. Planar noncrystallographic elements—s-surfaces in Sander's terminology—are structures such as bedding and foliation which are defined by preferred orientation of grain boundaries or by lithologic layering. Some aggregates contain more than one foliation. One of these may be parallel to axial planes of folds affecting an earlier foliation. Axial planes of folds may themselves be considered as fabric elements on a larger scale. Linear noncrystallographic fabric elements are structures such as lineations and fold axes. Lineations can be defined by such features as lines of intersection of two planar fabric elements, crenulations in a planar fabric element, alignment of boundaries of elongated grains, and so on.

The rigorous definition here adopted restricts the term fabric element to plane and rectilinear segments of noncrystallographic discontinuities. Crystallographic fabric elements are correspondingly plane and rectilinear. A fabric, therefore, is viewed as a three-dimensional array of plane and rectilinear segments even though a number of these may collectively define folded surfaces in the fabric. Our view of fabric elements and fabrics involves more precisely defined concepts than those current among most structural geologists; but we believe that it conforms closely to Sander's idea of *Gefüge*. Moreover it is only plane and rectilinear structures that can be measured by ordinary field and laboratory methods. And homogeneity and space-group symmetry (see page 42)—the very essence of fabric—can be rigorously defined only in terms of an infinite array of plane and rectilinear features.

Fabric elements, like fabrics, have both a geometric and a functional aspect. The descriptive phase of structural analysis is concerned mainly with geometric fabric elements divorced from the functions they reflect. Thus, we can speak of the spatial arrangement of lineations or mineral grains in a fabric in an abstract geometric sense without implying a related spatial arrangement of physical (functional) properties such as permeability or linear thermal expansion. Where genesis of a fabric is to be studied, however, the function of observed fabric elements in development of the fabric becomes important.

The attitude of any fabric element can be specified by its angular relation either to chosen orthogonal axes, called *fabric axes*, generally labeled *a*, *b*, and *c*, or to geographic coordinates. The measurements that specify the attitudes of fabric elements are termed *fabric data*.

A fabric is defined by the spatial array of all its elements. However, it is frequently sufficient or convenient to consider the array of only one kind of element. This array is called by Sander a *Teilgefüge* and here a *subfabric*.[18]

In a given fabric there may be many kinds of different elements and correspondingly numerous subfabrics. In practice, a few easily measurable elements are chosen and the subfabrics defined by these are combined to define the geometric properties of the fabric as a whole. For instance, in a quartz-mica schist some easily measurable subfabrics are defined by:

1. Attitude of one type of foliation
2. Attitude of one type of lineation
3. Preferred orientation of [0001] in quartz
4. Preferred orientation of {001} in mica

Although other subfabrics can be defined (for instance, by the preferred orientation of [100] in mica) their determination presents practical difficulties and does not always add materially to the geometric properties of the total fabric.

ISOTROPIC AND ANISOTROPIC FABRICS

Preferred Orientation of Fabric Elements. In the spatial arrangement of fabric elements two aspects are implicit:

1. The elements have *orientation;* that is, they have attitudes with respect to selected fixed reference axes (for instance, the attitude of a foliation surface as expressed by its strike and dip).

2. The elements have *location;* that is, they have a definite position with reference to elements of the same or different kinds (for instance, a slaty cleavage may be present in a shaly bed in a thick series of deformed sediments, but absent in a sandy bed).

Where fabric elements are not randomly oriented in a fabric they are said to possess a *preferred orientation*.[19] A random orientation of elements is extremely rare in nature. The elements in some igneous rocks and in hornfelses which have crystallized without deformation under effectively hydrostatic pressure most nearly approach random orientations. Even in these fabrics, however, sufficiently refined measurements

[18] Sander, *op. cit.*, pp. 5, 6, 1948. The term *subfabric* was introduced by Paterson and Weiss (*op. cit.*, p. 863).

[19] A comprehensive account of preferred orientation of grains is to be found in E. B. Knopf and E. Ingerson, Structural petrology, *Geol. Soc. America Mem. 6*, pp. 7–22, 1938.

on a sufficiently large number of elements will generally establish weak preferred orientation.

Preferred orientations are statistically defined so that they are of different degrees. A preferred orientation is generally expressed by the percentage of measured elements which have attitudes lying between arbitrarily chosen limits.

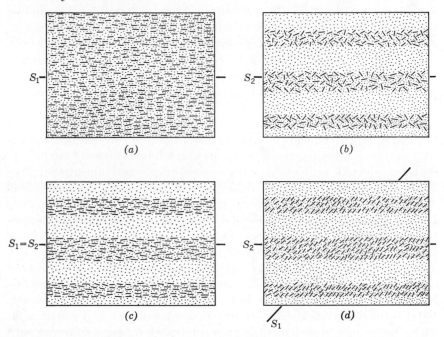

(a)   (b)

(c)   (d)

FIG. 2-8. S-surfaces defined by preferred orientation and preferred location of fabric elements. (a) Preferred orientation alone defines s-surfaces S_1. (b) Preferred location alone defines s-surface S_2. (c) Combination of (a) and (b) defines single s-surface, $S_1 = S_2$. (d) Combination of (a) and (b) defines two s-surfaces, S_1 oblique to S_2.

In structural analysis, fabric elements are said to possess preferred orientation where:

1. The preferred orientation is easily detectable by normal procedures employed in analysis (page 58). Some very weak preferred orientations detectable by special techniques are neglected in structural analysis of deformed rocks.

2. The pattern of preferred orientation is reproducible in comparable samples of the same elements similarly distributed in the same homogeneous domain.

A preferred orientation as defined above is a penetrative property of a body and is thus an aspect of its fabric. The preferred orientation exists whatever may be the position or location of elements in the body. Location of structures is by definition a nonpenetrative feature. Nevertheless, penetrative structures can be defined by preferred location of fabric elements as illustrated in Fig. 2-8, which shows the arrangement of planar elements such as {001} of mica crystals, lying normal to the plane of the figure. In Fig. 2-8a parallel preferred orientation of planar elements defines the family of penetrative surfaces S_1. In Fig. 2-8b similar elements lack preferred orientation but by their preferred location define nonpenetrative surfaces of discontinuity S_1. On a larger scale than Fig. 2-8b the surfaces S_1 could be a penetrative feature of a body and would then be fabric elements. In Fig. 2-8c a preferred orientation is combined with a preferred location to define a single surface S_1, and in Fig. 2-8d to define two mutually inclined surfaces S_1 and S_2 independent of each other in attitude.

Anisotropy of Fabric. A fabric lacking any preferred orientation or location of fabric elements is said to be isotropic. Conversely, an anisotropic fabric is a homogeneous fabric in which fabric elements are preferentially oriented or located. Because isotropy and anisotropy, like homogeneity, are statistically defined, both phenomena are dependent upon scale of domain.

Most fabrics—especially those of deformed rocks—are markedly anisotropic. Not every kind of fabric element present in a fabric need have preferred orientation for the fabric as a whole to be anisotropic. For instance, in some mica schists quartz and feldspar have no preferred orientation of lattice directions, so that the subfabrics for these crystallographic fabric elements are isotropic. In the same rock, however, {001} in mica may be in a state of strong planar preferred orientation. The subfabric for this element is anisotropic. A fabric is isotropic only where all determined subfabrics are isotropic.

THE CONCEPT OF THE TECTONITE FABRIC

Fabric and Deformation. Something of the origin and evolution of any rock is recorded in its fabric. Deformed rocks have the most diverse origins and the longest and most complicated histories of development. Their fabrics are likely to be correspondingly complex and they pose problems in fabric interpretation that are less amenable to conventional methods of geologic investigation than are the fabrics of undeformed sedimentary rocks. This is why structural detail of regionally metamorphosed rocks has been largely neglected in much routine geologic mapping.

Historically, structural geology begins almost with geology itself; but at first it was virtually synonymous with stratigraphy. Concern was initially mainly with fossiliferous rocks which, by their very nature, are relatively weakly deformed or internally reconstructed. Their structures are generally simple and were most easily studied as a corollary to stratigraphy and paleontology. The work of Lapworth[20] in the Lower Paleozoic rocks of the Southern Uplands of Scotland is an example of the way in which paleontology and stratigraphy complement each other in structural studies. Although the existence of isoclinal folds was established by Lapworth, their full geometric properties were not determined, nor was the nature of the internal movements accompanying the formation of the folds fully appreciated.

In 1843 John Phillips published a paper entitled "On certain movements in the parts of stratified rocks"[21] in which he noted the distortion of fossils in folded rocks. Sharpe[22] in 1846 noted the same phenomenon and stated that the internal structure of a rock is changed by differential movements of its smallest parts during the formation of large folds. He mentioned that fossils in some folded and cleaved rocks are distorted to some degree in every part of the rock. In this paper Sharpe also cautioned against confusion of bedding with cleavage, and noted that in many gneisses the foliation and layering that resemble bedding are more closely related to cleavage, which he correctly interpreted as being of dynamic origin. These early writers were among the first geologists to realize that deformation penetrates a rock body on all scales, that the formation of even a simple open large fold is effected by intergranular and even intragranular adjustments throughout the body.[23] Moreover, because the structural changes on different scales in the same act of deformation can be correlated with each other, the distortion of a small volume such as a fossil or even a group of grains tells something about the distortion of the whole body.

Componental Movements. Many strongly deformed rocks, which on the basis of laboratory behavior under room conditions would be classified as rigid and brittle, show evidence of a previous mobility similar to that of viscous fluid or a plastically flowing solid. To denote the process whereby a rock is deformed continuously in space without loss of cohesion, the descriptive term *flow* is used. The mechanisms of flow in solid rocks are varied and imperfectly understood. Certainly they include intracrystalline plastic flow (translation and twin gliding), intergranular slip and rotation, cataclasis, recrystallization, and neomineralization. Such relative movements of component particles of crystals or rocks Sander[24] called *componental movements* (*Teilbewegungen*). He recognized two kinds:

[20] C. Lapworth, The Moffat Series, *Geol. Soc. London Quart. Jour.*, vol. 34, pp. 240–346, 1878.

[21] J. Phillips, *Brit. Assoc. Adv. Sci.*, pp. 60–61, 1843 (Cork).

[22] D. Sharpe, On slaty cleavage, *Geol. Soc. London Quart. Jour.*, vol. 3, pp. 74–104, 1846.

[23] Sander, *op. cit.*, pp. 281–314, 1911.

[24] Sander, *op. cit.*, p. 115, 1930.

1. *Direct componental movements*, in which the relative movements of particles are highly correlated in a direct way, as in gliding processes within grains, and shearing and sliding movements between them.

2. *Indirect componental movements*, in which the correlation of relative movements can only be defined statistically, as in processes like ionic diffusion and migration along grain boundaries during recrystallization and neomineralization.

It is difficult to make any hard and fast distinction between these two kinds of movement.

The relative importance of these various processes in the history of most deformed rocks is unknown, but it may be presumed to influence their patterns of preferred orientation of grains or other structural features. Thus the patterns of preferred orientation of grains that arise when diffusion processes predominate will probably be different from those to which deformation by translation and twin gliding lead. However, our concern here is not with the patterns of preferred orientations themselves but with their symmetry, and from Curie's principles we may expect the symmetry of patterns of preferred orientation arising in given circumstances to be the same whatever the mechanism of deformation.[25]

Tectonites. *Definition.* Continuous solid flow of an aggregate is compounded of local componental movements differing amongst themselves and separated by discontinuities. Deformation is apparently continuous and homogeneous only in domains that are large in relation to these discontinuities in movement. On a microscopic scale surfaces of discontinuous movement in a flowing aggregate are either intragranular (surfaces of translation and twin gliding) or intergranular (boundaries between grains). Such movements together with indirect componental movements can lead to a preferred orientation of grains that is in some way an imprint of the deformation. Larger-scale discontinuities in movement occur (1) along discrete slip surfaces composed of aligned grain boundaries, that transgress a rock generally in parallel families, and (2) along surfaces which, while not actual slip surfaces, mark some change in the character of deformation—for instance, axial surfaces of some folds.

On a certain scale, penetrative discontinuities in structure are penetrative discontinuities in movement during flow, since on a smaller scale they separate domains with different kinds of behavior. Therefore, a fabric that has been deformed by flow in the solid state preserves in the preferred orientation and disposition of its fabric elements a record of the nature and extent of deformation. Such fabrics Sander[26] termed *tectonites*. In much the same way a worked metal retains in its grain fabric a complete or partial record of the manner and degree of working, and the alignment of inequidimensional particles suspended in a fluid indicates geometric features of flow.

[25] Paterson and Weiss, *op. cit.*, p. 860.
[26] Sander, *op. cit.*, p. 62, 1930.

Sander divides all rocks into tectonites and nontectonites. Nontectonites have fabrics whose every individual component acquired its position and orientation uninfluenced by movements of neighboring grains. Processes forming nontectonite fabrics include mechanical settling, precipitation from solution or fusion, progressive crystallization at a migrating nonpenetrative surface, and so on. Most veins are nontectonites possessing growth fabrics. Most sedimentary rocks and some igneous rock thus are not tectonites but have depositional or growth fabrics. However, even compaction following sedimentation involves some direct componental movements; and in diagenetic processes indirect componental movements play a role that may be highly correlated with compaction. As so often happens with regard to rock classification it is neither possible nor desirable to distinguish sharply between the two contrasted classes; some rocks are transitional between tectonites and nontectonites.

For practical purposes a rock is here termed a tectonite if its fabric clearly displays coordinated geometric features related to continuous flow during its formation.

Types of Tectonite. Knopf and Ingerson,[27] following Griggs, recognize several types of tectonite, as follows:

1. Primary tectonites: those in which fabric components have responded to movements in an enclosing medium without themselves undergoing deformation. Into this category fall igneous rocks in which early formed crystals become aligned by continuous movements in an enclosing melt—"fusion tectonites" in Sander's terminology. Here also belong many current-laid sediments, such as dune sands, whose bedding and ripple patterns reflect the flow of air from which they were deposited.

2. Secondary tectonites: those in which components and fabric elements have responded directly to moving influences. Most or all deformed rocks fall into this category.

3. Mimetic tectonites: those in which growth or enlargement of grains by post-tectonic recrystallization or neomineralization has been influenced by the anisotropy of an existing tectonite fabric. Componental movements affecting mimetic fabrics are entirely indirect; structures initially present may be greatly intensified by growth of new grains in parallel preferred orientations. The new grains may be preferentially grown from existing nuclei or may arise by nucleation in a structurally anisotropic field. The mica fabrics of many post-tectonically crystallized schists are mimetic in that the parallel orientation of newly crystallized mica flakes preserves and intensifies preexisting structural surfaces.

The above categories are defined on a genetic basis. Sander[28] has also subdivided tectonites descriptively into S-tectonites, which have fabrics

---

[27] Knopf and Ingerson, *op. cit.,* pp. 40, 41.
[28] Sander, *op. cit.,* p. 58, 1930.

dominated by planar features, and *B*-tectonites, which have fabrics dominated by linear features.   There is no sharp line of demarcation between the two classes, and the distinction will be pursued no further.

Metamorphic Tectonites.   The present work excludes weakly deformed rocks and both sedimentary and igneous tectonites of the primary class. Analysis of the fabric of primary igneous tectonites presents special problems of procedure and interpretation that have been developed in H. Cloos's classic treatment of "granite tectonics."[29]   This book is restricted to metamorphic tectonites, the geometric features of whose fabrics clearly reflect the componental movements—direct or indirect— of flow in the solid state.   The term tectonite is used henceforth in this restricted sense.

Fabric Elements of Tectonites.   In general, tectonites have geometrically more complicated fabrics than do other rocks.   Sedimentary rocks normally contain only one planar fabric element (bedding), commonly in a state of planar preferred orientation or some other geometrically simple condition; and only relatively rarely do they contain strongly defined linear fabric elements (for instance, groove and flute casts, lines of intersection of normal bedding and cross-bedding, and so on) of nontectonic origin.   Most of these sedimentary structures have developed at an interface between the sediment and the medium of deposition (water, air, or ice); and they represent variations at this interface in time as well as in space, the record being but slightly modified by diagenetic processes.

In most tectonites, on the other hand, initially simple fabrics of sedimentary or igneous origin have been grossly modified, and their planar and linear features geometrically transformed by deformation.   New structural features have appeared as a result of solid flow.   Some tectonites have been formed from earlier tectonites by repeated deformation giving rise to complicated fabrics difficult to interpret.   Sander[30] has distinguished between complete obliteration (*Umprägung*) of all initial geometric features of a fabric, and overprinting (*Uberprägung*) of new features on initial features without obliteration.   Fabrics developed by the former process are relatively simple geometrically because only structural features that may be correlated directly with deformation are present.   But such fabrics cannot be fully interpreted kinematically because no transformed structures inherited from the initial fabric remain as markers to show the nature and magnitude of deformation.   Fabrics developed by overprinting, on the other hand, contain structural features inherited from one or more previous conditions of the fabric, together

---

[29] E.g., H. Cloos, *Einführung in die tektonische Behandlung magmatische Erscheinungen*, Pt. I, Bornträger, Berlin, 1925; E. Cloos, The application of recent structural methods in the interpretation of the crystalline rocks of Maryland, *Maryland Geol. Survey*, vol. 13, pp. 36–49, 1937.

[30] Sander, *op. cit.*, pp. 29–31, 1930.

with structural features imposed entirely by deformation. Such fabrics commonly have great geometric complexity, but, because they contain fragments of their past history as distorted and transformed markers, they are the most fruitful subjects for structural analysis.

Most tectonites are products of overprinting. The fabric of a tectonite, therefore, generally contains fabric elements of the following kinds:[31]

1. Elements inherited in a transformed but recognizable condition from an initial or earlier fabric—*inherited fabric elements.* They may be geometrically transformed so that their orientation has changed with respect to external coordinates; but they have retained their identity as planar or linear elements. Examples are planar sedimentary bedding surviving in tectonites such as the "pebble-free bands" in a deformed conglomerate described by Flinn,[32] and the transformed linear structures described from parts of the Scottish Highlands by Ramsay.[33]

2. Elements imposed entirely by deformation—*imposed fabric elements,* e.g., slaty cleavage and other kinds of secondary foliation.

3. Elements arising by geometric combination of inherited and imposed elements—*composite fabric elements,* e.g., any fold axis formed in inherited bedding or foliation; or lineations marking the intersection of a transformed inherited s-surface and an imposed foliation.[34]

A similar terminology can be applied conveniently to the subfabrics defined by the spatial arrangement of elements. Thus a given tectonite fabric can contain inherited, imposed, and composite subfabrics as parts of its total fabric. Also, subfabrics which are composite or imposed at one stage in the evolution of a complex tectonite may become inherited subfabrics at a later stage. A given subfabric cannot always be assigned to one of the above categories, particularly where patterns of preferred orientation of crystallographic fabric elements are concerned. In the experimental deformation of Yule marble[35] an initial pattern of preferred orientation of [0001] in calcite is found to be progressively modified during deformation; but the final pattern always shows the influence of the initial pattern even where strain of specimen is large and the initial pattern itself has been completely obliterated (cf. pages 349 to 351).

The kinematic information provided by the three categories of subfabric is discussed in Chap. 10.

[31] See also Paterson and Weiss (*op. cit.,* pp. 876–879) for a more extended discussion.

[32] D. Flinn, On the deformation of the Funzie conglomerate, Fetlar, Shetland, *Jour. Geology,* vol. 64, p. 491, 1956.

[33] J. G. Ramsay, The deformation of early linear structures in areas of repeated folding, *Jour. Geology,* vol. 68, pp. 75–93, 1960.

[34] See for instance, L. E. Weiss and D. B. McIntyre, Structural geometry of Dalradian rocks at Loch Leven, Scottish Highlands, *Jour. Geology,* vol. 65, pp. 583–587, 1957.

[35] See, for instance, F. J. Turner, Lineation, symmetry and internal movements in monoclinic tectonite fabrics, *Geol. Soc. America Bull.,* vol. 68, pp. 12–16, 1957.

SYMMETRY OF TECTONITE FABRICS

Notion of Fabric Symmetry. The notion of fabric symmetry has been discussed in detail by Paterson and Weiss,[36] upon whose analysis the following general discussion is based.

The symmetry of a rock fabric has much in common with that of a crystal lattice. Both are infinitely extended structures so that their symmetry operations form space groups.[37] The symmetry of a fabric differs from that of a crystal lattice, however, in that it is defined statistically. The symmetry of a fabric, like that of a crystal, can be expressed in terms of the point-group symmetry (finite-body symmetry) of a small representative sample of the fabric, because to define statistical symmetry only arbitrary translations in all directions need be added to the operations of point-group symmetry. In a heterogeneous situation—e.g., in an individual small fold within a large array of similar folds—translations are absent and the symmetry of the heterogeneous structure is strictly of the point-group type. Individual fabric elements likewise have point-group symmetry; and this of course may differ from the space-group symmetry of their three-dimensional array in a subfabric.

The different types (point-groups) of fabric symmetry referred to below may conveniently be denoted by the standard Schönflies symbols of the crystallographer.[38] The reader should familiarize himself more particularly with the five types listed on page 44, as represented in natural rock fabrics. The symmetry of a fabric depends upon the symmetry of its subfabrics; and this in turn depends on the symmetry of the component fabric elements.

Symmetry of Fabric Elements. Fabric elements of tectonites are lines and planes of discontinuity in the fabric. With rare exceptions, such as graded bedding and primary flow structures inherited from sediments, they are nonpolar; and in structural analysis of tectonites any polar structures that may be measured have customarily been treated statistically as if nonpolar. Thus the symmetry of the individual fabric element has a unique axis of infinite symmetry (normal to a planar, parallel to a linear element) and perpendicular to this a plane of reflection. It is of the Schönflies type $D_{\infty h}$—the symmetry of a nonpolar line. Combinations of related noncrystallographic elements may have symmetry lower than $D_{\infty h}$. A fold is fully specified by an axial plane within which

---

[36] Paterson and Weiss, *op. cit.*, pp. 863–870.

[37] For discussion of space-group and point-group symmetry the reader is referred to standard texts on crystallography, e.g., F. C. Phillips, *An Introduction to Crystallography*, pp. 221–272, Longmans, London, 1946. Statistical symmetry is discussed by Paterson and Weiss, *op. cit.*, pp. 853–856.

[38] Paterson and Weiss, *op. cit.*, Table 2, p. 849, 1961.

lies the fold axis. The symmetry of the combined elements of the fold is D_{2h}—orthorhombic symmetry with three mutually perpendicular planes of symmetry, each normal to a twofold axis of symmetry.

Unique crystallographic elements such as $\{001\}$ in mica or $[0001]$ in quartz also have nonpolar axial symmetry $D_{\infty h}$. However crystallographic elements that are symmetrically repeated within each crystal will have other classes of symmetry. For example, the three $\{01\bar{1}2\}$ planes of calcite—even though they may be located by measuring a single visible $(01\bar{1}2)$ twin lamella plus the optic axis $[0001]$—collectively define a fabric element with symmetry D_{3d}—a triad axis normal to which are three diad axes of symmetry. Again $\{110\}$ in amphibole constitutes a fabric element with orthorhombic symmetry D_{2h}. Note that if only one of the crystallographically similar planes or lines is considered—e.g., the most conspicuously twinned of the three $\{01\bar{1}2\}$ planes in any grain of calcite—its symmetry is now $D_{\infty h}$.

Where fabric elements with crystallographic symmetry have a preferred orientation, the subfabric that they define can have pseudocrystallographic point-group symmetry, which is unlikely to arise from noncrystallographic elements. However, pseudocrystallographic symmetry does not necessarily follow from the preferred orientation of such fabric elements; for example, a calcite aggregate in which an a axis for each grain had for some reason become aligned parallel to a unique direction, but without accompanying alignment of c axes, would have symmetry $D_{\infty h}$. Pseudocrystalline symmetry occurs if there is preferred orientation of a set of equivalent nonunique crystallographic planes or lines. An example of a tectonite with pseudocrystallographic symmetry is the Poughquag quartzite studied by Higgs, Friedman, and Gebhart.[39]

Symmetry of Subfabrics and Fabrics. Because only centrosymmetric fabric elements have been measured so far in structural analysis only centrosymmetric subfabrics have been encountered. The study of natural tectonites has shown that, with respect to fabric elements of the kinds discussed in the previous sections, the natural tectonite fabrics have very few different kinds of symmetry. Excluding pseudocrystallographic symmetries defined by fabric elements with other than axial symmetry (that is, elements with symmetry other than $D_{\infty h}$), only 1-, 2-, and ∞-fold rotation axes, and planes and centers of symmetry, can be expected to arise. Therefore by putting $n = 1$, 2, and ∞ in a list of possible centrosymmetric groups of a homogeneous continuum,[40] only S_2 (C_i), C_{2h}, D_{2h}, $D_{\infty h}$, and $K_{\infty h}$ are obtained.

---

[39] D. V. Higgs, M. Friedman, and J. E. Gebhart, Petrofabric analysis by means of the X-ray diffractometer, *Geol. Soc. America Mem. 79*, chap. 10, fig. 6E, p. 285, 1960. This example has been considered in detail by Paterson and Weiss, *op. cit.*, pp. 864–865.

[40] Paterson and Weiss, *op. cit.*, p. 849, table 2.

These five symmetry classes are the observed classes of subfabrics of tectonites, and are named as follows:[41]

1. *Spherical fabrics*, symmetry $K_{\infty h}$: Fabrics have the symmetry of a sphere. Ideally this symmetry is shown by a random orientation of fabric elements and is therefore generally only approached in natural tectonites. Some hornfelses have subfabrics approaching this symmetry.

2. *Axial fabrics*, symmetry $D_{\infty h}$: Fabrics have the symmetry of a spheroid, that is, a unique axis which is the line of intersection of an infinite number of symmetry planes and is normal to another plane.

3. *Orthorhombic fabrics*, symmetry D_{2h}: Fabrics have the symmetry of a triaxial ellipsoid, that is, three mutually perpendicular planes of symmetry (plus three diad axes normal to them).

4. *Monoclinic fabrics*, symmetry C_{2h}: Fabrics have a single plane of symmetry (plus one diad axis normal to it).

5. *Triclinic fabrics*, symmetry $S_2 = C_i$: Fabric has no planes of symmetry.[42]

Each of the last three types has the symmetry of the holosymmetric class of the corresponding crystal system—(3) $m\,m\,m$, (4) $2/m$, (5) $\bar{1}$.

The symmetry of the total fabric is given by superposing the respective symmetries of the component subfabrics. Thus similarly oriented symmetry elements that are common to all the subfabrics are also symmetry elements of the total fabric. Symmetry elements not present in *all* subfabrics are not symmetry elements of the total fabric; and so the symmetry of a fabric cannot be higher than that of any of its subfabrics. Therefore, the five important types of symmetry listed for subfabrics above are also the important types that occur in fabrics.[43]

A subfabric can have the same symmetry as a total fabric, or it can have higher symmetry; it cannot have lower symmetry. This is in some respects analogous to the crystallographic situation where a given form can have the same symmetry as the crystal or a higher symmetry, depending on whether it corresponds to a general or a special form (e.g., {111} and {110}, respectively, in the orthorhombic sphenoidal crystal class 222). Fabrics in which all subfabrics agree in symmetry are termed by Sander[44] *homotactic fabrics;* those in which the subfabrics do not agree are termed *heterotactic fabrics*.

Experience shows that a few of the many possible subfabrics of a given fabric suffice to determine the symmetry of the total fabric. Thus if

---

[41] See also, Sander, *op. cit.*, p. 146, 1930, and *op. cit.*, p. 26, 1950.

[42] Figures 3-13 and 3-14 show patterns of preferred orientation of fabric elements with the five kinds of symmetry.

[43] Examples of natural tectonite fabrics on various scales analyzed in terms of superposition symmetry of their subfabrics are given by Paterson and Weiss, *op. cit.*, pp. 869–870.

[44] Sander, *op. cit.*, p. 165, 1930.

account is taken of the preferred orientation of axial crystallographic elements of two major, dissimilar minerals (e.g., quartz and mica, or calcite and mica) together with that of noncrystallographic elements such as foliations and lineations, the total symmetry so defined generally remains unchanged when other subfabrics are also taken into account. Structural analysis can be greatly simplified by careful selection of the elements to be measured.

The symmetry of a bulk physical property of a rock is likewise a guide to symmetry of its fabric (functional fabric). Neumann's principle[45] states that the symmetry element of any physical property of a crystal must include all the symmetry elements of its geometric (morphologic) symmetry. Where this principle is applied to aggregates, the study of easily determinable physical properties (such as bulk electrical, magnetic, or thermal properties) may be a convenient guide to the geometric symmetry of its fabric by showing which symmetry elements are lacking. Further, the measurement of properties such as piezoelectricity allows detection of the absence of a center of symmetry, not otherwise possible. Such investigations are likely to be most useful in determining fabric symmetry in very weakly deformed rocks where conventional methods of geometric analysis yield conclusions of doubtful statistical significance, and in very fine-grained rocks in which conventional microscopic study is impossible.[46] However, it must be remembered that the symmetry of a bulk physical property need not be the *same* as the structural symmetry of a body; it need only include the symmetry elements of the body (page 386). For example, the optical properties of an isometric crystal have spherical symmetry whereas the crystal structure is less symmetrical. On the other hand, examination of several bulk physical properties will generally reveal the true symmetry of the body.

[45] E.g., Paterson and Weiss, *op. cit.*, p. 857.
[46] E.g., R. Brinkmann, W. Giesel, and R. Hoeppener, Über Versuche zur Bestimmung der Gesteinsanisotropie, *Neues Jahrb. Geologie u. Paläontologie Mh.*, 1961, pp. 22–33, 1961.

CHAPTER 3

GRAPHIC TREATMENT OF FABRIC DATA

DATA OF STRUCTURAL ANALYSIS

Source of Data. Except where artificial surfaces such as road cuts, bore holes, mine workings, and so on are present, fabric data are obtained, as are most other geologic data, by direct observation on the topographic erosion surface separating the lithosphere from the atmosphere. Intersecting this irregular surface are surfaces and lines of structural, compositional, and stratigraphic discontinuity. The complexity of lines of intersection of intricately folded surfaces of discontinuity with an irregular topographic surface is clearly shown by any well-prepared geologic map of metamorphic rocks exposed in a mountainous terrain of high relief.

Rocks tend to weather and to break naturally in a manner conditioned by their anisotropy, so that foliation and bedding surfaces are commonly exposed (or can easily be exposed by artificial breakage) together with linear structures they may contain. On a mesoscopic scale, therefore, the attitude of planar and linear structures generally can be determined in three dimensions by direct measurement. On certain naturally developed surfaces, however, such as glaciated pavements, smooth roches moutoneéns, exfoliated inselbergs and tors (especially where these are cut in weakly anisotropic rocks), direct measurement of structural planes and lines without geometric extrapolation on a mesoscopic scale may be difficult or impossible (page 80). Extrapolation in observation is at a minimum in laboratory investigation of hand specimens and thin sections.

The data of structural analysis are drawn then from field observations supplemented by laboratory examination of hand specimens and thin sections. There are three kinds of data, relating respectively to location, dimension, and orientation.

Data of Location. These are concerned with positions of structures and fabric domains either on the bounding surface of a body as observed directly or within the body as determined by extrapolation of surface observations. Location of nonpenetrative structures is particularly important. In order to specify a fault or an unconformity it is insufficient to give only attitude; position also must be indicated with reference to known geographic lines and points. The data of location are conventionally represented on geologic maps. Inferred subsurface location can be indicated by geologic sections and profiles or by structure (stratum) contours drawn on a particular surface of discontinuity by extrapolation from surface information or from data from bore holes.

Location of fabric elements is not of prime importance in homogeneous bodies because fabric elements penetrate a body uniformly and have statistically the same attitude in all large samples. Most geologic bodies are, however, heterogeneous. In such bodies the spatial arrangement of fabric elements can outline homogeneous domains on a smaller scale than that of the whole body. The placing on a geologic map of suitable symbols indicates locations and orientations of particular measured fabric elements typical of the domains in which they occur.

Data of Dimension. These are concerned with shape and extent of fabric domains and discontinuities. The dimensions of grains in a thin section, and the surface extent of a large body of metamorphic rock shown to scale on a geologic map, both fall into this category.

Data of Orientation. These are concerned with the attitudes of structures in a body with respect to fixed axes of reference. For mesoscopic and macroscopic observations the reference axes are generally geographic. But some mesoscopic and many microscopic observations are more conveniently related to three orthogonal reference axes, termed *fabric axes*, chosen with respect to geometric features of a fabric. The criteria governing the selection of fabric axes are discussed on pages 87 to 90.

All fabric elements have the geometric properties of either a plane or a line. The attitude of a planar structure such as a surface of bedding or foliation is conventionally related to geographic axes in terms of *strike* (bearing from north of a horizontal line lying in the plane) and *dip* (angle between horizontal and the surface measured in the plane normal to the strike). The attitude of a rectilinear structure is conventionally related to geographic axes in terms of *trend* (strike of vertical plane containing the line) and *plunge* (angle between horizontal and the line in this plane). Where fabric axes are used as reference coordinates, the attitudes of structural planes and lines are similarly related to these in terms of measured angles.

Geometrically, the most significant feature of an anisotropic fabric is the preferred orientation of the elements determining the anisotropy. Investigation of preferred orientation is the essence of structural analysis. The rather complex procedures of measurement on different scales are described in Chaps. 4 to 6. In the present chapter we concentrate on graphic plotting and treatment of orientation data, for this is independent of scale.

Representation of Data on Maps and Sections. Conventionally in structural geology, location, dimension, and orientation of structural features are represented in three dimensions by means of geologic maps and cross sections, or by combination of these in block diagrams. Location and extent of nonpenetrative structural surfaces are shown as lines of *contact* separating domains of different lithologic, stratigraphic, or structural properties. Location and orientation of penetrative structures such as bedding and foliation are shown by symbols. Where topography is irregular and relief great, a measure of *depth* is inherent in a map; but where a topographic surface is smooth, planar, and level on a regional scale, a geologic map is effectively a horizontal planar cross section through a geologic body.

A well-prepared geologic map should be effectively a factual presentation of observations with little or no interpretive comment on the part of the geologist. The only limits to the quality of a geologic map should be set by accessibility, exposure, and time available for completion. Two equally competent geologists mapping the same well-exposed body of rocks should produce maps identical in all significant features.

A third dimension is commonly added to a geologic map by construction of cross sections. The value of these as additional indicators of geologic structure is in inverse proportion to the amount of inference used in their construction. A measure of inference is inevitable in all such constructions not based on detailed subsurface observations; but the amount can be reduced by observing two guiding principles, as follows:

1. Cross sections are significant only where constructed for bodies with relatively simple structure. Where bedded rocks contain simple open folds with horizontal or gently plunging axes, it is possible to construct a vertical cross section which is almost free of inference. On the other hand, a heterogeneous body of intensely deformed metamorphic rock containing several generations of large and complicated fold structures with divergent axes—affecting not only bedding but foliation—is not a suitable subject for construction of cross sections. So much inference is generally necessary to predict how structures in such bodies change below the topographic surface that cross sections drawn through them are largely conjectural and often a source of controversy.

2. Any construction of cross sections requires extrapolation from surface data. Extrapolation is only possible either where the rate at which the form of the body changes in the direction of extrapolation is known or where there is no change in this direction. Rarely is the rate of structural change in a given direction known in a geologic body. On the other hand, structurally simple homogeneous bodies commonly have a direction along which change is inappreciable or minimal, e.g., a rectilinear axis of folding. A cross section drawn normal to such a direction most clearly displays the structural character of the body in an undistorted form and gives a concise impression of the fold form. Such cross sections are termed *profiles*. For bodies with plunging fold axes, profiles may be constructed by orthographic projection of a geologic map onto a

surface normal to the fold axis.[1]   The advantage of this method of profile construction is that no contact line appears on the profile that is not also on the geologic map from which it was prepared.

Block diagrams are combinations of maps with cross sections viewed generally in orthographic projection.   A useful method of block-diagram construction that can be used in conjunction with axial projection is described by Goguel.[2]   Block diagrams are commonly used in structural geology in a schematic fashion to show the mutual relations of fabric domains and other structures.[3]

EQUAL-AREA PROJECTION IN STRUCTURAL ANALYSIS

Equal-area Net.   Structural analysis is concerned especially with orientation data relating to planes and lines (fabric elements) and their intersections.   In study of crystal morphology the relative orientations of planes and lines are conventionally represented and their geometric relations determined by means of the familiar *stereographic projection*— a tool which is commonly employed, too, in graphic solution of many problems of structural geology.[4]   In structural analysis, the necessity to evaluate preferred orientations of fabric elements imposes a peculiar limitation on graphic procedure.   All equal areas on the surface of the reference sphere must remain equal on the projection itself.   This is not true of the stereographic projection, in which centrally situated areas are diminished relatively to peripheral areas of equivalent size on the reference sphere.   To obviate this difficulty it is customary in structural

[1] For examples of the use of true profiles in structural analysis, the student is referred to the following papers: C. E. Wegmann, Beispieler tektonischer Analysen des Grundgebinges in Finnland, *Comm. géol. Finlande Bull.*, vol. 8, no. 87, pp. 98–127, 1929; D. B. McIntyre, The tectonics of the area between Grantown and Tomintoul (Mid-Strathspey), *Geol. Soc. London Quart. Jour.*, vol. 107, pp. 1–16, 1951; L. E. Weiss, Structural analysis of the Basement System at Turoka, Kenya, *Overseas Geology and Mineral Resources*, vol. 7, no. 2, pp. 135–139, London, 1959.

[2] J. Goguel, *Traité de Tectonique*, pp. 112–116, Masson et Cie, Paris, 1952.

[3] For examples of the use of schematic block diagrams see G. Wilson, The tectonics of the Tintagel area, North Cornwall, *Geol. Soc. London, Quart. Jour.*, vol. 106, p. 416, fig. 10, 1951; M. R. W. Johnson, The tectonic phenomena associated with the post-Cambrian thrust movements at Coulin, Wester Ross, *Geol. Soc. London, Quart. Jour.*, vol. 113, p. 264, fig. 11, 1957.   Construction of schematic block diagrams to scale is discussed in D. B. McIntyre and L. E. Weiss, Construction of block diagrams to scale in orthographic projection, *Geologists' Assoc. Proc.*, vol. 67, pp. 142–155, 1956.

[4] W. H. Bucher, The stereographic projection, a handy tool for the practical geologist, *Jour. Geol.*, vol. 52, pp. 191–212, 1944; F. C. Phillips, *Stereographic Projection in Structural Geology*, E. Arnold, London, 1954; D. V. Higgs and G. Tunell, *Angular Relations of Lines and Planes*, Wm. C. Brown, Dubuque, Iowa, 1959; P. C. Badgley, *Structural Methods for the Exploration Geologist*, pp. 187–242, Harper, New York, 1959; P. J. Haman, *Manual of Stereographic Projection*, West Canadian Research Publications, Calgary, pp. 1–67, 1961.

analysis to use a type of equal-area projection—also known as the Lambert projection (after its inventor) or the Schmidt projection (after W. Schmidt[5] who first used it in structural geology).

Both types of projection employ a reference sphere in which planes and lines passing through the center intersect the surface as great circles and points respectively. In equal-area projection, as in stereographic projection, these are projected—but from the lower hemisphere only[6]—onto the equatorial plane; but the graphic procedure employed maintains the desired equal-area specification that is absent from stereographic projection. Because of this property, density distribution of points on the projection faithfully reflects the preferred orientation of the corresponding lines passing through the center of the reference sphere. Stereographic projection is from a point source, and circles on the reference sphere appear as arcs of circles on the projection. This is not true of the equal-area projection; circles are projected as elliptical arcs, save where they lie in or normal to the plane of projection (the boundary circle and diameters of the projection respectively).

Fabric data are projected by means of a three-dimensional protractor made by equal-area projection of a hemisphere inscribed with parallels of latitude and meridians of longitude, generally at 2° intervals. The equatorial plane bounding this hemisphere appears as the peripheral circle of the projection—termed the *primitive circle*. The hemisphere is projected on a meridianal plane so that parallels and meridians appear in projection as in Fig. 3-1. The protractor is termed an *equal-area net*.[7] By its use, the attitude of any plane or line in relation to known axes of reference can be represented on a plane surface, and angles between planes and lines can be measured in any plane. The meridians of the net represent the traces on the reference hemisphere of planes passing through the center and the north and south poles of the hemisphere. These meridians are termed *great circles* of the net. The parallels represent traces of planes normal to the plane of projection but not passing through the center of the hemisphere. These parallels are called *small circles* of the net. The two diameters of the net are great circles normal to the plane of projection.

Nets are supplied printed on medium paper. For use in statistical analysis (Fig. 3-2), the net *N* is mounted (with transparent rubber-based paper cement) face upward on stout, smooth plywood or cardboard *B*. For protection a sheet of tracing acetate *A* is cemented to the face of

[5] W. Schmidt, Gefügestatistik, *Tschermaks mineralog. petrog. Mitt.*, vol. 38, pp. 395–399, 1925.

[6] The data taken from the upper hemisphere would be identical, but inverted through a center of symmetry, so long as the lines and planes have axial and not polar symmetry.

[7] Such nets of 20 cm diameter are at present commercially available from Department of Geology, The Johns Hopkins University, Baltimore 18, Maryland.

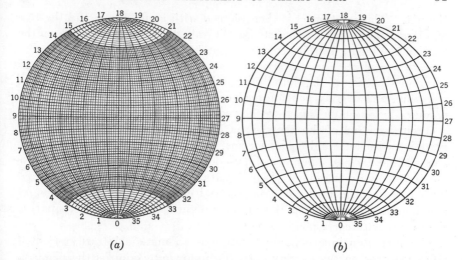

(a)   *(b)*

FIG. 3-1. Equal-area net. The diameters are the same as those of most projections and orientation diagrams throughout the book.

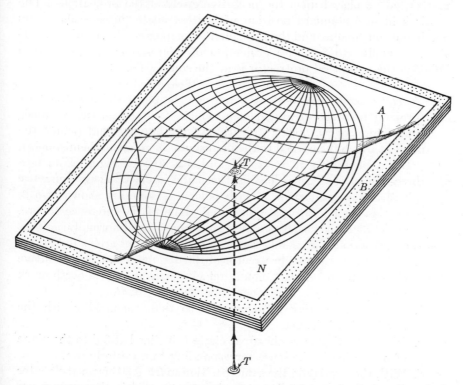

FIG. 3-2. Twenty-centimeter equal-area net mounted for use in structural analysis (*B*—stout board; *T*—thumbtack; *N*—net; *A*—sheet of transparent tracing acetate).

the net.   The *exact center* is then pierced with a small hole and the tine of a large thumbtack T is inserted and firmly glued into the hole from the back of the board until it projects about ¼ in. beyond the net.

Data are plotted on overlays of thin tracing paper which are free to rotate on the tine of the thumbtack.   To prevent tearing at the point of puncture, the overlay is reinforced centrally by a small piece of transparent adhesive tape affixed to the reverse side.

Geometric Use of the Equal-area Net.   Following are some general graphic operations and constructions, concerned with angular relations between planes and lines, widely used in structural analysis.   Each is illustrated by an example for which data are given, and is accompanied by a figure.   The reader can follow and check these constructions by plotting the given data in the manner described below and comparing the results with corresponding figures.

The first step in every construction is to mark arbitrarily selected reference axes on the overlay.   In the following examples the plane of projection is horizontal, the reference axes are geographic (*NS, EW* and vertical), and the draftsman is looking downward, so that only a north mark need be placed upon the primitive circle of the projection.   The net is held in a standard position with great circles intersecting in its north and south poles, and the two ruled diameters north-south and east-west.   Usually—to facilitate projection of microscopic data—the zero point on the peripheral protractor is at the south pole.

1. *To plot a plane* (Fig. 3-3): A plane may be plotted either as a *trace* (projection of the great circle on which it intersects the reference hemisphere) or as a *pole* (projection of the impingement point—the point at which the normal to the plane cuts the reference hemisphere).

    Let a plane P strike N25°W and dip 30°W.   Figure 3-3a is a three-dimensional view showing the plane intersecting the reference sphere in the great circle P with pole p.   These are shown also in projection on a horizontal equatorial plane of the reference sphere. Figure 3-3b is the corresponding projection viewed normally.   Steps in construction of Fig. 3-3b using an equal-area net are as follows:

    a. Using the peripheral protractor of the net, mark s on the primitive circle of the overlay 25° counterclockwise from N (the north mark on the overlay).   This represents the strike of P.

    b. Rotate the overlay 25° clockwise so that s coincides with the north pole of the net.

    c. On the overlay trace the great circle P inclined at 30° to the plane of projection in the sense corresponding to a westerly dip.

    d. With the overlay in the same position mark p 30° from the center along the east-west diameter of the net, again in the sense corresponding to a westerly dip.

e. Rotate the overlay 25° counterclockwise to bring N to the original N position (Fig. 3-3b).

2. *To plot a line* (Fig. 3-4a): Let the line L trend N42°E and plunge 62°. This statement implies that the *downward* end of the line is in the N42°E sense of the trend. Whereas either end of the strike of a plane may be specified, the trend of a line, although horizontal, is polar in that one end points in the same sense as the downward end

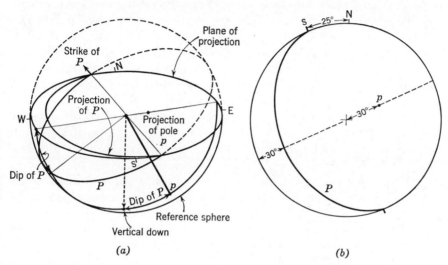

(a)   (b)

FIG 3-3. To plot a plane P (data in text). N—north mark on overlay.

of the datum line; this end must be specified. Steps in construction are as follows:

a. Mark the trend t on the primitive circle of the overlay. Rotate the overlay clockwise through 48° so that t coincides with the east-west diameter of the net D.

b. Mark L, the projection of the line to be plotted, 62° along D from the circumference.

c. Rotate the overlay to bring N to the north position on the net.

3. *To plot a plane containing a line* (Fig. 3-4b): If the attitudes of a plane and a contained line are known independently of one another these can be plotted separately as in operations 1 and 2. Commonly in structural geology the attitude of a line contained in a given plane is specified only by the angle and sense of *pitch* in the plane. Pitch is the angle between the line and the strike of some specified plane in which it lies.

Let the pitch of a line L in P of operation 1 be 53°SW. Rotate the strike of P to coincide with the north pole of the net. Now plot L 53° from the south pole of the net on the great circle of P.

4. *To find the orientation of a plane containing two given lines* (Fig. 3-4c):
Let the first line L_1 trend S78°W and plunge 40°, and the second line
L_2 trend N42°E and plunge 62°.   Since any two nonparallel lines lie
in only one plane, there can be only one great circle of the net that

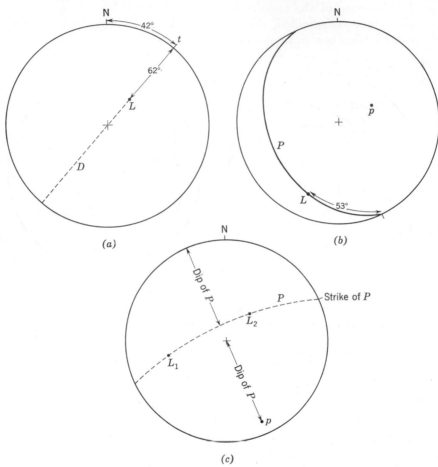

Fig. 3-4. Geometric operations in projection (data in text).   (a) To plot a line L.
(b) To plot a plane P containing a line L; p is the pole of P.   (c) To find the orientation of a plane P continuing two given lines L_1 and L_2; p is the pole of P.

passes through L_1 and L_2.   Rotate the overlay until L_1 and L_2 lie on
a great circle (P in Fig. 3-4c).   Then P is the plane containing L_1
and L_2; it strikes N67°E and dips 77°N.

5. *To find the line of intersection of two given planes* (Fig. 3-5a): Let
plane P_1 strike N25°W and dip 30°W, and plane P_2 strike N55°E
and dip 48°SE.   Their line of intersection L is the unique line common to both planes.   In projection, L (trend S32°W and plunge 16°)

is the point of intersection of the traces of P_1 and P_2. It is also p_3, the pole of the plane P_3 that contains the poles (p_1 and p_2) of P_1 and P_2. This plane is plotted as in operation 4.

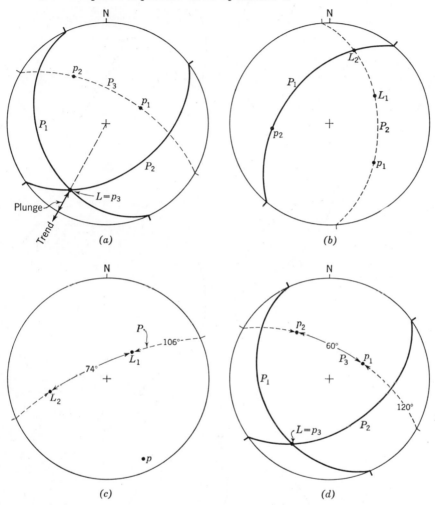

FIG. 3-5. Geometric operations in projection (data in text). P_1, P_2 are planes; p_1, p_2 are poles of P_1, P_2; L_1, L_2 are lines. (a) To find the line of intersection L of two given planes P_1 and P_2. (b) To find the orthographic projection of a given line L_1 on a given plane P_1. (c) To find angle between two given lines L_1 and L_2. (d) To find angle between two given planes P_1 and P_2.

6. *To find the orthographic projection of a given line on a given plane* (Fig. 3-5b): Let the plane P_1 strike N40°E and dip 50°NW, and the line L_1 trend N59°E and plunge 46°. The orthographic projection of a line on a plane is given by the trace on this plane of the plane normal to it containing the line. All planes normal to P_1 must con-

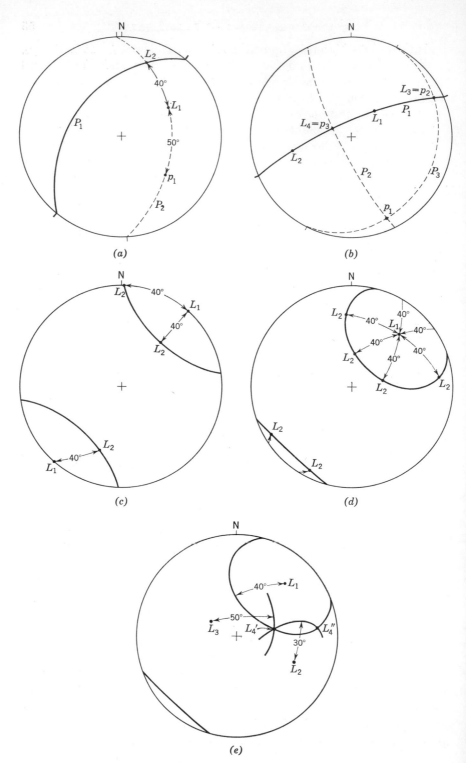

Fig. 3-6. For descriptive legend see opposite page.

tain its pole p_1. Only one of these planes also contains L_1. This unique plane P_2 is found as in operation 4; its intersection with the trace of P_1 (found as in operation 5) is L_2, the orthographic projection of L_1 on P_1. L_2 trends N19°E and plunges 14°.

7. *To find the angle between two given lines* (Fig. 3-5c): Let the line L_1 trend N42°E and plunge 62°, and let L_2 trend S78°W and plunge 40°. Rotate the overlay until L_1 and L_2 lie on a great circle of the net. The angle between the two lines can now be measured directly along this great circle. In Fig. 3-5c L_1 and L_2 intersect at 74° (supplementary angle 106°).

8. *To find the angle between two given planes* (Fig. 3-5d): Let the planes P_1 and P_2 be as in operation 5. The angle between two planes is measured in the plane P_3 normal to their line of intersection L. It is the angle between the poles p_1 and p_2 which can be measured directly as in operation 7. The supplementary angles are 60° and 120°.

9. *To find the angle between a given plane and a given line* (Fig. 3-6a): Let the plane P_1 and the line L_1 be as in operation 6. The angle required can be determined directly as the angle between L_1 and L_2, its orthographic projection on P_1. There are two supplementary angles, but the smaller angle (40° in Fig. 3-6a) is generally specified. This can be found more conveniently by measuring the angle between L_1 and p_1 in the plane P_2 (50°), as in operation 7, and taking the complementary angle.

10. *To bisect the angles between two given lines* (Fig. 3-6b): Let the lines L_1 and L_2 be as in operation 7. Plot the plane P_1 containing these lines, and on the great circle P_1 bisect the two supplementary angles between L_1 and L_2 at L_3 and L_4. The planes P_2 and P_3 normal to P_1 that bisect the angles between L_1 and L_2 can be found by constructing the planes of which L_3 and L_4 are poles.

11. *To find the locus of line at a given angle to a given line* (Fig. 3-6c, d): Where the given line L_1 is parallel to the plane of projection (Fig. 3-6c), the locus of lines L_2 at a given angle (40°) to L_1 is a small circle of the net centered on L_1. Where L_1 is inclined to the plane of projection (Fig. 3-6d), the locus of L_2 can be found by constructing a small circle about the inclined line L_1. Plot a number of points representing lines at the required angle to L_1 as follows: place L_1 on successive arbitrary great circles of the net by rotating the overlay a few degrees at a time in a constant sense, and for each great circle plot two points, one on either side of L_1, at 40° to L_1, measured along

---

FIG. 3-6. Geometric operations in projection (data in text). P_1, P_2 are planes; p_1, p_2 are poles of P_1, P_2; L_1, L_2 are lines. (a) To find angle between a given plane P_1 and a given line L_1. (b) To bisect angles between two given lines L_1 and L_2. (c–d) To find locus of a line L_2 at a given angle to a given line L_1. (e) To find a line L_4 at given angles to two or more given lines (L_1, L_2, and L_3).

the great circle.   The smooth curve connecting all such points is the required locus.

12. *To find a line at given angles to two or more given lines* (Fig. 3-6e): It is required to find the line L_4 inclined to three given lines L_1, L_2, and L_3 at angles of 40°, 30°, and 50° respectively.   Construct small circles of given angular radius around the given lines as in operation 11.   The small circles of appropriate radius around any two given lines (for instance, L_1 and L_2) intersect at two points, L_4' and L_4''; but only one of these points (L_4') is inclined at 50° to L_3.

Statistical Use of Equal-area Net.   *Patterns of Preferred Orientation.* The nature and degree of preferred orientation of a given type of planar or linear fabric element are expressed graphically by the distribution on an equal-area projection of points (poles, in the case of planar elements) representing the individual orientations of a large number of representative measured elements of the kind in question.   The points so plotted constitute a *pattern of preferred orientation* or an *orientation diagram* of the given element.   A statistically random orientation is expressed by a pattern in which there is no obvious tendency for *reproducible* local concentration of plotted points.   Most orientation diagrams representing tectonite subfabrics show marked reproducible local concentrations and complementary voids or sparsely populated areas.   These are graphic evidence of preferred orientation.   Such concentrations observed in diagrams for homogeneous domains conform to one of three types:

1. A maximum.   This is a single area of high concentration, generally with a well-defined center of gravity.   For linear elements this pattern indicates a linear preferred orientation, for planar elements a planar preferred orientation.   Some patterns show several maxima.   Figure 3-7a shows a symmetric maximum.

2. A girdle.   This is an arcuate maximum coinciding approximately with a great circle of the net.   The pole of the corresponding great circle is the center of a sparsely populated area and is termed the *girdle axis*. Most girdles contain one or more distinct maxima (Fig. 3-7b).   Rather rarely, two intersecting girdles are combined (generally with several well-defined maxima) in a single "crossed girdle" pattern (Fig. 3-7c).   For planar elements a girdle indicates a linear preferred orientation (the planar elements are statistically cozonal, with the girdle axis as zone axis); for linear elements it indicates a planar preferred orientation.

3. A small-circle girdle or cleft girdle.   This is an annular maximum occupying a small circle of the net.   Internal maxima generally are developed (Fig. 3-7d).   Both planar and linear elements have a preferred orientation at a fixed oblique angle to a line—the girdle axis.

Contouring Orientation Diagrams.   Most students will find it difficult to visualize fully the pattern of preferred orientation expressed by a point

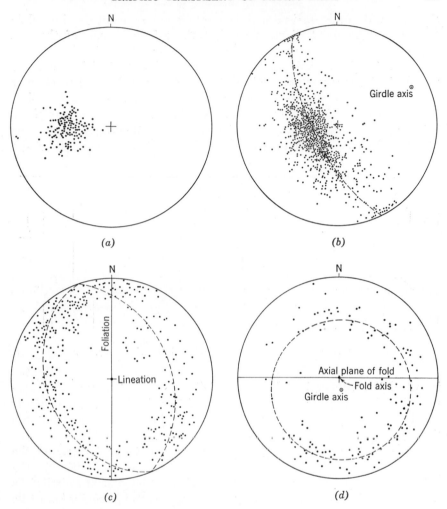

Fɪɢ. 3-7. Patterns of preferred orientation (median girdles shown by broken lines). (a) Maximum (symmetric): 150 lineations from Loch Leven, Scottish Highlands. (b) Girdle: 1,000 poles of foliation from Turoka, Kenya. (c) "Crossed girdle": 390 [0001] of quartz from quartzite, Barstow, California. (d) Small circle or "cleft" girdle: 140 [0001] of quartz from Orocopia schist, California. (After J. M. Christie.)

diagram such as Fig. 3-7b or 3-7c. To sharpen the pattern and render it more legible it is customary in structural analysis to draw density contours on the point diagram. Each contour delineates an area within which the density of distribution of plotted points exceeds some minimum value—e.g., 5 per cent of the total points per 1 per cent of the projection area. Contours may be drawn directly on the point diagram. More commonly, however, for clearer preservation of the recorded data, the contoured diagram is drawn separately on a second overlay while taped onto the point diagram so that the reference axes of the two coincide.

Contouring is done by means of a celluloid or plexiglass counter ($\frac{1}{16}$ to $\frac{1}{8}$ in. thick) illustrated in Fig. 3-8.[8] At each end is a circular hole or counting circle H, 2 cm in diameter, the area of which is thus 1 per cent of that of the projection (20 cm in diameter). Centers of the holes are 20 cm apart. A slot S wide enough to slide freely on the tine of a thumbtack, and about 2 cm long, is cut along the middle of the

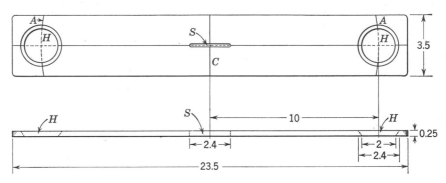

Fig. 3-8. Point counter (dimensions in centimeters).

inscribed line connecting the centers of the counting holes. A transverse inscribed line C marks the center of this slot and of the counter; and transverse arcs AA, of 10 cm radius, are inscribed to pass through the centers of the terminal holes.

To count the points lying within any 1 per cent circular area of the projection, place either counting circle in the appropriate position on the point diagram (Fig. 3-9a). Where the center of the counting circle falls within 1 cm of the circumference of the projection the procedure must be slightly modified (Fig. 3-9b): the thumbtack protruding from the center of the net is then inserted through slot S, and points falling in *both* counting circles are added. This gives the number of points in that counting circle whose center X lies within or close to the primitive circle of the projection. The object of counting is to draw density contours connecting centers of circular areas within which the measured points are equally concentrated. Contouring is an arbitrary procedure the statistical significance of which has not been rigorously evaluated. The following rules are recommended:

[8] This device is due to O. Schmidegg (see E. B. Knopf and E. Ingerson, Structural petrology, *Geol. Soc. America Mem. 6*, p. 245, 1938), and is not at present commercially available.

1. On any diagram the number of contours should not be more than six.

2. The highest contour is chosen to emphasize and differentiate maxima large enough to stand out clearly on a projection 2 to 3 in. in diameter. For instance, if the areas of local concentrations of 10 to 12 per cent are small, it may be advisable to draw the highest contour at 8 per cent.

3. In any diagram contour intervals should preferably be uniform.

4. It is customary, where possible, to draw the lowest contour to correspond to a concentration of 1 point per 1 per cent area. This contour defines the outer boundary of an area completely devoid of points (e.g., the *NE* area of Fig. 3-7*b*). Suitable contours in a diagram representing 300 plotted points might be 8, 6, 4, 2, 0.33 per cent, per 1 per cent area.

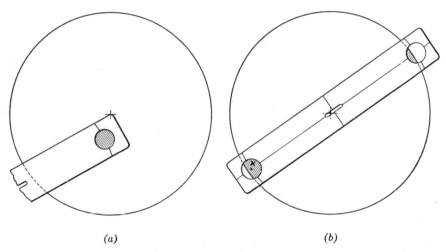

(a)　　　　　　　　　　　　　　　　(b)

Fig. 3-9. Use of point counter. (*a*) For counting points within the primitive circle. (*b*) For counting points close to or lying on the primitive circle.

5. In any analysis it is desirable, though not always possible, to measure the same number of points and to use the same contour intervals for diagrams representing data of one type from different fabric domains. This facilitates comparison of degree and pattern of preferred orientation within comparable domains.

6. Where a contour crosses the primitive circle of the projection it must reappear at the diametrically opposite point.

Several satisfactory contouring procedures are currently used:

1. Schmidt or grid method.[9] For diagrams with large numbers of points—in excess of 400—or with unusually high concentrations the most suitable method is that developed by Schmidt. The transparent point diagram is superposed on a 1-cm² grid, and counts are made with the center of the counting circle at each intersection. In the peripheral zone

[9] Schmidt, *op. cit.*, pp. 392–423; Knopf and Ingerson, *op. cit.*, pp. 245–251.

of the projection, intersections of the grid lines with the circumference are used for counting. At each intersection the number of counted points is noted in pencil on the second transparent overlay. Contours are now drawn on the latter (Fig. 3-10) at intervals corresponding to the appropriate point densities, e.g., in a count of 400 points, 24 (= 6 per cent), 20 (= 5 per cent), 16 (= 4 per cent) . . . , 1 (= 0.25 per cent).

2. Free-counter method. This is satisfactory where the number of points on the diagram is between 200 and 400, and individual concentrations are only moderately strong—fewer than about 12 points. After a quick preliminary trial with the counting circle to determine the range

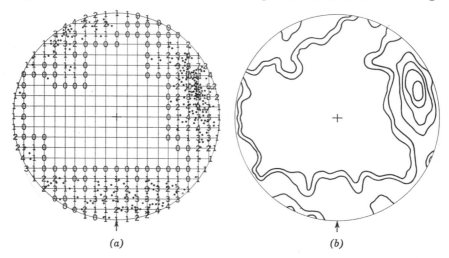

(a)   (b)

Fig. 3-10. Contouring point diagram by Schmidt method. (a) Diagram with 300 points counted out as per cent per 1 per cent area by means of 1-cm² grid. (b) Contours (13%, 10%, 7%, 4%, 1%, and ⅓%) per 1% area drawn by inspection of (a).

of concentrations, appropriate contour intervals are decided, e.g., in a 300-point diagram, 12 (= 4 per cent), 9 (= 3 per cent) . . . , 1 (= 0.33 per cent). The highest contour is now drawn as the locus of the center of the counting circle, so moved across the diagram as to maintain continuously a minimum of 12 points within its area (Fig. 3-11a). The remaining contours are added in order of decreasing density (Fig. 3-11b). The intersection of any contour with the circumference of the diagram is determined with the counter slot S fixed centrally by the thumbtack as in the grid method. The counting circle can then be moved continuously so that its center is constantly on the projection boundary. Points in both counting circles are counted.

3. Mellis or circle method.[10] This is most suitable for diagrams with few points—150 or less, for weak concentrations, and especially for draw-

[10] O. Mellis, Gefügediagramme in stereographischer Projecktien, Zeitschr. mineralog. petrog. Mitt., vol. 53, pp. 330–353, 1942.

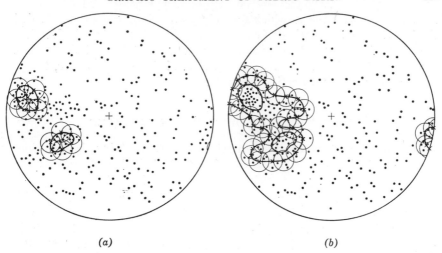

(a)   (b)

Fig. 3-11. Contouring point diagram by free-counter method. Circles represent successive positions of counting hole; crosses indicate centers of circles. Contours join centers of circles. (a) Four per cent contour (12 points) in diagram with 300 points. (b) Two per cent contour (6 points) in same diagram.

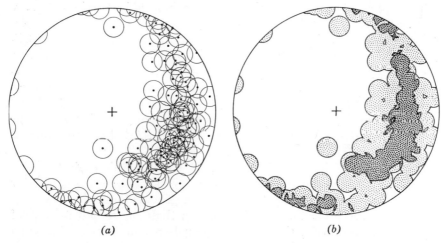

(a)   (b)

Fig. 3-12. Contouring point diagram by Mellis method. (a) Diagram with 100 points: circles of 2 cm diameter inscribed about each point. (b) One per cent contour (limit of circles) and 3 per cent contour (areas of overlap of three or more circles).

ing the contour of minimum density (usually the 1-point contour) of any diagram. The center of the counting circle is superposed successively on each plotted point, and a 1-cm circle is drawn by running a sharp-pointed pencil around the inside of the circle. When the operation is complete the second overlay carries a mesh of overlapping circles (Fig. 3-12). The contour representing a density of 4 points per 1 per cent area outlines the area in which four circles overlap, and so on.   This is the least subjective method of contouring—the only one by which strictly identical diagrams will be produced from the same point diagram by independent workers.   Its ready application is limited, however, to contours representing four or fewer points.

SIGNIFICANCE OF ORIENTATION DIAGRAMS

Statistical Significance of Orientation Diagrams.   There is a considerable literature dealing with criteria of statistical significance of preferred orientation diagrams, and with the possibility of maxima appearing in diagrams representing points with random distribution.[11]   The problem especially concerns fabrics with weak preferred orientation such as are common in sediments and in weakly deformed or post-tectonically recrystallized tectonites.   In general structural analysis of tectonites, however, kinematic interpretation can be applied with confidence only to strongly developed orientation patterns.   These alone fall within the scope of this book.   For such patterns the prime criterion of statistical significance of a diagram is reproducibility of its salient characters from other similar data taken from the same domain.   This criterion normally emerges in routine investigation of fabric homogeneity.   For example, if two orientation diagrams for [0001] in quartz are prepared from 300 measurements in each of two mutually perpendicular sections cut from one hand specimen, and if these are found to be essentially similar, it is concluded that the fabric is homogeneous within the domain of the specimen and that the orientation pattern is statistically significant.   If no such homogeneity can be established either the domain is heterogeneous and so has no fabric or the diagrams are not statistically significant owing to poor sampling procedure (page 152).

Symmetry of Orientation Diagrams.   A stereographic projection of a crystallographic form contains the symmetry elements of the symmetry class of the crystal.   Where the form is a general form, the symmetry elements of the projection are the same as those of the point group of the crystal.   Similarly, the contoured equal-area projection of a given fabric element contains the symmetry elements of a subfabric.   In struc-

---

[11] H. Winchell, A new method of interpretation of petrofabric diagrams, *Am. Mineralogist*, vol. 22, pp. 15–36, 1937; F. Chayes, Application of the correlation coefficient to fabric diagrams, *Am. Geophys. Union Trans.*, vol. 27, pp. 400–405, 1946; F. Chayes, in H. W. Fairbairn, *Structural Petrology of Deformed Rocks*, 2d ed., Addison-Wesley, Reading, Mass., chaps. 22 and 23, pp. 297–326, 1949; D. Flinn, On tests of significance of preferred orientation in three-dimensional diagrams, *Jour. Geology*, vol. 66, pp. 526–539, 1958; W. B. Kamb, Petrofabric observations from Blue Glacier, Washington, in relation to theory and experiment, *Jour. Geophys. Research*, vol. 64, pp. 1908–1909, 1959.

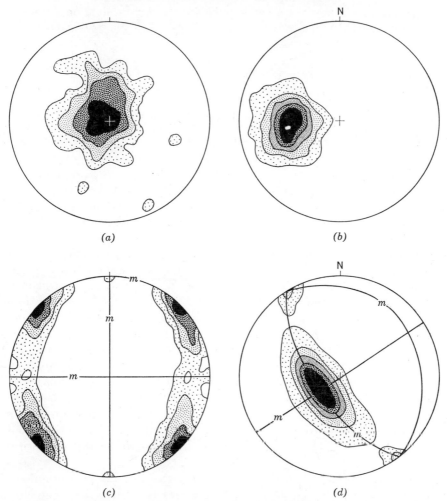

Fig. 3-13. Examples of axial and orthorhombic subfabrics. (a) Axial subfabric; 100 $[e_1:e_2]$ axes of calcite in marble from Barstow, California. (After L. E. Weiss.) Contours, 7%, 5%, 3%, 1%, per 1% area. (b) Axial subfabric; 171 lineations in quartzite from Ballachulish, Scottish Highlands. (After L. E. Weiss.) Contours, 13%, 10%, 7%, 4%, 1%, per 1% area. (c) Orthorhombic subfabric; 300 [0001] axes of quartz in mylonitized quartzite from the Moine Thrust, Stack of Glencoul, Scottish Highlands. (After J. M. Christie.) Contours, 8%, 5%, 3%, 1%, per 1% area. (d) Orthorhombic subfabric; 1,000 poles to foliation in gneisses from Turoka, Kenya. (After L. E. Weiss.) Contours, 9%, 7%, 5%, 3%, 1%, per 1% area.

tural analysis only centrosymmetric elements have so far been studied, so that only a single hemisphere (the lower) of the reference sphere is plotted. Because the types of symmetry observed in subfabrics are few in number and contain only ∞-fold and 2-fold axes, the only symmetry element observed in projection is the plane of symmetry (m).

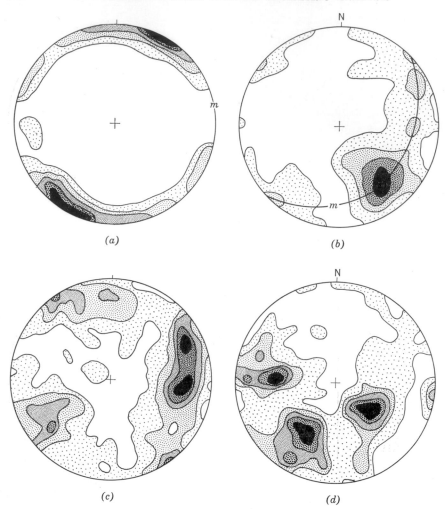

Fig. 3-14. Examples of monoclinic and triclinic subfabrics. (a) Monoclinic sub-fabric; 255 [0001] axes of quartz in mylonitized quartzite from Barstow, California. (*After L. E. Weiss.*)   Contours, 9%, 7%, 5%, 3%, 1%, per 1% area. (*b*) Monoclinic subfabric; 2,000 poles to foliation in schists and quartzites from Loch Leven, Scottish Highlands. (*After L. E. Weiss.*)   Contours, 4%, 3%, 2%, 1%, per 1% area. (*c*) Triclinic subfabric; 416 [0001] axes of quartz in deformed quartzite pebble from Panamint Range, California. (*After L. E. Weiss.*)   Contours, 5%, 4%, 3%, 2%, 1%, per 1% area. (*d*) Triclinic diagram (heterogeneous body); 193 poles to foliation in gneiss and schist near Lake O'Keefe, East Central Quebec, Canada. (*After G. Gastil and L. E. Weiss.*)   Contours, 5%, 4%, 3%, 2%, 1%, per 1% area.

Examples of subfabrics (one microscopic and one macroscopic) with the commonly occurring types of tectonite symmetry are given in the following figures: axial subfabrics—Fig. 3-13a and b; orthorhombic subfabrics—Fig. 3-13c and d; monoclinic subfabrics—Fig. 3-14a and b; and triclinic subfabrics—Fig. 3-14c and d.[12] Where every detail of the contoured patterns is taken into account orientation diagrams lack any plane of ideal symmetry. The main features (maxima and girdles) are, however, reproducible in different comparable sets of data from the same homogeneous body, whereas the detail of the contoured pattern is not. Symmetry of fabric is defined, therefore, only by the main features of orientation diagrams; the details of the contoured patterns cannot generally be evaluated although some may yet prove to be significant in rigorous study of statistical symmetry.

ROTATION OF FABRIC DATA

General Statement. In structural analysis it is commonly necessary either to change the angles between planes and lines in projection while keeping the plane of projection fixed or to compare or combine data measured and projected on planes of different orientation. So arises the general problem of how to rotate individual projections of planes and lines through a given angular distance in a given sense. The constructions involved are here termed *rotation operations*. All involve rotation of points on the projection—poles of planes, impingement points of lines. Each operation is made upon a second transparent overlay (here termed the *rotation overlay*) superposed on that carrying the initial data (here termed the *data overlay*).

Rotation Operations within a Fixed Projection. *General.* Graphic solutions of certain structural and crystallographic problems require rotation operations within a fixed projection having constant reference axes such as geographic coordinates or crystallographic axes. Some illustrative examples are as follows:

Rotation about a Diameter of the Projection (Fig. 3-15). Let the plane P strike N43°W and dip 52°SW; it is required to rotate P through some given angle about the horizontal line R whose trend is N81°E. Figure 3-15a shows P and R projected on the geographic horizontal plane. Rotate the two superposed overlays on the net until R coincides with the north-south diameter of the net (in the standard orientation of the net this is also the axis of all the small circles). The locus of rotation of p, the pole of P, about R is the small circle through p drawn around R. On the rotation overlay p can now be rotated in the desired sense through

[12] After M. S. Paterson and L. E. Weiss, Symmetry concepts in the structural analysis of deformed rocks, *Geol. Soc. America Bull.*, vol. 72, pp. 865–866, figs. 7, 8, 1961.

any required angle.   In Fig. 3-15b, *p* is rotated through 50° to *p′* and the plane *P* to *P′*.   The angle between *p* and *p′* (and hence between *P* and *P′*) is less than 50°.   Only for lines and poles lying on the great circle normal to *R* is the angle between the initial point (e.g., *L*) and the

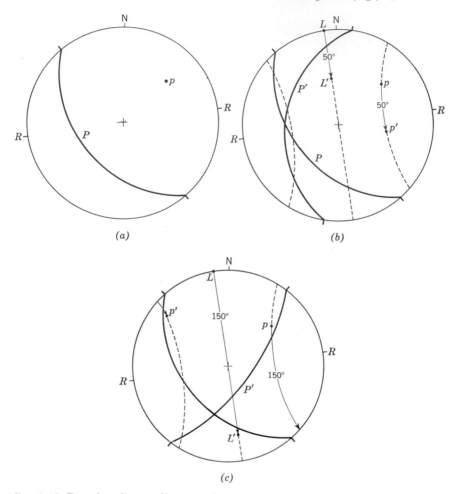

(a)   (b)

(c)

FIG. 3-15. Rotation about a diameter of projection (*R*—axis of rotation).   (*a*) Plane *P* and its pole *p* in initial orientation.   (*b*) Rotation of 50° counterclockwise (viewed eastward).   (*c*) Rotation of 150°.

rotated point (*L′*) exactly 50°.   Figure 3-15c illustrates a rotation in the same sense through 150°.

Rotation about an Axis Inclined to the Plane of Projection (Fig. 3-16). Let the plane P_1 (with pole p_1) strike N83°E and dip 52°S.   It is required to rotate P_1 80° in a clockwise sense (as viewed toward the NE) about an axis *R* trending N42°E and plunging 30°.   The path of rotation of a point (the projection of a line or the pole of a plane) is an inclined small circle constructed as in operation 11, page 57. Such small circles are not graduated; but rotation through a given angle can be made in any of three ways:

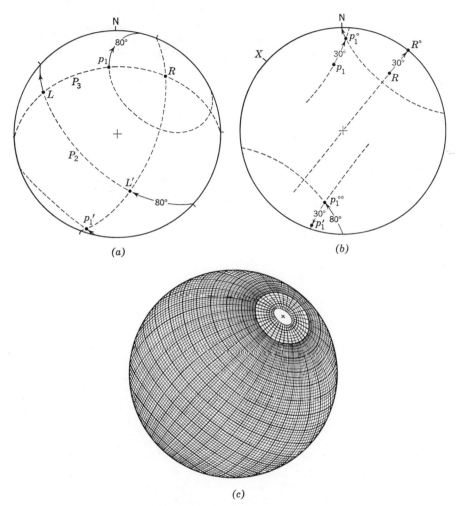

FIG. 3-16. Rotation about an axis inclined to the plane of projection. (a) and (b) Rotation of p_1 to p_1' about R. Explanation in text. Broken arcs in (b) are small circles about $R°$ and X respectively. (c) Inclined equal-area net for rotation about axis plunging at 40°.

1. In Fig. 3-16a construct the great circle of the plane P_2 normal to R and the great circle of the plane P_3 containing R and p_1. These planes intersect at L. Rotate L 80° along P_2 in the required sense to L'. The plane containing R and L' intersects the small circle in two points one of

which, from the sense of rotation prescribed, can be identified as the required point p_1', the pole of the rotated plane P_1.

2. In Fig. 3-16b bring R to the EW diameter of the net and rotate to $R°$ on the primitive circle; at the same time rotate p_1, through the same angle (30°) in the same sense on a small circle about the same axis (X), to $p_1°$. Now bring $R°$ to coincide with the north pole of the net; rotate $p_1°$, through 80° in the required sense about $R°$ to $p_1°°$. Return $R°$ to the EW diameter and rotate $p_1°°$ to p_1' through 30° in the same sense as $R°$ to R. Then p_1' is the required pole of the rotated plane P_1. This procedure is generally less time-consuming than that described in method 1.

3. Figure 3-16c[13] is an inclined equal-area net for rotation about any line inclined at 30° to the plane of projection. Separate nets must be prepared for different angles of inclination of the rotation axis. But a net of this kind greatly facilitates many rotations about an axis of given inclination.

Rotation of Dipping Plane to Horizontal. Figure 3-17a illustrates a common simple geologic problem, that of restoring a dipping plane to its initially horizontal position. A plane P strikes N43°W and dips 52°SW; it is required to rotate P to the horizontal, i.e., to bring its pole p to the center of the projection p'. Common procedure is to rotate p by the shortest path, i.e., through 52° about R_1, the strike of P. Any line L lying in P simultaneously moves through 52° to L' along the appropriate small circle about R_1. R_1 is the only horizontal rotation axis and the only axis lying in P that can restore P to the horizontal. But an infinite number of other axes, inclined both to P and to the horizontal, can be used for the same purpose. These lie in P_1 and P_2 (Fig. 3-17b), the normal bisecting planes of p and p' (cf. operation 10, page 57).

If P is restored to the horizontal by rotation about the axis R_2 (Fig. 3-17c), p moves to p' and L through the same angle (60°) to L'' along different small circles about R_2. L' of Fig. 3-17a does not coincide with L'' of Fig. 3-17c; in fact the two points are 32° apart. For each of the possible rotation axes on P_2 and P_3 of Fig. 3-17b, L is restored to the horizontal by a different path and the restored positions of L (L', L'', etc.) are different in every case. Where L is geologically significant (e.g., a direction of magnetization or of current lineation in an inclined sedimentary bed) rotation about the strike of the bed does not provide a unique solution of the trend of L in the initially horizontal bed. However, it is by far the most likely solution where the inclined bed is on the limb of a fold whose axis is horizontal.

Rotation of the Plane of Projection. *The General Problem.* It is commonly required to combine or to compare sets of fabric data measured and projected in two planes differently oriented with respect to the same reference axes. One projection and all points plotted upon it must

[13] Published with kind permission of G. Oertel.

be rotated into the plane of the second projection. The axis of rotation is the intersection of the two planes; so the procedure is that described above (page 67) for rotation about a diameter of the projection. All plotted points, including the reference axes, are rotated through the same

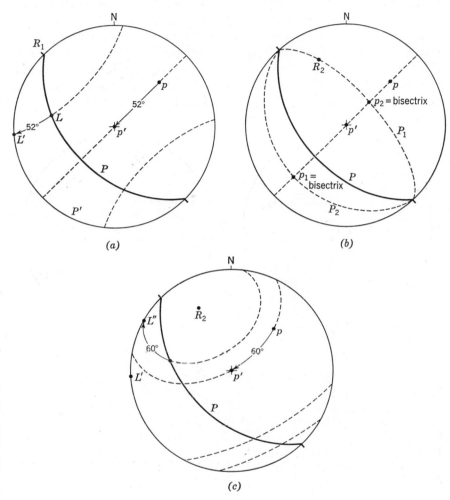

FIG. 3-17. Leveling of a plane P containing a line L. (a) Rotation about the strike of the plane R_1. (b) Loci of all possible rotation axes; these lie in two planes P_1 and P_2. (c) Rotation about an inclined axis R_2 (= R_2 of diagram b).

angle about the rotation axis. In the examples illustrated below only a few points are rotated; but in structural analysis it is not uncommon to rotate scores or even hundreds of points in a single operation. Special timesaving procedures have therefore been devised to facilitate rotation of many points through a given angle about the same diameter.

The problem is complicated by the fact that the reference axes are polar. Geographic axes are labeled *N-S*, *E-W*, *VU-VD* (vertically up, vertically down, respectively). Positive and negative ends of *a*, *b*, and *c* fabric axes likewise are distinguished. In rotation operations care must be taken to preserve the separate identities of opposite ends of each reference axis. Since fabric data are nonpolar any line in the fabric may equally well be represented by diametrically opposite impingement points on the reference sphere. For example the same line, or in an orientation diagram the same maximum, might appear in the $a^+b^+c^+$ quadrant of a projection on the *ab* plane (looking toward c^+) and in the $a^-b^-c^-$ quadrant of a projection on the *ac* plane (looking toward b^-).

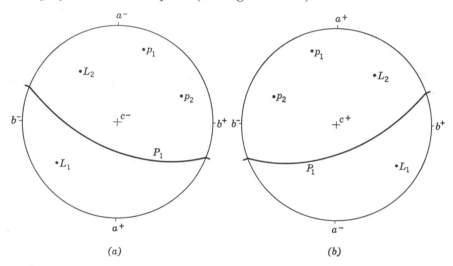

FIG. 3-18. Rotation (inversion) of plane of projection through 180°. (*a*) Data overlay before rotation. (*b*) The same data after rotation through 180°.

Three procedures are described below: the common cases where the angle of rotation is 180° or 90°, respectively, and the general case for rotation through any given angle.

Rotation through 180° (Fig. 3-18). Example: It is required to rotate data plotted on the *ab* plane looking toward c^-, so that they appear on the same plane looking toward c^+. This construction is commonly employed when comparing data measured on opposite parallel sides of a hand specimen. The operation is one of simple inversion. The data overlay (Fig. 3-18a) is turned face down (inverted) and all points and axes are traced on the superposed rotation overlay, the signs of each end of all three reference axes being reversed (Fig. 3-18b).

Rotation through 90° (Fig. 3-19). Example: It is required to rotate data plotted on the *ab* plane looking toward c^- (Fig. 3-19a) so that they appear on the *ac* plane looking toward b^+ (Fig. 3-19b). This is a common construction for comparison of data measured on mutually perpendicular faces of a hand specimen. In the example the a axis is common to the two projections. Superpose the rotation overlay upon the data overlay in such a way that the a axes of the two coincide in both position and sense. Since it is required that the center of the rotation overlay is b^+, the sense of c is uniquely fixed as in Fig. 3-19b. It is clear, then, that to bring b^+ to the center all points to the right of a^+a^- in Fig. 3-19a must be rotated through 90° toward the left as shown for p_1 and p_2. Now turn the data overlay face down by rotation through 180° about c^+c^-, the line

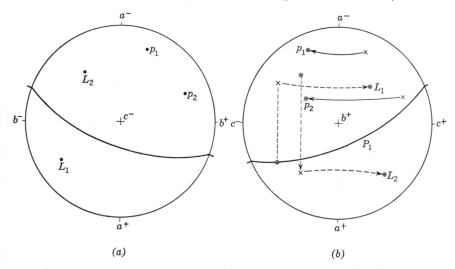

(a)   (b)

FIG. 3-19. Rotation of plane of projection through 90°. (a) Data overlay before rotation. (b) The same data after rotation through 90°. Paths of rotation (small circles about a) are shown as arcs connecting initial points (crosses) with rotated points (circled points). Double circles show positions of L_1 and L_2 before inversion.

normal to the common axis a^+a^-. Superpose the rotation overlay once more in its original position (taking no account of the changed sense of a). Points to the left of a^+a^- on the data overlay are now rotated through 90° toward the right as shown for L_1, L_2. To check the procedure make sure that one or two typical points appear in corresponding quadrants in both projections; thus L_2 is located in quadrant $a^-b^-c^-$ of Fig. 3-19a and in $a^+b^+c^+$ in Fig. 3-19b.

Rotation through Any Angle (Fig. 3-20). Example: It is required to rotate data plotted on a plane striking N50°W and dipping 40°NE into the geographic horizontal plane—looking down in both cases. The direction of strike, N50°W (R^+R^- in Fig. 3-20a), is common to the two projections. Superpose the rotation overlay (Fig. 3-20b) upon the data overlay (Fig. 3-20a) with the strike coinciding both in position and sense. To bring the arc R^+WSR^- of Fig. 3-20a to the horizontal, with the verti-

cal downward direction VD at the center of the projection, requires a
rotation about R^+R^- from right to left through 40°.   All points (such as
L_1, L_2) in the unshaded area may be rotated directly through 40° on
small circles about R^+R^- (see Fig. 3-20b).   Now turn the data overlay
face down by rotating it through 180° about the line normal to R^+R^-;
W is now inverted to E, and S to N.   Superpose the rotation overlay in
its original position (taking no account of the changed sense of R).
Points in the shaded area (e.g., L_3, L_4) are now rotated from left to right

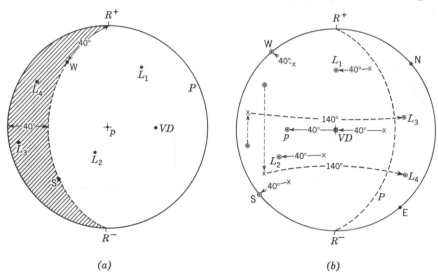

(a)   (b)

FIG. 3-20. Rotation of plane of projection P about strike (R^+R^-) through 40°.
(a) Data overlay before rotation. R^+WSR^- is the geographic horizontal plane; VD
is the vertical direction looking down; W = west, S = south.   (b) The same data
after rotation through 40° into the geographic horizontal plane.   Paths of rotation
(small circles about R) are shown as arcs connecting initial points (crosses) with
rotated points (circled points).   Double circles show positions of L_3 and L_4 before
inversion.

through the supplement of 40° (140°) along small circles about R^+R^-
(Fig. 3-20b).   Check the points of the compass and the VD direction
before and after rotation.

   Rotation of Contoured Diagrams.   It is customary to rotate data before
contouring rather than to rotate a complete contoured diagram.   However, it may be desirable, especially in macroscopic analysis of field data,
to rotate maxima and minima—or at least their centers of gravity—and
girdle arcs into a common plane such as the geographic horizontal or the
plane normal to the regional trend of macroscopic fold axes.   Centers of
gravity and girdles present no special problem.   To rotate a complete
contour, e.g., the 8 per cent contour bounding a given maximum, proceed
as follows (Fig. 3-21): Rotate selected points (1 to 6) on the contour

through the required angle (120° to the left), either directly as described on page 73 or according to one of the special procedures for many points. Now join the points by a smooth curve using the projection net as a grid of guidelines. The shape of a rotated maximum is not precisely the same

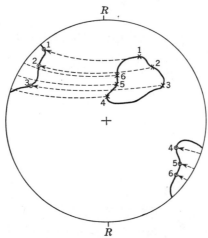

FIG. 3-21. Rotation of a contour through 120° about R. Corresponding initial points (crosses) and rotated points (circled points) are similarly numbered.

as the corresponding contour drawn after rotating individually the plotted points on which the maximum is based.

GENERAL PROCEDURE IN STRUCTURAL ANALYSIS

The geometric treatment of data—plotting, contouring, rotation, and so on—is the same on every scale. But different techniques of observation are employed for analysis on the microscopic, mesoscopic, and macroscopic scales respectively; and certain kinds of data are measured exclusively on one scale. For example, measurement of preferred orientation of mineral grains is essentially a microscopic procedure, whereas analysis of major folds must be carried out on the macroscopic scale.

A strictly logical account of technique and procedure should perhaps start with the microscopic and progress to the macroscopic scale. This is not, however, the order of procedure in most problems of structural analysis. Observation and analysis usually begin on the mesoscopic scale with work on the outcrop supplemented by laboratory study of hand specimens. The results so obtained, combined with regional mapping, are then extrapolated to the macroscopic scale. Microscopic analysis is usually the last phase of investigation; indeed some workers omit it altogether. In the three chapters which follow the technique of structural analysis is treated in the order normally followed in an actual investigation: mesoscopic, macroscopic, microscopic.

CHAPTER 4

MESOSCOPIC ANALYSIS—DESCRIPTIVE

GENERAL OBJECTIVES

Mesoscopic structural analysis is concerned with structures visible in hand specimens and exposures. Some of these structures are fabric elements on a mesoscopic scale (e.g., most lineations and foliations); others are fabric elements only of macroscopic domains (e.g., large folds and some bedding).

Descriptive mesoscopic analysis treats the following topics:

1. Detailed physical description of mesoscopic structures and their mutual relations
2. Measurement and recording of orientation of mesoscopic structures in the field
3. Collection of oriented hand specimens for more detailed laboratory study, and correlation of mesoscopic features with microscopic features discussed in Chap. 6
4. Determination of homogeneity of mesoscopic domains
5. Determination of symmetry of mesoscopic structures and fabrics
6. Determination of age relations of mesoscopic structures

MESOSCOPIC STRUCTURES AND FABRICS

Some mesoscopic domains—hand specimens or individual exposures—are homogeneous with respect to mesoscopic structures such as lineations and foliations, and so have their own individual fabrics. Others—e.g., a domain containing a few recognizable fold hinges—are heterogeneous but constitute parts of the fabric of some larger body that on the macroscopic scale is homogeneous. Yet other heterogeneous mesoscopic domains form no part of any recognizable homogeneous fabric even on the largest scale. The primary step in structural analysis is the recognition and investigation of homogeneous domains. So mesoscopic analysis focuses on structures that constitute fabric elements on either the mesoscopic or the macroscopic scale. Other geologically important but nonpenetrative structures, such as faults, intrusive contacts, and unconformities, that fail to qualify as fabric elements (cf. pages 24 to 28) are excluded from further discussion.

The simple mesoscopic structures of tectonites are treated geometrically as planes (e.g., foliation) or lines (e.g., lineation). However, some common structures are defined by a combination of the two, as for example a fold whose complete specification includes a fold axis plus an axial plane—the two being to some extent independent and possibly recording different aspects of deformation.

The role of statistical analysis of data is less prominent in mesoscopic than in microscopic and macroscopic analysis. Analysis of common heterogeneous structures such as single folds is mainly a matter of description combined with measurement of the attitude of the structure with respect to geometric coordinates. Preferred orientation of most mesoscopic structures emerges from analysis on the macroscopic scale.

Field measurement and recording of mesoscopic structures *in situ* during routine field mapping may profitably be supplemented by collecting oriented specimens for more detailed study in the laboratory. If it is then deemed desirable to proceed to microscopic analysis of oriented specimens, correlation of structures and fabrics on the microscopic with those on the mesoscopic scale ultimately follows. In some tectonites microscopic subfabrics, such as the patterns of preferred orientation of quartz and mica crystals, have symmetry elements in common with mesoscopic structures such as folds or lineations. In other tectonites symmetry of fabric and structure on the two scales is discordant.[1] Or again a microscopic subfabric may be homogeneous for a mesoscopic domain, which with respect to mesoscopic structures is heterogeneous.

Structures of a mesoscopic body may be identified under favorable conditions as being either inherited or imposed or composite. The distinction is important since structures of each category tend to record some different aspect of deformation (cf. pages 381 to 384). It involves investigating the relative ages of the observed structures. For example an inherited bedding foliation may be geometrically modified by folding in connection with which there develops an imposed axial-plane foliation. This in turn may be identified in some other domain as an inherited structure with respect to a later episode of superposed folding.

In this chapter mesoscopic structures will be considered under three headings:

1. Planar structures, e.g., bedding, foliation, joints.
2. Linear structures, e.g., lineation, rodding, mullion structures.
3. Folds. These are treated separately because they are usually specified in terms of a planar combined with a linear structure; their symmetry therefore can be lower than that of the generally axial symmetry of the individual planar or linear component. First we outline field and laboratory procedures for measuring and recording mesoscopic structures

---

[1] E.g., L. E. Weiss, Fabric analysis of a triclinic tectonite, *Am. Jour. Sci.*, vol. 235, pp. 225–236, 1955.

of each kind.   Then the nature and geometric properties of each structure are considered in turn.

PROCEDURES IN MESOSCOPIC ANALYSIS

Field Procedures.   *General.*   The following equipment (most of which is standard for a field geologist) is required for collecting data in the field:

1. Brunton compass or similar combination of prismatic compass with clinometer
2. Scale
3. Transparent protractor
4. Notebook and pencil
5. Equal-area or stereographic net 10 cm in diameter and supply of tracing paper in sheets of suitable size
6. 1½- or 2-lb hammer, large and small chisels
7. Felt-tipped ink pencil suitable for marking specimens
8. Small spirit level (3 to 6 in.)
9. Small stiff-bristled brush (e.g., a toothbrush)
10. Hand lens

The geologist proceeds as in routine geologic mapping; contacts between stratigraphic formations or lithologic types are mapped, specimens are collected for petrographic study; where they have significance, stratigraphic sections are studied and measured.   All structures, including nonpenetrative structures such as faults, unconformities, and so on, are mapped and investigated in the normal way.   The procedures of structural analysis are additional; *they in no way replace routine methods as outlined in standard textbooks.*

The additional procedures concentrate on accumulating orientation data for structures that on the mesoscopic or the macroscopic scale are penetrative.   The number of measurements depends on the complexity of the structure and is limited by available time.   Measurements should represent as uniform a sampling of the mapped body as exposure and accessibility make possible.   As mapping progresses, certain small domains, generally large exposures or groups of exposures showing the regionally prevalent structure with maximum clarity, are selected for further intensive study.   Of particular importance in such detailed studies are age relations of different structures.   It is usually possible to determine whether all foliations, lineations, and folds are of the same age or whether one foliation intersects and disrupts another, and whether lineations oblique to fold axes were bent by the folding and are therefore older than the folds or whether they were formed on an already folded foliation and so are younger than the folds.   Structures of different *tectonic styles* are recognized and separated.   The term *tectonic style* intro-

duced by Lugeon[2] refers to the total character of a group of related mesoscopic structures that distinguishes it from a group of comparable structures of another place or age, in the same way that the total character or
style of a building or an art object can distinguish it from similar objects
of other periods, places, or influences. Tectonic style is compounded of
features which, though subtly recognizable to the experienced eye, cannot
be defined precisely in geometric terms. It is properties of style rather
than geometric properties that most clearly delineate synchronous structures formed in one phase of deformation under approximately uniform
physical conditions different from those of preceding or following phases
of deformation.

Throughout the whole body to be investigated, the orientations of
penetrative structures are determined. This is done in terms of strike,
dip, trend, plunge, and pitch as defined in Chap. 3. Other useful geometric parameters of planar and linear structures are the following:[3]

A *face* is any effectively planar exposure surface, either natural or
artificial, e.g., a joint, foliation, or bedding surface, a road cut, and so on.

A *trace* is the visible expression of a penetrative structure on a face.
These are of two kinds:

1. Trace of planar structure—the line of intersection of the planar
structure with the face
2. Trace of linear structure—approximating the orthographic projection of an oblique linear structure on the plane of the face[4]

Measurement of Planar Structures. Where the planar structure can be
clearly seen in three dimensions its attitude (strike and dip) is determined in the usual way by compass. Representative attitudes are
recorded on the growing geologic map; but additional similar data, too
numerous to record directly, are noted in a notebook (see page 86) under
locality numbers corresponding to numbers located on the map or photograph. Where the orientation of one structure varies from place to
place in one exposure, measurement of several representative attitudes

[2] D. B. McIntyre (Alpine tectonics and the study of ancient mountain chains,
unpublished doctoral dissert., University of Edinburgh, p. 55, 1951) quotes an unpublished statement of Lugeon made in 1948: "I think that you are probably correct in
stating that it is I who introduced the term 'tectonic style.' I would have to search
through all my publications to find out when I used it for the first time. That this
expression should have come to my mind is understandable, for I am the son and
brother of artists and sculptors."

[3] R. H. Clark and D. B. McIntyre, A macroscopic method of fabric analysis, *Am.
Jour. Sci.*, vol. 249, p. 755, 1951. Note that *macroscopic* in the above paper is used in
the same sense as *mesoscopic* in this book.

[4] K. E. Lowe, A graphic solution for certain problems of linear structure, *Am.
Mineralogist*, vol. 31, p. 427, 1946.

reveals the nature of folding or other local structural perturbation (cf. pages 83 to 85).

Weak penetrative surfaces that cannot be seen clearly in three dimensions may appear only as traces on other surfaces. To determine the attitude of a planar structure of this kind, select three nonparallel planar faces (e.g., joints) F_1, F_2, and F_3 on each of which the trace of the surface S is visible. Measure the trend and plunge of the respective traces T_1, T_2, and T_3, and plot in projection (Fig. 4-1, cf. Fig. 6-8). Data for Fig. 4-1 are as follows:

F_1—strike N46°W, dip 63°SW; T_1—trend N62°W, plunge 23°
F_2—strike N24°E, dip 90°; T_2—trend N24°E, plunge 37°
F_3—strike N79°E, dip 75°NW; T_3—trend N66°E, plunge 9°

The attitude of S is given by the great circle most nearly passing through T_1, T_2, and T_3. Three attitudes are necessary to confirm that S is planar, and to establish that the traces express a planar and not a linear structure. In general practice, the faces themselves need not be projected, unless the pitch of the trace of S has been recorded instead of the plunge.

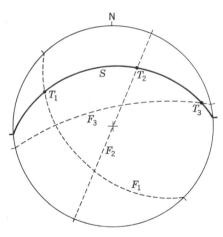

All kinds of planar structures in any exposure are described and their respective attitudes measured. Where several types, e.g., bedding, slaty cleavage, and fracture cleavage, are present in one exposure it is convenient to designate them, without implication as to relative age or prominence, by descriptive symbols S_1, S_2, S_3, etc. Age relationships are noted wherever possible. In this respect successive generations of joints may be recognized by their relationships to other structures as well as by individual characteristics—presence or absence of fillings (with calcite, quartz, epidote, and so on), evidence of displacement or folding during post-jointing deformation.

FIG. 4-1. Indirect determination of orientation of a planar structure S from traces T_1, T_2, and T_3 on three nonparallel plane faces, respectively F_1, F_2, and F_3 (data in text).

Measurement of Linear Structures. The most convenient way of measuring and plotting a given linear structure depends on the character of the lineation in question and its relation to readily measured associated planar structures.

1. Where a linear structure is a fold axis or is the most conspicuously developed structure of a tectonite (a B-tectonite), its trend and plunge are measured directly with a Brunton compass. This is the simplest and most direct method of measuring lineation.

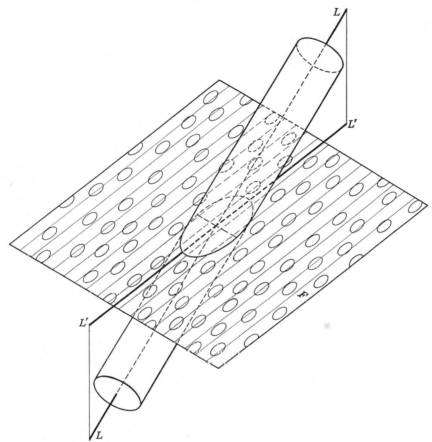

Fig. 4-2. Cylindrical domains with equant cross sections with preferred orientation of axes L forming a trace (apparent lineation) L' on an oblique plane face F.

2. The attitude of a lineation lying in a measured plane of easy breakage, S_1, may be determined by measuring, with a protractor, its pitch—the angle it subtends with the strike of S_1. To plot such a lineation, knowing also the strike and dip of S_1, the pitch is recorded on the net along the great circle of S_1; but this great circle itself need not necessarily be plotted.

3. The attitude of a lineation defined by intersection of S_1 and S_2 need not be measured separately. It is plotted on the net as the normal to the great circle drawn through the poles of S_1 and S_2 (page 54, operation 5).

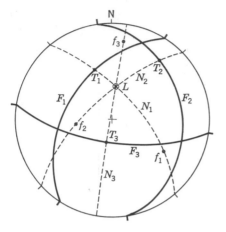

FIG. 4-3. Indirect determination of orientation of a linear structure L from traces T_1, T_2, and T_3 on three nonparallel plane faces, respectively F_1, F_2, and F_3 (data in text). Poles of F_1, etc., are f_1, etc.

4. In lineated rocks lacking any surface of easy breakage the attitude of a lineation can be determined by measuring its trace on each of three nonparallel faces.[5] It is assumed that the lineation is defined by prismatic or cylindrical domains of equant cross section. On an oblique face F (Fig. 4-2) the cross section of each such domain is elongated parallel to the orthographic projection L' of the length of the domain L. Thus on F appears a statistically defined linear structure here termed the trace of the lineation (equals "apparent lineation" of den Tex[6]). The three faces F_1, F_2, and F_3 and the three traces, respectively T_1, T_2, and T_3, are measured and plotted in projection (Fig. 4-3). Data for Fig. 4-3 are as follows:

F_1—strike N34°E, dip 52°NW; T_1—trend N19°W, plunge 45°
F_2—strike N8°W, dip 30°NE; T_2—trend N39°E, plunge 23°
F_3—strike N81°W, dip 70°SW; T_3—trend S12°W, plunge 70°

For each face draw a great circle N passing through the lineation trace T and the pole f of the face F on which it occurs. The three great circles N_1, N_2, and N_3 intersect ideally in a point—actually in a small triangle of error—defining the attitude of the lineation L.

Where a particular lineation is locally curvilinear—e.g., where it crosses a visible fold—its local orientation is determined at several points. This brings out the form of curvature which may be significant in dating the lineation with reference to other structures. Where lineations of more than one kind are visible in a single exposure all should be described and measured. Common practice is to label them L_1, L_2, L_3, etc.

Much of the procedure described above applies not only to lineation in the strict sense but also to large or heterogeneous linear structures such as rods, mullions, boudins, stretched pebbles, and so on. The methods of measurement most commonly employed in such cases are numbers 1 and 4 above.

[5] Lowe, *op. cit.*, pp. 425–434; Clark and McIntyre, *op. cit.*, pp. 757–758; E. den Tex, Stereographic distinction of linear and planar structures from apparent lineations in random exposure planes, *Geol. Soc. Australia Jour.*, vol. 1, p. 59, 1953.
[6] Den Tex, *ibid.*, p. 57.

Measurement of Folds. The attitude of a regular fold or a regular segment of a fold on the mesoscopic scale is defined by measurement of two geometric parameters—the fold axis and the axial plane. The attitude of the rectilinear axis of a small fold can generally be determined directly by measuring the trend and plunge of an exposed hinge (cf. pages 106 to 108). Where no hinge is exposed, it is customary to measure the strike and dip of the folded surface at several points; the planes so measured intersect ideally in the fold axis. In Fig. 4-4 attitudes of three segments of a folded surface S are as follows:

1. S_1—strike N30°E, dip 41°NW
2. S_2—strike N87°W, dip 52°N
3. S_3—strike N42°W, dip 79°SW

Since all attitudes of a folded surface are ideally cozonal with reference to the fold axis (cf. page 154) the great-circle traces of the three segments should intersect in a point corresponding to the fold axis, and the poles of the segments should fall on a great circle normal to the axis. Usually the great-circle traces are found to define a small triangle of error, whose center (B in Fig. 4-4) is the fold axis (trend N50°W, plunge 39°, in Fig. 4-4).

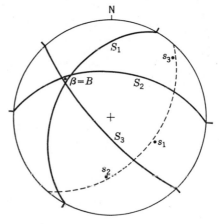

Fig. 4-4. Indirect determination of a fold axis B as the line of intersection β of planar segments of the folded surface, S_1, S_2, and S_3 (data in text).

Sander has denoted the axis of intersection of a set of cozonal s-surfaces by one of the symbols B, β, or π, depending on the particular geometric construction used for its determination.[7] Following Sander's usage in part we denote any proved fold axis as B. A β axis is the line of intersection of two or more segments of a surface S, or the statistical maximum of intersections between measured s-surfaces of one type, S, in a homogeneous fabric. π is the normal to the great circle which the poles of the measured segments of S most closely approximate. β and π are exactly equivalent, for they represent the same geometric property of the

[7] B. Sander, Über Flächen- und Achsengefüge (Westende der Hohen Tauern, III Bericht), *Sonderabdruck aus den Mitt. Reichsamts für Bodenforsch.*, Vienna, p. 7, 1942; *Einführung in die Gefügekunde der Geologischer Körper*, Pt. I, pp. 132–146, 177–179, Springer, Berlin, Vienna, 1948. Unfortunately Sander's definition of B is not purely descriptive but includes genetic implications as to forces and movements as well as the geometric criterion that B is normal to a plane of fabric symmetry.

fabric determined in two different ways. Moreover, a β axis of intersection very commonly represents a rectilinear axis of folding. So β is
very commonly equivalent to B. However, the two symbols are not
completely synonymous for there are some situations in which β is the
statistical intersection of s-surfaces not related by folding. Axial-plane
cleavages, for example, may have a radial disposition about a common
axis of intersection which has the character of β but not of B. Where a
β maximum determined from projected data does not correspond with a
directly observable B axis the possibility that the plotted attitudes of S
are indeed related by folding should still be tested by further field observations and plotting of data on the macroscopic scale. It may even be

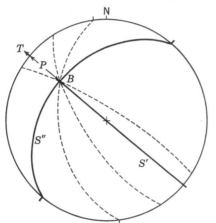

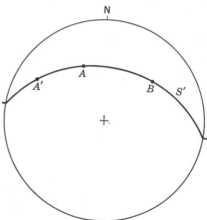

FIG. 4-5. Trend T of fold axis B given by strike of vertical planar segment S' of folded surface: plunge P of B is given by dip of planar segment S'' of folded surface striking normal to S'.

FIG. 4-6. Indirect determination of orien-tation of axial plane S' as the plane con-taining the fold axis B and the trace of the axial plane A or A' on a random planar face (data in text).

found on the other hand that the supposed β maximum has no direct
geologic significance—as when s-surfaces of two kinds or s-surfaces separated by a fault or an unconformity have been mistakenly plotted on a
single diagram. The use of B, β, and π is discussed further in connection
with procedure on the macroscopic scale (pages 154 to 158).

The attitude of a curvilinear fold axis can be determined indirectly
by determining β intersections for a series of effectively rectilinear segments of the axis. Where folds are reclined (see pages 117 to 120) or
inclined with opposite limbs dipping in the same sense, the trend of the
fold axis is the strike of any vertical attitude of the folded surface and
the plunge is the dip of any segment of the folded surface striking normal
to the plunge (Fig. 4-5).

In many tectonites, e.g., where an axial-plane foliation is present, the
axial planes of folds can be measured directly. More usually the axial

plane must be determined indirectly as illustrated in Fig. 4-6. Here the fold axis B trends N50°E and plunges 38°; on some planar face F (the attitude of which need not be measured) the trace A of the axial plane by direct measurement is found to trend N23°W and to plunge 41°. Since both these lines lie in the axial plane, the latter is the great circle passing through B and A. In Fig. 4-6 the axial plane S' so determined strikes N82°W and dips 45°N. Many tectonites carry prominent joints at high angles to B, and these provide most convenient faces on which to measure the traces of axial planes of folds and to observe details of style of folding. Such is the trace A' in Fig. 4-6. Any two traces (e.g., A and A') on nonparallel faces completely define the axial plane.

Recording Data. Orientation data should be recorded in a form readily accessible for plotting and projection. Ideally they are kept separate from descriptive data. It is convenient to reserve one page of a field notebook for orientation data from one or more localities and to place the descriptive data from the same localities on a facing page. Figure 4-7 shows a recommended notebook layout for data from one locality.

Collecting Oriented Hand Specimens. Oriented hand specimens for laboratory (including microscopic) analysis should be as far as possible of fresh unweathered rock free of open fractures. They should be large enough for several surfaces of different orientation to be cut and polished as required. Of several methods for collecting and marking of oriented specimens the following is recommended:

Break the specimen from the exposure but do not trim it. Chisels may be used to break the specimen along prominent surfaces of foliation or jointing. At least two such natural bounding surfaces should be effectively planar (joint, foliation, or plane fracture surfaces). Clean these surfaces carefully with a stiff-bristled brush and remove all dust and loose fragments from the artificial fracture surfaces both on the specimen and on the exposure. Where conditions are moist, it may be necessary to remove superfluous water. Then carefully fit the specimen back onto the fracture surfaces until it is held firmly in its initial orientation. Where the fracture surface is overhanging (a condition to be avoided if possible) a specimen should be selected that can be wedged in position with loose rocks or a hammer handle.

Measure and record the attitudes of all visible planar and linear structures on the specimen. By means of a small spirit level (a Brunton compass is generally too bulky for the purpose) draw a strike line with a felt-tipped ink pencil on each of the two planar outside surfaces of the specimen. Indicate the sense of dip by short lines (Fig. 4-8a). These marks give the trace of the horizontal plane on the specimen. Using a Brunton compass, then mark on any convenient nearly horizontal surface a small arrow with a known trend (generally north). This arrow need not be horizontal (Fig. 4-8a). The specimen is now uniquely oriented

LITHOLOGIC DESCRIPTIONS, GENERAL DESCRIPTIVE DATA AND SKETCHES
FROM SAME LOCALITY ON FACING PAGE.

PROJECT *Lake Isabella : Photograph - ABL - 3K - 181 :*   DATE *August 15, 1960*

LOCALITY	STRUCTURE		STRIKE OR TREND	DIP OR PLUNGE	NOTES
106 I	S - surfaces	S_1	N.18 W N 68 W N 89 W	81 NE 67 SW 65 SW	Three measurements on bedding taken from a small fold in a thin quartzite layer in mica schist.
		S_2	N 40 W	84 SW	Foliation of mica schist defined by preferred orientation of mica. Parallel to axial plane of fold.
		S_3	N 69 E	60 NW	Second "strain-slip," cleavage oblique to fold axis.
	Fold axis B		S 30 E	54	Similar asymmetric fold in bedding defined by thin quartzite (5 inches thick)  NE— mica schist —SW quartzite 3 feet
	Fold axial plane S_2		N 40 W	84 SW	Parallel to S_2 - foliation in mica schist.
	Lineations	L_1	S 28 E	55	Fine striation parallel to fold axis B and to intersection of S_1 & S_2.
		L_2	S 80 W N 85 W N 4 W	18 32 57	Crenulation on S_1 parallel to intersection of S_1 & S_3. Three measurements from different attitudes of S on the B-fold.
		L_3	N 48 W	58	Crenulation on S_2 parallel to intersection of S_2 & S_3
	Joints	J_1	N 27 E	36 NW	Subnormal to B
		J_2	N 40 W	7 NE	Approximately symmetrical to B ?
		J_3	N 52 E	78 NW	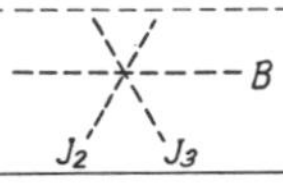 ----X---- B J_2 J_3
	Oriented specimen 106 I		Top	N 80 W 65 S	From thin quartzite in schist.
					Photograph of fold-down axis looking S.E. Roll 9, frame 6.

FIG. 4-7. Recommended layout of notebook page for recording of orientation data from a single exposure. Orientations of s-surfaces, lineations, fold elements, and joints are recorded. Descriptive information from the same exposure can be recorded on the facing page of the notebook.

and all that need be recorded in the notebook is the number of the specimen and the trend of the arrow if this is other than north.

Where only one planar surface can be obtained on a specimen (Fig. 4-8b), mark this surface with a strike and dip symbol as before, but barb one end of the strike line and record the sense of this in the notebook (note also if the surface is overhanging). Record also the amount and sense of dip along with a sketch of the strike and dip symbol on the specimen (Fig. 4-7, bottom). These marks give a unique orientation for the specimen. The first method is to be preferred since it is more rapid and generally permits reorientation of the specimen in the laboratory without reference to the notebook.

As soon as possible, paint the ink marks on the specimen with enamel or other durable paint.

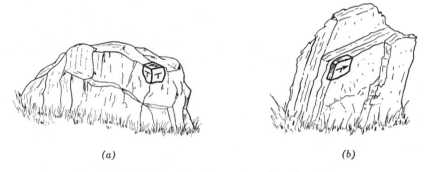

(a)　　　　　　　　　　　　　　　　(b)

Fig. 4-8. Methods of marking oriented hand specimens.

Laboratory Procedures. *General.* Mesoscopic field observations should always be supplemented by study of selected oriented hand specimens in the laboratory. The surfaces of a hand specimen are examined with a hand lens or a low-power binocular microscope with a view to determining in as great detail as possible the nature and mutual relations of s-surfaces and lineations already familiar through field observation. Structures that passed unnoticed in the field are sometimes revealed in this way. Since field observations comprise the first and the most important phase of mesoscopic analysis, it is customary in subsequent laboratory work on the mesoscopic scale to employ geographic coordinates as reference axes. To replace the specimen in its initial field orientation and to measure visible planar and linear structures, Ingerson[8] has devised useful types of orienting apparatus.

Selection of Fabric Axes. Where a specimen is apparently homogeneous, other reference axes or *fabric axes* may be more convenient than

[8] E. B. Knopf and E. Ingerson, Structural petrology, *Geol. Soc. America Mem. 6,* pp. 216, 217, 1938; E. Ingerson, Apparatus for direct measurement of linear structures, *Am. Mineralogist,* vol. 27, pp. 721–725, 1942.

geographic axes and are selected according to arbitrary rules designed to emphasize the dominant structural features of the specimen. Three orthogonal axes a, b, and c are selected and opposite ends are designated as plus or minus as in the reference axes for an orthorhombic crystal (Fig. 4-9). Choice and use of fabric axes are in fact closely analogous to crystallographic usage, since in both cases the selected axes are related to symmetry elements recognizable on the mesoscopic scale; but fabric axes, unlike crystallographic axes, are always at right angles whatever the symmetry of the fabric. Fabric axes can be selected only in a fabric that is sensibly homogeneous at least with respect to some of its subfabrics. In block diagrams of fabrics with lineations or folds, the front face (in which graphic distortion is minimal) is usually normal to b, i. e., parallel to the transverse profile of folds (contrast Figs. 4-9 and 4-10).

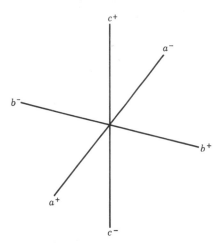

Fɪɢ. 4-9. Orthogonal system of fabric axes a, b, and c.

In this book the following rules have been adopted for designating fabric axes:

1. Fabrics dominated by a prominent planar structure S: $S = ab$; any regular lineation in S, especially if normal to a plane of symmetry of the fabric $= b$; in the absence of lineation, any direction in S is arbitrarily designated b.

2. Fabrics with two or more planar structures intersecting in a common axis: The most prominent planar structure $= ab$; the common axis of intersection $= b$.

3. Fabrics with more than two planar structures not intersecting in a common axis: The most prominent planar structure $= ab$; the intersection of this with the next most prominent $= b$.

4. Fabrics dominated by a strong lineation: Lineation $= b$; any direction normal to $b = a$ (preferably lying in a planar structure).

Adherence to these rules gives fabric axes a relation to the symmetry of mesoscopic subfabrics (inclusion of all subfabrics, especially microscopic subfabrics, may destroy this relation in heterotactic fabrics), as follows:[9]

---

[9] Cf. F. J. Turner and J. Verhoogen, *Igneous and Metamorphic Petrology*, 2d ed., p. 620, McGraw-Hill, New York, 1960.

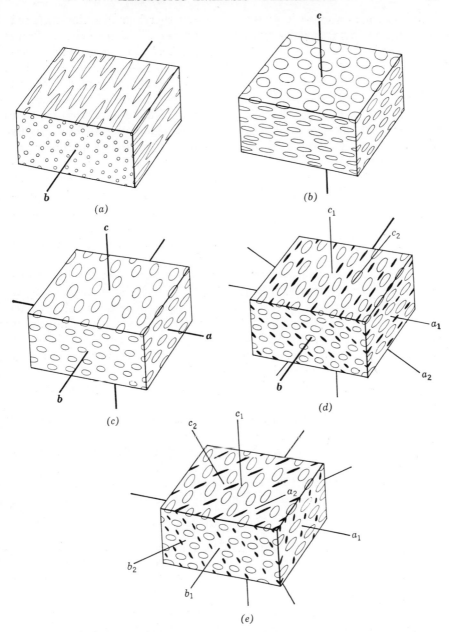

FIG. 4-10. Relation between fabric axes a, b, and c and symmetry. (a) and (b) Axial fabrics. (c) Orthorhombic fabric. (d) Monoclinic fabric. (e) Triclinic fabric.

1. In axial fabrics with symmetry $D_{\infty h}$, either b or c is the principal axis of symmetry (respectively Fig. 4-10a and b).

2. In orthorhombic fabrics a, b, and c are normal to planes of symmetry (Fig. 4-10c).

3. In monoclinic fabrics b is normal to the single plane of symmetry; a choice of a and c is possible (e.g., a_1, a_2, and c_1, c_2 in Fig. 4-10d).

4. In triclinic fabrics a, b, and c have one of the above relations to a prominent subfabric or subfabrics with higher symmetry. Thus in most triclinic fabrics, e.g., one with two obliquely intersecting foliations each containing a lineation, a choice of axes is possible within the above specifications. The foliation and the most prominent lineation are together orthorhombic and can be used to determine a possible set of axes as outlined above. In Fig. 4-10e two possible choices of axes (a_1, b_1, c_1 and a_2, b_2, c_2) are illustrated.

The procedure outlined above conforms in general to Sander's definition of fabric coordinates.[10]

It cannot be emphasized too strongly that our definitions are completely free from kinematic and dynamic implications of any kind. Sander[11] has used a, b, and c also to denote kinematic axes, that is, axes of reference for displacements, translations, rotations, strains, and so on (pages 395 to 400). This usage has led to a confusion between observation and inference. To avoid this, the definition of fabric axes here adopted is framed solely in terms of criteria observable in a geometric fabric.[12] Completely independent kinematic axes, also termed a, b, and c, will be defined later (pages 399 and 400). Speculation on the kinematic and dynamic interpretation of fabrics is also postponed to a later section.

Study of Hand Specimens. For detailed study of mesoscopic structures, several nonparallel faces are cut, polished, and, sometimes, etched with acids. Commonly the faces left after cutting slices for thin sections are used for this purpose. On such surfaces, traces of planar and

[10] B. Sander, *Gefügekunde der Gesteine*, Springer, Berlin, Vienna, p. 119, 1930; Sander, *op. cit.*, p. 125, 1948.

[11] Sander, *op. cit.*, pp. 56, 57, 1930; *op. cit.*, pp. 68, 69, 1948.

[12] Many tectonites in the Scottish Highlands and Scandinavia have monoclinic mesoscopic fabrics with a strong lineation normal to a single plane of symmetry. This lineation, by definition, is a b fabric axis. Past controversy (see, for instance, E. M. Anderson, On lineation and petrofabric structure, *Geol. Soc. London Quart. Jour.*, vol. 104, pp. 99–126, 1948; A. Kvale, Petrofabric analysis of a quartzite from the Bergsdalen Quadrangle, Western Norway, *Norsk Geol. Tidssk.*, vol. 25, pp. 193–215, 1945; A. Kvale, Linear structures and their relation to movement in the Caledonides of Scandinavia and Scotland, *Geol. Soc. London Quart. Jour.*, vol. 109, pp. 51–73, 1953) was concerned with the nature, symmetry, and scale of the differential movements concerned in the evolution of these fabrics. It was not, as is so commonly stated, a controversy regarding a versus b lineations. Rather it was a question of whether a b lineation should be correlated with an a or a b kinematic axis.

linear structures can be clearly seen, and with the aid of a transparent protractor and a contact goniometer all angular relations between faces and the traces visible on them can be determined. Where specimens contain few structures their traces are relatively simple and easily distinguished. However, in specimens containing several s-surfaces and more than one lineation, correlation of the respective traces of each kind of structure on several faces presents special problems that have been discussed by Clark and McIntyre and by den Tex.[13] Age relations between various kinds of structure in a hand specimen, although sometimes obvious from mesoscopic study, can be determined in greater detail in thin sections. They belong more properly to the subject matter of microscopic analysis.

PLANAR STRUCTURES

General. Almost all deformed rocks contain one or more families of penetrative planar (including curviplanar) structures. These are commonly surfaces of easy fracture (e.g., slaty cleavage) and consequently tend to appear as natural or artificial bounding surfaces of tectonites in hand specimens and exposures. We adopt Sander's general term s-surface to denote such penetrative planar structures. Where more than one s-surface is present they are descriptively designated S_1, S_2, S_3, and so on.

s-Surfaces in tectonites are genetically of three kinds:

1. Inherited surfaces of premetamorphic origin. By far the commonest, and most important in structural analysis, is sedimentary bedding.

2. Surfaces of metamorphic origin such as cleavage, schistosity, and layering due to metamorphic differentiation. In this book all such structures are termed foliations.

3. Joints. These are sets of parallel surfaces of fracture postdating metamorphic flow but commonly symmetrically related to the flow pattern revealed by analysis of foliation and lineation.

Bedding. *General.* Whereas bedding in sedimentary rocks is initially planar and more or less horizontal, in deformed rocks, including tectonites, it is tilted or folded. Where still recognizable in tectonites, bedding thus furnishes an internal marker whose geometric configuration reflects the nature and degree of deformation. Moreover if bedding survives throughout a deformed body something of the original stratigraphy can be inferred; and it may even be possible to correlate local stratigraphic sequences within the deformed body with more completely preserved sections in adjacent less deformed bodies. Because of the great interpretive significance attached to bedding, it is particularly important in structural analysis of tectonites to identify bedding beyond reasonable doubt and to make sure that the layered structure in question has not

---

[13] Clark and McIntyre, *op. cit.*, pp. 755–768; den Tex, *op. cit.*, pp. 55–66.

originated in some other way—e.g., by metamorphic differentiation controlled by s-surfaces resulting from deformation.   It may be possible to establish that, in a tectonite body in which bedding is definitely recognizable (albeit in a distorted condition), the original continuity of layers and contacts still survives, and the gross disposition of layers still reflects something of the initial gross stratigraphic sequence prior to deformation.

Transposition of bedding.   Apart from that arising by metamorphic differentiation—a very common type—most of the lithologic layering of deformed rocks arises directly from the bedding of sedimentary rocks. There can be no doubt, for instance, that continuous thick layers of marble and quartzite in biotite gneisses represent original sedimentary units.   But bedding in deformed rocks is commonly violently disturbed; original continuity of layers may be lost, sequences may be repeated by intense folding and sliding along surfaces of discontinuity, original sequences may be differentially thickened and thinned, and the gross lithologic pattern of the beds may be changed.   The commonest cause of disturbance of bedding is folding.   On a mesoscopic scale the effect of intense folding and sliding on bedding can be seen very clearly in sequences of exposures showing progressively greater deformation as described, for instance, by King and Rast, Knill, and Baird.[14]   These sequences generally correspond to a *transposition* of an initial layering or foliation from one dominant orientation to another, with the appearance of what is effectively a new foliation discordant to the rotated gross orientation of the initial layering.   Such a structure has been called by Sander a *transposition foliation* (*Umfaltungsclivage*).[15]   Figure 4-11 shows an idealized sequence of stages in the transposition of bedding, as follows:

1. Similar folding of bedding S_1 (Fig. 4-11a).   The gross orientation of the bedding as a stratigraphic unit is preserved in the orientation of the surface joining successive hinges in a single folded surface ("enveloping surface"—see page 111).

2. Alternate limbs are attenuated where folding is asymmetric (Fig. 4-11b).

[14] B. C. King and N. Rast, Tectonic Styles in the Dalradians and Moines of parts of the Central Highlands of Scotland, *Geologists' Assoc. Proc.*, vol. 66, pp. 243–269, 1955; B. C. King and N. Rast, The small-scale structures of south-eastern Cowal, Argyllshire, *Geol. Mag.*, vol. 93, pp. 185–195, 1956; J. L. Knill, The tectonic pattern in the Dalradian of the Craignish-Kimelfort district, Argyllshire, *Geol. Soc. London Quart. Jour.*, vol. 115, pp. 339–364, 1960; A. K. Baird, Superposed deformations in the central Sierra Nevada Foothills, east of the Mother Lode, *Univ. California Geol. Sci. Pub.*, vol. 42, pp. 1–70, 1962.

[15] B. Sander, Über Zusammenhänge zwischen Teilbewegung und Gefüge in Gesteinen, *Tschermaks mineralog. petrog. Mitt.*, vol. 30, pp. 305, 306, 1911; A. I. Jonas, Tectonic studies in the crystalline schists of southeastern Pennsylvania and Maryland, *Am. Jour. Sci.*, vol. 34, pp. 364–388, 1937; Knopf and Ingerson, *op. cit.*, pp. 189, 190.

3. The attenuated limbs are replaced by glide surfaces parallel to a secondary foliation S_2 in "incompetent" layers (Fig. 4-11c).

4. The isolated hinges so formed are further appressed to form lenticles flattened in the plane of S_2. Some of these may still be recognizable as appressed hinges (Fig. 4-11d). The attitude of S_2, although everywhere conformable to lithologic contacts, is discordant with regard to the rotated gross orientation S_1 of the initial layering. S_1 is now obvious only as crude lithologic layering such that lenses of competent material are concentrated in particular zones bounded by S_1 (the large-scale enveloping surface of small-scale fold remnants)—cf. domain IV, Fig. 5-26.

At the final stage of transposition (4 above) if lenses of competent material are individually long and thin they define a lithologic layering which in small domains simulates bedding. Generally origin by transposition is indicated by survival of small tightly appressed fold hinges in some lenses;[16] but intense deformation may remove even this evidence on a mesoscopic scale, and the true relation of bedding to foliation may then be determined only by macroscopic mapping of distribution of rock types. To term the foliation S_2 in Fig. 4-11d "bedding" is clearly inaccurate and misleading. Many deformed rocks with mesoscopically uniform layering prove when studied on a larger scale to be composed of extended overlapping lenses, some of which are appressed hinges of folds, representing the disrupted and transposed remnants of bedding. As indicated in Fig. 4-11, the attitude and sequence of such layers are no indication of the true attitude and sequence of stratigraphic units, although the gross form of these may still emerge from detailed mapping (see pages 165 to 169).

At what stage in the cycle of transposition of bedding the term "bedding" should no longer be applied is arbitrary. Some geologists hesitate to recognize any laminated structures in metamorphic rocks as "bedding"; others seem ready to apply stratigraphic principles to any kind of layering. Both views are extreme.

Mesoscopic Criteria of Bedding in Tectonites. Bedding can be recognized on a mesoscopic scale by the following criteria:

1. Where lithologic layers (especially of carbonates, quartzites, and other peculiarly sedimentary lithologic types) are continuous and consistent in thickness (disregarding thickening in fold hinges) and in sequence they commonly represent bedding.

2. Gross lithologic layering discordant to the most conspicuous foliation usually represents bedding. Flinn[17] has described strongly deformed conglomerates in which bedding survives only weakly as pebble-free layers markedly discordant with regard to the plane of flattening of the peb-

---

[16] E.g., L. E. Weiss and D. B. McIntyre, Structural geometry of Dalradian rocks at Loch Leven, Scottish Highlands, *Jour. Geol.*, vol. 65, p. 579, pl. 1A, 1957.

[17] D. Flinn, On the deformation of the Funzie conglomerate, Fetlar, Shetland, *Jour. Geol.*, vol. 64, p. 491, 1956.

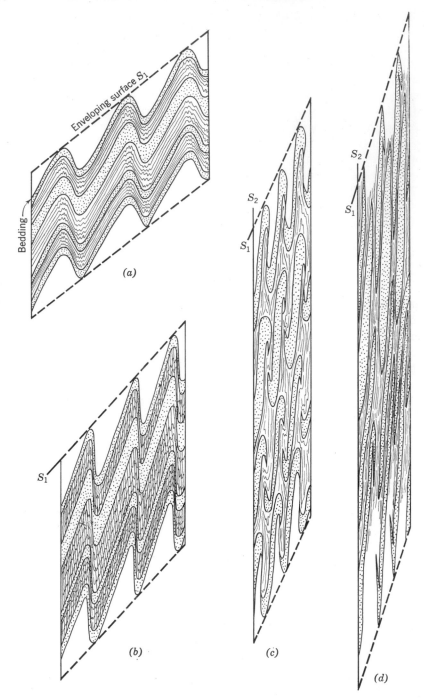

FIG. 4-11. Sequence of transposition of bedding S_1 into a foliation S_2.

bles—which is by far the most obvious mesoscopic structure. Figure 4-12a illustrates contacts S_1 between calcareous and pelitic layers in a series of schists. Both rock types are strongly foliated parallel to a common plane S_2; but the form of the bedding is still indicated by the gross distribution of the two lithologic types and becomes still more

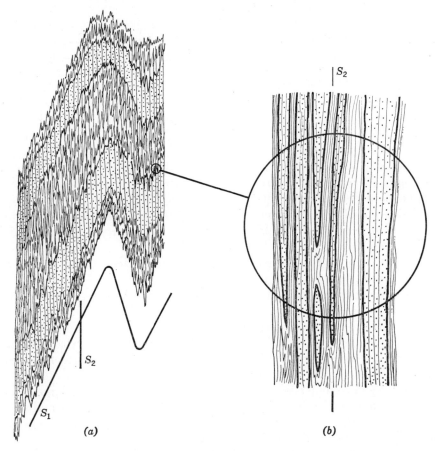

S_2

S_2

S_1

(a)   (b)

FIG. 4-12. Lithologic contact on two scales. (a) Large scale; generalized contact is S_1. (b) Small scale; contact is S_2.

obvious when mapped on the macroscopic scale. In smaller domains (Fig. 4-12b) the contact is more complicated in detail and clearly reflects the dominant influence of S_2.

3. Bedding may be indicated by the presence of sedimentary structures[18] preserving their initial relations to individual beds; e.g., cross-

[18] The term *sedimentary structure* is used here to denote any of the structures typical of sedimentary rocks, including structure formed by processes of sedimentation and by local movements in unconsolidated sediments.

bedding, graded bedding, ripple marks, convolute laminae, groove and flute casts, fossils, and so on. Particularly important are planar polar structures such as cross-bedding and graded bedding, because they allow the initial order of deposition to be determined and indicate tectonic inversions of layers where such has occurred.[19]

Purely tectonic structures in tectonites are easily confused with inherited sedimentary structures such as those just described. Intersecting foliations can resemble normal and cross-bedding;[20] small crenulations can resemble ripple marks.[21] Some apparently pebbly layers in schists can be shown to be composed of the disrupted remains of veins or thin beds.[22] Structures simulating graded bedding can be formed by mechanical or chemical processes accompanying metamorphism.[23] Detailed study, especially on the microscopic scale, will generally distinguish pseudodepositional deformational features from structures of truly sedimentary origin.

Symmetry of Bedding. Two principal features define bedding: alternation of lithologically different layers, and planar preferred orientation of inequant detrital grains such as mica flakes. The symmetry of bedding defined solely by these characters is axial $(D_{\infty h})$; but associated sedimentary structures commonly impart a total symmetry of a lower order to the mesoscopic fabric.

1. Bedding with groove casts or linear preferred orientation of inequant grains lacking imbrication—orthorhombic (D_{2h}).

2. Bedding intersected rectilinearly by cross-bedding—monoclinic (C_{1h}); or, where the cross-bedding is planar, monoclinic (C_{2h}).

3. Graded bedding—axial polar $(C_{\infty v})$.

4. Bedding combined with poorly correlated sedimentary structures (flute casts, groove casts of variable orientation, convolute laminae, slump structures, and so on)—triclinic (C_1).

These are point-group symmetries of small domains. Where a large body contains constantly oriented sedimentary structures throughout and so is homogeneous (e.g., a body with thin planar regularly graded beds), the symmetry may extend to the whole body.

[19] See, for example, T. Vogt, On the chronological order of deposition of the Highland schists, *Geol. Mag.*, vol. 67, pp. 68–73, 1930; E. B. Bailey, New light on sedimentation and tectonics, *Geol. Mag.*, vol. 67, pp. 77–92, 1930; G. Wilson, J. Watson, and J. Sutton, Current-bedding in the Moine series of north-west Scotland, *Geol. Mag.*, vol. 90, pp. 377–387, 1953; H. H. Read, A centenary lecture: stratigraphy in metamorphism, *Geologists' Assoc. Proc.*, vol. 69, pp. 83–102, 1958.

[20] D. R. Bowes and K. A. Jones, Sedimentary features and tectonics in the Dalradian of Western Perthshire, *Edinburgh Geol. Soc. Trans.*, vol. 17, pp. 135–137, 1958.

[21] E. Ingerson, Fabric criteria for distinguishing pseudo-ripple marks from ripple marks, *Geol. Soc. America Bull.*, vol. 51, pp. 557–569, 1940.

[22] E.g., J. Ramsay, The supposed Moinian basal conglomerate at Glen Strathfarrar, Inverness-shire, *Geol. Mag.*, vol. 93, pp. 32–40, 1956.

[23] Bowes and Jones, *op. cit.*, pp. 137–139.

Foliation. *Definition.* Following usage widely prevalent in the United States we use the term foliation to cover all types of mesoscopically recognizable s-surfaces of metamorphic origin. Lithologic layering, preferred dimensional orientation of mineral grains, and surfaces of physical discontinuity and fissility resulting from localized slip may all contribute to foliation of different kinds (Fig. 4-13). British petrologists[24]

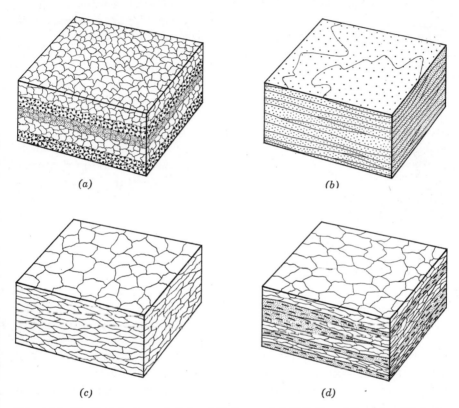

(a)

(b)

(c)

(d)

FIG. 4-13. Physical features defining foliations. (*a*) Foliation defined by lithologic layering. (*b*) Foliation defined by discrete fractures or other surfaces of discontinuity. (*c*) Foliation defined by planar preferred orientation of grain boundaries. (*d*) Foliation defined by combination of features (*a*), (*b*), and (*c*).

restrict "foliation" to s-surfaces defined by lithologic layering and use "schistosity" and "cleavage" to cover other types of s-surface.

In the descriptive phase of structural analysis it is better to avoid genetic terms such as "flow cleavage" for particular kinds of foliation. We advocate distinction of the different categories observed in a given domain as S_1, S_2, S_3, and so on. The observable characteristics of each

[24] A. Harker, *Metamorphism*, p. 203, Methuen, London, 1932.

kind of S should be listed, and according to the preference of the individual worker, a descriptive general term consistent with current usage may be added. There are a number of these descriptive terms which, although in part overlapping, are so well established in geologic literature as to warrant retention here:

Slaty Cleavage.[25] This term denotes the regular planar parting characteristic of slates and phyllites. It is independent of bedding—which it commonly intersects at high angles—and reflects a highly developed preferred orientation of grain boundaries, especially those of tabular crystals of micaceous minerals. Slaty cleavage attracted the attention of the earliest workers on tectonites[26] because it is conspicuous even in weakly metamorphosed rocks and is so clearly independent of still recognizable bedding that it is obviously of tectonic origin. Speculation as to its dynamic significance was inevitable and has proved to be far from unanimous;[27] but use of the term *slaty cleavage* in this book carries no dynamic or kinematic implications.

Fracture Cleavage; Strain-slip Cleavage.[28] Fracture cleavage is a parting defined by closely spaced discrete parallel fractures, ideally independent of any planar preferred orientation of grain boundaries that may exist in the rock.[29] It is closely allied to strain-slip cleavage which is a foliation defined by parallel narrow domains or discrete surfaces of incipient transposition of a preexisting foliation. Fracture cleavage can occur in almost all rock types; it is not restricted, as is slaty cleavage, to rocks containing inequidimensional minerals. Strain-slip cleavage, on the other hand, can occur only in rocks already possessing a platy foliation or bedding. The distinction, however, is not wholly satisfactory because the structures appear to be mutually gradational, and both are commonly secondary *s*-surfaces—incipient transposition foliations— appearing in previously foliated rocks. Fracture cleavage in one type of rock may be synchronous with and dynamically equivalent to strain-slip cleavage in associated beds of another type. The two would be denoted by the same S symbol.

[25] E.g., E. S. Hills, *Outlines of Structural Geology*, pp. 106, 111, Methuen, London, 1953; C. H. Behre, Observations on structures in the slates of Northampton County, Pennsylvania, *Jour. Geol.*, vol. 34, pp. 481–506, 1926; C. H. Behre, Slate in Pennsylvania, *Penn. Geol. Survey Bull. 16*, pp. 7–32, 1933.

[26] E.g., J. Tyndall, Comparative view of the cleavage of crystals and slate rocks, *Phil. Mag.*, ser. 4, vol. 12, pp. 35–48, 1856.

[27] E.g., G. Wilson, The relationship of slaty cleavage and kindred structures to tectonics, *Geologists' Assoc. Proc.*, vol. 57, pp. 263–302, 1946.

[28] These types of foliation together with associated structure have been superbly figured and described by R. Balk, Structural and petrologic studies in Dutchess County, New York, part I, *Geol. Soc. America Bull.*, vol. 47, pp. 685–774, 1936.

[29] C. K. Leith, Rock cleavage, *U.S. Geol. Surv. Bull. 239*, p. 12, 1905; Harker, *op. cit.*, p. 158, fig. 68, 1932 (strain-slip cleavage).

Axial-plane Foliation or Cleavage. Foliations and cleavages—especially slaty cleavage and strain-slip cleavage—commonly bear symmetric relations to the axial planes of folds in some preexisting sets of *s*-surfaces. The commonest arrangements are as follows:

1. Foliation parallel to an axial plane. This is probably the commonest situation, particularly in strongly metamorphosed phyllites, schists, and gneisses, and it may be the ultimate condition toward which the other arrangements converge.

2. Foliation in a fan symmetric to an axial plane. The fan opens either toward the core of a fold or away from it. De Sitter[30] believes that the former arrangement is typical of fracture cleavage and the latter of slaty cleavage. Where layers of different lithologic type are folded, the angle of the fan may be different in different layers. So arises the so-called "refraction" of cleavage across the boundary between adjacent beds of different composition.

3. Two or more conjugate foliations symmetric to an axial plane. This relation, described by Knill,[31] is probably much more widespread than has been previously appreciated by geologists. Closely related to this structure is an axial-plane cleavage of type 1 developed in a system of related folds having conjugate axial planes (cf. pages 114 and 115).

Layering and Lamination. The most conspicuous *s*-surfaces of many tectonites are parallel layers or tabular lenticles, commonly a fraction of a centimeter thick, consisting alternately of contrasted mineral assemblages such as quartz-albite and chlorite-muscovite-epidote. This structure has been widely identified—though often without justification—as bedding or as "bedding foliation." We have here reserved the term bedding—as distinct from foliation—for structure clearly recognizable as such and having true stratigraphic significance. More often than not one cannot be sure that metamorphic layering on the mesoscopic scale is indeed undisturbed bedding. Rather commonly it can be shown to be a transposed preexisting *s*-surface of some kind and should then be denoted by some convenient descriptive symbol—e.g., "S_2 = transposed layering, possibly bedding."

Much the most widespread type of metamorphic lamination in tectonites is the result of metamorphic differentiation;[32] an initially homogeneous rock has become differentiated into alternating layers of contrasted composition controlled by and emphasizing some cleavage or

[30] L. U. De Sitter, *Structural Geology*, pp. 99–100, fig. 71, McGraw-Hill, New York, 1956.

[31] Knill, *op. cit.*, pp. 317–324.

[32] F. L. Stillwell, The metamorphic rocks of Adelie Land, *Australasian Antarctic Exped. 1911–1914 Sci. Repts.*, ser. A, vol. 3, pt. 1, pp. 76, 77, 1918; F. J. Turner, The development of pseudo-stratification by metamorphic differentiation in the schists of Otago, New Zealand, *Am. Jour. Sci.*, vol. 239, pp. 1–16, 1941; Turner and Verhoogen, *op. cit.*, pp. 583–586, 1960.

other s-surface of metamorphic origin. Some of the characteristic criteria by which layering of this origin may be recognized are as follows:

1. The scale of metamorphic layering is independent of the scale of bedding of the parent rock, which may be inferred in a general way from its chemical composition. Thus fine differentiation lamination may be equally well developed in pelitic schists derived from shale (presumably finely bedded), in quartzo-feldspathic schists derived from graywacke (presumably coarsely bedded), and in greenschists derived from basalt.

2. On the macroscopic scale transition may be demonstrated between coarsely bedded or massive parent rocks, well-cleaved schists without layering, and conspicuously laminated schists.

3. Individual layers on close examination prove to be very flat discontinuous lenses.

4. Chemically there is no correspondence between many common types of layer and any ordinary sediments. Such are quartz-albite layers of metagraywackes, epidote-chlorite-actinolite layers of greenschists, glaucophane layers in glaucophane schists, and so on.

5. Microscopic examination may prove that a layered structure closely resembling bedding in the field crosses an earlier s-surface itself characterized by layering on a fine scale.

Schistosity. The term schistosity may be used to cover foliations defined by preferred orientation of tabular crystals, especially of micas; it is commonly emphasized on the mesoscopic scale by layering of metamorphic origin. Some geologists use the term schistosity in the same sense as foliation is used here; others have used it synonymously with slaty cleavage.[33] There is complete transition between cleavage of fine-grained rocks and schistosity of coarser-grained schists.

Joints. Joints are regularly spaced subparallel planar fractures which may be open or cemented with fillings of minerals such as quartz, calcite, or albite. They may be parallel and related to closely spaced micro-fractures pervading the rock on a microscopic scale. Joints differ from other deformational structures in tectonites in that they form by brittle rupture of the rock after cessation of flow. Some joints are products of late stresses unrelated to flow. But other types are symmetrically related to flow structures and probably reflect response to residual stresses remaining in the tectonite after flow ceased. Two common types of joints in this latter category are as follows:

1. Cross joints (also called *ac* joints by some writers) approximately—but rarely exactly—normal to any strong linear structure (lineation, fold axis, mullion axis, and so on). Such joints tend to be very regular in a body that is homogeneous with respect to a strong linear structure.

---

[33] E.g., Leith, *op. cit.*, p. 23, 1905; J. L. Knill, A classification of cleavages with special reference to the Craignish District of the Scottish Highlands, *21st Internat. Geol. Cong. Rept.* (1960), pt. XVIII, p. 318, 1960.

They range in size from widely spaced continuous master joints to closely spaced fractures confined to small domains such as garnet porphyroblasts or quartzose laminae.

2. Conjugate or oblique joints (also called $0kl$ joints[34]). These tend to occur in pairs symmetrically inclined to a conspicuous lineation to which their line of intersection is normal. Either kind of joint may occur separately, but both commonly occur together.[35]

LINEAR STRUCTURES

Lineation. Cloos[36] defines lineation as ". . . a descriptive and non-genetic term for any kind of linear structure within or on a rock. It includes striae on slickensides, fold axes, flow lines, stretching, elongated pebbles or oöids, wrinkles, streaks, intersections of planes, linear parallelism of minerals or components, or any other kind of linear structure of megascopic, microscopic or regional dimensions." In this book the term lineation is restricted to linear structures penetrative in hand specimens or in small exposures. Slickenside striae are excluded because they occur on discrete surfaces of discontinuous movement and do not pervade the surrounding rocks, which may even be undeformed. Folds likewise are excluded because they combine the geometric properties of both a plane and a line. The latter—the fold axis—may be treated as a lineation in a body that is homogeneous with respect to folding on a small scale. Larger-scale linear features such as mullions, rods, and elongated pebbles are here treated separately as *linear structures*.

Four features either singly or in any combination define lineations in tectonites:

1. Parallel elongate aggregates of individual minerals forming parallel streaks, trains, or bodies of cylindrical, prismatic, or spindle-shaped form (Fig. 4-14a). The grains of any kind of aggregate are not necessarily elongate; they may equally well be equant, tabular, or prismatic. To this general category also belong elongate rock fragments and ellipsoidal ooliths and microfossils whose inequidimensional outlines are due to deformation.

2. Linear preferred orientation of boundaries of prismatic or tabular crystals (Fig. 4-14b, c).

3. Axes of microcrenulations of a set of s-surfaces (Fig. 4-14d).

4. Intersection of two or more cozonal s-surfaces—the trace of one s-surface upon another (Fig. 4-14e).

[34] Use of the symbols ac and $0kl$ refers to orthogonal fabric axes in which b is identified with a lineation normal to a conspicuous plane of symmetry in the mesoscopic fabric.

[35] E.g., M. Kürsten, The metamorphic and tectonic history of parts of the Outer Hebrides, *Edinburgh Geol. Soc. Trans.*, vol. 17, p. 17, figs. 12, 13, 1957.

[36] E. Cloos, Lineation, *Geol. Soc. America Mem. 18*, p. 1, 1946.

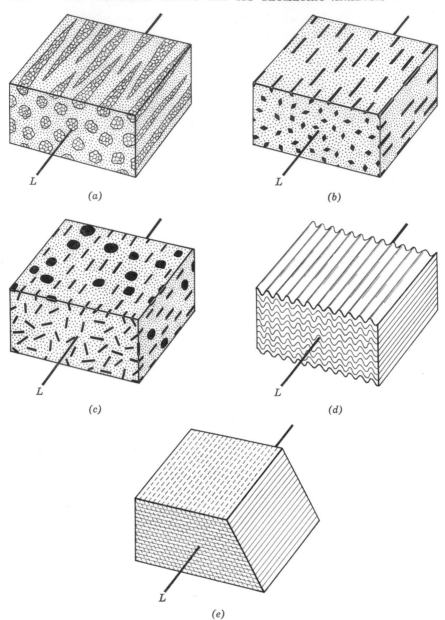

Fig. 4-14. Physical features defining lineations L. (a) Lineation defined by pre-ferred orientation of elongated domains of equant grains. (b) Lineation defined by linear preferred orientation of prismatic grains. (c) Lineation defined by linear preferred orientation of platy grains. (d) Lineation defined by small crenulations of an s-surface. (e) Lineation defined by intersecting s-surfaces.

Lineations of the first two types are independent of s-surfaces; the last two types occur only in conjunction with s-surfaces. Many tectonites contain more than one lineation. An *apparent lineation*[37] is the trace of a lineation of any kind upon an obliquely intersecting s-surface.

Until Sander's work became known most geologists paid more attention to foliation than to lineation. In English-speaking countries work on lineation was stimulated in 1946 by the appearance of E. Cloos's invaluable survey with its accompanying annotated bibliography.[38] Today there is still no satisfactory generally adopted classification of lineations. Some terms in current use—stretching, rolling, streaming, flow lines, and so on—are undesirable because they have a genetic connotation that is difficult to verify. Others such as a and b lineation, defined kinematically in terms of assumed "movement" and "tectonic transport," must be rejected for the same reason. The term a or b lineation may indeed be used if the symbols refer strictly to fabric axes defined by symmetry alone; but misunderstanding is almost inevitable because of the kinematic significance so widely attached to a and b in the literature on tectonites. We recommend use of the descriptive symbol L,[39] different lineations being designated L_1, L_2, etc. The descriptive attributes of the lineation may be added, e.g., "$L_1 =$ axis of alignment of hornblende prisms and intersection of S_1 and S_2, normal to the single symmetry plane and parallel to the b axis of the fabric." All lineations in tectonites are nonpolar and have axial symmetry $D_{\infty h}$.

Linear Structures. In some tectonite bodies occur structures closely related to lineations but on a much larger scale. Of these, mullion structures and rods[40] are most widespread, and are generally associated with folding. Wilson contrasts mullions and rods as follows:[41] " . . . mullions are formed of the normal country-rock, while rodding is developed from quartz that has been introduced into, or has segregated in, the rocks." He distinguishes three kinds of mullions:

1. Bedding or fold mullions, formed by the parting of the rock along curving undulations or flexures of the bedding. In examples from areas other than those discussed by Wilson, the folded surface can be foliation.

2. Cleavage mullions, formed by a roughly prismatic parting of the rock along intersecting bedding and cleavage surfaces (or along intersecting foliation surfaces).

3. Irregular mullions, formed by the intersection of irregular curving, parting surfaces that seem to bear little relation to bedding or foliation;

[37] Den Tex, *op. cit.*, p. 57.

[38] Cloos, *op. cit.*, pp. 50–113; Lineation: review of literature, 1942–1952, *Geol. Soc. America Mem. 18 Suppl.*, 1953.

[39] Cf. Cloos, *op. cit.*, p. 5.

[40] G. Wilson, Mullion and rodding structures in the Moine series of Scotland, *Geologists' Assoc. Proc.*, vol. 64, pp. 118–151, 1953.

[41] Wilson, *op. cit.*, p. 119.

but they tend to be elongated parallel to associated fold and cleavage mullions.   Possibly Wilson's irregular mullions are in part equivalent to mullions bounded by intersecting deformed cross and normal bedding as noted by other workers in the same area.[42]

Both mullions and rods are especially prominent in hinges of large folds. Indeed they are rather reliable indicators of the existence of such structures, reflecting as they do a general increase in intensity of linear structures that is also manifested in fold hinges by local profusion of small folds and by the locally oblique or transverse relation of axial-plane cleavage to the folded s-surface.   The symmetry of an individual mullion or rod, taking the form of the typical cross section into account, is almost invariably monoclinic C_{1h}, with a single plane of symmetry normal to the length of the mullion.[43]

Other large-scale linear structures of tectonites are elongate boudins and deformed pebbles.   Elongate boudins[44] apparently form by disruption of competent layers along planar partings in the course of transposition or lateral stretching.   Careful investigation on the macroscopic scale has shown that some pseudoconglomerates are actually products of transposition and boudinage of alternating quartzite and shaly beds. The elongated pebbles of many deformed conglomerates also impart a large-scale linear structure to the deformed body.   Where the individual pebble is lensoid (triaxial) rather than spindle-shaped, the linear structure may be combined with a large-scale planar structure resulting from parallel alignment of the planes of flattening as well as the axes of maximum elongation.[45]

FOLDS

General Terminology.   Because they are the commonest and most obvious structures of deformed rocks, folds have long occupied the attention of geologists.   There is a large literature dealing with folds and folding; but no completely satisfactory descriptive classification of folds is in general use.   The situation in part reflects the great variety and complexity of fold forms that may occur even in a single deformed body; and in part it arises from the need for parallel independent classifications based respectively on geometric properties, style, orientation, and symmetry.   The classifications and terminology here adopted are descriptive.

---

[42] J. M. Christie, D. B. McIntyre, and L. E. Weiss, *Appendix*, in D. B. McIntyre, The Moine thrust: its discovery, age and tectonic significance, *Geologists' Assoc. Proc.*, vol. 65, p. 220, 1954.

[43] Cf. Wilson, *op. cit.*, pp. 129, 137.

[44] E.g., E. Cloos, Boudinage, *Am. Geophys. Union Trans.*, vol. 28, pp. 626–632, 1947; L. U. De Sitter, Boudins and parasitic folds in relation to cleavage and folding, *Geologie en Mijnbouw (N.W. ser.) 20e Jaar.*, pp. 277–286, 1958.

[45] E.g., Flinn, *op. cit.*, pp. 486–490.

They are drawn as far as possible from accepted current usage, but it has been necessary to introduce some new or unfamiliar terms, and to frame a comprehensive geometric classification of fold forms.

Folds range in size from small crenulations, too large to be considered lineations, to great nappe structures many miles in amplitude. In this chapter only mesoscopic folds are considered. These are folds, generally of small size, whose geometric elements can be measured directly. They range from an inch or two to tens of feet in amplitude and correspond to the *minor* or *small-scale folds* recognized by workers in the Scottish Highlands and elsewhere. Folds exist wherever a set of s-surfaces is curviplanar in form. Most folds have formed in s-surfaces that were initially planar; but such an origin is not necessarily implicit in the term fold.

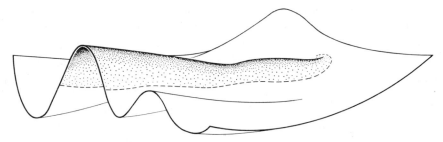

Fig. 4-15. The domain of a single fold (stippled) in a curviplanar surface.

Where folds have formed from initially planar structures they are important indicators of distortion in a geologic body, and their geometric features can be correlated with local stresses, strains, rotations, translations, and so on.

The following general terminology of folds is geometric and nongenetic and it can be used equally well for mesoscopic and macroscopic structures:

1. The term *fold* can be applied to any segment of a set of surfaces which are curviplanar. The limits of an individual fold are somewhat arbitrarily defined. Most folds are elongate bodies, and the fold is considered to include the extension of the structure in the direction of elongation, regardless of detailed changes in form. In directions normal to the elongation the fold persists only so long as the sense of curvature is effectively constant. The presence of a marked inflection line defines the boundary of a second fold. Thus, in Fig. 4-15 the stippled portion can be taken to outline the domain of a single fold.

2. A fold is said to *close* in the region where the curvature is greatest; where exposed on a topographic surface such a region is sometimes termed a *closure*.

3. That portion of a fold where the folded surface is plane or approximately so, between opposing closures, is a *fold limb*.

4. A group of spatially related folds closing in opposite senses may be termed a *fold system*.   Where these are demonstrably of common origin, they may be termed a *fold generation*.

5. The terms *anticline* and *syncline* are reserved for folds in bedding in which stratigraphic relations are known.   Following one common usage[46] we define an anticline as a fold closing upward with older beds in its core (i.e., toward the center of curvature), and a syncline as a fold closing downward with younger beds in its core.   A fold closing downward with older beds in its core we term a *synformal anticline* and a fold closing upward with younger beds in its core an *antiformal syncline*.

6. Following Bailey,[47] we term a fold closing upward with unknown or no stratigraphic features (e.g., a fold in foliation) an *antiform* and a fold closing downward a *synform*.

Geometric Classification of Folds.   *General.*   To be discussed in relation to strain of the body in which it occurs, the fold must be regarded as a single geometric system, regardless of origin.   From this viewpoint develops a nongenetic classification of folds based on purely geometric criteria.   Such a classification is useful because although folds give some idea of strain it is not always possible to reconstruct their kinematic development from initially planar surfaces, to evaluate the relative roles of flexure and slip, or to establish whether one or several phases of deformation have been involved in folding.   The geometric properties of many folds are simple and can be defined in terms of simple elements such as a rectilinear fold axis and an axial plane.   Systems of such folds— or of simple portions of more complex folds—are amenable to statistical analysis, for this technique is applicable only to homogeneous domains whose fabric elements are measurable straight lines and planes.   Other folds are complex and require curvilinear and curviplanar elements for their complete definition.   Some of these are shown later in this chapter (pages 129 to 143) to be compound systems of superposed folds of more than one age.

The geometric classification developed below includes all common folds, simple or complex.   It is framed in terms of a linear element (the hinge or the axis) and a planar element (the axial surface) either of which may be curved in the more complex types.   There is wide divergence in current usage of these terms.   The definitions adopted below are strictly geometric (descriptive); but they are framed to facilitate kinematic analysis.

Hinge or Hinge Line.   This is the line on a single folded surface joining points of greatest curvature.   Where there is no *point* of greatest curvature in a closure but only a circular arcuate segment, as is true of some

---

[46] E.g., M. P. Billings, *Structural Geology*, Prentice-Hall, New York, p. 38, 1942.

[47] E. B. Bailey, in E. B. Bailey, J. Weir, and W. J. McCallien, *Introduction to Geology*, p. 121, Macmillan, London, 1939.

open folds, the hinge line is symmetrically situated in this segment. Hinges are geometrically of three kinds, as follows:

1. Rectilinear hinge (Fig. 4-16a)
2. Curvilinear hinge lying in a plane (Fig. 4-16b)
3. Curvilinear hinge not lying in a plane (Fig. 4-16c)

Fold Axis. Some folds with rectilinear hinges can be generated geometrically by a line parallel to the hinge moving with constant orientation.[48] This line or generator is termed a *fold axis* and is designated B.

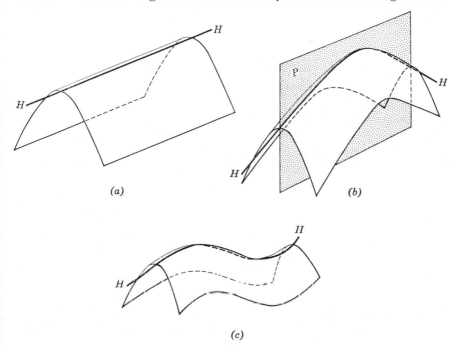

Fig. 4-16. Hinges H of folds. (*a*) Rectilinear. (*b*) Curvilinear lying in a plane P. (*c*) Curvilinear not lying in a plane.

All attitudes of the folded surface ideally contain this line which may be considered as a penetrative feature of the fold, present at every point in the folded surface. Such folds are termed *cylindroidal* or, preferably, *cylindrical folds.*[49] Where all the folds in a system share the same fold

[48] R. H. Clark and D. B. McIntyre, The use of the terms pitch and plunge, *Am. Jour. Sci.*, vol. 249, p. 594, 1951.

[49] C. H. Stockwell, The use of plunge in the construction of cross-sections of folds, *Geol. Assoc. Canada Proc.*, vol. 3, p. 98, 1950; C. D. A. Dahlström, Statistical analysis of cylindrical folds, *Canadian Inst. Mining Metallurgy Trans.*, vol. 57, p. 1, 1952; L. E. Weiss, Geometry of superposed folding, *Geol. Soc. America Bull.*, vol. 70, pp. 92, 93, 1959; J. B. Mertie, Classification, delineation and measurement of nonparallel folds, *U.S. Geol. Surv. Prof. Paper 314E*, pp. 95–99, 1959.

axis, the system may be termed cylindrical. All other folds are termed *noncylindrical*. Ideally, one type of noncylindrical fold, namely, a *conical fold*,[50] can be generated by a straight line passing through a fixed point. Each very small segment of the folded surface at a particular distance from the fixed point has a fold axis of different orientation.

Axial Surface. This is the surface containing hinge lines on successive folded surfaces. Axial surfaces are of three kinds:

1. Planar. This is the commonest kind of axial surface and is generally termed an *axial plane*. Where folds of a system share the same axial plane it may be considered a penetrative structure present at every point. Commonly a cleavage or foliation is parallel to the axial plane and marks its orientation at all points in the fold. Penetrative axial planes are conveniently treated as a variety of *s*-surface. Folds with axial planes are here termed *plane folds*. Plane folds can be either cylindrical (*cylindrical plane folds*) or noncylindrical (*noncylindrical plane folds*) as illustrated respectively by Fig. 4-17*a* and *b*. Most folds that can be measured directly on an outcrop are cylindrical plane folds or fold segments on this scale; on the macroscopic scale they may prove to be noncylindrical or nonplane.

2. Cylindrically curviplanar: the axial surface is cylindrically curved. The folds themselves may be either cylindrical, so that the fold axis is shared by the folded surface and the axial surface (Fig. 4-17*c*), or noncylindrical with fold axis inclined to the axis of curvature of the axial plane (Fig. 4-17*d*). The former are termed *nonplane cylindrical folds;* the latter, *nonplane noncylindrical folds*.

3. Noncylindrically curviplanar: the axial surface is noncylindrically curved. Folds with such axial surfaces lack any kind of geometric regularity and these too are termed *nonplane noncylindrical folds* (Fig. 4-17*e*). Orientation of axes and axial surfaces of noncylindrical and nonplane folds can only be expressed in terms of a number of measurements made respectively on cylindrical and plane segments. No single measurement can specify the orientation of such a fold.

In most folds the axial surface approximately bisects the angle between the fold limbs where these are effectively planar (Fig. 4-18*a*). But in some asymmetric folds, especially those with marked attenuation of one limb, the axial surface as defined by hinge lines may depart significantly from the true bisecting surface (Fig. 4-18*b*). The angle of divergence between these two surfaces is a measure of the degree of asymmetry of a fold.[51]

---

[50] Dahlström, *op. cit.*, pp. 5–6; P. J. Haman, *Manual of Stereographic Projection*, pp. 32–36, West Canadian Research Publications, Calgary, 1961.

[51] For a detailed account of relation between axial plane and bisecting surface in folds of different kinds, see Haman, *ibid.*, pp. 21–30.

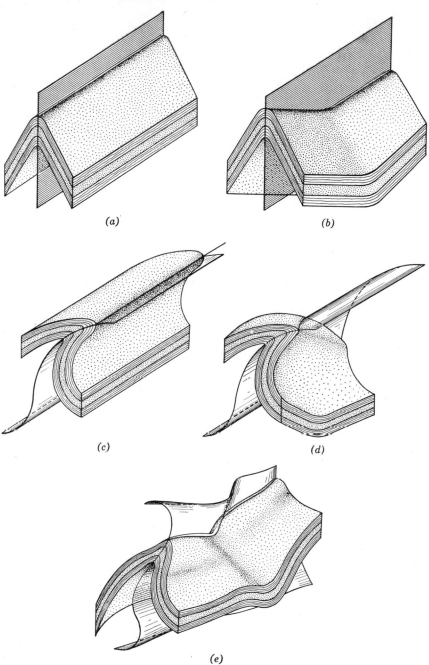

FIG. 4-17. Geometric properties of folds. (a) Cylindrical plane fold. (b) Non-cylindrical plane fold. (c) Nonplane cylindrical fold. (d) Nonplane noncylindrical fold with cylindrical axial surface. (e) Nonplane noncylindrical fold with noncylindrical axial surface.

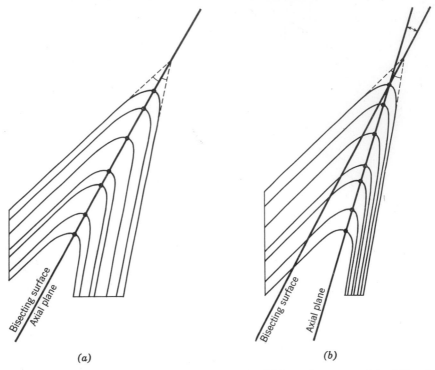

(a)   *(b)*

FIG. 4-18. Axial plane and bisecting surface of a fold; sections normal to fold axis. (*a*) Symmetric fold; axial plane and bisecting surface coincide. (*b*) Asymmetric fold; axial plane and bisecting surface inclined.

TABLE 4-1. GEOMETRIC CLASSIFICATION OF FOLDS

		Axis or hinge		
		Rectilinear	Planar curvilinear	Nonplanar curvilinear
Axial surface	Planar	1. Plane cylindrical	2. Plane non-cylindrical	
	Cylindrical curviplanar	3. Nonplane cylindrical		4. Nonplane non-cylindrical
	Noncylindrical curviplanar			4. Nonplane non-cylindrical

Classification. From the foregoing discussion emerges a geometric classification of folds in four classes, based on relations between the fold axis (or hinge) and the axial surface. This is summarized in Table 4-1.[52]

The Enveloping Surface (Faltenspiegel).[53] The enveloping surface is a structure pertaining to a group of adjacent folds or a fold system. On the mesoscopic scale it is measured as the approximately plane surface that is tangential to successive antiforms or synforms developed in a single folded surface—the *form surface*.[54] The form surface is any recognizable surface of contact between lithologically different layers—whether these are stratigraphic, transposed, or of metamorphic origin. On a large scale, especially on the full macroscopic scale, the enveloping surface of a fold system, as reconstructed from measurement of a number of nearly planar segments, may prove to be planar (Fig. 4-19a), curviplanar (Fig. 4-19b), or very commonly regularly folded (Fig. 4-19c). If the component folds of the system are appressed and symmetric, their axial surfaces and limbs may be almost normal to the enveloping surface (Fig. 4-19d).

In much the same way as the form of transposed lithologic layering can be defined by bands of transposed competent lenticles (Fig. 4-11d), the enveloping surface of a fold system defines the gross form of the folded surface (Fig. 4-12). An enveloping surface may intersect the axial planes of the fold system at any angle (cf. pages 122 to 124). Where the intersection is oblique and the form surface is bedding, the attitude of the axial plane in relation to the enveloping surface has the same stratigraphic implication—though on a larger scale—as the familiar bedding-cleavage relations in individual folds: if the enveloping surface dips more steeply than the axial planes of the component folds, large-scale inversion of gross bedding may be indicated.

Style, Orientation, and Symmetry of Folds. On the basis of geometric relations between hinge and axial surface, folds fall into one of the categories summarized in Table 4-1. Folds are also classified according to equally important criteria of three other kinds:

1. Style (general form, as seen in profile)
2. Orientation (attitude of linear and planar elements relative to geographic coordinates)

---

[52] Intentionally omitted are true domes which cannot be defined in terms of axis or axial surface.

[53] See, for instance, R. Hoeppener, Zur Tektonik des SW-Abschnittes der Moselmulde, *Geol. Rundschau,* vol. 46, pp. 324–325, 1958. Good examples of what is here termed the enveloping surface are figured and discussed by A. Engel (Studies of cleavage in the metasedimentary rocks of the northwest Adirondack Mountains, *Am. Geophysical Union Trans.,* vol. 30, p. 773, 1949) and by R. Balk (*op. cit.,* pp. 702–715).

[54] D. B. McIntyre and L. E. Weiss, Construction of block diagrams to scale in orthographic projection, *Geologists' Assoc. Proc.,* vol. 67, p. 149, 1956.

3. Symmetry (innate symmetry of the structure with respect to elements and total form, independent of orientation)

Classification of Folds According to Style. The style of a fold—recognized especially from its form and general character as seen in profile (cf. page 48)—can be defined and classified only in a rather arbitrary and subjective manner. Yet in comparing parts of a geologic body, folds of a given generation in a given rock type usually can be recognized and

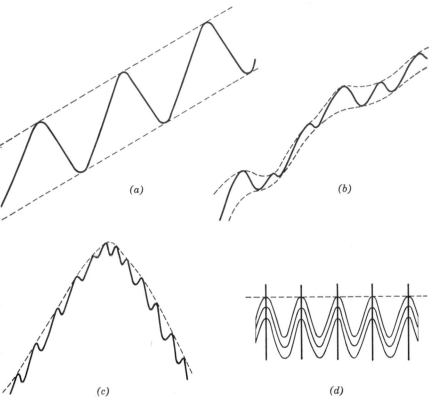

Fig. 4-19. Types of enveloping surface shown by broken lines (explanation in text).

correlated by identity of style more than by any other character. Many descriptive terms relating to style are in common use. Perhaps ten such are sufficient to classify folds by style.

1. *Concentric or Parallel Folds.*[55] Locally important in tectonites, these are the common *competent* folds of sedimentary rocks. The folded layers maintain more or less constant thickness in one fold, with the result that their radius of curvature decreases toward the core of the fold. Such folds cannot persist through many layers without becoming cuspate, dying out or terminating in décollements or thrusts (Fig. 4-20a). In

[55] E.g., De Sitter, *op. cit.*, pp. 189–191, 196–201, 1956; Mertie, *op. cit.*, pp. 97–99.

tectonites they occur mainly in isolated layers of one rock type enclosed in another having different mechanical properties (e.g., thin sandstone layers in slate in Fig. 4-20b). They do not penetrate a rock body in a harmonic fashion.

2. *Similar Folds.*[56] These are the common folds of tectonites. The name connotes their most characteristic feature, namely, that each folded surface is approximately similar in form to the others, so that geometrically a fold can be generated by arbitrary translations of a single folded surface in the axial surface. Similarity in form requires that individual

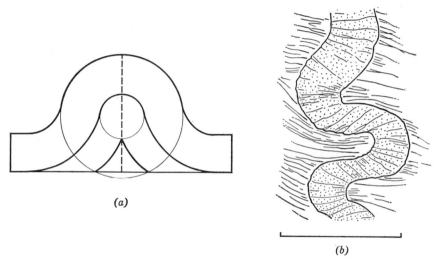

(a)

(b)

FIG. 4-20. Features of concentric folds in sections normal to fold axes. (a) General form of a concentric fold, assuming circular arcs. (b) Concentric folds in sandstone layer. (*After L. U. de Sitter.*)

layers between form surfaces be radially thickened in the hinges relative to the limbs (Fig. 4-21a). Theoretically, individual folds can persist indefinitely in a direction normal to the hinge. Some natural similar folds that have been fully explored in three dimensions persist with only minor changes in form through thousands of feet along the axial surface (e.g., the folds from Broken Hill, Australia, illustrated in Fig. 4-21b).[57]

3. *Cleavage Folds.*[58] Where used in a descriptive sense, this term denotes folds of similar type which have secondary foliations or cleavages symmetrically related to their axial surfaces. The possible arrangements of such cleavages have already been discussed (page 99).

[56] E.g., Billings, *op. cit.*, p. 53, 1942; Mertie, *op. cit.*, pp. 99–103.

[57] J. K. Gustafson, H. C. Burrell, and M. D. Garretty, Geology of the Broken Hill ore deposit, Broken Hill, N.S.W., *Geol. Soc. Amer. Bull.*, vol. 61, pp. 1397–1406, 1950. Cf. also Hills, *op. cit.*, fig. 50, p. 84, 1953.

[58] E.g., De Sitter, *op. cit.*, pp. 94–98, 1956; *op. cit.*, p. 277, 1958.

4. *Disharmonic Folds.*[59] In a disharmonic fold successive surfaces have markedly different form without destroying the individual identity of the fold.   In some disharmonic folds the same geometric elements are approximately common to all folded surfaces (Fig. 4-22a); in others the geometric relations are more complex (Fig. 4-22b).

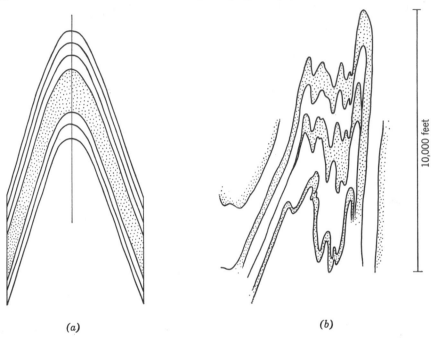

(a)   (b)

Fig. 4-21. Features of similar folds in sections normal to fold axes. (a) General form of a similar fold.   (b) Large macroscopic similar folds at Broken Hill, Australia. (*After J. K. Gustafson, H. C. Burrell, and M. D. Garretty.*)

5. *Chevron or Kink Folds.*   These are folds which have planar limbs connected by closures so sharply curved that hinges are really angular bends (Fig. 4-22c).   They occur characteristically in very thinly laminated or foliated rocks and are commonly asymmetric.   The kinking of foliation in such folds closely resembles the kinking of a glide plane in a crystal containing kink bands.

6. *Isoclinal Folds.*   Ideally, these have parallel limbs.   A concentric fold can be truly isoclinal (Fig. 4-22d), but similar folds can only approach this form (Fig. 4-22e).

7. *Conjugate Folds.*   This term was coined by Johnson[60] to designate closely associated folds of identical style, occurring in pairs with mutually

[59] E.g., Billings, *op. cit.*, pp. 52–54, 1942; De Sitter, *op. cit.*, pp. 229–234, 1956.

[60] M. R. W. Johnson, Conjugate fold system in the Moine thrust zone in the Lochcarron and Coulin Forest areas of Wester Ross, *Geol. Mag.*, vol. 93, pp. 345–350, 1956.

inclined approximately conjugate axial surfaces (Fig. 4-23a).   Each fold
of a conjugate pair is approximately a mirror image of the other.   They
are a special case of Greenly's polyclinal folds,[61] in which axial surfaces
of a group of adjacent related folds have approximately random orientation (Fig. 4-23b) but a common line of intersection (the fold axis B).
Conjugate folds commonly appear near the intersections of conjugate

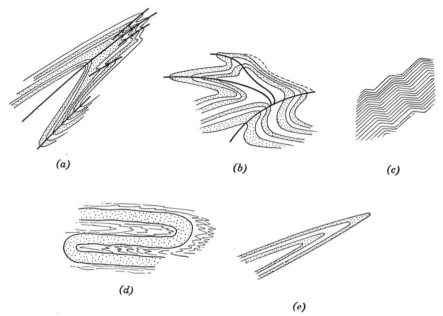

(a)   *(b)*   *(c)*

(d)

(e)

FIG. 4-22. Fold styles (diagrammatic); sections normal to fold axes. (a) Disharmonic folds; axial planes shown as dark lines. (b) Disharmonic folds; axial surfaces
shown as dark lines. (c) Chevron or kink folds. (d) Isoclinal concentric fold.
(e) "Isoclinal" similar fold.

sets of kink folds (see pages 475 to 478).   The axis of intersection of the
kink surfaces generally lies in the foliation, but in some conjugate folds
this axis is inclined to the folded surface.
    8. *Convolute Folds.*   This term is convenient for folds resembling dis-
harmonic, conjugate, or polyclinal folds, but having axial surfaces that
are curved, smoothly branching, or whorled, and hinges that are complex and convolute (Fig. 4-23c).   The individual folds are generally
cylindrical in extension and resemble folds which have been called
refolded folds.[62]

[61] E. Greenly, The geology of Anglesey, vol. 1, *Geol. Surv. Gt. Britain Mem.*, pp.
190–191, 1919.
[62] P. Clifford, M. J. Fleuty, J. G. Ramsay, J. Sutton, and J. Watson, The development of lineation in complex fold systems, *Geol. Mag.*, vol. 94, pp. 8–11, 1957.

9. *Ptygmatic Folds.*[63]   Ptygmatic folds are distinguished from convolute folds by their lobate form (Fig. 4-23*d*).   They typically occur in thin layers of one rock type (generally pegmatite or granite) enclosed in another (e.g., schist or gneiss).   The limbs are commonly attenuated and the hinges are sensibly concentric in form.   Ptygmatic folds are not widespread in tectonites other than migmatitic gneisses.

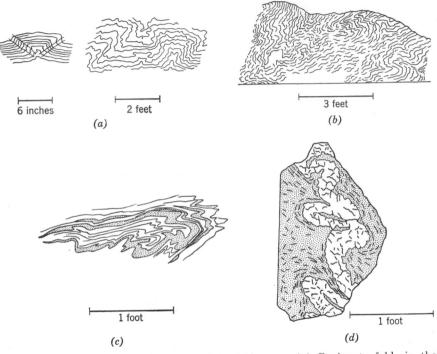

Fig. 4-23. Fold styles; sections normal to fold axes. (*a*) Conjugate folds in the Moine Thrust zone, Scottish Highlands. (*After M. R. Johnson.*) (*b*) Polyclinal folding in the Mona complex of Anglesey, Wales. (*After E. Greenly.*) (*c*) Convolute folds from Swedish Lapland. (*After photograph by M. Lindström.*) (*d*) Ptygmatic folds. (*After G. Wilson.*)

10. *Intrafolial Folds.*   Isolated folds with distinctive characters are commonly observed in otherwise unfolded tectonites.   They are tightly appressed plane folds occurring sporadically as relatively slight distortions of dominantly planar foliation (Fig. 4-24*a*).   They commonly grow from an unfolded foliation surface only to die out again at a higher level. The axial planes either conform approximately or are significantly inclined

---

[63] G. Wilson, Ptygmatic structures and their formation, *Geol. Mag.*, vol. 89, pp. 1–21, 1952; Turner and Verhoogen, *op. cit.*, pp. 372–374, 1960; H. Ramberg, Evolution of ptygmatic folding, *Norsk geol. tiddsk.*, vol. 39, pp. 99–151, 1959.

to the average attitude of the surrounding unfolded foliation; and this usually curves gently around the local swelling caused by folding. Closely related are *rootless intrafolial folds* which consist generally of an isolated closure or of a pair of opposing closures in a disrupted portion of a layer now "floating" as a tectonic inclusion in relatively unfolded foliation (Fig. 4-24b). The presence of intrafolial folds is one of the criteria of transposition of s-surfaces (cf. Fig. 4-11d). Because of its genetic connotation the term "drag fold," sometimes applied to intrafolial folds, is not used in this book. In tectonites produced from sedimentary rocks

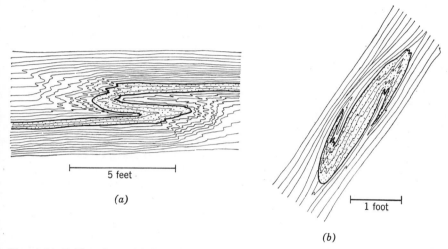

5 feet

(a)

1 foot

(b)

FIG. 4-24. Fold styles. (a) Intrafolial fold of feldspathic gneiss in biotite gneiss near Turoka, Kenya. (b) Rootless intrafolial fold of calc-silicate layer in marble near Weldon, California.

inherited slump folds of sedimentary origin are easily confused with intrafolial folds of tectonic origin.

Orientation of Folds. *General.* It is sometimes convenient to classify folds according to their orientation, which is defined by the attitude of fold elements with respect to external coordinates. Orientation is not to be confused with symmetry, which is independent of external coordinates. The attitude of any fold is specified by the orientation of the axis and the axial plane, so that classification based on orientation is directly applicable only to plane or cylindrical folds. Since the orientation of geometric elements in other folds is inconstant, the attitude of such folds can be specified only in terms of orientation measured in each of several plane or cylindrical segments. A number of well-recognized terms in current use suffice to define common folds on the basis of orientation in relation to the geographic horizontal plane (cf. Figs. 4-25, 4-26 for projections on the horizontal plane).

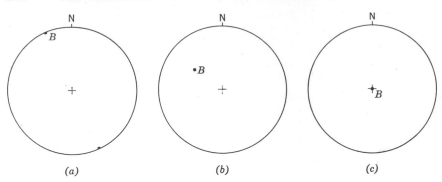

FIG. 4-25. Orientation of axes (B) of cylindrical folds projected on a horizontal plane. (*a*) Horizontal fold. (*b*) Plunging fold. (*c*) Vertical fold.

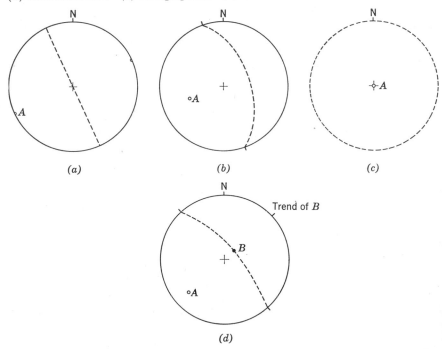

FIG. 4-26. Orientation of poles to axial planes A of plane folds projected (as broken arcs) on a horizontal plane. (*a*) Normal or upright fold. (*b*) Inclined or overturned fold. (*c*) Recumbent fold. (*d*) Reclined fold (cylindrical folds only); B = fold axis.

Classification of Plane and Cylindrical Folds by Geographic Orientation

1. Orientation of axes of cylindrical folds, plane and nonplane:
     Horizontal fold—with horizontal or subhorizontal axis (Fig. 4-25*a*)
     Plunging fold—with axis inclined obliquely to the horizontal (Fig. 4-25*b*)

Vertical fold—with vertical axis (Fig. 4-25c)

2. Orientation of axial planes of plane folds, cylindrical or noncylindrical:

Normal or upright fold—axial plane vertical (Fig. 4-26a)

Inclined or overturned fold—axial plane dipping at less than 90° (Fig. 4-26b)

Recumbent fold—axial plane horizontal (Fig. 4-26c)

Reclined fold[64] (cylindrical only)—axial plane striking normal to the trend of the axis (Fig. 4-26d)

The commonest mesoscopic folds belong to the plane cylindrical class; and in these the various standard orientations of fold axis and axial plane listed above may be combined in only seven ways. The seven types are shown in projection in Fig. 4-27 and tabulated in Table 4-2. From Fig. 4-27 it is clear that the trend of the fold axis may be inclined at any angle to the strike of the axial plane.

TABLE 4-2. CLASSIFICATION OF PLANE CYLINDRICAL FOLDS BY
GEOGRAPHIC ORIENTATION

		Orientation of fold axis		
		Horizontal	Plunging	Vertical
Orientation of axial plane	Vertical	Horizontal normal	Plunging normal	Vertical
	Dipping	Horizontal inclined	Plunging inclined (Strike of axial plane oblique to trend of fold axis)	
			Reclined (Strike of axial plane perpendicular to trend of fold axis)	
	Horizontal	Recumbent		

Orientation of the Enveloping Surface. The attitude of a planar segment of the enveloping surface of a fold system can be measured directly only where exposures are sufficiently continuous or the individual folds are small enough for at least three or four—preferably more—successive crests or troughs to be exposed on a planar face. The trend and plunge of the trace of the enveloping surface on such a face—e.g., on a cross-joint surface—are measured. Since the enveloping surface also contains the axis of the individual fold, the unique attitude of the planar segment is determined graphically by the construction in Fig. 4-6.

[64] This term is noted by J. Sutton (Some crossfolds and related structures in northern Scotland, *Geologie en Mijnbouw, 39e. Jaar.*, no. 5, p. 155, 1960). The same kind of fold is discussed by K. Naha (Steeply plunging recumbent folds, *Geol. Mag.*, vol. 96, pp. 137–140, 1959).

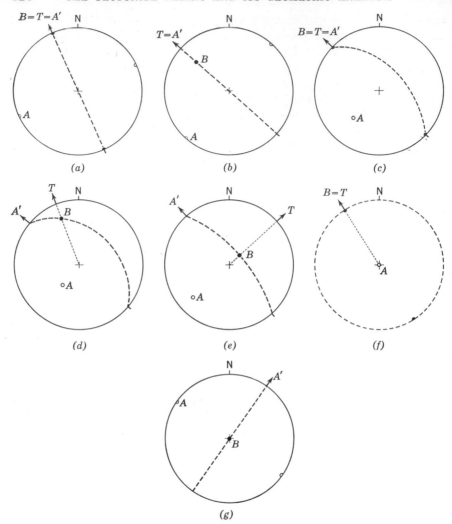

FIG. 4-27. Orientation of axes B and poles to axial planes A, of plane cylindrical folds projected on a horizontal plane. T is the trend of the fold axis and A' the strike of the axial plane. (a) Horizontal normal fold. (b) Plunging normal fold. (c) Horizontal inclined fold. (d) Plunging inclined fold. (e) Reclined fold. (f) Recumbent fold. (g) Vertical fold.

Relative Orientation of Spatially Related Folds. In current terminology of folds are many terms describing the orientation of folds relative to spatially associated macroscopic structures such as large folds, fold systems, and orogenic zones. These relations, which do not necessarily imply any genetic or chronological connection between the associated structures, are discussed in greater detail in Chapter 5, for they can be fully established only by macroscopic analysis of the major structures. Meanwhile a number of generally recognized definitions are listed:

1. *Longitudinal folds*[65] have axes trending parallel to the regional elongation of an orogenic body. The fold axes must be horizontal or gently plunging. Longitudinal folds are thought generally to be early formed folds of large amplitude whose form accounts for the existing gross distribution of lithologic types.

2. *Cross folds* or *oblique folds*[66] have axes either at right angles or oblique to longitudinal or main folds. They have many different origins, but in general they are smaller than the main folds. Some share axial planes with associated longitudinal folds[67] and form with them a geometric system that would be termed plane noncylindrical in the descriptive classification given above. Other cross folds have axial planes inclined to those of associated longitudinal folds; and some are even associated with folds developed in a foliation that parallels the axial planes of the longitudinal folds. Such cross folds are clearly later than the main folds on whose limbs they appear. They have been termed *superposed* or *superimposed folds*,[68] and their geometric properties are discussed in detail on pages 129 to 143.

3. *En échelon folds*[69] are arranged en échelon, generally on the limbs of larger folds.

4. *Discordant folds*[70] are varieties of oblique folds with axes inclined to those of the longitudinal folds in the same area.

5. *Parasitic folds*[71] appear as mesoscopic folds on the limbs of a large fold sharing the same geometric elements. This term is preferred to the term "drag folds," which has been used in somewhat the same way by earlier writers.

6. *Inconstant folds*[72] are associated folds varying in both trend and

---

[65] E.g., Sutton, *op. cit.*, p. 151.

[66] H. J. Koark, Über Querfaltung, Bewegung ‖ B und Erzlagerung mit Beispielen aus Malmberget/Gällivare, *Upsala Geol. Inst. Bull.*, vol. 34, pp. 251–278, 1952; King and Rast, *op. cit.*, pp. 243–269, 1955; King and Rast, *op. cit.*, pp. 185–195, 1956; J. Haller, Gekreutze Faltensysteme in Orogenzonen, *Schweizer mineralog. petrog. Mitt.*, vol. 37, pp. 11–30, 1957; Sutton, *op. cit.*, pp. 149–162.

[67] King and Rast, *op. cit.*, pp. 188–189, 1956.

[68] E.g., W. S. White and M. P. Billings, Geology of the Woodsville Quadrangle, Vermont–New Hampshire, *Geol. Soc. America Bull.*, vol. 62, pp. 681–683, 1951; Weiss and McIntyre, *op. cit.*, pp. 575–602, 1957; J. G. Ramsay, Superimposed folding at Loch Monar, Inverness-shire and Ross-shire, *Geol. Soc. London Quart. Jour.*, vol. 113, pp. 271–308, 1958a; Weiss, *op. cit.*, pp. 91–106, 1959.

[69] J. D. Campbell, En échelon folding, *Econ. Geology*, vol. 53, pp. 448–472, 1958.

[70] J. L. Knill and D. C. Knill, Some discordant fold structures from the Dalradians of Craignish, Argyll and Rosguill, Donegal, *Geol. Mag.*, vol. 95, pp. 426–510, 1958.

[71] De Sitter, *op. cit.*, pp. 279–280, 1958.

[72] P. Clifford, M. J. Fleuty, J. G. Ramsay, J. Sutton, and J. Watson, *Geol. Mag.*, vol. 94, pp. 6–8, 1957.

plunge. They can be either plane noncylindrical or nonplane non-cylindrical folds.

Symmetry of Folds. In structural analysis one of the most significant attributes of a fold or a fold system is its symmetry. *Symmetric* and *asymmetric* are terms familiar enough in current terminology of folds.[73] But their generally accepted usage is unsatisfactory in that it carries implications relating to geographic orientation as well as to symmetry. The symmetry and the orientation of a geologic structure are independent properties and in structural analysis must be treated separately.

The symmetry of an individual fold is defined by its geometric elements (hinge or axis, and axial surface) and by the form of the folded surface. The geometric elements of a plane or cylindrical fold can be measured directly and plotted on a projection, from which their combined symmetry is obvious. The symmetry of a fold form on the other hand is not so readily treated by graphic means. That of a plane cylindrical fold is directly observed on the mesoscopic and microscopic scale in any section normal to the fold axis; and it is convenient to combine this with the projection of the axis and plane to bring out the total symmetry of the fold. On the macroscopic scale inferences regarding symmetry of fold forms may be drawn from the outcrop pattern of the folded beds or from statistical analysis of numerous attitudes of the folded surface measured by uniform sampling over a large area (cf. pages 158 to 160).

Because a fold as an individual unit is not a homogeneous domain it can possess only point-group symmetry. A large body, uniformly folded on a small scale and hence structurally homogeneous, has statistical space-group symmetry (including a center of symmetry), and this may be either isomorphous with the point-group symmetry of the individual fold[74] (e.g., a fold system in which antiforms are consistently different from synforms) or have different symmetry.

The symmetry of all geometric classes of fold shown in Table 4-1 is summarized in Table 4-3. For each of the four geometric categories is listed first the symmetry of the combined geometric elements, and then the modified symmetry resulting from considering as well the form of the fold. The symmetry of combined fold elements (second column of Table 4-3) includes a center of symmetry—as indeed must be the case for any projection of fabric data. But inclusion of the fold form (third and fourth columns of Table 4-3) eliminates the center of symmetry.

Symmetric and asymmetric folds may be distinguished on the basis of the fold form alone. A symmetric fold is a plane fold whose profile is bilaterally symmetric across the axial plane; other folds are classed as

---

[73] E.g., Billings, *op. cit.*, p. 39, fig. 21, 1942; C. M. Nevin, *Principles of Structural Geology*, 4th ed., p. 43, fig. 25, Wiley, New York, 1949.

[74] M. Paterson and L. E. Weiss, Symmetry concepts in the structural analysis of deformed rocks, *Geol. Soc. America Bull.*, vol. 72, pp. 849–853, 1961.

TABLE 4-3. SYMMETRY OF MESOSCOPIC FOLDS

		Symmetry		
		Geometric elements alone (hinge line and axial surface)	Geometric elements plus folded surface	
			Bilaterally symmetric across axial plane: symmetric folds	Bilaterally asymmetric across axial plane: asymmetric folds
Fold type	Plane cylindrical	Orthorhombic D_{2h}	Orthorhombic C_{2v}	Monoclinic C_{1h}
	Plane noncylindrical	Monoclinic C_{2h}	Monoclinic C_{1h}	Triclinic C_1
	Nonplane cylindrical	Monoclinic C_{2h}		Triclinic C_1
	Nonplane noncylindrical	Triclinic C_i		Triclinic C_1

asymmetric. Because symmetry and orientation are independent, both classes of fold may be normal, inclined, recumbent, and so on, according to their orientation with respect to the horizontal plane (cf. Fig. 4-28a to d). Since on the mesoscopic scale measurements are confined to fold axes and to plane segments of axial surfaces, the symmetry of plane cylindrical folds (first horizontal row of Table 4-3) has particular significance in mesoscopic analysis. It is easy to identify the symmetry of such a fold if its complete profile between adjacent closures of the same sense is exposed. If not, the attitude of the axial plane in relation to the enveloping surface is a useful criterion: In a symmetric fold the axial plane is normal to the enveloping surface (Fig. 4-28a and c); in an asymmetric fold the intersection is oblique (Fig. 4-28b and d).

MUTUAL RELATIONS OF ASSOCIATED MESOSCOPIC STRUCTURES

General Relations of Foliation, Lineation, and Folds. Two widely prevalent relationships between mesoscopic structures of foliated folded rocks have long been recognized and used by structural geologists:

1. Foliation S_2 is commonly parallel to the axial surfaces of folds affecting an earlier s-surface S_1.

2. Lineation is commonly parallel to the axes of cylindrical folds. As field investigations of tectonites have become more intensive, however, these two relationships have proved to be by no means universal. Rocks

with plane cylindrical folds may have more than one lineation—one parallel to the fold axis, the other oblique and curvilinear; associated axial-plane foliation may contain lineation oblique to the fold axis.   Complex relations of lineation to fold axes have proved, indeed, to be characteristic of noncylindrical folds in particular.[75]   Some of these complexities arise from difference in ages of associated structures.   Different lineations

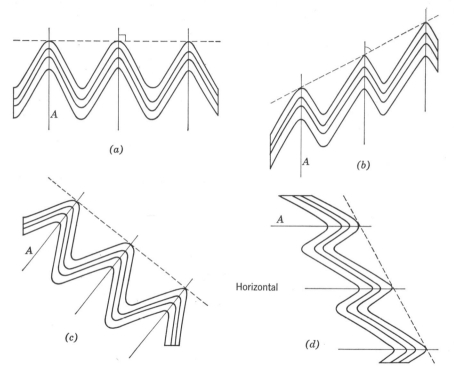

FIG. 4-28. Symmetric and asymmetric folds.   Broken line is enveloping surface; axial plane is A.   (a) Symmetric folds with axial plane normal to enveloping surface. (b) Asymmetric folds with axial plane oblique to enveloping surface.   (c) Inclined symmetric folds.   (d) Recumbent or reclined asymmetric folds.

may have formed before, simultaneously with, or after the associated folds; and early lineations may have been bent by subsequent folding of the s-surfaces in which they lie.   Likewise a late foliation S_2 may cut obliquely across the axial planes of earlier folds in another s-surface S_1; or two sets of s-surfaces may be simultaneously folded about divergent axes; or two interfering sets of folds of different age may affect a single set of s-surfaces.

In the remainder of this chapter structures that overprint or interfere with each other, either in space alone or in both space and time, are said

[75] E.g., Clifford, Fleuty, Ramsay, Sutton, and Watson, *op. cit.*, pp. 1–24.

to be superposed. Superposed structures, then, may record either different geometric aspects of one deformation or two partially or completely unrelated phases of deformation. To determine relative ages of superposed structures, which from geometry alone might seem to belong to one phase of deformation, it is necessary to turn to mineralogic and petrographic microscopic criteria.

We now review some of the established geometric features of superposed structures. The discussion is introductory rather than comprehensive, for structural analysis of superposed structures is still in its infancy.

Superposed Foliation and Lineation. *Age Criteria.* Foliations and lineations of tectonic origin clearly must be younger than associated inherited structures such as bedding. Where two intersecting foliations appear in the same rock the following are useful criteria of the relative age of the earlier foliation S_1 and the later foliation S_2:[76]

1. S_2, defined by discrete surfaces of slip, intersects and offsets S_1 (Fig. 4-29a).

2. S_2 is defined by attenuated limbs or axial planes of microfolds in S_1 (Fig. 4-29b).

3. S_2 is defined by preferred orientation of grain boundaries of a mineral (e. g., mica) local concentration of which defines layering (foliation) S_1 (Fig. 4-29c).

4. Planar s-surfaces S_2 (defined, for example, by mineral layering) cut microscopically folded S_1 (Fig. 4-29d).

5. Flakes of mica with preferred orientation in S_1 are locally bent parallel to discrete slip surfaces S_2 (Fig. 4-29e) which define a slip cleavage.

Intersecting foliations are not necessarily of different ages. In some tectonites two conjugate foliations of the same age intersect without offset; e.g., closely spaced slip surfaces develop locally between widely spaced more continuous conjugate slip surfaces. Conjugate statistical s-surfaces are commonly defined, too, by preferred orientation of grain boundaries (notably of micas) as revealed by microscopic analysis.

A lineation marking the line of intersection of two s-surfaces of different ages is synchronous with the later s-surface. Lineation defined by preferred orientation of prismatic or tabular crystals may be synchronous with or later than the foliation in which it lies; it may be a syntectonic structure related to internal displacements accompanying deformation, or it may be post-tectonic, preserving and emphasizing a linear structure of deformational origin. Lineation defined by penetrative crenulation of s-surfaces is clearly later than these. On the other hand an early lineation is sometimes curved or bent by uneven displacement on slip surfaces that define a later foliation.

[76] E.g., B. Sander, Typisierung von deformierten Tonschiefern, mit optischen und röntgenoptischen Mitteln, *Zeitschr. Kristallographie*, A, vol. 89, pp. 97–124, 1934.

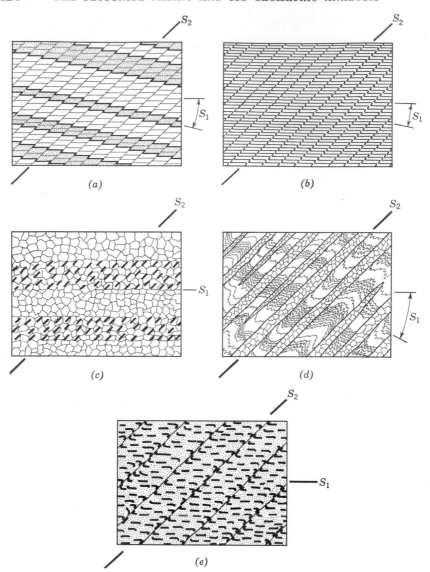

FIG. 4-29. Age relations between foliations: S_2 is later than S_1.

The relative ages of intersecting lineations L_1 and L_2 may be inferred from such critertia as (1) disturbance of L_1 by later crenulations L_2, or (2) microscopic relations of micas and hornblendes to L_1 and to L_2.   Or the age relation may emerge only from analysis of lineation attitudes.

Geometric Properties of Foliation and Lineation Superposed on Early Folds.   Consider first a plane cylindrical fold (axis B and axial plane S_2) in a set of s-surfaces S_1 cut by a later planar foliation S_3 (Fig. 4-30a).

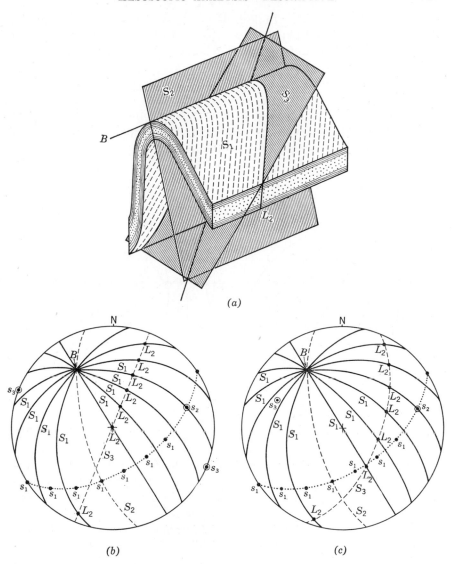

FIG. 4-30. Superposition of planar foliation S_3 and lineations L_2 on cylindrically folded s-surface S_1 (axis B, axial plane S_2). Explanation in text. S_1, etc., segments of s-surfaces; s_1, etc., poles of S_1, etc.

The lineation L_2 marking the intersection of S_3 with folded S_1 is curvilinear; but all attitudes of L_2 lie in the plane of S_3. The geometric properties of L_2 are shown projected in Fig. 4-30b in terms of several attitudes of L_2 on planar segments of S_1.[77] In Fig. 4-30b, S_3 is shown vertical, so that although the plunge of L_2 is variable, its trend (= the

[77] Weiss and McIntyre, op. cit., pp. 584–585, fig. 5a, 1957.

strike of S_3) is constant.   In Fig. 4-30c, S_3 dips at a moderate angle, so that both trend and plunge of L_2 vary.   In both diagrams the angle between L_2 and B is different for each attitude of S_1.[78]   Two special cases are noted:

1. S_3 is normal to the fold axis B, and L_2 consequently is everywhere normal to B.

2. S_3 is parallel to B, so that L_2 everywhere coincides with B.   This applies not only to the common case where S_3 is an axial-plane foliation, but also where S_3 intersects the axial plane in B but at any angle.

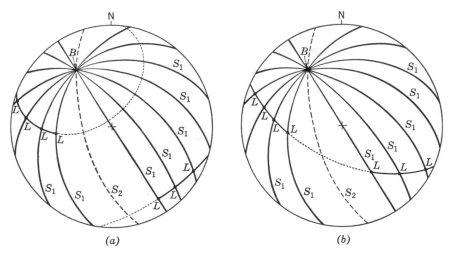

(a)   (b)

FIG. 4-31. Distortion of older lineation L by later cylindrical folding of S_1 with axis B and axial plane S_2.   (a) L lies on a small circle in projection.   (b) L lies on a great circle in projection.

Since regularity in orientation of L_2 is controlled by S_3, the same geometric relations hold even when the initial folds are nonplanar or noncylindrical.   If, however, S_3 is curviplanar, the attitudes of L_2 are more variable and the general pattern of L_2 more complex.

Geometric Properties of Foliation and Lineation Affected by Subsequent Folds.   First consider late cylindrical folding of an s-surface S_1 containing a lineation L.   Again the fold axis is B and the axial plane is S_2. The deformed linear structure L generally conforms to one or another of the following patterns, each of which may be correlated with a particular mechanism of folding (pages 474 to 490).

1. The angle between L and B is constant,[79] so that in projection L lies on a small circle centered on B (Fig. 4-31a); if L is normal to B it lies on a great circle.

[78] Cf. Sander, *op. cit.*, pp. 174–175, 1948.
[79] Sander, *op. cit.*, p. 172, 1948.

2. L does not maintain a constant angle to B but lies in a plane, i.e., on a great circle oblique to B in a projection (Fig. 4-31b).[80] Geometrically, this condition is indistinguishable from that shown in Fig. 4-30b and c for superposition of younger lineations on an older fold, except that in the present case the various attitudes of L need not lie in a *plane* foliation.

3. The plotted attitudes of L lie on an arc intermediate between a great and a small circle with B as center.[81]

4. The pattern of L is irregular, in which case it is likely that prior to cylindrical folding L was not rectilinear.[82]

Deformation of a body which already contains s-surfaces S_1 and S_2 intersecting in a lineation L may cause simultaneous folding of both s-surfaces with the result that L becomes curved. Commonly the folds in S_1 and in S_2 are approximately harmonic and share a common axial plane.[83] The same geometric relations hold for simultaneous folding of normal and cross-bedding and of beds above and below an angular unconformity. Figure 4-32 illustrates harmonic cylindrical folding of s-surfaces S_1 and S_2, with a common axial plane S_3. The respective fold axes are B_1 and B_2. The manner in which L becomes deformed depends on the mechanism of folding (see pages 474 to 490); in one common pattern all attitudes of the folded L lie in a single plane (Fig. 4-32b). After folding, L preserves its initial character as the local intersection of S_1 and S_2.

Superposed Mesoscopic Folds. *General Character and Terminology.* Interfering mesoscopic fold systems are characteristic of many tectonite bodies. Indeed some complex noncylindrical folds already treated geometrically as individual structures are more properly to be regarded as interfering systems. In some tectonite bodies the two fold systems are clearly different in age, but in others they appear to record different components of a single deformation. While it is by no means rare for

---

[80] Weiss, *op. cit.*, pp. 100–102, 1959; J. G. Ramsay, The deformation of early linear structures in areas of repeated folding, *Jour. Geology*, vol. 68, pp. 78–80, 1960.

[81] Weiss, *op. cit.*, p. 105, 1959; Ramsay, *op. cit.*, pp. 90–92, 1960.

[82] Some lineations form with an initial curvature as a result of heterogeneous deformation. Others, initially rectilinear in a planar foliation, can become curved within the plane of the foliation as a result of deformation not involving folding (cf. Weiss, *op. cit.*, p. 92, 1959).

[83] Such relations are characteristic of the Mariposa formation west of Mariposa, Calif.; here obliquely intersecting bedding S_1 and slaty cleavage S_2 on the limbs of large early folds have been harmonically refolded about a common axial plane marked by a late cleavage S_3 [M. Best, Petrology and structural analysis of metamorphic rocks in the southwestern Sierra Nevada foothills, *Univ. California Geol. Sci. Pub.*, (in press). See also J. Ramsay, Moine-Lewisian relations at Glenelg, Inverness-shire, *Geol. Soc. London Quart. Jour.*, vol. 113, p. 492, 1958].

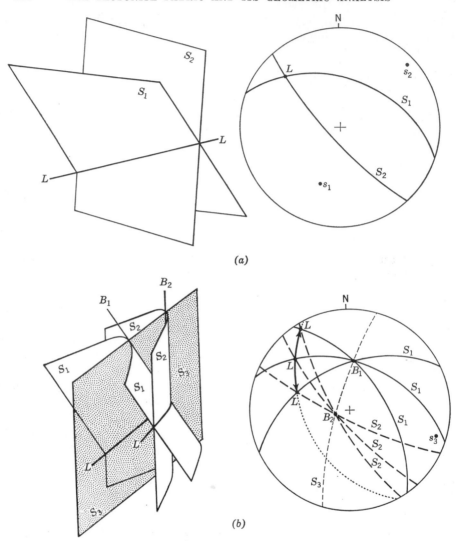

Fɪɢ. 4-32. Simultaneous cylindrical folding of two planar surfaces S_1 and S_2 intersecting in a lineation L. S_1 is seen in b to be folded about B_1 and S_2 about B_2.   The folds share the same axial plane S_3.

Figure 4-32 and subsequent diagrams of superposed folds in chapters 4, 5, 13, and 14 are simplified by representing "S_3" as a single plane surface connecting hinges of particular folds in differently oriented surfaces S_1 and S_2.   For certain types of fold, "S_3" so drawn is significantly inclined to the true common axial plane as determined by connecting hinges of folds in several form surfaces of one orientation—either S_1 or S_2.   The form of folds simultaneously generated in obliquely inclined surfaces by slip folding has been discussed by O'Driscoll (E. S. O'Driscoll, Experimental patterns in superposed similar folding, *Alberta Soc. Petroleum Geologists Jour.*, vol. 10, pp. 164–167, 1962).

three or four systems of folds to be superposed,[84] we shall here concentrate on relatively simple systems where two sets of folds are superposed. Our illustrations, moreover, are simple examples whose geometric features may be clearly represented in projection. In applying our conclusions to naturally superposed folds the reader is reminded that every decipherable case has its individual peculiarities of scale, style, orientation, and complexity of folding.

On the basis of geometric criteria, each of three cases will be considered separately:

1. Both fold systems are plane.
2. Only one fold system is plane.
3. Neither fold system is plane.

To avoid tedious repetition of such phrases as "axial surface of the earlier folds" or "folds of the second generation," the following symbols, incorporating Sander's usage of S and B, have been adopted. The use of symbols is concise, unambiguous and devoid of genetic implications. It may be applied equally well to folds on any scale.

1. s-Surfaces, including axial planes of folds, are designated S_1, S_2, S_3, etc. S_1 is the earliest recognizable s-surface; and where the relative order of development of other s-surfaces can be determined the subscripts denote that order.

2. Fold axes are designated B. A subscript denotes the folded surface, and a superscript the axial surface of the fold (where this is recognizable). Thus $B_{S_1}^{S_2}$ is the axis of a fold in S_1, the axial surface of which is S_2, and is therefore also the intersection of S_2 and S_1.

3. Lineations are designated L_1, L_2, L_3, etc. The subscript carries no necessary connotation of relative age, nor is it necessarily the same as the subscript of the s-surface in which the lineation lies (in fact, a lineation commonly is the intersection of two s-surfaces).

Geometric Relations

1. *Both fold systems plane.* It is recognized that two systems of plane folds with different geometric elements may develop simultaneously or in successive phases of deformation. The discussion which follows refers specifically to the second case; but synchronous superposed folds could be analyzed geometrically in much the same manner. No undoubted example of this class of superposed fold is yet known to us.[85]

[84] E.g., J. Sutton and J. Watson, Structures in the Caledonides between Loch Duich and Glenelg, North-west Highlands, *Geol. Soc. London Quart. Jour.*, vol. 114, pp. 231–257, 1959; P. Clifford, The geological structure of the Loch Luichart area, Ross-shire, *Geol. Soc. London Quart. Jour.*, vol. 115, pp. 365–388, 1960; A. Baird, *op. cit.*; M. Best, *op. cit.*

[85] The example described by J. L. Roberts (Fold structures in the Dalradian rocks of Knapdale, Argyllshire, *Geol. Mag.*, vol. 96, pp. 221–229, 1959) may illustrate this class.

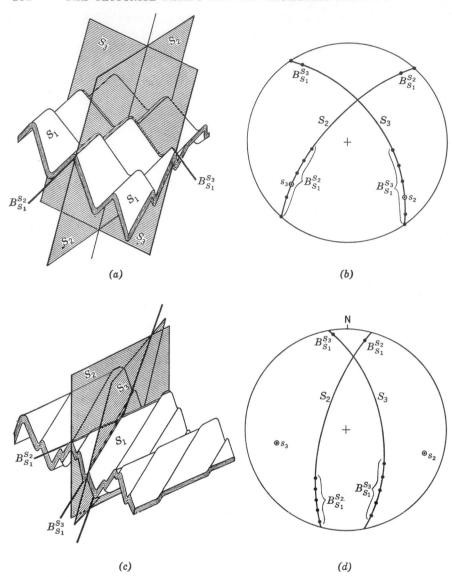

FIG. 4-33. Superposition of two systems of plane folds; S_2 and $B_{S_1}{}^{S_2}$ are respectively axial planes and axes of one system; S_3 and $B_{S_3}{}^{S_1}$ are respectively axial planes and axes of the other.   (a) and (b) $S_2 \perp S_3$.   (c) and (d) $S_2 \wedge S_3$.   Diagram c is simplified as in Fig. 4-32a.

Let S_2 and S_3 be axial planes of two systems of plane noncylindrical folds in S_1; the individual folds may have any style and may be symmetric or asymmetric. Figure 4-33 illustrates the geometry of the compound system where S_2 alternatively is (a) normal to S_3 (Fig. 4-33a and b) and (b) oblique to S_3 (Fig. 4-33c and d). The projections represent the general situation where S_2 and S_3 dip at any angle. The compound system cannot be referred to any rectilinear fold axis pervading the body as a whole. Each cylindrical segment of any fold has a fold axis lying in either S_2 or S_3 and having its own unique trend and plunge. In projection the axes $B_{S_1}{}^{S_2}$ (folds in S_1 with S_2 as axial plane) fall on the great circle defined by the trace of S_2. Similarly axes $B_{S_1}{}^{S_3}$ fall on the great circle of S_3.

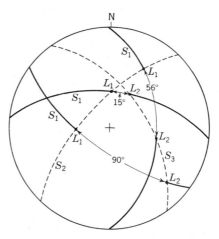

Fig. 4-34. Angles between L_1 and L_2 in three randomly selected planar segments of S_1 from the superposed fold system, Fig. 4-33a and b (explanation in text).

Lineations L_1 and L_2, respectively parallel to the intersections of S_1 with S_2 and with S_3, have the same distribution as the two kinds of fold axes. Figure 4-34 shows three plane segments of S_1 (taken diagrammatically from Fig. 4-33a) and corresponding attitudes of lineations L_1 (intersection of S_1 and S_2) and L_2 (intersection of S_1 and S_3) measured in these segments. Note that the angle L_1 to L_2 is different in each segment of S_1 (15°, 56°, and 90°). Whereas a single measurement of $L_1 \wedge L_2$ is no guide to the angle of intersection of S_2 and S_3, the attitudes of these two surfaces (broken arcs) can be determined by measuring L_1 and L_2 in each of several segments of the complexly folded surface S_1. Similar relations hold where S_2 and S_3 intersect obliquely as in Fig. 4-33c and d.

In any cylindrical fold segment one lineation is rectilinear and one curvilinear. The rectilinear structure is parallel to the fold axis of the segment, and the curvilinear structure lies in the axial plane of the second fold system: e.g., L_1 rectilinear, parallel to $B_{S_1}{}^{S_2}$, L_2 curvilinear in S_3 (Fig. 4-35a). The measured attitudes of S_1 within the cylindrical segment intersect in a β axis $= B_{S_1}{}^{S_2} = L_1$. In any system of superposed folds L_1 is rectilinear in cylindrical fold segments with axis $B_{S_1}{}^{S_2}$, and curvilinear in other segments with axis $B_{S_1}{}^{S_3}$ (Fig. 4-35b).

2. *One fold system plane, one nonplane.* In most described examples of superposed mesoscopic folds one system is plane, the other nonplane—

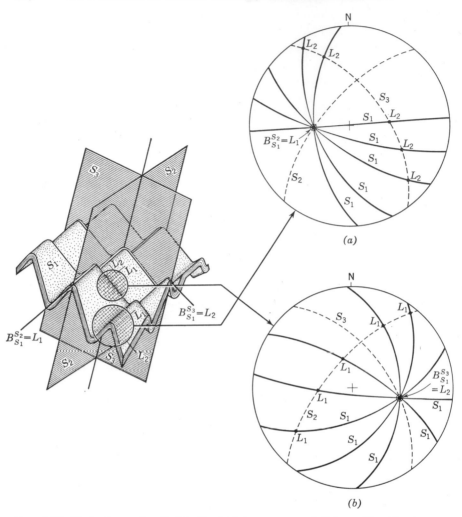

FIG. 4-35. Projections of cylindrically folded segments of S from Fig. 33a (reproduced on left-hand side of figure, simplified as in Fig. 4-32a). (a) Cylindrical with respect to $B_{S_1}{}^{S_2}$. (b) Cylindrical with respect to $B_{S_1}{}^{S_3}$.

generally having a cylindrically folded axial surface.[86]   Figure 4-36 illustrates a general case.   From inspection it is obvious that folds with the curviplanar axial surface S_2 must be earlier than those with the axial plane S_3.   Fold axes $B_{S_1}{}^{S_3}$ of the second generation lie in S_3.   The earlier axes $B_{S_1}{}^{S_2}$ may have any of several geometric patterns in projection,

[86] E.g., Weiss and McIntyre, *op. cit.*, pp. 586, 1957; Ramsay, *op. cit.*, pp. 297–299, 1958a; T. Nureki, Structural investigation of the Ryôké metamorphic rocks in the area between Iwakuni and Yanai, Southwestern Japan, *Hiroshima Univ. Jour. Sci.*, ser. C, vol. 3, no. 1, pp. 81–82, 1960.

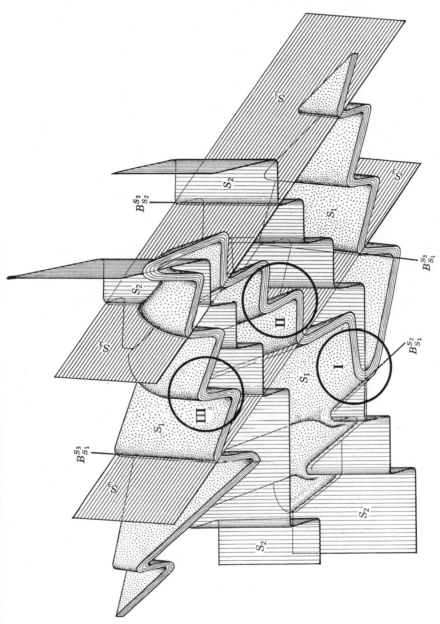

Fig. 4-36. Superposition of a system of plane folds (axial plane S_3) on a system of nonplane folds (axial surface S_2), simplified as in Fig. 4-32a. I, II, and III are three domains of cylindrical folding.

corresponding to patterns of deformed lineation illustrated in Fig. 4-31, and depending on the mechanism of the second folding (see pages 474 to 490).

Geometric properties of the fold system are illustrated by projection of cylindrical segments of both generations of fold. Figure 4-37a is a

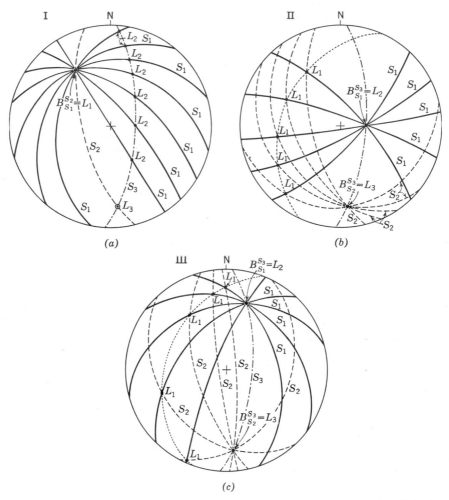

Fig. 4-37. Projection of domains of cylindrical folding from Fig. 4-36. (a) Cylindrical with respect to $B_{S_1}{}^{S_2}$ (domain I). (b and c) Cylindrical with respect to $B_{S_1}{}^{S_3}$ (respective S domains II and III).

projection of planar segments of S_1 measured in a plane cylindrical domain (I of Fig. 4-36) with axis $B_{S_1}{}^{S_2}$ and axial plane S_2. Where S_2 is a visible foliation its intersection with S_1 defines a lineation L_1 coinciding with $B_{S_1}{}^{S_2}$. S_3 is everywhere planar, and its intersection with S_1 marks a second lineation L_2, the attitude of which of course varies from one segment of S_1 to another. The lineation L_3, marked by intersection of the axial planes S_2 and S_3, is the same in every domain of Fig. 4-36, provided the curvature of S_2 is due to folding with S_3 as axial plane (the usual case).

Figure 4-37b and c shows projections of domains (II and III of Fig. 4-36) of folds of the second generation, cylindrical with respect to the axis $B_{S_1}{}^{S_3}$. In these both S_1 and S_2 are cylindrically folded (cf. Fig. 4-32), with axes respectively $B_{S_1}{}^{S_3}$ and $B_{S_2}{}^{S_3}$ and the common axial plane S_3. The lineation L_1 (intersection of S_1 and S_2) is deformed by the second folding and is shown occupying a great circle in Fig. 4-37b and c (other patterns of L_1 are possible—cf. Fig. 4-31). Figure 4-37b and c illustrates the common situation where prior to the second folding S_2 (e.g., an axial-plane cleavage) was planar: after the second folding, $B_{S_2}{}^{S_3}$ has a constant orientation in all domains of plane cylindrical folding about $B_{S_1}{}^{S_3}$, but $B_{S_1}{}^{S_3}$ can occupy any position within the plane S_3. The geometry may be more complex where S_2 was initially curviplanar and late folds about both $B_{S_1}{}^{S_3}$ and $B_{S_2}{}^{S_3}$ consequently are noncylindrical.

To compare the geometry of superposed folds with axes $B_{S_1}{}^{S_2}$ and $B_{S_1}{}^{S_3}$ and to establish their order of superposition in time the most profitable approach is to measure the elements of both structures in selected domains wherein each is cylindrical. A random section such as a joint face generally shows hinges of both generations of folds, as illustrated from published examples in Fig. 4-38. In each example the folded axial surface of the first folds is termed S_2, the axial plane of the second generation of folds S_3. Neither S_2 nor S_3 need necessarily be represented by a visible foliation. Projections such as those of Fig. 4-37 may help to check the relations inferred from direct mesoscopic inspection of the outcropping face; but extensive use of the projection belongs more properly to macroscopic analysis.

3. *Both fold systems nonplane.* No complete analysis of superposed nonplane folds has yet been published. Such systems are geometrically more complex and are more difficult to represent in projection than the case just considered. Take, for example, the simplest possible situation, in which the superposed system resembles that of Figs. 4-36 and 4-37 except that S_3—the axial surface of the second generation of folds—is cylindrically curved as the result of a third episode of folding such that the latest axial planes S_4 are planar and not geometrically related to earlier structures. The full complement of structures that could develop in the thrice-folded body is listed below:

a. Initial structures:

S_1—initial s-surface (bedding or foliation: where S_1 is bedding other sedimentary structures, such as cross-bedding, current lineations, and so on, may be present, further complicating the structure)

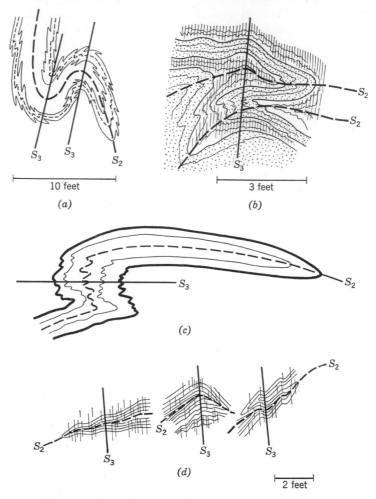

FIG. 4-38. Random sections through bodies with superposed folding. S_2 is axial surface of first generation, S_3 is axial plane of second generation. (a) From central Vermont. (*After W. S. White and R. H. Jahns.*) (b) From Loch Leven, Scottish Highlands. (c) From Lochcarron, Scottish Highlands. (*After M. R. Johnson.*) (d) From Loch Monar, Scottish Highlands. (*After J. G. Ramsay.*)

b. First generation structures:
   S_2—axial-surface foliation of folds in S_1
   $B_{S_1}{}^{S_2}$—axes of folds in S_1 with S_2 as axial surface
   L_1—lineation parallel to the intersection of S_1 and S_2
c. Second generation structures:
   S_3—axial-surface foliation of folds in S_1 and S_2
   $B_{S_1}{}^{S_3}$—axes of folds in S_1 with S_3 as axial surface
   L_2—lineation parallel to the intersection of S_1 and S_3

$B_{S_2}{}^{S_3}$—axes of folds in S_2 with S_3 as axial surface

L_3—lineation parallel to the intersection of S_2 and S_3

d. Third generation structures:

S_4—axial-plane foliation of folds in S_1, S_2, and S_3

$B_{S_1}{}^{S_4}$—axes of folds in S_1 with S_4 as axial plane

L_4—lineation parallel to intersection of S_1 and S_4

$B_{S_2}{}^{S_4}$—axes of folds in S_2 with S_4 as axial plane

L_5—lineation parallel to intersection of S_2 and S_4

$B_{S_3}{}^{S_4}$—axes of folds in S_3 with S_4 as axial plane

L_6—lineation parallel to intersection of S_3 and S_4

By no means will all of the sixteen possible structures listed above appear in any tectonite body. Some will fail to develop; others will be

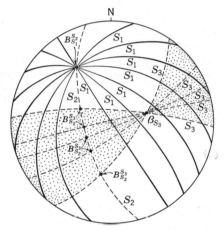

Fig. 4-39. Superposition of fan of conjugate axial surfaces S_3 on preexisting cylindrical fold (axis $B_{S_1}{}^{S_2}$, axial plane S_2). Second folds $B_{S_1}{}^{S_3}$ and $B_{S_2}{}^{S_3}$ can form with axes only in the stippled area.

too obscure to permit measurement of their orientation. A structure present in one exposure may be absent in another. Moreover, one essential condition for mesoscopic analysis will only rarely be fulfilled— namely, that mesoscopic domains can be found which are homogeneous with respect to one or more of the planar or linear structures. The geometric relations to be expected in a complex system of this kind can be illustrated in projection by considering in turn domains homogeneous with regard to $B_{S_1}{}^{S_2}$, $B_{S_1}{}^{S_3}$, or $B_{S_1}{}^{S_4}$ and plotting the other mesoscopic structures in each domain.

Superposed Folds with Fanned or Conjugate Axial Surfaces. It seems that in many tectonite bodies—especially on the macroscopic scale (pages 175 to 185)—a single system of folds has nonparallel axial planes that are fanned or conjugate in that they intersect in a common axis. Suppose that this condition applies to axial planes S_3 of a second generation of folds affecting a body in which S_1 was first folded with an axial plane S_2. Figure 4-39 is a projection of data measured in a domain of plane cylindrical folding of S_1 about $B_{S_1}{}^{S_2}$. The fold axis $B_{S_2}{}^{S_3}$ is not unique (as in Fig. 4-37b and c), but is distributed through the plane S_2—a great circle of the projection. Orientation of $B_{S_1}{}^{S_3}$ is even more variable: It is distributed through a sheaf-like sector (shown stippled in Fig. 4-39), the narrowest point (β_{S_3}) of which is the axis of intersection of the conjugate s-surfaces S_3.[87] If the angle of divergence of S_3 is large, the spread of $B_{S_1}{}^{S_3}$ axes is correspondingly great.

Relative Size of Superposed Folds. In mesoscopic analysis of superposed folds attention is concentrated on domains within which folds of

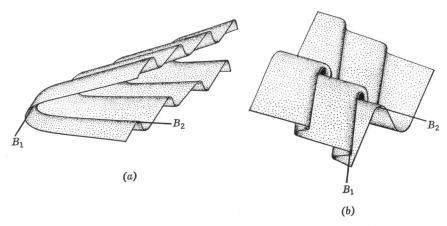

(a)

(b)

Fig. 4-40. Superposed folds of different amplitude. B_1—axes of first folds; B_2—axes of second folds. (a) B_1 folds of larger amplitude than B_2 folds. (b) B_1 folds of smaller amplitude than B_2 folds.

a given type are essentially cylindrical. Recognizable cylindrical segments of folds of two generations commonly differ in both amplitude and axial extent. Some general relations in this connection are as follows:

1. Late folds of small amplitude commonly are superposed on limbs of early folds of larger amplitude (Fig. 4-40a); but it is also possible for folds of the second generation to have the greater amplitude (Fig. 4-40b).

2. Where S_1 undergoes two phases of folding, a single fold limb or a series of limbs in an isoclinal system of early folds can provide a plane segment of S_1 for cylindrical folding in the second phase of deformation (Fig. 4-40b).

3. The axes $B_{S_1}{}^{S_3}$ of second-generation folds in S_1 maintain a constant orientation over distances that are inversely proportional to the angle of divergence between the two axes of folding $B_{S_1}{}^{S_3}$ and $B_{S_1}{}^{S_2}$.

[87] Cf. Weiss and McIntyre, *op. cit.*, p. 588, fig. 7d, 1957; Weiss, *op. cit.*, p. 104, fig. 11, 1959.

Symmetry of Superposed Folds. In a previous section (pages 106 to 111) superposed folds were treated geometrically as single systems, the symmetry of which, except for special cases, is generally triclinic. Neglecting associated subfabrics such as secondary foliations and lineations, cylindrical segments of superposed folds can have symmetry of a higher order—in fact any of the types listed in Table 4-3. Folds of a second

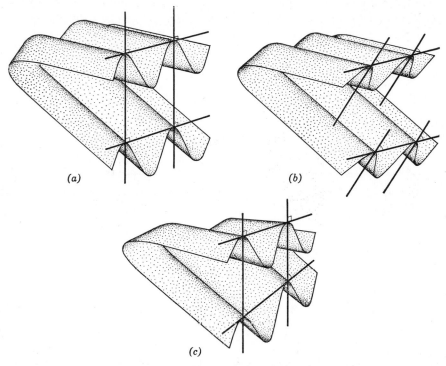

FIG. 4-41. Symmetry of second-generation folds. (*a*) Symmetric on both limbs of a first-generation fold. (*b*) Asymmetric on both limbs of a first-generation fold. (*c*) Symmetric on one limb of a first-generation fold, asymmetric on the other.

generation need not have the same symmetry when developed on different limbs of a fold, of an earlier generation. In Fig. 4-41*a* folds about $B_{S_1}{}^{S_3}$ are symmetric on both limbs of an earlier fold about $B_{S_1}{}^{S_2}$. In Fig. 4-41*b* the $B_{S_1}{}^{S_3}$ folds are asymmetric on both limbs of the earlier $B_{S_1}{}^{S_2}$ fold. In Fig. 4-41*c* the later folds are symmetric on the upper limb, asymmetric on the lower limb of the earlier fold.[88]

Bodies containing superposed folds, although generally triclinic, can still be homogeneous. Where each small sample contains statistically the same array of superposed folds the geometric and symmetric properties of this sample extend to the whole body. The arrays of mesoscopic

[88] Cf. Ramsay, *op. cit.*, p. 287, figs. 7 and 8, 1958.

elements, i.e., fold axes, foliations, lineations, and so on, of one kind, are then subfabrics of the whole homogeneous body (pages 146 to 152).

Folds with Steeply Plunging Axes. Mesoscopic folds with steeply plunging axes, long ago recognized as important by Sander,[89] are a common feature of bodies of strongly deformed rock. Where the folded surface is bedding, the presence of steeply plunging folds in what was an initially plane subhorizontal set of s-surfaces usually indicates superposition of more than one generation of folds.

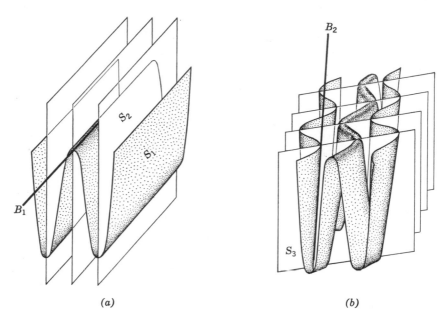

(a)   (b)

Fig. 4-42. Steeply plunging mesoscopic folds—two stages of deformation. (a) Macroscopic isoclinal folds in bedding S_1 with subhorizontal axes B_1 and subvertical axial planes S_2. (b) Superposed mesoscopic folds with subvertical axial planes S_3 and steeply plunging axes B_2.

A complex type of deformation can admittedly transform a plane horizontal surface into a set of steeply plunging folds in a single act by noncylindrical folding of an extremely heterogeneous kind. More commonly, however, two distinct phases seem to be recognizable:

1. Effectively isoclinal large-scale folding of the bedding about subhorizontal axes with subvertical axial planes (Fig. 4-42a).

2. Superposition of mesoscopic folds with steeply dipping axial planes. Regardless of the strike of the second generation of axial planes the second folds will in general plunge very steeply (Fig. 4-42b).

[89] B. Sander, Petrofabrics (Gefügekunde der Gesteine) and orogenesis, *Am. Jour. Sci.*, vol. 28, p. 43, 1934.

Systems of Basins and Domes Arising by Superposition and Interference of Folds. The superposition of folds of similar size can transform a given form surface into a pattern of generally inequant *basins* and *domes* that can have a systematic spatial distribution and orientation reflecting both the relative orientation of the interfering folds and the mechanism of folding.[90] Where the interfering folds are very tightly appressed these domes and basins may be so sharply inflected and elongated that they are effectively cylindrical in form throughout significant extensions. On approximately planar exposure surfaces such structures leave exposure traces that are closed and ring-like in form, and measurement of attitudes shows them to have apparently uniform axial plunge. In general form they resemble true diapiric structures, but unlike these they may be inclined at any angle to the horizontal.[91]

[90] By means of ingenious card-deck models, E. S. O'Driscoll (Experimental patterns in superposed similar folding, *Alberta Soc. Petroleum Geologists Jour.*, vol. 10, pp. 145–169, 1962) has established the detailed geometric form of such interference folds for some hypothetical cases.

[91] The gently plunging cylinder-like fold described by L. E. Weiss (Structural analysis of the Basement System at Turoka, Kenya, *Overseas Geology and Mineral Resources*, vol. 7, no. 2, pl. V, 1959) may in depth be a structure of this kind, although on presently available evidence the previously suggested interpretation seems equally probable.

CHAPTER 5

MACROSCOPIC ANALYSIS—DESCRIPTIVE

OBJECTIVES

The subject matter of macroscopic structural analysis is twofold: it embraces lithologic configurations too large to be observed directly in a single exposure, and it deals with the spatial arrangement of mesoscopic structures within large tectonite bodies. On this scale we are concerned mainly with three topics:

1. Form, orientation, geometric relations, and relative age of macroscopic structures, notably folds
2. Preferred orientation of mesoscopic structures—particularly s-surfaces, lineations, and fold elements—that are penetrative with respect to macroscopic domains
3. Homogeneity and symmetry of macroscopic domains

MACROSCOPIC BODIES

The fabric of a homogeneous macroscopic body is defined mainly by mesoscopic structures whose planar and linear segments have some constant pattern of preferred orientation on the macroscopic scale, and thus constitute penetrative elements of a macroscopic fabric. Among mesoscopic structures in this category only folds have macroscopic equivalents. In a large body, homogeneous by virtue of penetrative folding on a medium scale, the folds may be considered as truly macroscopic elements of the fabric. Otherwise macroscopic fabric elements are uncommon, for few structures are too large to be classed as mesoscopic and at the same time small enough to be penetrative within a large domain. Large folds are important subjects of macroscopic analysis. But they are heterogeneous structures and do not themselves constitute fabric elements. The large fold is a macroscopic structure; only its constituent homogeneous domains may have true fabrics on the macroscopic scale.

MACROSCOPIC STRUCTURES

General Nature. The term macroscopic is applied to structures whose form and orientation can be established only by geologic mapping.

144

Macroscopic structures of tectonites include folds, faults, unconformities, and miscellaneous domain boundaries such as igneous intrusive contacts. In structural analysis by far the most important of these are folds. Macroscopic folds though generally too large to be penetrative structures may have axes or axial planes parallel to corresponding elements of penetrative mesoscopic folds. So macroscopic folds may be present without destroying the homogeneity of a tectonite body with respect to mesoscopic fold axes and axial planes (e.g., in domains II, III, IV, and V of Fig. 5-2). Macroscopic structures other than folds may form boundaries of internally homogeneous domains, or they may merely be discrete discontinuities within a structurally homogeneous domain (cf. Figs. 2-3a and 2-5c).

Measurement and Elucidation of Macroscopic Structures. For a geologic map to serve as a basis for structural analysis it must show standard geologic data such as distribution and, where determinable, stratigraphic relations of lithologic units, and location and orientation of macroscopic structures (folds, faults, etc.) and of typical mesoscopic structures (notably s-surfaces, lineations, and folds). From the outcrop patterns and orientation symbols on a map, domains can be outlined as broadly structurally uniform. For instance, the general form and distribution of large folds can be determined, domains of broadly uniform trend and plunge of lineations or strike and dip of foliation can be detected. For each domain the available mesoscopic data are plotted separately to establish the unity, form, and symmetry of the macroscopic structure—e.g., the mean orientation and geometric relations of lineations, intersections of s-surfaces (β axes), and elements of mesoscopic plane and cylindrical folds. Finally any subfabrics so revealed in particular domains are compared and related to the principal macroscopic structures.

Where complex major folds are not readily visualized from mere inspection of the map, their geometry may sometimes be demonstrated in areas of high topographic relief by structure (stratum) contours drawn on selected form surfaces.[1] These are especially helpful, too, where the preferred orientation of mesoscopic structures does not obviously reflect the form of associated macroscopic structures, or where the most conspicuous mesoscopic layering is transposed bedding now obliquely inclined to gross lithologic contacts (cf. pages 92 to 96). In Fig. 5-1a small valleys cut a macroscopically plane lithologic contact between two rock units A and B. Apparently conformable to the contact are the local attitudes of foliation in both types of rock. By means of structure contours the surface of contact is found to have a regional orientation S_1 expressed by strike N19°W, dip 50°W. This is plotted in projection (Fig. 5-1b) along with the mean orientation of the foliation—the great circle S_2

---

[1] E.g., A. Berthelsen, Structural contour maps applied to the analysis of double fold structures, *Geol. Rundschau*, vol. 49, pp. 459–466, 1960.

normal to the foliation-pole maximum.   The discordance between S_1 and S_2 demonstrates that S_2 is a transposed surface, and the axis of transposition L is the intersection of S_1 and S_2.   In actual examples of transposition L is commonly found to coincide with a prominent lineation (pages 168 and 169).

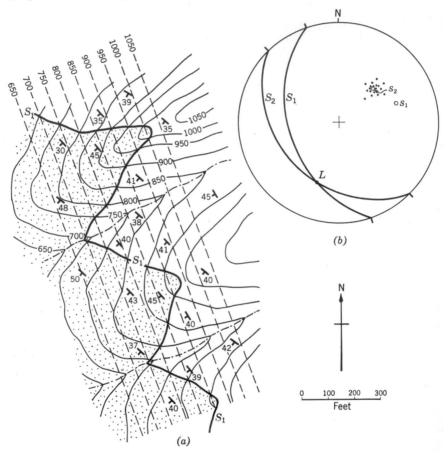

FIG. 5-1. Diagrammatic demonstration of angular discordance between mesoscopic transposition foliation and macroscopic form surface. (a) Contoured map of contact S_1 between two rock units A (stippled) and B. Structure contours (broken lines) on mapped contact (heavy line) determine strike N19W° and dip 50°W.   Orientation of mesoscopic transposition foliation S_2 given by symbols. (b) Trace of contact S_1 and poles of mesoscopic foliation S_2 from diagram a. Trace of mean orientation of S_2 intersects S_1 at L.

MACROSCOPIC FABRICS

General.   Any homogeneous macroscopic domain has a macroscopic fabric.   It will be remembered that such a domain need not necessarily be homogeneous with respect to all measured structures.   For example in many bodies containing penetrative, plane noncylindrical, mesoscopic folds, the orientation of the axial planes of the folds is everywhere constant although the preferred orientation of fold axes varies from place to place.   On the macroscopic scale the body is then heterogeneous with respect to fold axes but homogeneous with respect to axial planes.   It has a subfabric defined by the array of axial planes, but none with respect to the heterogeneous array of fold axes.

The fabric elements most commonly used to define macroscopic fabrics are mesoscopic s-surfaces, lineations, and axes and axial planes of folds. Microscopic structures, though less intensively studied by many geologists, may also build arrays that are homogeneous on a large scale, thus contributing to the fabric of a macroscopic domain.

Investigation of Homogeneity.   *General Procedure.*   Rarely homogeneity on the macroscopic scale is demonstrable by simple inspection. Thus throughout an intensely deformed schist complex in southeastern New Zealand the configuration of surface outcrops and even the drainage pattern are so completely controlled by a subhorizontal mesoscopic lineation of constant trend that a glance at an air photograph reveals this as a dominant element of the macroscopic fabric of any large domain.[2] By contrast in many deformed bodies superposed structures are so complex that simple inspection of an outcrop or of a structural map reveals an apparently chaotic structure.   Yet even in such bodies the existence of a macroscopic subfabric, homogeneous with respect to one or more kinds of structure (fabric element), can emerge from a well-planned geometric analysis.

The procedure of analysis is designed to suit each individual case. Consider, for example, Fig. 5-2 representing a hypothetical large body with macroscopic plane noncylindrical folds in an s-surface S_1 (an individual S_1 surface is indicated in heavy lines on small inset figure).   A second s-surface S_2, parallel to axial planes of folds, striking north-south and dipping vertically, intersects S_1 in a lineation L.   With respect to its total structure the body as a whole is clearly heterogeneous.   Routine procedure, designed to bring out any homogeneity that may exist, is as follows:

1. Data are collected from a large number of stations uniformly distributed (within the limits imposed by the nature of the exposure) on the topographic surface (top surface, Fig. 5-2).

2. A number of small domains are chosen, each encompassing some 20 or 50 stations and having a uniform or simple outcrop pattern on the map.   For example in Fig. 5-2 areas I_1 and I_2 are domains in each of

[2] F. J. Turner, "Gefügerelief" illustrated by "schist tor" topography in central Otago, New Zealand, *Am. Jour. Sci.*, vol. 250, pp. 802–807, pl. 1, 1952.

which the gross bedding strikes uniformly northwest and dips northeast; in domain II the strike of the bedding is northeast.

3. For each small domain orientation diagrams are constructed for each of the measured structures—S_1, S_2, L, and so on (Fig. 5-3). Strong preferred orientation in any diagram shows that the domain is homogeneous with respect to the corresponding structure. By trial and error it is found that certain contiguous small domains with identical orientation

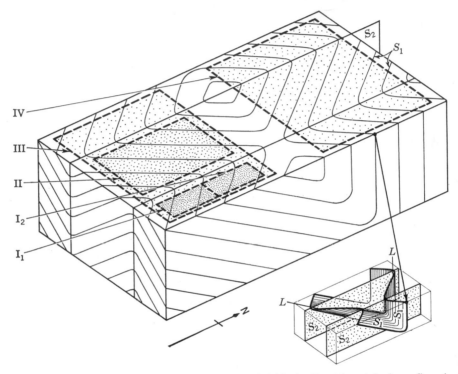

FIG. 5-2. Body containing plane noncylindrical folds in S_1 with axial plane S_2. A lineation L marks the intersection of S_1 and S_2. Homogeneous domains each with structural characteristics pecular to itself are shown by roman numerals. Inset figure shows the form of one S_1 surface and its relation to S_2 and L.

diagrams may be combined into a larger homogeneous domain—e.g., domain I, homogeneous with respect to S_1, S_2, and L, is compounded from the smaller domains I_1 and I_2 (cf. Fig. 5-3a to f). Ultimately the whole body could be divided by this means into a few homogeneous domains I, II, III, and IV, each in some respects structurally different from its neighbors. Thus in Fig. 5-2, whereas domains I and II are both homogeneous with regard to S_1, S_2, and L, they differ from each other regarding preferred orientation of S_1 (Fig. 5-3a and g), for they lie on opposite limbs of a major fold in S_1. Again domains III and IV,

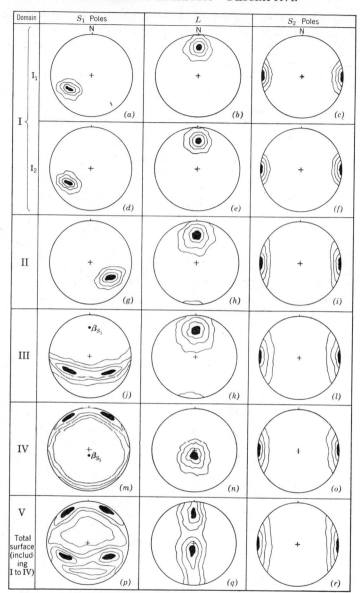

FIG. 5-3. Schematic representation in projection of S_1, S_2, and L in domains outlined by roman numerals in Fig. 5-2.   Diagrams such as p, q, and r have been termed *synoptic*.

each homogeneous with respect to β_{S_1} (the axis of the S_1-pole girdle), L, and S_2, resemble each other only in the identical attitude of S_2.

4. Comparison of the subfabrics of the various domains now reveals which structures, if any, maintain a constant orientation throughout the

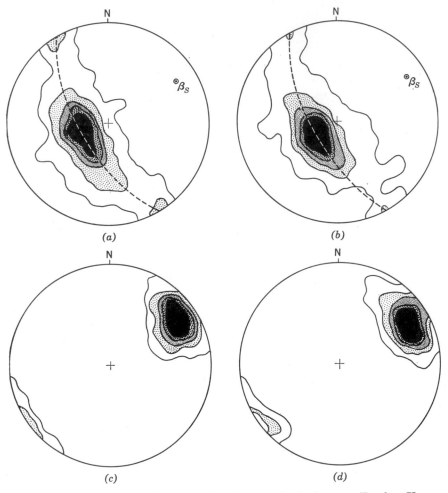

Fig. 5-4. Demonstration of homogeneity in tectonite body near Turoka, Kenya. (*After L. E. Weiss.*) Contours, 9%, 7%, 5%, 3%, 1%, per 1% area. (*a*) 429 foliation poles from northern half of area: girdle axis β_S. (*b*) 573 foliation poles from southern half of area: girdle axis β_S. (*c*) 284 lineations from northern half of area. (*d*) 502 lineations from southern half of area.

whole body (domain V). In Figs. 5-2 and 5-3 only one structure fulfills this condition—the foliation S_2. The body as a whole is homogeneous with respect to S_2 which thus has the properties of an all-pervasive fabric element. The fact that S_2 is parallel to the axial plane of the noncylindrical folds in S_1 has genetic implications as to the folding process; but discussion of this topic must be postponed to a later section dealing with interpretation of fabric.

Types of Homogeneous Bodies

1. A totally homogeneous body is homogeneous with respect to all measured penetrative structures. Each such structure is a fabric element on the macroscopic scale, and its preferred orientation defines a subfabric of the body. Figure 5-4 shows orientation diagrams for mesoscopic structures in schists and gneisses of a large segment of the basement complex of Kenya.[3] The only mesoscopic structures pervading the whole body are a foliation S, a lineation L, and axes B_S of small folds coinciding with L. Separate plots of these structures for two arbitrarily defined halves of the body give identical orientation patterns for S, for β_S, and for L ($= B_S$). All three therefore are fabric elements on the macroscopic scale, and the body is totally homogeneous.

2. A partially homogeneous body is homogeneous with respect to some but not all penetrative structures. A body of Dalradian quartzite and schist at Loch Leven[4] in the Scottish Highlands proves to be heterogeneous with respect to early lithologic layering S_1, lineation L_1, and axes of small folds B_{S_1}.[2] However, S_2—a later foliation parallel to the axial plane of folds in S_1—has almost the same orientation pattern in the eastern as in the western half of the body (Fig. 5-5). The pattern of S_2 poles is a girdle with axis β_{S_2}. The body is homogeneous with respect to S_2 alone.

3. Heterogeneous bodies (the most common kind of arbitrarily outlined macroscopic body) are heterogeneous with respect to all penetrative structures. Very commonly such bodies may be divided into partially or completely homogeneous domains[5] (e.g., the body in Fig. 5-2); heterogeneous features of partially homogeneous bodies usually exhibit this kind of regularity.[6] In other heterogeneous macroscopic bodies no homogeneity can be detected on a scale larger than that of a hand specimen, so that there is no macroscopic fabric or subfabric.

Determination of structural homogeneity, as outlined above, clearly involves broadly statistical procedures. However, the nature of the problem prohibits strict statistical treatment for reasons to be discussed.

[3] L. E. Weiss, Structural analysis of the Basement System at Turoka, Kenya, *Overseas Geology and Mineral Resources*, vol. 7, no. 2, pp. 133, 134, London, 1959.

[4] L. E. Weiss and D. B. McIntyre, Structural geometry of Dalradian rocks at Loch Leven, Scottish Highlands, *Jour. Geology*, vol. 65, p. 590, fig. 8, 1957.

[5] For illustrative examples see J. G. Ramsay, Superimposed folding at Loch Monar, Inverness-shire and Ross-shire, *Geol. Soc. London Quart. Jour.*, vol. 113, pp. 276–277, fig. 3, 1958a; A. Baird, Superposed deformations in the Central Sierra Nevada foothills, east of the Mother Lode, *Univ. California Geol. Sci. Pub.*, vol. 42, pp. 1–70, 1962.

[6] Weiss and McIntyre, *op. cit.*, p. 576, fig. 2.

Limitations in Statistical Study of Macroscopic Fabrics. From the pattern of preferred orientation of samples of mineral grains in thin sections cut from a homogeneous hand specimen, statistically sound estimates can be made of the preferred orientation of the whole population of grains within the specimen. Such estimates are possible because sampling procedures can be designed to yield significant results for the fabric element concerned: e.g., thin sections can be cut in desired locations and orientations, measuring traverses can be made in particular directions,

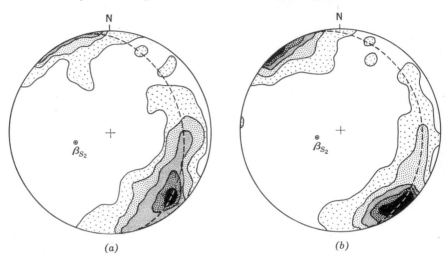

(a)   (b)

FIG. 5-5. Example of homogeneous subfabric from heterogeneous tectonite body at Loch Leven, Scottish Highlands. (*After L. E. Weiss and D. B. McIntyre.*) Contours 9%, 7%, 5%, 3%, 1%, per 1% area. (*a*) 241 poles to secondary foliation S_2 from eastern half of area: girdle axis β_{S_2}. (*b*) 354 poles to secondary foliation S_2 from western half of area: girdle axis β_{S_2}.

and, if necessary, the orientation of all the grains present within a chosen domain can be measured. Thus the data themselves can be subjected to tests of significance and other standard statistical procedures.[7]

Although sampling procedures are generally less under the direct control of the investigator, a similar statement can be made for mesoscopic fabrics, especially in domains of small or moderate size. But the geometric analysis of macroscopic domains as outlined below can make no such claims to statistical soundness. They are generally "statistical" in a purely qualitative sense. By these procedures a geologist is able to establish the general geometric form of a body. In particular, he is able to establish patterns of preferred orientation of mesoscopic fabric elements where these are strongly defined. But he is at present unable to

---

[7] By this statement we do not imply that *all* published orientation diagrams for microscopic structures are suitable subjects for statistical evaluation. Only where sampling procedures are carefully designed can the diagrams be taken as representative samples of populations.

make the rigorous determination of structural homogeneity in a given domain that would be required were strict statistical procedures subsequently to be applied to orientation data.

The main restrictions to the application of rigorous statistical methods stem from the necessarily somewhat fortuitous nature of the sampling. Except in unusually completely exposed bodies, data can be gathered only at localities decided by the whims of subaerial erosion. Areas of excellent exposure may be surrounded by areas of poor or no exposure; and even where exposed, rocks may be inaccessible to the geologist, as on vertical cliffs. The statistical evaluation of data from macroscopic domains is made questionable also by the extent of necessary extrapolation into unsampled parts of the body. Data are measured in a relatively thin skin of exposed material of large areal extent. As the size of this area increases the depth to which structural observations must be extrapolated increases, if full geologic use is to be made of the data. Added to these difficulties is an almost complete ignorance of the sources and relative magnitude of errors in measurement and observation. For example, are the errors involved in measuring the attitude of a dipping surface with a Brunton compass of the same magnitude as those involved in measuring a plunging lineation? Are either of these errors as large, in a given situation, as the errors associated with superficial gravitational creep of rocks exposed on steep slopes?

In applying the geometric procedures outlined in the following pages, therefore, a geologist must be constantly aware that he is not making rigorous statistical analyses. Rather, he is making geometric images of the internal configuration of specific domains within a geologic body and from these he is, by extrapolation, drawing general conclusions concerning the structure of the body as a whole. Because from sampled portions of a population generalizations are made about the properties of the whole population the techniques involved are nevertheless broadly of a "statistical" nature.

The statistical approach is valuable because it eliminates much of the personal, intuitive element in structural interpretation. Diagrams are prepared by a standard, almost mechanical, procedure and when complete are impersonal summaries of fact from which interpretations may be made. When the diagrams are clear ones prepared from abundant data, the interpretations are self-evident and may be considered to be as reliable as observed fact. . . . Application of the statistical method emphasizes the variation between facts, intelligent guesses, and guesses, a distinction which one does not always otherwise make. . . . Ideally the technique requires uniform sampling. Since this is the aim of geologists doing other than detail mapping, the only insurmountable obstacle is lack of outcrop. Uneven sampling produced by large areas of poor outcrop is a factor which must be considered in the interpretation.[8]

[8] C. Dahlström, Statistical analysis of cylindrical folds, *Canadian Mining Metall. Bull.*, p. 5, April, 1952.

ANALYSIS OF MACROSCOPIC FOLDS AND FOLD SYSTEMS

General. The transverse dimension of macroscopic folds ranges between a few tens of feet and several miles. Such folds have cylindrical or plane properties much less commonly than do mesoscopic folds. If the folded surface is one of mappable lithologic layering the fold form is revealed on a geologic map. But where macroscopic folding has affected closely spaced s-surfaces, such as foliation in schist or bedding in thinly bedded uniform sedimentary units, the fold form may emerge— and then somewhat imperfectly—only from statistical treatment of many measured attitudes of the s-surface in question.

Analysis of macroscopic folding is usually focused upon the most prominent s-surface—generally some kind of lithologic layering—in the tectonite body. Where more than one s-surface has been folded macroscopically each should be investigated. It is not unusual to find that the most conspicuous s-surface S_1 of one domain elsewhere becomes progressively transposed into S_2 which consequently may be the dominant s-surface of the fabric in an adjoining domain. The object of analysis is to determine the pattern of preferred orientation of the most prominent s-surface in each of several domains homogeneous with respect to that surface. Patterns of this kind provide the only available information regarding macroscopic folding where (1) the form of individual folds is not revealed by mappable markers, and (2) mesoscopic folds, which elsewhere might provide a clue as to the nature of macroscopic folding, are absent. Where mappable markers are present, structural analysis amplifies the picture of folding that emerges from the map.

The measured segments of the folded s-surface everywhere are planar. From their state of preferred orientation in various domains of the body may be deduced the attitude and configuration of axes and axial surfaces of macroscopic folds. It is possible also to tell whether folds are cylindrical or noncylindrical, plane or nonplane; and something of the style of macroscopic folding also emerges from the analysis.

The β Axis of a Cylindrical Fold System. The most consistent characteristic of preferred orientation of any particular s-surface in a macroscopic tectonite body is a tendency—seldom perfectly realized—for all measured segments to intersect in a common axis. On a projection the traces of the individual segments intersect in points that cluster around a center of gravity which Sander[9] has termed a β axis. This is then an important element in the macroscopic fabric. A β axis refers to surfaces of only one kind and of one generation. Thus β_{S_1} is the statistically defined intersection of measured segments of S_1 in a given domain, which must be homogeneous with respect to β_{S_1}. To locate β, the s-surface

---

[9] B. Sander, *Einführung in die Gefügekunde der Geologischer Körper*, Pt. I, pp. 132– 133, Springer, Berlin, Vienna, 1948.

intersections are plotted and contoured (Fig. 5-6a to c). A β axis is not necessarily an axis of folding (B) of the plotted s-surface; e.g., a fan of axial-plane cleavages S_2 will yield a β axis approximating the axis of folding $B_{S_1}S_2$ of an earlier surface S_1 even though S_2 itself is not folded.[10] However, where a surface S is folded cylindrically on the macroscopic scale, β_S defines statistically the axis of folding B_S (cf. Fig. 4-4). This is a very common situation, and determination of β_S is then the most satisfactory statistical procedure for investigating the nature of folding of S on the macroscopic scale. If folding is ideally cylindrical all traces of S segments intersect in β; and the β axis is defined by the intersection of two or more traces. The scattering of trace intersections around the statistically defined β axis expresses the degree of deviation from strictly cylindrical folding plus errors in field measurements.

Since the number of intersections of n segments is $n(n-1)/2$, it is impracticable to plot and contour intersections of many traces on a projection (25 traces yield 300 intersections). The statistically defined axis of folding in such cases is more readily obtained by plotting poles of measured S segments[11] and drawing the great circle of best fit to these (Fig. 5-6d and e). This Sander[12] has termed the "π circle," the normal to which is the axis π. Now β and π represent the same property of the fabric—the statistically defined axis of intersection of segments of S. Theoretically the two methods of utilizing the same data should yield precisely coincident β and π axes. This is true where the poles of S are evenly spread through a wide arc (Fig. 5-6d). But where most of the S poles are closely clustered it is the few poles that depart widely from

[10] A β axis need not necessarily coincide with an axis of folding (B) of any kind. For further discussion of this aspect of the significance of β axes see pp. 184–185. Note that if s-surfaces of two kinds or generations are mistakenly identified with each other and plotted on one diagram, the resulting concentration of trace intersections is not a β axis.

[11] This is the method first developed by C. E. Wegmann (Beispiele tektonischer Analysen des Grundgebirges in Finnland, *Comm. géol. Finlande Bull. 87*, pp. 104, 105, 1929) and used by his students, e.g., D. B. McIntyre, The tectonics of the area between Grantown and Tomintoul (mid-Strathspey), *Geol. Soc. London Quart. Jour.*, vol. 107, pp. 4, 5, 1951.

[12] B. Sander, Über Flächen und Achsengefüge (Westende der Hohn Tauern, III Bersicht), *Sonderabdruk aus den Mitt. Reichsamts für Bodenforsch.*, Wien, p. 7, 1942; *op. cit.*, p. 179. 1948.

Sander's original definitions of π, cited above, are clear. Elsewhere (e.g., Sander, *op. cit.*, p. 138, fig. 41, p. 139, 1948) he has used "π" as equivalent to "S-pole," and has designated the position of the π axis on the projection as the "π-pole." This terminology has been followed by a number of writers (e.g., L. E. Weiss, *op. cit.* p. 18), and has been confused further by misuse of "π-pole" as being equivalent to "s-pole" (e.g., L. E. Weiss, A study of tectonic style, *Univ. California Geol. Sci. Pub.*, vol. 30, p. 14, 1954). Because of current confusion in usage of π, and because π and β are different symbols for the same element of the fabric, we recommend that π be dropped from the terminology of structural analysis.

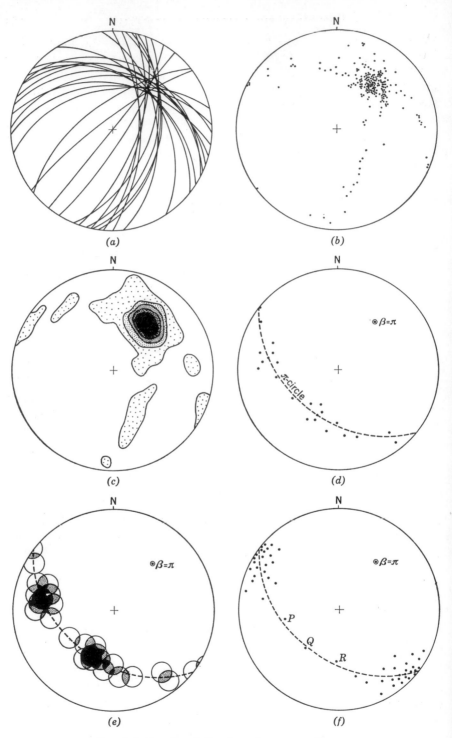

FIG. 5-6. For descriptive legend see opposite page.

the mean orientation (e.g., P, Q, R in Fig. 5-6f) that define most clearly the fold axis. These are given due weight in drawing the π circle, but are weighted equally with all other measured attitudes of S in the β construction. It has become common practice to designate the statistical axis of intersection of S segments as β, whether it has been located by contouring β intersections or by drawing the π circle; and this is the usage that we now advocate. Another reason why the use of β intersections to determine structure is unsatisfactory is more psychological than geologic. Because relatively few S traces yield a very large number of β intersections a geologist can be deluded into thinking that he is dealing with very large samples of orientations. Once the relative sparseness of the truly measured data is forgotten, statistical treatment of hundreds or thousands of β intersections may lead to complicated structural interpretations not at all warranted by either the quantity or the accuracy of initial measurements.

The uncritical use of β intersections is particularly suspect where folding is extremely weak so that the s-surfaces are broadly homoclinal. The characteristic pattern of β for such domains is an unusually perfect girdle in the plane of the uniformly dipping S, generally with scattered maxima; and the corresponding S-pole diagram shows a single maximum, perhaps with recognizable elongation on a great circle normal to one of the β maxima. Such a combination may possibly be significant. But to date there has been no statistical analysis of the effects of such factors as error in field measurement and different sampling procedures on the significance of weak or scattered β maxima. In this situation complex structural interpretation of β diagrams with scattered maxima—especially those based on measurements of acutely intersecting attitudes of S—are unwarranted, and kinematic inferences drawn from such data are valueless.[13]

---

[13] Such, for example, are some of the published analyses of M. Lindström, e.g., Structural geology of a small area in the Caledonides of Arctic Sweden, *Lunds Univ. Årssk.*, N.F. Avd. 2, vol. 51, no. 15, pp. 3–31, 1955; Tectonics of the area between Mt. Keron and Lake Allesjaure in the Caledonides of Swedish Lapland, *Lunds Univ. Årssk.*, N.F. Avd. 2, vol. 53, no. 11, pp. 3–33, 1957.

Equally dubious are axes β_2, β_3, . . . , β_6, and so on, constructed by some European writers from measurements of a single S in subdomains of a large domain (e.g., M. Kirchmayer, Zur Nomenklatur der Makrogefügekunde, *Neues Jahrbuch Geol. Paläont. Mh.*, 1961, pp. 337–339, 1961). Whereas β_S is a penetrative material element of the fabric and expresses a clear relationship between individual S surfaces, β_3, β_4, and so on, exist only on the projection net.

Fig. 5-6. Projections of 25 planar segments of cylindrically folded s-surface S. (*a*) Traces of S (S diagram). (*b*) 300 intersections from diagram a (β diagram). (*c*) Contoured β diagram: contours 17%, 13%, 9%, 5%, 1%, per 1% area. (*d*) 25 S poles (S-pole diagram). (*e*) Contoured S-pole diagram: contours 32%, 16%, 8%, 4%, per 1% area. Broken line is great circle of best fit to the girdle (π circle). Normal to circle is $\beta = \pi$. (*f*) Schematic S-pole diagram showing great influence of relatively few points (P, Q, R) upon placing of the π circle.

For most purposes we strongly favor the use of S-pole diagrams to determine β.

The S-pole Girdle of a Cylindrical Fold System. Under favorable conditions something of the geometry of folding may be inferred from the form of the girdle in the orientation diagram constructed for poles of S. Some guiding principles are as follows:

1. The crude form of a macroscopic fold may sometimes be reconstructed by drawing on the map extrapolated continuous strike lines everywhere parallel to measured attitudes (Fig. 5-7a). However, this is not always possible: Fig. 5-7b shows the same attitudes as those of Fig. 5-7a, but distributed apparently randomly; probably the scale of folding is relatively small and the domain of the map is homogeneous with respect

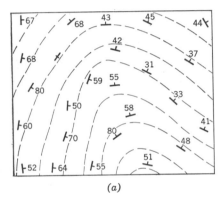
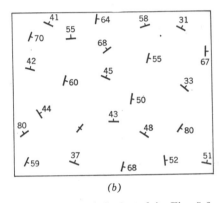

(a)   (b)

FIG. 5-7. Possible distributions on maps of the attitudes of S plotted in Fig. 5-6. (a) Extrapolation between orientation symbols clearly outlines a single large fold. (b) Scale of folding is smaller and individual folds cannot be outlined by extrapolation.

to the folded s-surface. The only indication of folding is the existence of an S-pole girdle (Fig. 5-6c) and a β maximum (Fig. 5-6c). The form of the S-pole girdle yields no information as to fold dimensions.

2. The distribution of maxima and voids in an S-pole girdle representing data measured at uniformly distributed stations provides evidence relating to style (as seen in profile) of cylindrical folds (Fig. 5-8).

a. Absence of maxima indicates open concentric folds; the pole of the axial plane is marked by a void or at least a minimum concentration within the girdle (Fig. 5-8a).

b. A pair of maxima, corresponding to the limbs, a near-void at the pole of the axial plane and a minimum at the hinge, are characteristic of the S-pole girdle for open similar folds (Fig. 5-8b).

c. In the diagram for tightly appressed similar folds the two limb maxima tend to merge into a single elongate maximum the center of which is the pole of the axial plane (Fig. 5-8c).

d. Polyclinal, convolute, and other nonplane folds yield an unusually complete *S*-pole girdle lacking prominent maxima or minima (Fig. 5-8*d*).

3. The symmetry of the *S*-pole girdle reflects the symmetry of folding. Figure 5-9*a* illustrates a system of symmetric folds, with symmetry planes m_1 (profile), m_2 (axial plane), and m_3 (enveloping surface). By contrast the unbalanced maxima of Fig. 5-9*b* indicate that alternate limbs are long and short, i.e., that the folds are asymmetric; the only plane of symmetry—that of the diagram—is normal to the fold axis, and the class of symmetry is monoclinic.

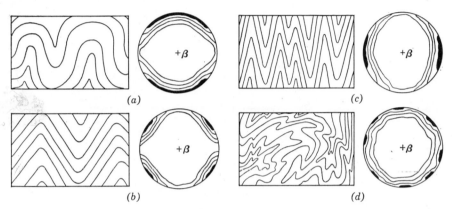

(a)   (c)

(b)   (d)

FIG. 5-8. Styles of cylindrical folds suggested by configuration of *S*-pole diagrams. (*a*) Open concentric folds. (*b*) Open similar folds with planar limbs. (*c*) Tightly appressed similar folds with planar limbs. (*d*) Polyclinal or convolute folds.

The commonest folds in macroscopic tectonite bodies are appressed plane similar folds, cylindrical segments of which yield *S*-pole girdles with a single elongate maximum the center of which approximates the pole of the axial plane (Fig. 5-8*c*). Figure 5-10*a* shows the *S*-pole diagrams, plotted on the geographic horizontal plane, for (*a*) horizontal normal, (*b*) plunging normal, (*c*) plunging inclined, and (*d*) reclined folds of this kind.[14]

In all analyses of the above kind there must constantly be borne in mind the effect of sampling procedures imposed by uncontrollable influences (e.g., nature of exposure, relief, accessibility, scale, and complexity of structure relative to completeness of exposure, and so on) upon the statistical significance of the conclusions. At present such procedures can be statistically sound only to a crude degree, and consequently are valid only where the geometric relations are obvious and reproducible in different sets of data.

[14] An excellent account of analysis of the style and orientation of cylindrical folds from projections of *S* poles is to be found in Dahlström, *op. cit.*, pp. 1–6.

β **Axes of Noncylindrical Folds.** In a body pervaded by a noncylin-drically folded s-surface S there can be no single β_S axis common to all domains. The problem of analysis of preferred orientation of S is to delineate the minimum number of domains each of which is homogene-ous with respect to β_S and to explore the regularity and variation in orientation of β_S within the body as a whole.

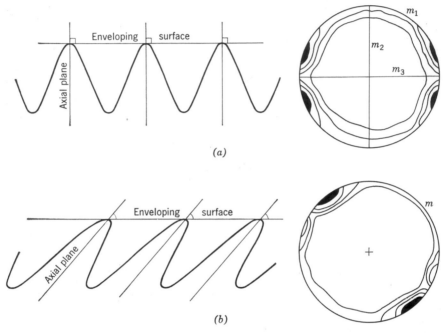

(a)

(b)

Fig. 5-9. Symmetry of plane cylindrical folds from S-pole diagrams prepared by uni-form sampling. (a) Symmetric folds: S-pole diagram has three planes of sym-metry; m_1—normal to fold axis, m_2—parallel to axial plane, m_3—parallel to envelop-ing surface. (b) Asymmetric folds: S-pole diagram has one plane of symmetry, m—normal to fold axis.

Consider the noncylindrically folded s-surface S shown in Fig. 5-11a and assume that the scale of folding is macroscopic and that S is a pene-trative structure. In Fig. 5-11 the mean attitudes of S on each of the four planar limbs l_1, l_2, l_3, and l_4 are projected as four great circles (traces). Diagrams b to d represent three domains in each of which S is cylindri-cally folded, the fold axes being the hinges (b) $l_1:l_2$, (c) $l_2:l_3$, and (d) $l_3:l_4$, with corresponding β_S axes respectively β_1, β_2, and β_3. Each of these β_S axes is a fabric element for one domain only. Any regular relation that may exist between β_1, β_2, and β_3 may be brought out by plotting them together on a collective β_S diagram. The same three axes appear on a more comprehensive diagram (e) on which all measured attitudes of

S are plotted collectively; but they are here accompanied by three other intersections—$l_1:l_3$, $l_1:l_4$, and $l_2:l_4$ (circles)—which are not fold axes and have little if any tectonic significance, in that they merely reflect a geometric procedure applied to a structure in different domains of a hetero-

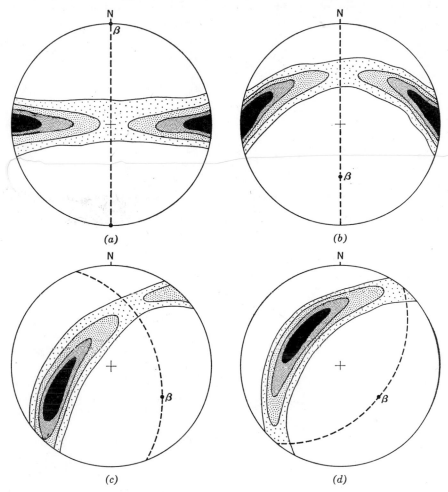

FIG. 5-10. Orientation of appressed plane cylindrical similar folds from S-pole diagrams. Broken line is axial plane; β is axis of S-pole girdle (fold axis). (a) Horizontal normal (on upright) folds. (b) Plunging normal folds. (c) Plunging inclined folds. (d) Reclined folds.

geneous body. Clearly it is essential in analyzing noncylindrical folding to construct β diagrams only for domains homogeneous with respect to β. If several β maxima appear in any preliminary plot of attitudes of S, then S is noncylindrically folded within the domain in question and this is heterogeneous with respect to β_S. It must then be resolved into sub-

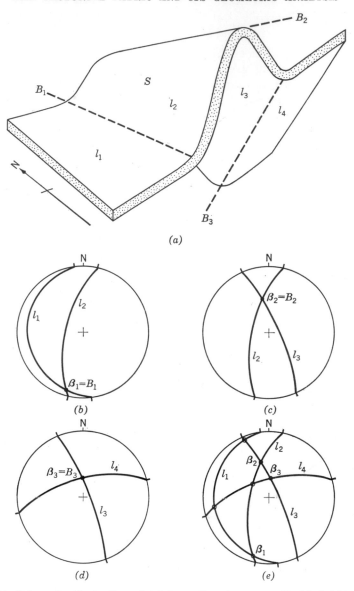

Fɪɢ. 5-11. Schematic illustration of β intersections in a noncylindrical fold system. (a) Four planar limbs, l_1, l_2, l_3, and l_4 connected by three nonparallel hinges, B_1, B_2, and B_3. (b) $\beta_1 = B_1$ defined by intersection of l_1 and l_2 in a cylindrical domain. (c) $\beta_2 = B_2$ defined by intersection of l_2 and l_3 in a cylindrical domain. (d) $\beta_3 = B_3$ defined by intersection of l_3 and l_4 in a cylindrical domain. (e) β intersections for whole system include some (circles) corresponding to no fold hinges.

domains each of which yields a single β_S maximum, indicating local cylindrical folding of S.

Geometric Properties of Macroscopic Cylindrical Folds.   *The Problem.*
On a geologic map the gross configuration of folded marker beds represents a distorted section across the system of macroscopic folds.   Distortion is due to two factors—the irregularity of the topographic surface and the plunge of the fold axes.   A general problem in structural geology is to eliminate distortion of both kinds and to reconstruct the geometry of macroscopic folding from the mapped pattern of folded beds together with representative measured attitudes of the folded surface.   It has already been shown that the axis B of a cylindrical fold may be determined graphically as β, the statistical intersection of segments of the folded surface (page 154, Fig. 5-6).   In addition to the orientation of B, we require to know the configuration and orientation of the axial surfaces and to draw appropriate plane sections—particularly transverse profiles—through the folded structure.   Since a noncylindrical fold may be divided into cylindrical segments the problem refers especially to cylindrical folds.

Construction of a Horizontal Plane Section.   Distortion caused by topographic relief is heterogeneous and is most marked where a surface of high relief intersects folds with gently plunging axes.   It is corrected by constructing a horizontal plane section through the fold.   The plane of projection may be drawn at any elevation; but a plane at sea level is most convenient since it permits direct use of elevations recorded on the map, and the sense of projection is the same for all points on the map.[15]
On a transparent overlay rule a series of closely spaced lines parallel to the trend of the fold axis B.   Each of a series of selected points on the marker contact is now projected onto the plane of section by moving it parallel to the trend of B, in the sense of the plunge, through a distance $h/\tan \alpha$, where h is the elevation of the point and α is the angle of plunge of B.   Figure 5-12*b* shows a horizontal section at sea level through a fold whose outcrop pattern is shown in Fig. 5-12*a*.

In any horizontal section through a plunging cylindrical fold—a state realized precisely in Fig. 5-12*b* and approximately on any topographic surface of low relief—the form of the fold is homogeneously distorted to a degree inversely proportional to the plunge of B.   But in the distorted profile the features of style are still preserved, and so it is possible to identify the fold as concentric, similar, disharmonic, isoclinal, and so on, and to determine whether the axial surface is plane or curved.   Thus in Fig. 5-13 the line joining hinges of successive form surfaces in any fold is the trace of the axial surface $(A A)$.   This is straight in plane folds (Fig. 5-13*a*), curved in nonplane folds (Fig. 5-13*b*); on a horizontal surface it is the strike of the axial surface.   It is not to be confused—though

[15] Except those rare cases where parts of the topographic surface are below sea level.

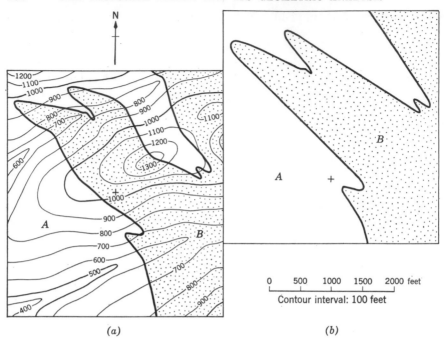

(a)   (b)

FIG. 5-12. Correction of profile of plunging cylindrical fold in contact between two rock units (*A* and *B*) to a horizontal surface. (*a*) Map of plunging cylindrical fold showing topographic distortion. (*b*) Profile of fold in *a* corrected to a horizontal surface at sea level.

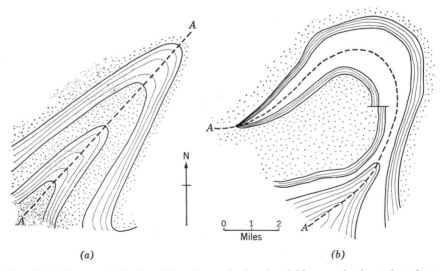

(a)   (b)

FIG. 5-13. Traces (*AA*) of axial surfaces of plunging folds on a horizontal surface. (*a*) Plane folds. (*b*) Nonplane folds (*After D. M. Scotford*).

this has been done on some maps—with the trend of the fold axis B, for this may be inclined at any angle to the strike of the axial surface (cf. Fig. 4-27).

Construction of a Transverse Profile.   Whereas the general geometric properties of folds are apparent in any plane section inclined at a moderate angle to the fold axis, the homogeneous distortion in such sections due to plunge may be corrected by constructing a true profile normal to the fold axis.   A simple geometric construction used by Wegmann[16] is generally employed.   It is based on the assumption that the profile of a fold tends to maintain its form for long distances measured parallel to the axis.   This assumption is amply confirmed for certain types of fold by observations of mesoscopic folds and by the demonstrated axial persistence of subhorizontal macroscopic folds in regions such as the Alps where high relief makes it possible to view the largest structures in three dimensions.[17]

Construction of the Axial Surface of a Plane Cylindrical Fold.   In Fig. 5-14 attitudes of measured segments of (*a*) a folded surface S have been plotted as (*b*) an S-pole diagram which gives the orientation of $\beta_S = B$. The trace A of the axial plane upon the horizontal plane surface of Fig. 5-14*a* is plotted in Fig. 5-14*c* together with B.   The axial plane is the great circle containing A and B (cf. Fig. 4-6).   It is conveniently designated S'; thus S' is the geometrically constructed axial plane of folds in S.

It is of course possible to estimate roughly the orientation of B in some folds by mere inspection of the geologic map.   Thus in Fig. 5-14*a* the trend of B is parallel to the strike of a vertical segment of the folded surface at X; and the plunge of B is defined by the dip (at Y) of the segment that strikes normal to this direction (cf. Fig. 4-5).

Gross Configuration of Fold Affected by Mesoscopic Transposition of S. Where bedding lamination S_1 has been partially transposed mesoscopically into a later foliation S_2, it may be possible under favorable circumstances to determine the gross configuration of major folds in S_1 from the gross outcrop pattern of contacts between lithologic units.   Figure 5-15*a* shows on the macroscopic scale a large fold defined by the disposition of four different rock types with gross contacts S_1.   The rocks share a secondary foliation S_2.   On the limbs of the broadly isoclinal fold, transposition of S_1 into S_2 is effectively complete, so that only their combined orientation can be measured mesoscopically (Fig. 5-15*b*).   The axis of transposition is, however, marked by a prominent and regularly plunging lineation L.   Partial transposition of S_1 into S_2 by folding is seen in the hinge of the fold at the contact between two of the units

---

[16] C. E. Wegmann, *op. cit.*, pp. 107–120, 1929.   See also D. B. McIntyre, *op. cit.*, p. 12; L. E. Weiss, *op. cit.*, pp. 47–49.

[17] Cf. E. Argand, Les nappes de recouvrement des Alpes pennines et leurs prolongements structuraux, *Materiaux carte géol. Suisse*, n.s., 31, 1911.

(marble and quartz schist in Fig. 5-15c). The folds are very tightly appressed and in places are actually so disrupted that only S_2 (here an axial-plane foliation) can be measured. The lineation L is more prominent and is accompanied by mullions that plunge regularly parallel to the axes of the small folds. At other places in the hinge S_1 survives

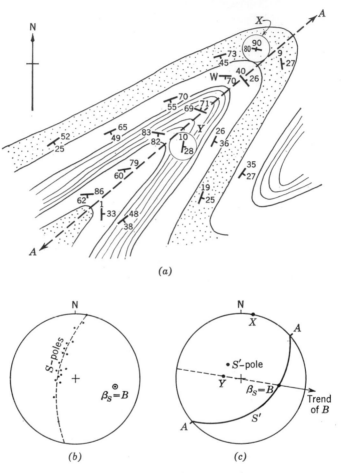

(a)

(b)   (c)

FIG. 5-14. Determination of orientation of plane cylindrical folds in untransposed S. (a) Map of plunging folds showing configuration of folded S and trace of axial plane (AA). (b) S-pole diagram and $\beta_S = B$. (c) Orientation of axial plane S' determined from β_S and AA.

gently folded, with S_2 expressed only as a weak foliation or merely as the axial plane of the folds (Fig. 5-15d). The data for this structure are given in Fig. 5-16. Measurements of L (dots) for the whole fold define a maximum effectively coincident with that of axes of small folds (crosses) measured in the hinge area (Fig. 5-16a). The poles of S_2 (on the limbs of the fold the measurements are of S_2 and the transposed S_1) lie in an elongated maximum expressing the gently curved form of the axial surface of the main fold (Fig. 5-16b).   In the hinge poles of surviving untransposed S_1 lie in a girdle centered on β_{S_1} (Fig. 5-16c) which

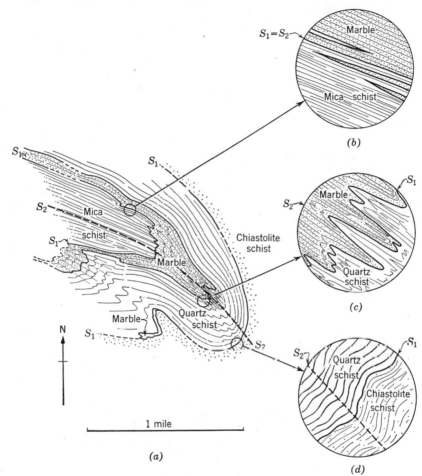

FIG. 5-15. Transposition of lithologic contacts demonstrated by rocks of the Kernville Series, Lake Isabella, California. (*After L. E. Weiss.*) (*a*) Map of large fold involving four rock types.   (*b*) Detail of contact on fold limb; lithologic contact S_1 transposed into foliation S_2.   (*c*) Detail of contact in hinge: folding of S_1, with S_2 as axial-plane foliation.   (*d*) Detail of contact in hinge; weak folding of S_1, with S_2 as axial plane only.

has almost the same orientation as the maximum of L and axes of small folds.   The large fold is clearly cylindrical and almost plane and its form is closely mirrored by the nature and preferred orientation of mesoscopic structures.

In some macroscopic folds transposition of S_1 into S_2 is complete on all scales so that the gross configuration of the fold survives only as a pattern on the map. But from the foregoing example a construction is suggested by which the form of the large fold can still be determined if it

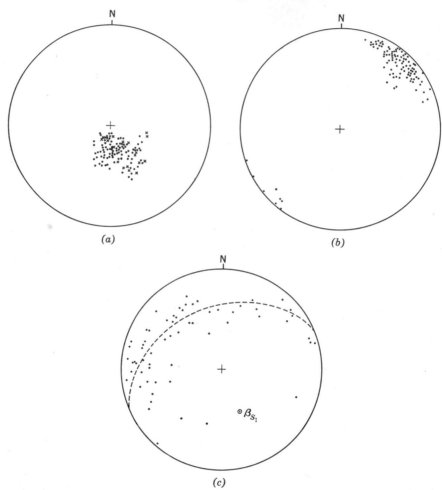

FIG. 5-16. Orientation data for area in Fig. 5-15. (a) Orientation diagram for L—lineation parallel to intersection of S_1 and S_2— for the whole fold (dots), and axes of mesoscopic folds in the hinge area (crosses). (b) S_2 poles for the whole fold. (c) S_1 poles in hinge area; fold axis given by β_{S_1}.

corresponds to a more advanced stage of development of the same structural phenomena. The construction is shown diagrammatically in Fig. 5-17: attitudes of foliation (S_2) transferred from the map (a) give a maximum concentration of poles (in b) defining the axial plane of the macroscopic fold; attitudes of lineation (in c) give statistically the macroscopic fold axis B_{S_1}.   The construction should, however, be used with caution because some tightly appressed folds in transposed surfaces have axes with significantly different plunge from that of the lineations on their limbs (see also, Fig. 5-34).   In cases where the main lineation appears to have formed after folding of S_1 such discordance may be very marked, and some other means must be employed to locate B_{S_1}.   For instance, by use of structure contours (cf. Fig. 5-1) the gross attitude of the contact is determined for each of several areas where it cuts a topographic surface of high relief.   These attitudes, plotted as great circles on a projection, should give a recognizable β axis equivalent to B_{S_1}.

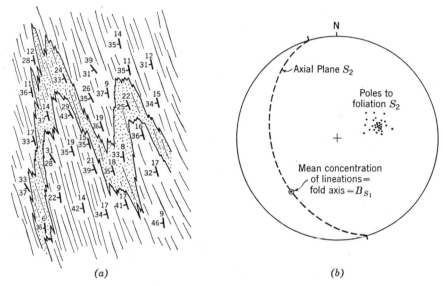

(a) $\qquad\qquad\qquad\qquad\qquad\qquad\qquad$ (b)

Fig. 5-17. Determination of orientation of plane cylindrical folds in mesoscopically transposed lithologic layering S_1. (a) Map showing gross folded form of S_1 and attitudes of mesoscopic transposition foliation S_2. (b) Axial plane S_2 and axis B_{S_1} of fold determined respectively from maximum of S_2 poles and lineations.

Geometric Properties of Macroscopic Noncylindrical Folds.   *General.* Noncylindrical folds so oriented that cylindrical segments plunge in opposite senses generally can be recognized as such from their outcrop patterns.   Where plunge is in one sense, however, the outcrop patterns of plane noncylindrical folds closely resemble those of plane cylindrical folds.   The noncylindrical nature of the structure becomes obvious from the appearance of several maxima in the β diagram constructed for the body as a whole.   By trial and error the body is then subdivided into domains each having a single β axis which characterizes a fold as being locally cylindrical and defines the local orientation of the fold axis B. It is now possible to construct a horizontal plane section through the fold system, giving the pattern of folding corrected for distortion due to topographic relief (cf. page 163).   On this section appears the trace of the axial surface (cf. Fig. 5-12b).

Plane Noncylindrical Folds.   The trace of the axial plane of any plane noncylindrical fold upon a plane section such as Fig. 5-18a (AA) is rectilinear.   The axial plane itself is defined as the great circle of best fit through the β axes of cylindrical segments; it must also contain the trace AA transferred from the map.   Figure 5-18b to f shows β diagrams constructed for the respective domains I to V of Fig. 5-18a; construction of the mean axial plane for the body as a whole is illustrated in Fig. 5-18g. Note that the trend of the local β axes is variable and independent of the strike of the axial plane.

Superposed Folds.   Superposed folds constitute the commonest type of nonplane noncylindrical folds encountered in tectonites.   The method of analysis is much the same as that just described for plane noncylindrical folds.   By trial and error the body is divided into domains of plane cylindrical folding; however, not only does the fold axis vary in orientation throughout the body but so also does the axial plane.

Consider the common case where late plane folds have been superposed obliquely on an early generation of folds.   The geometry of the complex system is identical with that of superposed mesoscopic folds already discussed on pages 129 to 143 (Figs. 4-36 and 4-37).   Analysis on the macroscopic scale is complicated, however, by two factors which do not apply to mesoscopic analysis: (1) fold axes cannot be measured directly; (2) structural data, unless the topographic surface is one of unusually high relief, can be measured on only one approximately planar surface— and this, being randomly oriented with respect to the structures, does not necessarily display with maximum clarity the geometric form of the fold system.

Let S_1 be a primary s-surface (e.g., bedding) folded first about an axis $B_{S_1}{}^{S_2}$, with S_2 as the axial surface; and let both S_1 and S_2 be folded later about respective fold axes $B_{S_1}{}^{S_3}$ and $B_{S_2}{}^{S_3}$, where S_3 is the common axial plane of all folds of the late generation.   Two geometric factors particularly influence the macroscopic outcrop pattern as seen on a map:

1. The angle between the second axial plane S_3 and the enveloping surface of the folded early axial surface S_2.   Where this angle is acute the late folds tend to be highly asymmetric, and their form is not obvious on the map.

2. The angles at which the geometric elements of both fold systems intersect the horizontal plane.

Upon these factors depends the angle subtended by the respective generalized axial-surface traces of folds of the two generations as seen on the map.   Where this angle is large it is generally clear from the map that the system is one of superposed folds; but where it is small, superposition may be revealed only by statistical analysis.   The apparent

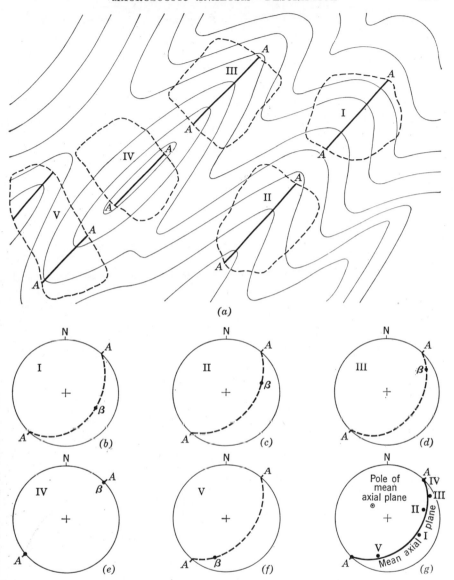

FIG. 5-18. Schematic geometric analysis of a system of macroscopic plane noncylindrical folds. (a) Outline map showing gross form of folded contacts S. Traces of axial planes are AA. Cylindrical domains are I to V. (b–f) Determination of fold axis as β respectively in domains I to V. (g) Collective diagram for β for the whole body. The plane of the girdle of β is the axial plane of the fold system.

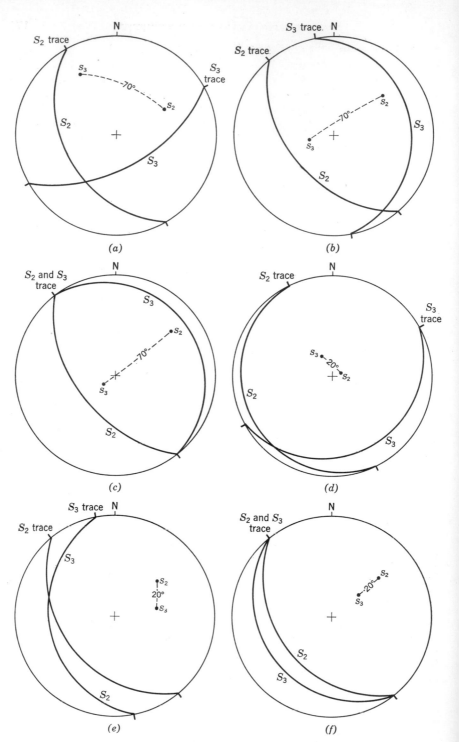

Fig. 5-19. For descriptive legend see opposite page.

angle on the map reflects not only the true angle between the axial planes S_2 and S_3, but also the dips of S_2 and S_3 relative to the horizontal surface. Possible variation from 90° to zero is illustrated in Fig. 5-19a to c which shows three different attitudes of S_2 and S_3, the angle $S_2 \wedge S_3$ being in each case 70°. The same range of variation is possible where $S_2 \wedge S_3$ has any other value (e.g., 20° in Fig. 5-19d to f).

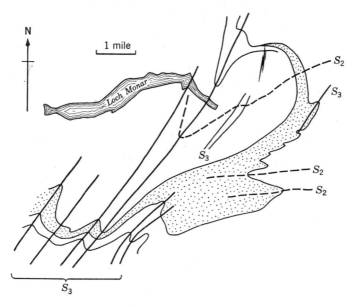

Fig. 5-20. Map of superposed folds with axial-surface traces inclined at a moderate angle; Moine Series, Loch Monar, Scotland. (*After J. G. Ramsay.*) Broken lines, traces of axial surface S_2 of first generation; full lines, traces of axial planes S_3 of second generation.

Natural outcrop patterns of superposed fold systems are illustrated in Figs. 5-20 to 5-22. Figure 5-20 shows schematically the gross orientation of rock units on the map, where the surface traces of S_2 and S_3 intersect at a moderate angle.[18] Since both S_1 and S_2 dip steeply their traces intersect at an angle that is close to the true angle of intersection $S_2 \wedge S_3$. Figure 5-21 is a horizontal section through the Homestake Mine, South

[18] Ramsay, *op. cit.*, pp. 271–308.

Fig. 5-19. Variation of angle between horizontal traces of two nonparallel dipping axial surfaces (S_2 and S_3) with change in (1) angle between planes and (2) plunge of their line of intersection. (*a*) $S_2 \wedge S_3 = 70°$; traces perpendicular. (*b*) $S_2 \wedge S_3 = 70°$; traces inclined at 30°. (*c*) $S_2 \wedge S_3 = 70°$; traces parallel. (*d*) $S_2 \wedge S_3 = 20°$; traces perpendicular. (*e*) $S_2 \wedge S_3 = 20°$; traces inclined at 30°. (*f*) $S_2 \wedge S_3 = 20°$; traces parallel.

Dakota.[19]   An early fold with axial surface S_2 (broken lines) has smaller folds with axial planes S_3 (full lines) superposed on its limbs.   The traces of S_2 and S_3 intersect at an acute angle.   In Fig. 5-22 axial surfaces S_2 of an older fold system (broken lines) dip NW or SE.   The axial planes

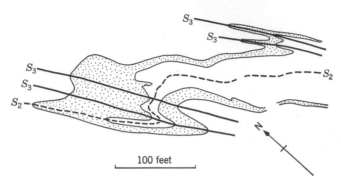

Fig. 5-21. Map of superposed folds with axial-surface traces inclined at small angle; 2,300-ft level, Homestake Mine, South Dakota.   (*After J. A. Noble, J. O. Harder, and A. L. Slaughter.*)

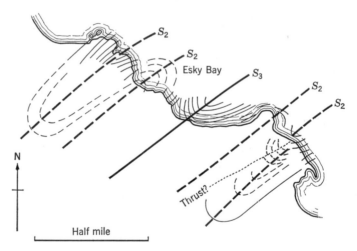

Fig. 5-22. Map of superposed folds with parallel axial-surface traces; Dalradian Series, Donegal, Eire.   (*After D. L. Reynolds and A. Holmes.*)

S_3 of a later generation (full lines) also strike NE, but dip vertically. There is nothing in the outcrop pattern to indicate the presence of superposed folds.

For certain orientations of superposed folds relative to the exposure

[19] J. A. Noble, J. O. Harder, and A. L. Slaughter, Structure of a part of the northern Black Hills and the Homestake Mine, Lead, South Dakota, *Geol. Soc. America Bull.*, vol. 60, pp. 321–352, 1949.

surface, complex patterns of closed rings and symmetric or asymmetric "mushroom"-like lobate patterns may appear.[20]

β Analysis of a Superposed Fold System. *General.* The general procedure in macroscopic analysis of a superposed fold system is to recognize and define domains each of which is homogeneous with respect to β_S, S being any prominent s-surface, not necessarily the same one in each domain. From the geometric relations between β_S in different domains emerges a picture of the total geometric configuration of S and of the stages of folding by which S has been affected. It may also turn out that the most prominent s-surface in one part of the body is of different origin from that in other domains. We shall consider two hypothetical idealized examples, each of which has its counterpart among published accounts of structural analysis.

Case 1 (Figs. 5-23 to 5-25). The outcrop pattern of a hypothetical geologic body on a roughly plane topographic surface is shown schematically in Fig. 5-23.[21] Conjectural contacts below alluvium are shown by fine broken lines. Form surfaces (S_1) are defined by contacts between lithologic units $(A$ to $G)$. By inspection of the map the presence of superposed folds appears likely because two kinds of axial-surface trace are present:

1. Those shown by the broken lines (S_2) which are visibly folded

2. Those shown by the full lines (S_3) which are not consistently folded and are also, in fact, traces of axial surfaces of folds in axial surfaces of the first kind (S_2)

Geometric analysis proceeds by the following stages:

1. By trial and error the map is divided into domains of plane cylindrical folding of S_1. This is done by plotting S_1 poles for areas in which the traces of axial surfaces are rectilinear, and modifying the areas until adjacent S_1 poles define a single β_{S_1} axis. Orientation data for S_1 in fourteen such domains (I to XIV) are shown plotted on the map in Fig. 5-24 and in projection in Fig. 5-25. For each domain there is a unique β_{S_1} axis and an axial plane (either S_2 or S_3 shown by full lines in Fig. 5-25). The fold axis $B_{S_1}{}^{S_2}$ or $B_{S_1}{}^{S_3}$ in each domain is given by β_{S_1}. Note that domains of cylindrical folding could be chosen as overlapping areas

[20] D. L. Reynolds and A. Holmes, The superposition of Caledonoid folds on an older fold-system in the Dalradians of Malin Head, Co. Donegal, *Geol. Mag.*, vol. 91, pp. 417–444, 1954.

[21] For broadly analogous natural examples, see Weiss and McIntyre, *op. cit.*, pp. 575–602; Ramsay, *op. cit.*, pp. 271–308; J. G. Ramsay, Moine-Lewisian relations at Glenelg, Inverness-shire, *Geol. Soc. London Quart. Jour.*, vol. 113, pp. 487–523, 1958b; T. Nureki, Structural investigations of the Ryoké metamorphic rocks of the area between Iwakuni and Yanai, southwestern Japan, *Hiroshima Univ. Jour. Sci.*, vol. 3, pp. 69–141, 1960; W. D. Means, Structure and stratigraphy in the central Toiyabe Range, Nevada, *Univ. California Geol. Sci. Pub.* (in press). The geometric properties of superposed folds in general have been discussed by Weiss, *op. cit.*, pp. 91–106, 1959.

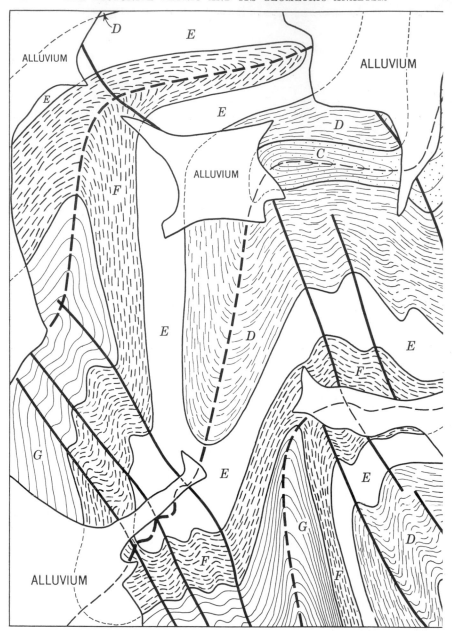

Fig. 5-23. Diagrammatic map of body containing superposed folds in a lithologic lines, traces of axial surfaces of second generation S_3. A, B,....,E are mappable

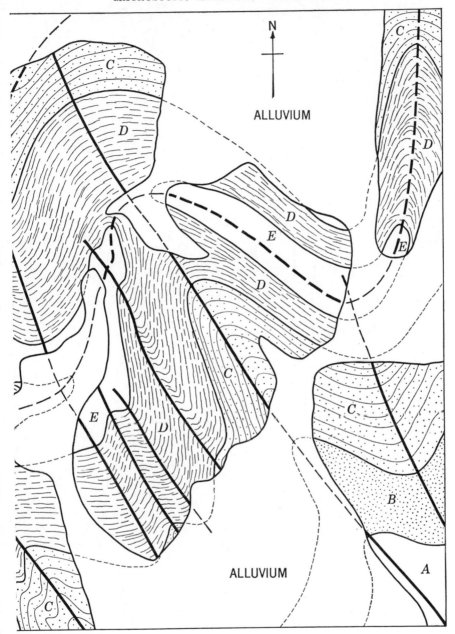

layering S_1. Broken lines, traces of axial surfaces of first generation S_2; full dark
lithologic units.

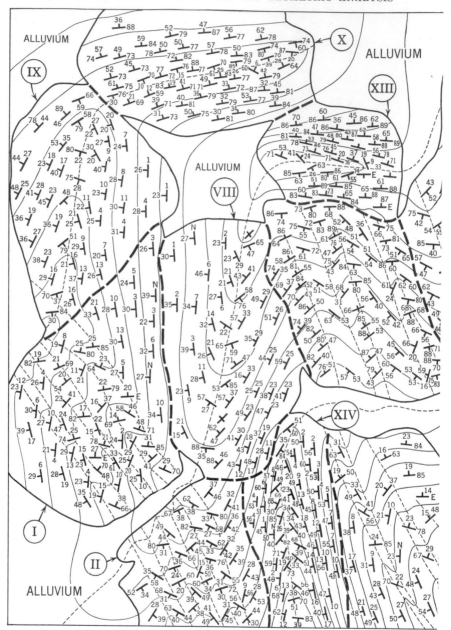

FIG. 5-24. Domains of plane cylindrical folding of S_1 with S_3 as axial plane

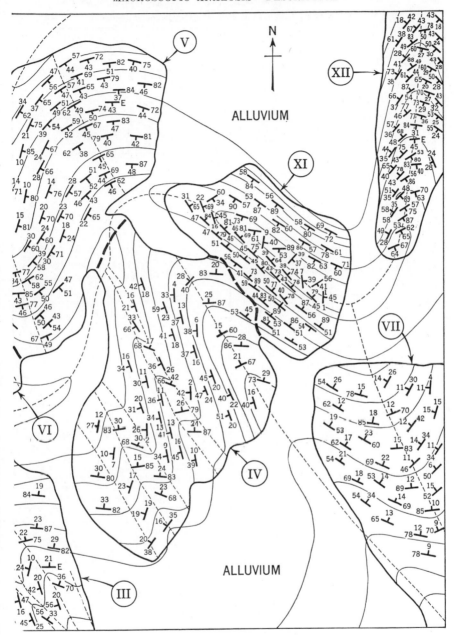

(I to VII) and with S_2 as axial plane (VIII to XIV) (from Fig. 5-23).

S_1 – pole diagrams for domains of plane cylindrical folding

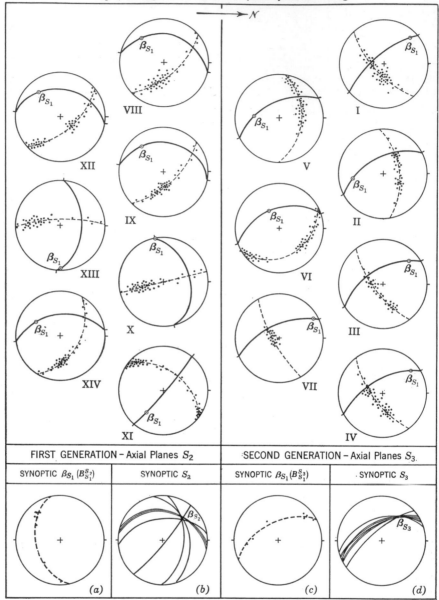

FIG. 5-25. Projections of data from Fig. 5-24 (explanation in text).

because a domain of planar S_1 can form the limb of adjacent folds with differently oriented β_{S_1} (cf. Fig. 5-11).

2. The domains of cylindrical folding are grouped so that folds of the same generation fall together. Under favorable conditions, such as those illustrated, this can be done by inspection, because axial planes are clearly of two different kinds (S_2 and S_3). Data for domains I to VII with S_3 as axial plane and for domains VIII to XIV with S_2 as axial plane are given in Fig. 5-24. Synoptic diagrams (Fig. 5-25, below) are then prepared for β_{S_1} and S_2 or S_3 for each group of domains. As an example we have chosen a very simple case in which the synoptic patterns are of a regular kind, as follows:

a. For domains I to VII β_{S_1} ($B_{S_1}{}^{S_3}$) lie on a great-circle girdle (Fig. 5-25c) and S_3 are almost coplanar (they are shown defining a weak β_{S_3} in Fig. 5-25d; this is not a fold axis).

b. For domains VIII to XIV β_{S_1} ($B_{S_1}{}^{S_2}$) lie on a second great circle (Fig. 5-25a). In natural examples the pattern of distorted older folds is generally much less regular owing to local heterogeneity. The axial planes S_2 are cozonal defining a β_{S_2} axis (a fold axis $B_{S_2}{}^{S_3}$) lying in the $B_{S_1}{}^{S_3}$ circle (Fig. 5-25b).

3. Where the distinction between S_2 and S_3 cannot be made by inspection the grouping of β_{S_1} axes can be attempted either (a) by trial and error involving the detection of regular patterns of synoptic β_{S_1} (this is a highly subjective and somewhat dubious procedure), or (b) by the use of associated mesoscopic structures (small folds, secondary axial-plane foliations parallel to S_2 and S_3, intersecting lineations, and so on) to establish age relations as described in Chap. 4. In actual practice, no satisfactory macroscopic analysis of complex folding can be made without the extra information provided by relations of mesoscopic structures to one another and to the large folds (pages 185 to 193).

The example outlined above corresponds to the mesoscopic example of superposed folds pictured in Figs. 4-36 and 4-37. The body has been affected by two episodes of folding:

1. Plane cylindrical folding about an axis $B_{S_1}{}^{S_2}$ whose initial orientation is indeterminate. Scattered domains (VIII to XIV) of the body preserve distorted plane cylindrical segments of this first generation of folds. The initially plane form of these folds is demonstrated by the cylindrical folding of their axial planes (denoted by β_{S_2} in Fig. 5-25b) in the later episode of folding.

2. Plane noncylindrical folding about axes $B_{S_1}{}^{S_3}$ of variable orientation. Domains I to VII represent segments of S_1 that were effectively planar after the first episode of folding and in which cylindrical $B_{S_1}{}^{S_3}$ folds formed in the second episode.[22]

[22] An instructive exercise for the student is to prepare for himself the orientation diagrams in Fig. 5-25 from the orientation data given in Fig. 5-24. Although no

Case 2. This resembles Case 1 except that the second episode of fold-ing leads to transposition of the initial layering of the body.[23]   Figure 5-26 is a simplified outcrop map showing the traces of two visible s-sur-faces, one (S_1) a layering defined by a single stippled bed, the other (S_2) an axial-plane foliation to folds in S_1.   On the basis of fold style and degree of development of S_1 and S_2 the map is divided into major domains I to IV.   During passage from I to IV, S_1—the sole s-surface of domain I—is transected by S_2 (domains II and III), which leads to complete transposition of S_1 into S_2—the sole s-surface of domain IV.   Through-out the body domains of plane cylindrical folding of S_1 can be outlined as in Case 1: all of these domains have fold axis β_{S_1}, but some have axial plane S' and others have axial plane S'' (Fig. 5-26).   Salient geometric features of major domains I to IV are as follows:

Domain I is homogeneous with respect to β_{S_1} and S' (Fig. 5-27a).

Domain II resembles in its properties the body analyzed above as Case 1.   Some folds in S_1 have S' as axial plane, others S''.   Some sub-domains in II (e.g., IIA in Fig. 5-26) are heterogeneous except for the orientation of S'' (Fig. 5-27b); the β_{S_1} intersections are irregularly dis-tributed, but some, corresponding to second-generation fold axes, lie in the plane of S'' (Fig. 5-27c).   Other subdomains (e.g., IIB in Fig. 5-26) contain plane cylindrical folds in S_1 with axial plane S''.

Domain III contains a second foliation S_2 parallel to S''.   Most sub-domains are heterogeneous with respect to β_{S_1} which characteristically lie in the plane of $S_2 = S''$ (Fig. 5-27d).   Transposition of S_1 to S_2 is well advanced.

Domain IV contains only one mesoscopic s-surface S_2 which repre-sents also transposed S_1. S_2 has a constant attitude and no β axes can be determined.   But small-scale relics of mesoscopic and microscopic folds (in S_1) persist locally and their axes B have a wide range of orien-tation within a girdle approximating the plane of S_2 (Fig. 5-27e).[24]

The picture that emerges from this analysis is one of folding in two stages:

1. Plane cylindrical folding of S_1 about an axis B_{S_1} ($= \beta_{S_1}$ of domain I), plunging gently SW; axial planes dip steeply SE.

2. Plane noncylindrical folding of S_1 about variable fold axes B_{S_1} ($= \beta_{S_1}$ of domain III and B of domain IV); axial planes ($= S_2$) strike

---

natural body will approach this hypothetical case in regularity of geometric properties, only from knowledge of ideal relations can one hope to detect the less definite geo-metric order imposed by nature.   It will be found that, as in some but not all natural instances, β_{S_3} coincides with β_{S_2}.

[23] A partial counterpart of Case 2 has been described by Baird, *op. cit.*

[24] Possibly this is the condition figured for certain Lewisian gneisses of Scotland by B. C. King, The tectonic pattern of the Lewisian around Clashnessie Bay near Stoer, Sutherland, *Geol. Mag.*, vol. 92, pp. 72, 73, figs, 2, 3, 1955.

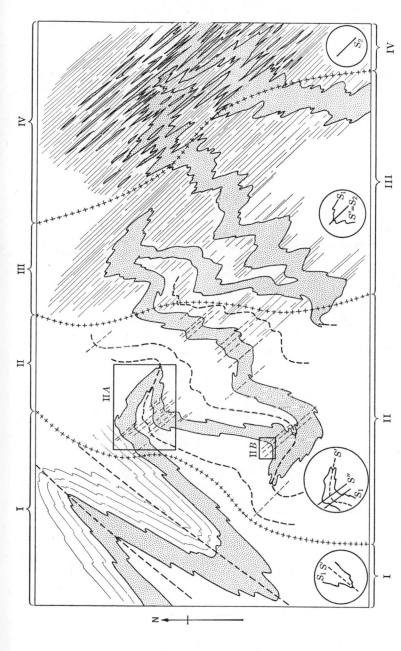

FIG. 5-26. Diagrammatic geologic map (plane horizontal section) of a body containing superposed folds involving transposition. The four domains I to IV represent progressive stages of superposition of folds with axial planes striking NW on earlier folds with axial planes striking NE. Transposition of the initial s-surface S_1 (given by the stippled layer) into the secondary foliation S_2 is complete on a mesoscopic scale in domain IV.

consistently NW and dip steeply NE. This folding, not recorded in domain I, progressively becomes more intense in the eastern domains, and culminates in domain IV in complete transposition of S_1 into S_2. The condition now attained in domain IV could be the initial state for further episodes of folding.

β *Axes Unrelated to Folding.* By definition a β axis is the statistically defined axis of intersection of s-surfaces of one kind and generation within

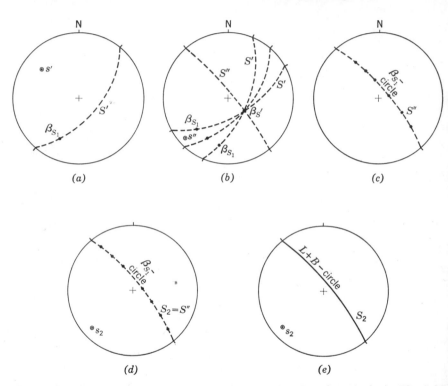

Fig. 5-27. Diagrammatic representation of orientation data from body in Fig. 5-26 (explanation in text). (*a*) Domain I; (*b* and *c*) Domain IIA; (*d*) Domain III; (*e*) Domain IV, L—lineation, B—remnant fold axes.

some specified domain. Where it can be shown that the domain is one of plane cylindrical folding of S then β_S is a fold axis B_S. But true or apparent β axes are not invariably fold axes.

1. A secondary foliation S_2 in a large body commonly varies percepti-bly in orientation forming a fan of cozonal surfaces intersecting in a common axis.[25] This axis is not an axis of folding of S_2 but is by defi-nition a β_{S_2} axis. Where the S_2 surfaces are axial-plane foliations inclined at small angles to the axial planes of folds in an earlier surface S_1, β_{S_2} usu-ally coincides with B_{S_1}.

[25] Weiss and McIntyre, *op. cit.*, p. 588, fig. 7.

2. s-Surfaces of the same type, S_1, measured on both sides of a fault transverse to S_1, yield a β axis whose orientation may be used in estimating rotation accompanying faulting. It is unrelated to folding of any kind.

3. s-Surfaces mistakenly identified as of the same type and measured in different domains—e.g., S_1 in domain I and S_2 in domain IV of Fig. 5-26—may yield statistically defined axes of intersection. But these are neither B nor β axes.

MACROSCOPIC ANALYSIS OF LINEATIONS

The Problem. Lineations are mesoscopic structures. However, their significance in the tectonic picture is brought out mainly by determining the pattern of preferred orientation in macroscopic domains that are homogeneous with respect to one or more of the geometric elements of folding of the s-surface S in which the lineations lie. Such domains have first been delineated by β analysis of S as described in the previous section. In a domain homogeneous with respect to a given lineation, the pattern of orientation of the lineation supplies a significant element in the overall symmetry of the fabric of that domain. It may prove to coincide with or to be geometrically related to other fabric elements such as β axes, B axes, and the girdles of quartz or mica diagrams. Moreover, the nature of a given kind of lineation—e.g., an axis of intersection of S_1 and S_2 or an axis of microfolding of S_1—may provide a clue to the mechanics of strain. Some lineations, for example, provide the only sure indication that an early surface S_1 has been completely transposed into S_2.

Lineations in Domains of Cylindrical Folding. In the smallest partially homogeneous domains emerging from β analysis, the analyzed s-surface S_1 has been affected by plane cylindrical folding; and a number of these in some cases collectively constitute a larger domain in which the system of folds in S_1, although nonplane, has a single fold axis B_{S_1} ($= \beta_{S_1}$) and so is cylindrical. Several patterns of lineation L in relation to B_{S_1} are commonly encountered:

1. The diagram for L has a single maximum parallel to B_{S_1}. It may represent the intersection of the folded surface S_1 with an axial-plane foliation S_2; or in nonplane folds it may be an axis of microcrenulation of S_1; and in either case it is commonly parallel to the average long dimension of nonequant crystals such as mica or hornblende. Development of the lineation must be connected in some way with the process of folding.

2. The lineations L fall in a small circle the center of which is the fold axis B_{S_1} (cf. Fig. 4-31a). This pattern[26] suggests that the lineation is an early structure that has been folded with S_1.

[26] E.g., Sander, *op. cit.*, pp. 172–179, 1948.

3. L is distributed on a great-circle girdle which generally is obliquely inclined to B_{S_1} (compare the statistically equivalent mesoscopic structure illustrated in Fig. 4-31b).   There are three alternative possibilities:

a. L is the intersection of a late plane s-surface S_2 with a previously folded surface S_1, and the pole of the L girdle coincides with the unique maximum of the diagram for poles of S_2 (Fig. 5-27e; cf. also Fig. 4-30).[27] L has been imprinted on the body after folding of S_1.

b. In the absence of a late plane foliation S_2, L may be an early lineation that has been deformed simultaneously with S_1, but in such a manner that it has been dispersed within a plane (cf. Fig. 4-37b and c).

c. A special situation in which the great-circle girdle of L is normal to B_{S_1} might be interpreted as a limiting case of 2 above.   It seems likely, however, from the symmetrical relation of lineation to folding of S_1 that there is some genetic connection between development of L and folding of S_1.   A kind of penetrative slickensiding normal to B_{S_1} has been suggested.

4. Patterns intermediate between 2 and 3 are also known.

Lineations in Domains of Noncylindrical Folding.   The most satisfactory method of analyzing orientation of lineations in an extensive system of noncylindrical folds is to subdivide the region into domains of plane cylindrical fold segments and then to proceed as described in the previous section.   If, however, the system is treated instead as a single heterogeneous domain, any particular lineation is not uncommonly found to have a regular orientation pattern—usually approximating a great-circle girdle (including sheaf girdles, cf. pages 139 and 140).

Figure 5-28a is a diagrammatic representation of a system of plane noncylindrical folds in a prominent s-surface S_1; within S_1 are three distinct kinds of lineation, L_1, L_2, and L_3, each of a type commonly encountered in tectonites:

1. L_1 is the earliest lineation.   It has been deformed during the folding of S_1 and is now dispersed in a great-circle girdle (corresponding to plane P_1) oblique to the axial plane of the system (Fig. 5-28b).

2. L_2 is the intersection of S_1 with an axial-plane foliation S_2 (corresponding to plane P_2).   It occupies a great circle coinciding with the mean orientation of S_2 (Fig. 5-28c).   If the noncylindrical condition of the fold system is due to superposition of later upon earlier folds, then S_2 and L_2 developed synchronously with folds of the second generation.

3. A still later lineation L_3 is the intersection of a late foliation S_3 (corresponding to plane P_3) with S_1; it occupies a girdle coinciding with S_3 (Fig. 5-28d).

Other patterns are also possible.   One such is an irregular cluster of early lineations, analysis of which can proceed only by breaking down

[27] Sander, *op. cit.*, pp. 172–179, 1948; Weiss and McIntyre, *op. cit.*, pp. 597–598; Ramsay, *op. cit.*, pp. 293–295, 1958a.

the system into domains of plane cylindrical folding. The kinematic significance of all these patterns, and especially the relative roles of

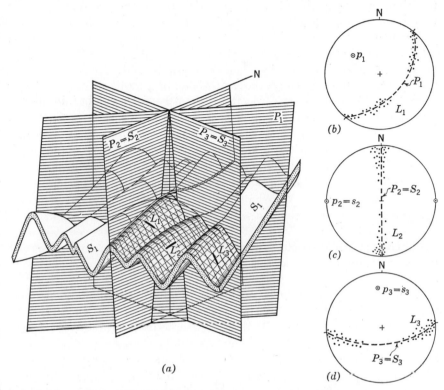

FIG. 5-28. Diagrammatic representation of three generations of lineations (L_1, L_2, L_3) associated with macroscopic noncylindrical folds in s-surfaces S_1. (a) Block diagram of noncylindrical folds in S_1 showing planes of preferred orientation P_1, P_2, P_3, respectively, for lineations L_1, L_2, and L_3. (b) Preferred orientation of L_1. (c) Preferred orientation of L_2 (= intersection of S_1 and S_2). (d) Preferred orientation of L_3 (= intersection of S_1 and S_3).

flexure and slip in their development, will be discussed in a later chapter (pages 474 to 490).

MACROSCOPIC ANALYSIS OF MESOSCOPIC FOLDS

General. Long known to geologists as "Pumpelly's rule" the regular geometric relation between associated small and large folds was expressed by T. N. Dale[28] as follows: "The degree and direction of pitch of a fold

[28] R. Pumpelly, J. E. Woff, and T. N. Dale, Geology of the Green Mountains, Part III, Mount Greylock: its areal and structural geology, *U.S. Geol. Survey Mon.*, vol. 22, p. 158, 1894.

are often indicated by those of the axes of the minor plications on its sides." Dale elaborated further thus: "The strikes of the stratification, foliation, and cleavage foliation often differ in the same rock, and are then regarded as indicating a pitching fold.

"Such a correspondence exists between stratification and cleavage foliations of the great folds and those of the minute plications that a very small specimen, properly oriented, gives, in many cases, the key to the structure over a large portion of the side of a fold."

These relationships, obvious as they are for cylindrical folds with which Dale was largely concerned, are valid also for mutually associated lineations, foliations, and folds of all sizes in macroscopic systems of superposed folds. In any tectonite body, however complex its structure, it is generally possible to find a hand specimen or a single exposure in which all the geometric properties of the macroscopic body are displayed on the mesoscopic scale. We shall now examine the observed relations between the geometric elements of mesoscopic folds and those of associated macroscopic folds.

Domains of Macroscopic Cylindrical Folding. The commonly observed patterns of preferred orientation of mesoscopic fold elements are as follows:

1. In a domain of macroscopic plane cylindrical folding, axes and planes of mesoscopic folds (Dale's "plications") are approximately parallel to corresponding elements of macroscopic folds. Folds on the two scales are of the same age. Not uncommonly the orientation diagram for poles of mesoscopic axial planes (S') yields a maximum that is somewhat dispersed in an incomplete girdle about the axis maximum—indicating a *fanning* of minor axial planes about the macroscopic axial plane (Fig. 5-29).

2. Where a system of mesoscopic plane cylindrical folds in a surface S_1 has a prominent axial-plane foliation S_2, subsequent deformation of a general kind can cause refolding of S_1 and S_2 and bending of the axes of the first formed folds $B_{S_1}{}^{S_2}$. Because S_2 was planar before the appearance of the second folds, plane cylindrical folds in S_2 with axes $B_{S_2}{}^{S_3}$ can develop (cf. Figs. 4-36, 4-37). If the second folds are macroscopic the first folds can remain plane cylindrical on the mesoscopic scale, but their attitude is no longer constant (Fig. 5-30a). Two limiting patterns are likely:

a. S_2 poles lie in a great circle normal to $B_{S_2}{}^{S_3}$ (β_{S_2}), and $B_{S_1}{}^{S_2}$ axes (mesoscopic) lie on a small circle centered on β_{S_2} (Fig. 5-30b; cf. Fig. 4-31a).

b. S_2 poles lie on a great circle normal to β_{S_2}, and $B_{S_1}{}^{S_2}$ axes lie in a great circle oblique to β_{S_2} (Fig. 5-30c; cf. Fig. 4-31b).

The kinematic significance of these two patterns is discussed on pages 474 to 486.

3. Axes of mesoscopic folds $(B_{S_1}{}^{S_2})$ occupy a great circle (as in 2b above), but their axial planes (S_2) are constantly oriented and may be a plane of secondary foliation (Fig. 5-31). The mesoscopic folds are a younger system superposed on macroscopic folds (cf. Fig. 4-33).

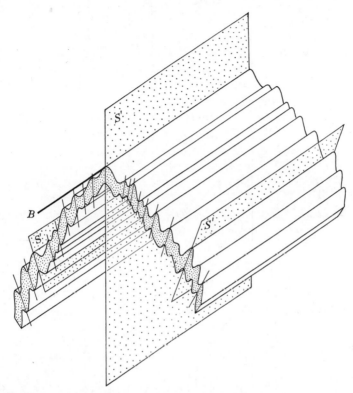

FIG. 5-29. Macroscopic and mesoscopic *(parasitic)* folds with common fold axis B and symmetrically disposed *(fanned)* axial planes S'.

Domains of Macroscopic Noncylindrical Folding. As in the case of lineations, mesoscopic fold axes may occupy great-circle girdles corresponding to any of three different situations (cf. pages 186 and 187; see also Fig. 5-28):

1. Mesoscopic folds are the older. Poles of their axial planes also lie in a girdle which usually is oblique to the girdle of fold axes.

2. Mesoscopic and macroscopic folds are synchronous and have geometric elements in common within any plane cylindrical segment of the macroscopic folds. Where macroscopic folds are plane, the axial plane coincides with the girdle of mesoscopic fold axes.

3. Younger mesoscopic folds are superposed on older macroscopic folds. Mesoscopic fold axes are dispersed in a girdle coinciding with

the mean orientation of mesoscopic axial planes.   This plane is not regularly related to geometric elements of the major folds.

Relative Orientation of Axial Planes and Enveloping Surface.   The attitude of axial planes of "drag folds" in relation to their enveloping

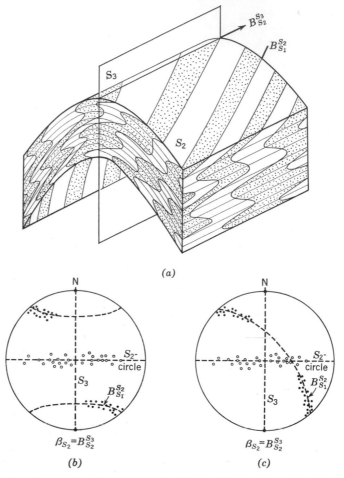

(a)

(b)   *(c)*

Fig. 5-30. Axes $B_{S_1}{}^{S_2}$ of earlier mesoscopic folds in lithologic layering S_1 with axial-plane foliation S_2 distorted by later macroscopic cylindrical folding of S_2 with axis $B_{S_2}{}^{S_3}$. (a) Block diagram. (b) $B_{S_1}{}^{S_2}$ occupy a small circle of the projection centered on β_{S_2}. (c) $B_{S_1}{}^{S_2}$ occupy a great circle of the projection oblique to β_{S_2}.

surface has long been used to distinguish opposite limbs of synchronous macroscopic folds and to locate anticlinal as opposed to synclinal hinges where these are tightly appressed.[29]   However, where mesoscopic and

[29] E.g., M. P. Billings, *Structural Geology*, pp. 76–81, Prentice-Hall, New York, 1942; G. Wilson, The relation of slaty cleavage and kindred structures to tectonics, *Geologists' Assoc. Proc.*, vol. 57, pp. 291, 292, 1946.

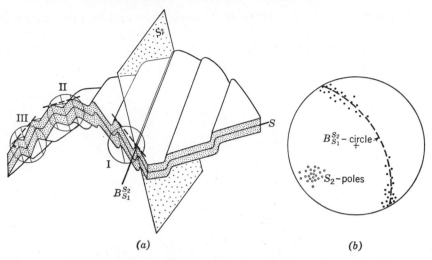

(a)   *(b)*

Fɪɢ. 5-31. Superposition of a system of plane noncylindrical mesoscopic folds in S_1 (axes $B_{S_1}{}^{S_2}$, axial plane S_2) on an older macroscopic fold.

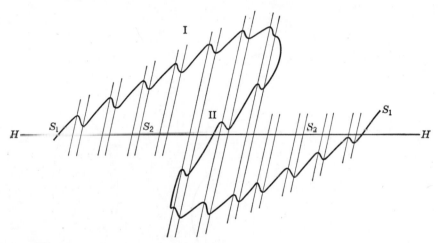

Fɪɢ. 5-32. Asymmetry of mesoscopic folds superposed on macroscopic folds (HH, trace of horizontal).

macroscopic folds are not of the same generation the orthodox interpretation of such relations need no longer be valid.[30] For example, Fig. 5-32 shows mesoscopic folds superposed on the limbs of a macroscopic fold. Folds at I and II have the same sense of asymmetry although they are situated on opposite limbs of a large antiform. Clearly, therefore, the sense of asymmetry of the small folds is no simple guide to the

[30] Cf. E. S. Hills, *Outlines of Structural Geology*, p. 98, Methuen, London, 1953; Billings, *op. cit.*, p. 232, fig. 193, 1942.

site of the fold hinge.   The same relation of S_1 and S_2 can be seen in three dimensions in domains I, II, and III of Fig. 5-31; but here the sense of asymmetry agrees more closely with that of the macroscopic fold.

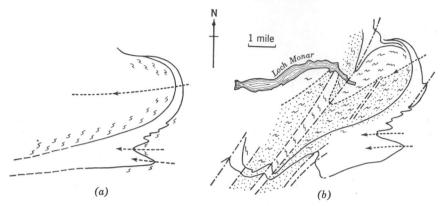

Fig. 5-33. Difference in sense of asymmetry of two generations of mesoscopic folds associated with synchronous macroscopic folds. Loch Monar, northwest Scotland. (*After J. G. Ramsay*).

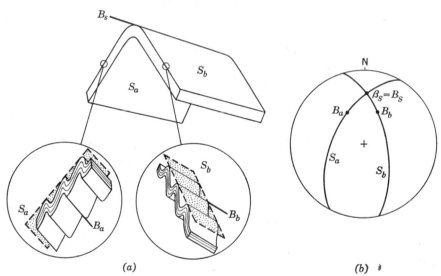

Fig. 5-34. Use of enveloping surface of mesoscopic folds to determine axis of macroscopic fold (explanation in text).

Ramsay[31] has elegantly demonstrated that where each of two generations of mesoscopic folds is associated with synchronous macroscopic folds, separation of the two generations of mesoscopic structures may be possible on the basis of their sense of asymmetry in relation to the form

[31] Ramsay, *op. cit.*, pp. 297, 298, fig. 16, 1958a.

of the large folds. On the limbs of an early large fold, mesoscopic folds had the sense of asymmetry shown in Fig. 5-33a. Subsequent refolding of the limbs of the first large fold formed a second generation of macroscopic folds associated with the asymmetric mesoscopic folds shown in Fig. 5-33b.

Certain macroscopic folds are associated with mesoscopic folds that are not obviously of different axial orientation. The enveloping surface of the small folds can be used under these conditions to estimate the axial orientation of the large fold. The construction is shown diagrammatically in Fig. 5-34. On opposite limbs of the macroscopic fold in S (Fig. 5-34a) the attitudes of planar segments of the enveloping surface of mesoscopic folds are determined by the construction given on page 85. These two attitudes (S_a and S_b) represent the gross orientation of the macroscopically folded S. Their line of intersection in projection (β_S) is the statistically defined macroscopic fold axis (B_S). This axis may not coincide with the axis of the small folds (B_a, B_b) measured on its limbs (Fig. 5-34b). More than two determinations of the enveloping surface are necessary to give a realistic estimate of $\beta_S = B$.

HOMOGENEITY AND SYMMETRY OF MACROSCOPIC DOMAINS

Homogeneity of a macroscopic domain is a function of its total extent and of the scale of sampling. A large domain containing many macroscopic folds may be homogeneous with respect to macroscopic fabric elements (such as axial planes and axes of major folds), provided the scale of sampling also is large. But a smaller constituent domain such as that comprised by a single major fold is heterogeneous with respect to such structures as the folded s-surface, though it may still be homogeneous with regard to such mesoscopic elements as minor folds and lineations. Mesoscopic domains of the same body may be heterogeneous with regard to most mesoscopic structures.

Since a domain must be homogeneous with respect to one or more structures (fabric elements) in order to have a fabric, the symmetry concept is applied only to domains that are at least partially homogeneous. Totally homogeneous macroscopic bodies, e.g., those that have been affected by a single episode of simple deformation, may have total fabrics with axial, orthorhombic, or monoclinic symmetry. On the other hand complex deformation involving repeated folding usually results in a total macroscopic fabric with triclinic or at the most monoclinic symmetry. Within such a body individual subfabrics may have higher symmetry; and smaller constituent domains may have a total symmetry that is also of a higher order. In an earlier chapter (cf. Figs. 3-13b and d, 3-14b and d) we have given examples of macroscopic subfabrics with four kinds of symmetry.

CHAPTER 6

MICROSCOPIC ANALYSIS—DESCRIPTIVE

GENERAL OBJECTIVES

Some aspects of the tectonite fabric already analyzed on the mesoscopic scale can be examined in greater detail beneath the microscope. To this category belong s-surfaces, lineations, joints, and some of the smaller domains such as sedimentary beds, segregation laminae, joint fillings, pisolites, porphyroblasts, and so on. There are yet smaller domains—notably the crystallographic domains of individual grains, twin lamellae, and deformation lamellae—that can be studied only on the microscopic scale. This applies, too, to one of the most widely developed and significant characteristics of the tectonite fabric—the state of preferred orientation of the principal constituent minerals. The general objective of microscopic analysis thus is to corroborate, modify, and amplify analysis of mesoscopic bodies, and to obtain additional information that is accessible only through the microscope. Special emphasis is placed on the following topics:

1. Homogeneity and symmetry of microscopic fabric
2. Direct evidence of strain and of movement—as revealed, for example, by grain shape, the folded configuration of originally planar s-surfaces, bending and twinning of crystals, presence of spiral trains of inclusions in rotated porphyroblasts, and so on
3. The time sequence of crystallization and development of various fabric elements
4. The state of preferred orientation of component minerals, notably quartz, micas, and carbonates
5. Correlation of microscopic with mesoscopic analysis

Standard procedure is to examine each of several oriented thin sections cut from the same hand specimen. Since we are concerned with the geometric relations between surfaces and directions that in general are inclined to the plane of the section, it is necessary for full analysis to use a petrographic microscope equipped with a universal stage.

The most time-consuming phase of microscopic analysis is the determination of the state of preferred orientation of individual minerals. This can be carried out satisfactorily only with a universal stage, and many measurements must be made in each of several sections. It is advisable therefore to omit analysis of preferred orientation unless there is some carefully defined objective which seems to offer a reasonable prospect of attainment. Complete analysis of the orientation patterns of several minerals in a few carefully chosen specimens closely associated in the field, though it may take several weeks to carry out, is likely to sharpen and perhaps modify the picture of fabric symmetry based solely on mesoscopic fabric elements. It may also clarify time relations between crystallization and various phases of deformation. It will still tell us little— in the absence of adequate experimental data—regarding the manner in which the state of preferred orientation itself evolved.

The procedure outlined below does not cover every aspect of microscopic analysis.[1] It includes most measurements that are commonly undertaken, and it constitutes a basis for developing modified techniques to suit particular problems. Although access to a universal stage is assumed, a partial but still valuable analysis of the microscopic fabric can and should be made if this instrument is unavailable. Much of Sander's philosophy of structural analysis (Gefügekunde) developed from early field and microscopic studies in which the universal stage played no significant part.[2]

PREPARATION OF ORIENTED SECTIONS

Several oriented sections are cut from the hand specimen on which reference axes a, b, and c have already been marked according to some suitable convention (e.g., a planar foliation is commonly designated ab and a strong lineation within it b—cf. pages 87 to 90). Sections should be of normal thickness (0.02 to 0.03 mm)[3] and mounted on short slides (e.g., $1\frac{3}{4} \times 1$ in.) suitable for use on a universal stage. A common procedure is to cut three mutually perpendicular sections respectively normal to a, b, and c and respectively designated the a, b, and c sections. It may be advisable, especially with monoclinic fabrics dominated by a single lineation b, to cut several sections normal to b, for this is the orientation that displays in greatest detail the configuration of microscopic structures and domains and permits the fullest possible investigation of fabric. It is advisable to cut one of the b sections at about 80° rather than strictly normal to b. This allows more satisfactory compari-

[1] For additional suggestions see E. B. Knopf and E. Ingerson, Structural petrology, Geol. Soc. America Mem. 6, pp. 216–262, 1938; H. W. Fairbairn, Structural Petrology of Deformed Rocks, pp. 248–296, Addison-Wesley, Reading, Mass., 1949.

[2] E.g., Über Zusammenhänge zwischen Teilbewegungen und Gefüge in Gesteinen, Tschermaks mineralog. petrog. Mitt., vol. 30, pp. 281–314, 1911; Über einige Gesteinsgefüge, Tschermaks mineralog. petrog. Mitt., vol. 33, pp. 103–113, 1915.

[3] To facilitate observation and measurement of such fabric elements as s-surfaces, microjoints, or intragranular lamellae, somewhat thicker sections may sometimes be necessary.

son of the respective symmetries of the mesoscopic subfabrics and the orientation patterns of various component minerals (cf. page 44).

Errors in orienting thin sections are easily made. To minimize them we recommend strict adherence to some simple routine procedure such as the following (Fig. 6-1):[4]

1. With a diamond saw cut a slice having the desired orientation. Roughly polish the cut surface of the specimen, and on it mark directions and signs of appropriate fabric axes, and a single-barbed arrow (usually parallel to a fabric axis). Mark the cut surface of the rock slice with an identically oriented arrow.

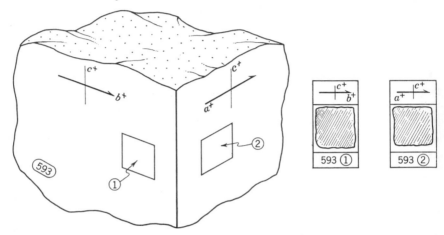

FIG. 6-1. Orientation and marking of sections and corresponding hand specimen.

2. Mount the slice (cut surface to glass) on a glass slide, orienting the arrow on the slice to correspond with an arrow previously scratched on the glass parallel to one edge. This ensures a unique orientation of the slide, looking into the hand specimen. Usually one or both fabric axes will be parallel to an edge of the slide.

3. When the section has been ground and covered, paint the ends (upper surface only) with fast-drying white paint. On one end inscribe fabric axes, reference arrow, and section number in India ink; when dry cover the label with a thin coat of lacquer which preserves it against mineral oil or other fluid used for mounting on the universal stage.

4. With a hand lens check visible structural details in the section against the cut surface of the hand specimen, and in this way localize the section and verify its orientation. Mark (using paint, ink, and lacquer) the site of the section on the hand specimen.

Analysis of the microscopic fabric is greatly aided by photomicrographs of the whole section, or of restricted areas in which the full structural

[4] Similar procedures have been described by Knopf and Ingerson (op. cit., pp. 216–220) and by Fairbairn (op. cit., pp. 248–251, 1949).

detail is visible only under high magnification. Identification and trends of various structures, domains, and individual grains in relation to fabric axes, and location of traverses or of areas of particular study are then readily recorded on a transparent overlay attached to each photograph. The trouble and expense of photomicrographs are repaid especially if a section is to be the subject of full analysis of preferred orientation of the constituent minerals.

UNIVERSAL-STAGE PROCEDURE

The Universal Stage and Its Adjustment. For preliminary scanning of foliation and other surfaces of discontinuity and of microscopic domains of homogeneity in thin sections some students use a binocular microscope. However, the principal—in our experience usually the sole—instrument for microscopic analysis is a petrographic microscope equipped with a universal stage. Accessories for convergent light are unnecessary. Only three axes of the universal stage itself are used: the innermost rotation axis A_1, the NS tilting axis A_2, and the EW tilting axis A_4. For this reason and because of its larger working area, a three- or four-axis universal stage is preferable to one equipped with five axes. Necessary accessories are a set of universal-stage objectives (such as the UM series provided by Leitz), and a rectangular guide sledge permitting free mobility of the section while maintaining it at a constant orientation. Two sets of stage hemispheres are essential: one with $RI = 1.56\pm$ for measuring quartz, feldspars, calcite, and dolomite; one with $RI = 1.65\pm$ for measuring minerals such as olivine, pyroxene, or biotite. For a mounting fluid, to lubricate the surfaces of the section and of the glass hemispheres, we recommend colorless medicinal mineral oil, which is stable and noncorrosive.

The universal-stage procedure employed in fabric analysis is simple. It involves measurement of the orientation (in relation to the plane of the section) of (1) discrete visible planar surfaces of discontinuity such as s-surfaces, twin lamellae, and mineral cleavage cracks, and (2) the axes X, Y, and Z of the indicatrix in individual grains. The measured directions and normals to measured surfaces are plotted individually on an equal-area projection (as described on pages 52 to 64). The plane of projection is that of the thin section and so may be correlated directly with a plane surface of the hand specimen. In all cases it is the lower hemisphere of reference that is projected.

Preliminary adjustments of the stage[5] are four in number; the first three need be repeated only once every few weeks, but the fourth must

---

[5] These adjustments apply especially to the Leitz stage as manufactured in 1959. Some recently manufactured universal stages are fitted with a centering device, facilitating adjustment 2.

be made individually for each thin section: (1) Screw the universal stage firmly to the microscope stage in any preliminary setting.   Now center each objective individually with reference to the vertical axis of the microscope itself (rotation axis A_5).   (2) With NS and EW tilting axes set at zero, and using a high-power objective (e.g., Leitz UM 3), focus on the section, and bring some small index grain to coincide with the cross-hair intersection.   Rotate through 180° about the innermost rotation axis A_1; the index grain becomes displaced from its centered initial position.   Loosen the two screws holding the universal stage to the microscope stage; this allows a small degree of play sufficient for the

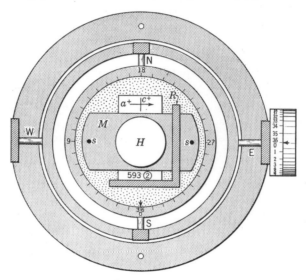

Fig. 6-2. Simplified diagrammatic representation of universal stage looking down the vertical rotation axes.   The section is covered by the upper glass hemisphere H set in a metal mount M held to the inner stage by screws s.   The sledge R moves vertically in a slot cut in the hemisphere mount. NS and EW are tilting axes.

index grain to be brought back by manual adjustment toward the initial centering.   By half correcting the displacement of the index grain, followed by rotation once more through 180° about A_1, and repeated half correction, the index grain is readily centered.   Now carefully tighten the stage screws so as to hold the universal stage firmly in the corrected position.   The inner and outer rotation axes A_1 and A_5 now coincide.   (3) With the microscope stage clamped in the zero position (so that the two tilting axes A_2 and A_4 are approximately NS and EW) focus the objective on a dust speck on the outside of the upper hemisphere.   Tilt back and forth on the EW tilting axis, observing the motion of the speck in relation to the cross hairs.   Unclamp the microscope stage and rotate a degree or two until the speck moves exactly parallel to the *NS* cross hair on repeated tilting on *EW*. Clamp the microscope stage and note its reading—say $1\frac{1}{2}°$. This is the zero reading for this setting of the stage, with the two tilting axes parallel to the cross hairs; and every time the microscope stage is unclamped and rotated it must be brought back to this reading. (4) Slightly loosen the upper hemisphere and rotate the centering ring in which the lower hemisphere is mounted, until the surface of the section coincides with the plane of the *NS* and *EW* tilting axes. Tilting on either axis now causes minimum deviation from focus. This adjustment is simple and rapidly carried out. It should be repeated whenever necessary during an analysis.

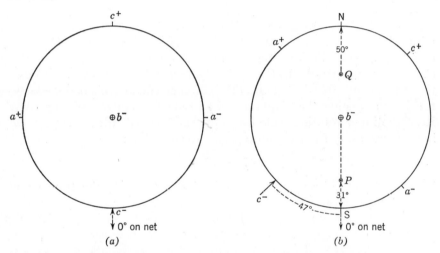

(a)   (b)

Fig. 6-3. (*a*) Orientation of fabric axes in mounted section (cf. Fig. 6-2) with reference to indicator arrow on inner rotation scale (= scale of projection net). (*b*) Plot of poles of {001}—*P* and *Q*—in two mica flakes measured in the same section as *a*. (For data, see text.)

Universal-stage technique is illustrated below by five specific simple exercises. The student who has mastered these will find himself competent to carry out the general microscopic analysis of rock fabrics and to develop such minor variations in procedure as may be required in particular cases.

To Orient the Section. All fabric data must ultimately be referred to the fabric axes *a*, *b*, and *c*. A preliminary step, therefore, in any measurement is to orient the section so that the fabric axes maintain a fixed relation to the graduated scale of the innermost rotation axis A_1 throughout the analysis. This is accomplished by means of the accessory rectangular guide sledge (*R* in Fig. 6-2) set in a groove in the upper hemisphere mount *M* so that it is free to move in one direction only (*NS* in Fig. 6-2). The base of the mounted section is brought into parallel contact with the lower arm of the sledge; and this relation is maintained throughout the analysis. The section is free to move EW along the lower arm, while sledge and section together can move NS as a unit.

The orientation of the section markings (a and c axes in Fig. 6-2) corresponding to the zero reading on the inner rotation scale is noted. This, when transferred to the projection overlay (Fig. 6-3a), provides axes of reference against which all fabric data may be plotted. The engraved scale of the innermost rotation circle of the stage must correspond with the scale on the margin of the projection net; usually both are numbered clockwise from a zero reading at the south point. When the sledge arms are NS and EW, the indicator arrow may equally well read $0°$ or $180°$.

To Locate {001} Cleavage in Muscovite. In a section of granite or mica schist, select, center, and sharply focus on a large isolated flake of muscovite. With both tilting axes at zero, rotate on A_1 to bring visible cleavage cracks parallel to the EW cross hair. Now tilt on EW to give the sharpest possible definition to the cleavage cracks (this may be facilitated by adjusting the diaphragm set inside the Leitz UM objective). Read the inner rotation scale (say $47°$) and the EW tilt scale (say $31°$, in the sense away from the observer). Record thus:

$$47° - 31°\uparrow$$

To plot this measurement on a projection net, rotate the transparent overlay until the index arrow coincides with $47°$ on the peripheral protractor of the net. Plot the pole of the cleavage, P on the NS diameter of the net, $31°$ from the S end (Fig. 6-3b). P represents a cleavage which, for a stage setting of $47°$, dips N (away from the observer) at $59°$ ($= 90° - 31°$). The point Q in Fig. 6-3b represents a cleavage dipping at $40°S$. Note that cleavage surfaces dipping at high angles to the plane of the section—and thus requiring small angles of tilt—are most readily measured. Inaccuracies due to construction and adjustment of the stage become intensified with increasing angles of tilt on EW or NS. Moreover, tilts beyond $50°$ result in total reflection, so that no surface inclined at angles of $40°$ or less to the plane of the section can be investigated on a universal stage.

To Locate the Indicatrix Axes in Plagioclase. In a section of greenschist or amphibolite, select and center a large clear crystal of albite or oligoclase-andesine. With the tilting axes approximately at zero and nicols crossed, rotate on the innermost axis A_1 to extinction. Tilt through about $30°$ on EW; in most cases the grain will become illuminated. Now tilt on NS to the nearest position of extinction. Reverse the tilt on EW through about $60°$, and again rotate on A_1 to extinction. By repeated tilting on NS and rotation on A_1 (for various tilts on EW) the section is brought to complete extinction, which is maintained for any angle of tilt on EW. An indicatrix axis is now aligned parallel to the EW cross hair. Readings of the inner rotation scale (say 226°) and the NS tilting scale (say 28° upward from the left) are recorded thus:

$$226° \rightarrow 28°$$

The EW indicatrix axis must now be identified as X, Y, or Z. Unclamp the microscope stage and rotate 45° so that the section becomes fully illuminated. Now tilt on EW through an arc of 45° to 50° in each sense. If the EW indicatrix axis is Y (provided $2V$ is large) the section will pass through an extinction position as one of the optic axes is brought parallel to the vertical axis A_5 of the microscope. (In the case illustrated in Fig. 6-4 this would occur for a tilt of 12° on EW in the sense toward the observer.) The full record, including orientation of the optic axis O, is

$$Y = 226° \rightarrow 28° \qquad O—12°\downarrow$$

If the EW indicatrix axis were X or Z there would be no extinction during tilting on EW in the 45° setting; instead the interference colors would tend to rise for high tilts as a result of increased effective thickness of the section. Compensation or addition with a gypsum plate will identify the EW axes as Z or X.

The microscope stage is now returned to the zero setting and clamped. A second indicatrix axis may now be aligned with the EW cross hair by rotating the section on the inner axis A_1 to the second extinction position and repeated tilting on NS and rotation on A_1 for various tilts on EW. Suppose that the axis X is so located for a reading of 150° on the inner rotation scale and a tilt of 22° upward from the right on NS. The full record of measurements is

$$X = 150° \leftarrow 22°$$
$$Y = 226 \rightarrow 28° \qquad O—12°\downarrow$$

These data may now be plotted on a transparent overlay (representing the plane of the section) superposed on the projection net. Set the index arrow of the overlay at 150° and plot X 22° in from the right on the EW diameter of the net (22° from Q on PQ in Fig. 6-4). Now set the index arrow at 226° (the position shown in Fig. 6-4) and plot Y 28° in from the left on the EW diameter of the net. If X and Y have been accurately measured each should fall on the great circle normal to the other (broken arcs in Fig. 6-4). A discrepancy of two or three degrees is tolerable in fabric analysis since many approximate measurements have more significance than one perfect measurement. The third axis Z is located by intersection of the great circles respectively normal to X and Y.

The reader unfamiliar with universal-stage procedure is advised to plot out the above data and compare his plot with Fig. 6-4. With a little practice X, Y, and Z can be measured, identified, and plotted within three to five minutes.

To Locate the Optic Axis [0001] in Quartz. Since quartz is uniaxial and positive the problem is to locate Z of the indicatrix. Set both tilting axes of the stage approximately at zero. Between crossed nicols identify the fast (X) and slow (Z') directions of a quartz grain by means of a gypsum plate, and rotate the section on the inner axis A_1 to extinction with Z' EW. Tilt to any angle on EW, and bring the section back

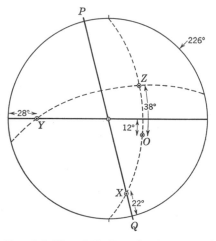

FIG. 6-4. Plot of X, Y, and Z in a crystal of albite. (For data, see text.) The projection is shown in position (with indicator arrow at 226° on the net scale) for plotting Y. Broken arcs are great circles normal to X and Y.

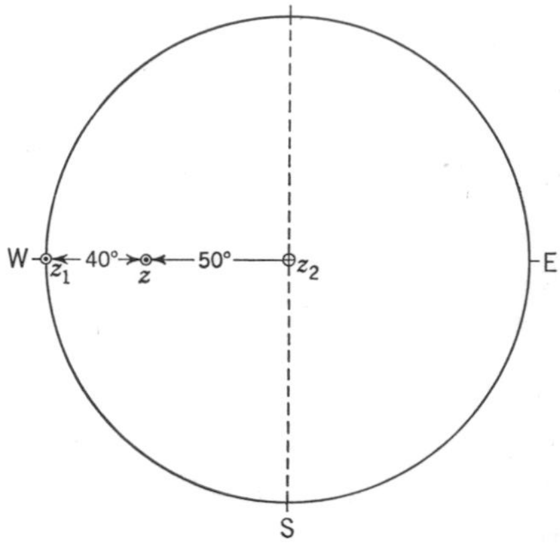

FIG. 6-5. Alternative orientations (Z_1 and Z_2) of optic axis of quartz permitting extinction for all angles of tilt on EW. Z is initial orientation of optic axis. Projection plane is that of the microscope stage.

to extinction by tilting on NS. The section should now remain in extinction for any angle of tilt on EW. (If not, correct the extinction by repeated rotation on A_1 and tilting on NS.) There are two possible orientations of Z (relative to EW and NS axes of the stage) which are compatible with this behavior: either (1) Z is parallel to the EW axis (Z_1 in Fig. 6-5), or (2) Z is normal to both EW and NS axes (Z_2 in Fig. 6-5). These orientations are mutually distinguishable by simple optical criteria and involve different plotting procedures as outlined below:

1. Orientation with Z parallel to EW is most readily achieved where Z is inclined to the section at angles of less than 45°. Such sections show interference colors at the higher end of the range appropriate for quartz (white to pale yellow). If EW is set at zero and the microscope stage as a whole is rotated the section becomes brightly illuminated (clear

white or pale yellow). Suppose the reading of the inner rotation scale is 320° and the NS tilt is 30° upward from the right, record thus:

$$Z = 320° \leftarrow 30°$$

and plot as P in Fig. 6-6.

2. Orientation with Z normal to both EW and NS stage axes is most readily achieved where Z is steeply inclined to the plane of the section. The interference color is distinctively low (gray). With EW set at zero, the section remains dark between crossed nicols when the microscope stage as a whole is rotated about A_5. Moreover, there is a subtle difference in the appearance of the grain as it is brought to extinction in the first instance by tilting on NS: for case 2 extinction is a shade less complete but the arc of tilt is more narrowly defined than for case 1. With a little experience the observer needs no other criterion to distinguish which of the two alternatives applies to any particular grain. Suppose that for an orientation of type 2 the inner rotation scale reads 320°, and the NS tilt is 20° upward from the right, thus:

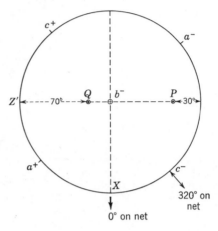

FIG. 6-6. Plot of optic axes P and Q of two quartz grains. (For data, see text.)

$$320° \leftarrow 20°$$

We recommend recording the complementary tilt angle (opposite in sense) that would bring the Z axis parallel to EW, thus:

$$Z = 320° \rightarrow 70°$$

With the index arrow on the overlay at 320° on the net scale, Z is then plotted 70° from the left along the EW diameter of the net (Q in Fig. 6-6). A single plotting procedure then serves for grains of all types.

A practiced observer can locate and plot the optic axis of a quartz grain in less than a minute.

To Correct Tilt Angles for Refraction Effects. Tilting of the section about either axis involves error due to refraction. Since most of the layers of different materials traversed by a ray of light are parallel-sided (e.g., oil films, glass slide, cover glass), refraction effects in these cancel out. In the standard treatment hitherto employed in universal-stage petrography, the problem is reduced to the passage of a ray from the mineral slice with refractive index RI_m, through a glass hemisphere with

refractive index RI_g, and so into air (Fig. 6-7).   The spherical outer surface of the glass eliminates refraction at glass-air contacts such as Y.
Suppose that we are measuring a direction PR (e.g., an optic axis, or a
normal to Z) in the section SS', by bringing it parallel to the microscope
axis A_5 (= XY in Fig. 6-7).   The path of the measured ray is PRY.
Because of refraction at R it appears to be aligned in XY when within
the mineral slice it is actually inclined to XY at a small angle.   The

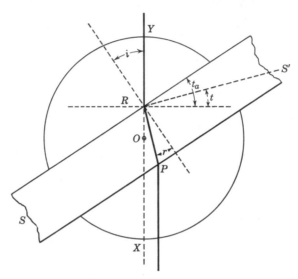

FIG. 6-7. Refraction of ray PR in a mineral slice SS' enclosed in segments of a glass
sphere. XY = vertical axis of microscope.   Refracted ray is RY. t_a = measured
angle of tilt = i; t = corrected angle of tilt = r.

measured angle of tilt t_a equals the angle of incidence i in the refractive
system.   The true (or corrected) angle of tilt t equals the angle of refraction r.   So

$$\frac{\sin t_a}{\sin t} = \frac{\sin i}{\sin r} = \frac{RI_m}{RI_g}$$

Some typical corrections computed from this relation are given in Table
6-1.   In fabric analysis, where an error of 1° is of little significance, there
is usually no need to correct tilts of less than 15° to 20°.   Note however
that corrections of 3° to 4° may be necessary for tilts of 40° to 45° if the
refractive index of the mineral differs markedly from that of the glass.
Moreover, for minerals of high birefringence (see, for example, calcite in
Table 6-1) there is some uncertainty as to the value of RI_m to be used
for any particular orientation of the measured grain.   Obviously meas-

urements involving low angles of tilt are more accurate than those for which high tilts are necessary.[6]

TABLE 6-1. CORRECTION OF ANGLES OF TILT (RI FOR
HEMISPHERE GLASS = 1.56)

Albite An$_5$	0°–15°	20°	30°	. . . . .	45°	Measured tilt
$\beta = 1.535$	0°	$+\frac{1}{2}°$	$+\frac{3}{4}°$	. . . . .	$+1\frac{1}{4}°$	Correction
Calcite	10°	20°	30°	40°	45°	Measured tilt
$\alpha = 1.48$	$+\frac{1}{2}°$	$+1\frac{1}{4}°$	$+2°$	$+2\frac{1}{2}°$	$+3°$	Correction
$\gamma = \omega = 1.65$	$-\frac{1}{2}°$	$-1°$	$-1\frac{1}{4}°$	$-2\frac{1}{2}°$	$-3°$	Correction
Biotite	0°–15°	20°	30°	. . . . .	45°	Measured tilt
$\alpha = 1.59$	0°	$-\frac{1}{2}°$	$-\frac{3}{4}°$	. . . . .	$-1°$	Correction
Olivine, Fo$_{80}$	10°	20°	30°	40°	45°	Measured tilt
$\beta = 1.69$	$-\frac{3}{4}°$	$-1\frac{1}{2}°$	$-2\frac{1}{2}°$	$-4°$	$-4\frac{1}{2}°$	Correction

MICROSCOPICALLY VISIBLE FABRIC ELEMENTS AND DOMAINS

General Procedure. Microscopic analysis of a rock fabric falls into two parts: study of microscopically visible fabric elements and the small domains whose boundaries they delineate, and analysis of preferred orientation of the crystal lattices of constituent minerals. Whether or not this latter phase is undertaken, analysis of fabric on the macroscopic or mesoscopic scale should always be supplemented by microscopic study of the fabric elements visible in the hand specimen. Observations in this category are most readily recorded on a transparent overlay attached to a photomicrograph of the section. This is particularly useful in correlating microscopic fabric elements with structures already observed in the hand specimen. It also helps to clarify geometric relations between the various fabric elements and the patterns of preferred orientation of minerals that emerge from complete analysis of the fabric. If photographs are not available free use of camera lucida sketches is recommended. No rigid procedure of microscopic analysis is laid down. Rather the following notes are intended to guide the student in developing his own approach to any particular problem.

s-Surfaces and Joints. Any visible line, such as the intersection of an s-surface with the plane of the section, may be measured by aligning it EW by rotation of the inner stage on A_1. What is normally required is the mean trend of a set of s-surfaces or joints within a section or some

[6] Since the book went to press, the standard correction procedure here described has been criticized by W. B. Kamb (*Am. Mineralogist*, vol. 47, pp. 227–245, 1962). He finds that the correction is negligible for a uniaxial crystal with the optic axis brought parallel to the EW axis of the stage.

smaller domain.   This can usually be estimated by inspecting the domain as a whole under low magnification, rather than by measuring the individual trends of many separate elements.   Figure 6-8 shows a hypo-

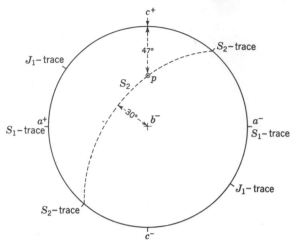

Fig. 6-8. Projection of traces of S_1, S_2, and J_1 upon the plane of a b section.   Broken arc is unique orientation of S_2 as determined by p, its trace on an a section.

thetical case in which the traces (on a b section) of s-surfaces S_1 and S_2 and of a quartz-filled joint J_1 have been measured and recorded as follows:

	Reading for
Element	EW alignment
a Axis	180°
S_1	180°
S_2	231°
J_1	145°

Unless the section is unusually thick or the s-surfaces are very sharply defined it is seldom possible to measure accurately the inclination of an s-surface to the plane of the section.   For complete determination of its attitude the orientations of its intersections with each of two nonparallel sections must be measured (cf. page 80).   Thus in Fig. 6-8 the broken arc represents completely the orientation of S_2 as determined from the measured trend of its trace on the plane of the diagram (b section) plus the observation that its trace on an a section is inclined to c at 47° on the arc $\overset{+-}{cb}$.

From microscopic study comes the most reliable information as to time relationships between various types of s-surfaces and crystallization of individual minerals.   Figure 6-9a shows a phyllonitic schist with two visible s-surfaces maintaining more or less constant trends in the microscopic domain of the drawing. S_1 is defined by mineral layering: thin, pigmented, micaceous bands alternate with wider quartz-mica layers; and there are less numerous still thicker layers of nearly pure quartz (at top). A cleavage S_2, crossing and displacing S_1 in a constant sense, is defined by concentration of mica and dark pigment. Much of the mica aligned in the micaceous layers S_1 and all the mica in the interleaved quartz-mica layers is sharply crystallized and shows no sign of strain. The mica flakes in and adjacent to S_2 commonly are bent, apparently in response to slip on S_2. The inferred sense of the component of slip lying in the plane of the section is shown by arrows on

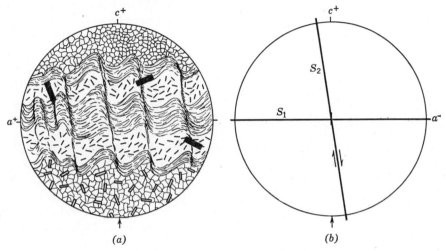

(a)   (b)

FIG. 6-9. (a) Sketch of fabric details in b section of phyllonitic mica schist, Brisbane, Australia. S_1 and S_2 are defined by pigmented micaceous layers. Dashed domains are quartz-muscovite; band at top is pure quartz; dark tabular porphyroblasts are sulfide. (b) Projection of mean traces of S_1 and S_2 in schist of diagram a.

S_2 in Fig. 6-9b.[7] Quartz throughout the rock is unstrained. Tabular crystals of sulfide are randomly oriented and cut across both S_1 and S_2. Clearly S_2 formed later than S_1. Crystallization of quartz and sulfide has outlasted the development of both S_1 and S_2; all the mica postdates S_1 but some of it finished crystallizing before movement on S_2 ceased. Figure 6-9b shows the geometric relations of the mean trends of S_1 and S_2 to the fabric axes inscribed on the section.

Microscopic Domains. *General.* Some deformed rocks are homogeneous within the domain of a thin section. But more commonly inspection under low magnification reveals the existence of microscopic domains

---

[7] As far as possible inference should be postponed until the descriptive phase of analysis is complete. Some inferences, however, especially those relating to direction and sense of movement and to order of development of different fabric elements in time, must be made while the section is under microscopic scrutiny. The kinematic significance of strain-slip cleavages such as S_2 is discussed on pp. 463–467.

each with its own textural and mineralogic individuality.   Some are relics of a premetamorphic state, e.g., sedimentary beds, pisolites, phenocrysts. Others such as segregation laminae and porphyroblasts are products of diffusion and localized crystallization during metamorphism.   Yet others, such as lensoid aggregates of quartz or calcite in phyllonites, are bounded by surfaces directly related to the deformation process.   Petrographic evidence pointing to one or another such an origin should be sought and noted; but as far as possible each type of microscopic domain should be described in nongenetic terms.   It is preferable to record lamination as such, rather than as bedding—even though evidence suggesting sedimentary origin (e.g., relict heavy-mineral films) may have been noted.

Lamination Domains.   Most tectonites are laminated parallel to one or more sets of s-surfaces.   Alternating layers of different mineral composition and texture may represent original bedding.   More commonly, perhaps, they are due to segregation of relatively simple mineral assemblages by metamorphic differentiation[8] in some way influenced by discrete surfaces of slip.   Long continued metamorphism, alternately dominated by crystallization and by ruptural deformation, tends to yield an intricate pattern of microscopic domains formed by contortion and disruption of once planar laminae.   In relating drawings or photographs of such patterns to the fabric axes, allowance must be made for microscopic inversion of the image that has been recorded.   Trends of boundaries are not affected; but the curvature of any line—and hence the total configuration of a fold—is inverted in relation to the fabric axes.   To correct for inversion, rotate the drawing or photograph (Fig. 6-10a) through 180° before superposing it on the fabric axes (Fig. 6-10b).   The figure may also be checked by direct comparison with the section as seen with a hand lens.

Porphyroblasts.   A porphyroblast constitutes a microscopic domain within which there may be an internal fabric or subfabric defined by mineral inclusions.[9]   Commonly recorded types of internal fabric include the following:

1. Strings of inclusions delineate an early set of internal s-surfaces (*si* in Sander's terminology) that can be matched and correlated in time with external s-surfaces *se* of the enclosing matrix (Fig. 6-11a and b). Growth of the porphyroblasts postdates development of the s-surfaces.

[8] F. J. Turner, The development of pseudostratification by metamorphic differentiation in the schists of Otago, New Zealand, *Am. Jour. Sci.*, vol. 239, pp. 1–16, 1941; F. J. Turner and J. Verhoogen, *Igneous and Metamorphic Petrology*, 2d ed., pp. 583–586, McGraw-Hill, New York, 1960.

[9] B. Sander, *Gefügekunde der Gesteine*, Springer, Berlin, Vienna, pp. 138–139, 162–165, 264–266, 1930; or *Einführung in die Gefügekunde der Geologischen Körper*, Pt. II, pp. 122–125, 298–300, Springer, Berlin, Vienna, 1950; H. J. Zwart, Relations between folding and metamorphism in the Pyrenees and their chronological succession, *Geologie en Mijnbouw, 39e Jaar.*, pp. 163–180, 1960.

The geometric relation of *si* to *se* allows additional inferences as to later phases of deformation:

a. Comparable microfolding of both *si* and *se* (helicitic texture) records a phase of deformation preceding growth of the porphyroblasts (Fig. 6-11*b*).

b. S-shaped or spiral trends of *si* (Fig. 6-11*c* and *d*), commonly displayed by albite of greenschists and by garnet of mica schists, indicate

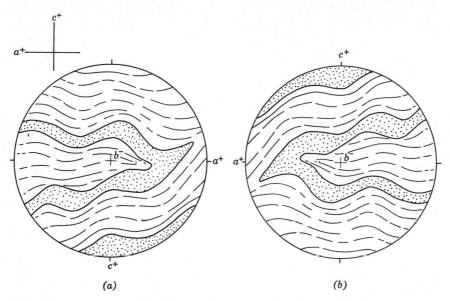

(a)   (b)

Fig. 6-10. Correction of microscopically observed fold pattern for inversion. Detail of microfolding in laminated phyllonitic mica schist, Brisbane, Australia. (*a*) Pattern as observed beneath the microscope; orientation of the section is indicated by fabric axes, top left. (*b*) Observed pattern in true relation to fabric axes.

rotation of the porphyroblast (paracrystalline deformation) during its development. The sense of rotation shown in a given thin section may yield valuable information as to the sense of one component of displacement on contemporary slip surfaces S_2 (Fig. 6-11*c*); but sections of several orientations must be studied to gain a comprehensive picture of movement in three dimensions.

c. Abrupt discontinuity in trend between *si* and adjoining *se* (Fig. 6-11*e*)[10] indicates rotation of the porphyroblast after cessation of growth (postcrystalline deformation).

2. In the second class of internal subfabric, inclusions of one mineral have a pattern of preferred orientation that is related to the lattice of the

[10] Sander, *op. cit.*, p. 164, fig. 63, 1930; F. J. Turner and C. O. Hutton, Some porphyroblastic albite schists from Waikouaiti River, *Royal Soc. New Zealand Trans.*, vol. 71, pt. 3, pp. 233, 234, 1941.

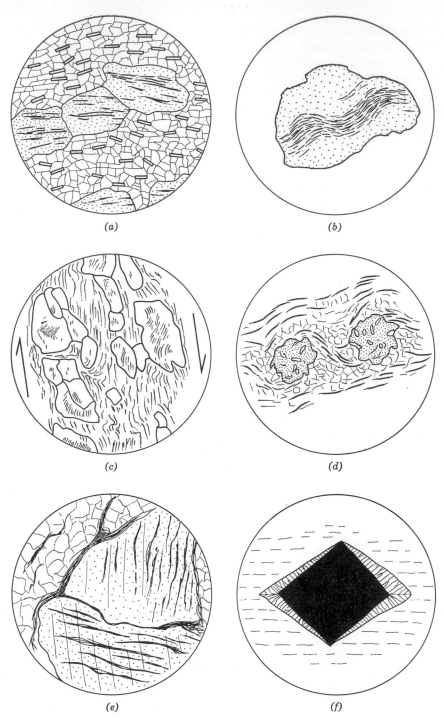

FIG. 6-11. For descriptive legend see opposite page.

host porphyroblast. This situation can be demonstrated and explored only by full analysis of preferred orientation as described below. It is possible that growth of porphyroblast and inclusions may have been simultaneous, as is probably the case with plagioclase and enclosed quartz of myrmekite. Alternatively the inclusions may be of later origin, as seems likely with small flakes of white mica aligned with {001} parallel to {010}, {001}, or {110} of albite porphyroblasts in some albite-mica schists of eastern United States.[11]

3. Irregular scattered inclusions, e.g., of quartz in porphyroblasts of biotite, showing no obvious alignment in any kind of s-surfaces, are simply recorded as defining the *quartz-in-biotite* subfabric. Their pattern of preferred orientation may prove to be different from that of the *quartz-in-quartz* subfabric of quartzose laminae of the same rock.

External domains of distinctive mineralogy and texture are developed in the immediate vicinity of porphyroblasts in some tectonites. To this category belong "pressure shadows" of quartz, chlorite, or carbonate, bordering cubic porphyroblasts of pyrite or octahedrons of magnetite in slates and schists.[12] These domains clearly postdate the development of the porphyroblasts with which they are associated. Their structure is commonly characterized by radial or tangential orientation of prismatic or tabular crystals. Pressure shadows usually are elongated in the plane of schistosity of the enclosing matrix (Fig. 6-11*f*), and from this it has been inferred that their growth has been controlled by late tension acting parallel to the schistosity.

The Individual Grain as a Microscopic Domain. The individual mineral grain is a microscopic domain (crystallographic domain) of peculiar

---

[11] E. Ingerson, Albite trends in some rocks of the Piedmont, *Am. Jour. Sci.*, vol. 35A, pp. 127–141, 1938.

[12] A. Pabst, "Pressure shadows" and the measurement of the orientation of minerals in rocks, *Am. Mineralogist*, vol. 16, pp. 55–70, 1931; J. J. Frankel, Abraded pyrite crystals from the Witwatersrand gold mines, *Mineralog. Mag.*, vol. 31, pp. 392–401, 1957.

FIG. 6-11. (*a–e*) Relations of internal s-surfaces (*si*) in porphyroblasts to s-surfaces (*se*) of the enclosing aggregate. (*a*) Porphyroblastic albite schist, New Zealand. *si* is continuous with *se*. Growth of albite porphyroblasts postdates *se* (= *si*). (*b*) Porphyroblastic albite schist, New Zealand. Folding of *si* predates growth of albite porphyroblast. (*c*) Albite schist, Scotland. (*After E. B. Bailey, Geol. Mag., vol. 60, pp. 328–330, 1923.*) S-shaped *si* in porphyroblasts of albite indicates rotation of growing crystal in the sense of the arrows (syntectonic crystallization). (*d*) Garnet-schist, Loch Leven, Scottish Highlands. Curved trains of inclusions *si* indicate rotation of growing garnet crystal (syntectonic crystallization). (*e*) Porphyroblastic albite schist, New Zealand. Sharp change in trend of *si* at boundary between two albite porphyroblasts indicates relative movement after cessation of crystallization. (*f*) Pyritic slate, Mother Lode, California. Quartz crystallized in "pressure shadows" around cube of pyrite. (*After A. Pabst.*)

individuality deriving from its lattice structure. Characteristics to be noted microscopically are size, shape (see below, page 214), and nature of the boundary surfaces. Minerals high in the crystalloblastic series,[13] such as kyanite, epidote, and garnet, persistently occur as idioblastic grains bounded by simple rational crystal faces. Quartz, calcite, and other minerals low in the series tend to be xenoblastic. Their mutual boundaries may be sutured and irregular or approximately planar. Where monomineralic rocks like quartzite or dolomite rock are composed of grains with planar but crystallographically irrational boundaries, it seems reasonable to infer that recrystallization has advanced to a state of equilibrium such that any surface common to two grains has the same surface energy with respect to each of the two lattices.

In many tectonites internal variation in optical behavior of some grains indicates internal heterogeneity which is generally attributed to some kind of strain (postcrystalline deformation, cf. page 209). Detailed measurements of crystallographic orientation and of boundary surfaces of subgrains are necessary to bring out the internal structure of a heterogeneous grain. This is tedious and time-consuming work; but it may lead to significant inferences regarding the dynamics and kinematics of the later phases of rock deformation. Familiar examples of intragranular heterogeneity in tectonites are discussed briefly below:

1. In many tectonites grains of quartz, olivine, or calcite display undulatory extinction between crossed nicols. Heterogeneity is gradational within the domain of a grain, and homogeneous subdomains cannot be microscopically identified. There is general agreement that bend gliding is involved in the development of this condition.[14] But only by experiment (cf. page 356) will it be possible to identify the glide system—probably {0001} translation in quartz.

2. Closely allied to the condition just described is one in which undulatory extinction is not strictly gradational. Rather the grain consists of small sharply bounded optically homogeneous sectors, each differing slightly in orientation from its neighbors.[15] In quartz grains the boundary surfaces of subgrains are close to [0001]; in olivine they approximate {100}. The structure is highly reminiscent of that developed in single crystals of metal that have been bent at room temperature and subsequently heated to temperatures below that critical for full annealing recrystallization. Metallurgists call the phenomenon *polygonization*. It

---

[13] Turner and Verhoogen, *op. cit.*, pp. 594–598, 1960.

[14] A. Hietanen, *On the Petrology of the Finnish Quartzites*, pp. 31–35, Government Press, Helsinki, 1938; S. W. Bailey, R. A. Bell, and J. Peng, Plastic deformation of quartz in nature, *Geol. Soc. America Bull.*, vol. 69, pp. 1443–1466, 1958.

[15] Bailey, Bell, and Peng, *op. cit.*, pp. 1452, 1453; D. T. Griggs, M. S. Paterson, H. C. Heard, and F. J. Turner, Annealing recrystallization in calcite crystals and aggregates, *Geol. Soc. America Mem. 79*, pp. 23–24, 1960.

is believed that lattice imperfections (especially dislocations), randomly distributed in the cold-strained crystal, later migrate under the influence of heat, and congregate in planar arrays that now define the boundaries of newly homogenized subgrains.

3. In some tectonites and lavas, tabular crystals of mica (Fig. 6-12b) are crossed by wedge-shaped or lensoid sectors in which the {001} cleavage is sharply deflected through as much as 25° to 50°. Sector boundaries tend to cut {001} of the host at high angles. In deformed basic plutonic rocks crystals of orthopyroxene likewise may be divided sharply

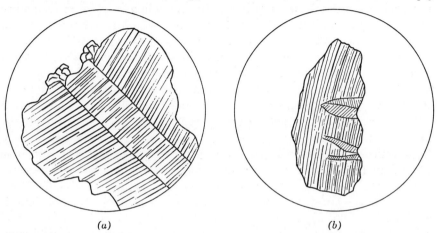

(a)   (b)

Fig. 6-12. Kink bands in naturally deformed crystals. (a) Enstatite in pyroxenite, Coast Ranges, California. Kink bands, bounded by irrational surfaces parallel to [010] = X and 80° to 90° to [001] = Z, are rendered obvious by sharp deflection of {100} exsolution lamellae. (b) Muscovite, quartz-mica-staurolite-garnet schist, near Innsbruck, Austria. Kink bands are inclined at high angles to {001} cleavage, which is sharply deflected.

into sectors whose planar boundaries are generally transverse to ubiquitous {100} exsolution lamellae (Fig. 6-12a). Precisely similar structures have been produced experimentally in biotite of granite and in enstatite of pyroxenite in the course of deformation at 500° to 800°C and 5,000 bars confining pressure.[16] They are believed to be kink bands resulting from rotation of crystal sectors in which gliding (on some plane transverse to the sector boundaries) has been active. Such structures are commonly produced during experimental deformation of single crystals of metals and of calcite.[17]

4. Twin lamellae are intragranular domains familiar to every petrographer. Some types of lamellar twin, notably {01$\bar{1}$2} in calcite, {02$\bar{2}$1} in

[16] D. T. Griggs, F. J. Turner, and H. Heard, Deformation of rocks at 500° to 800°C., Geol. Soc. America Mem. 79, pp. 60–66, 1960.

[17] F. J. Turner, D. T. Griggs, and H. Heard, Experimental deformation of calcite crystals, Geol. Soc. America Bull., vol. 65, pp. 883–934 (especially pp. 896, 897), 1954.

dolomite and {010} in sodic labradorite have been produced experimentally by straining initially homogeneous crystals.[18]   The mechanism of deformation—crystal gliding involving displacements of precisely defined geometry and magnitude—is well known in each case.   This information has been applied to the dynamic analysis of the orientation of calcite and dolomite twins in marble tectonites (see pages 413 to 425).[19]

5. Swarms of thin lamellae, differing slightly from the host grain in orientation or in refractive index, are commonly present in quartz grains of tectonites, especially in quartzites.   They have been widely recorded as "Boehm lamellae" or as "deformation lamellae."[20]   Their crystallographic orientation is irrational and varied, but the majority are inclined at between 10° and 20° to [0001].   There is no agreement as to their dynamic significance: they have been variously interpreted as translation lamellae and as kink bands.   It is certain, however, that they represent the latest, and probably a minor, phase of deformation of the rocks in which they occur.   "Deformation lamellae" have also been recorded in other minerals of tectonites—notably in olivine of sheared peridotites.[21] In olivine they approximate {100} and can be recognized only between crossed nicols.   For no adequate reason they have been termed "translation lamellae."   Measurement of "deformation lamellae," just as with cleavage and twin planes, is accomplished by rotating the lamella trace parallel to EW and tilting on EW to the point of sharpest definition of the lamella boundaries.

Dimensional Data.   A complete description of the microfabric should include at least a rough estimate of grain dimensions of the principal minerals, as determined by inspection of a few representative grains with a micrometer ocular.   In many tectonites the dimensional characteristics of a mineral will be found to vary from one kind of domain to another.

---

[18] E.g., Turner, Griggs, and Heard, *op. cit.*, 1954; F. J. Turner, D. T. Griggs, H. Heard, and L. E. Weiss, Plastic deformation of dolomite rock at 380°C., *Am. Jour. Sci.*, vol. 252, pp. 477–488, 1954; I. Borg, J. Handin, and D. V. Higgs, Experimental deformation of plagioclase single crystals, *Jour. Geophys. Res.*, vol. 64, p. 1094, 1959.

[19] F. J. Turner, Nature and dynamic interpretation of deformation lamellae in calcite of three marbles, *Am. Jour. Sci.*, vol. 251, pp. 276–298, 1953; R. H. Clark, A study of calcite twinning in the Strathavon marble, Banffshire, *Geol. Mag.*, vol. 91, pp. 121–128, 1954; J. Christie, Dynamic interpretation of the fabric of a dolomite from the Moine Thrust zone in north-west Scotland, *Am. Jour. Sci.*, vol. 256, pp. 159–170, 1958.

[20] For a clear account of the nature and preferred orientation patterns of these lamellae see J. M. Christie and C. B. Raleigh, The origin of deformation lamellae in quartz, *Am. Jour. Sci.*, vol. 257, pp. 385–407, 1959.   See also H. W. Fairbairn, Deformation lamellae in quartz from the Ajibik formation, Michigan, *Geol. Soc. America Bull.*, vol. 52, pp. 1265–1278, 1941; N. A. Riley, Structural petrology of the Baraboo quartzite, *Jour. Geology*, vol. 55, pp. 453–475, 1947; K. Naha, Time of formation and kinematic significance of deformation lamellae in quartz, *Jour. Geology*, vol. 67, pp. 120–124, 1959.

[21] F. J. Turner, Preferred orientation of olivine crystals in peridotites, *Royal Soc. New Zealand Trans.*, vol. 72, pt. 3, pp. 281, 282, 1942.

Quartz of monomineralic laminae tends to be notably coarser than the same mineral in interlayered domains composed of several minerals. Mica in micaceous laminae S, oriented with {001} subparallel to S, tends to have a much more pronounced tabular habit than crystals of the same mineral randomly oriented in adjacent quartz-rich layers.

The grain dimensions of quartz, calcite, and dolomite—minerals that typically occur in tectonites as xenoblastic grains lacking any recognizable crystallographic habit—may give some indications of the nature and degree of metamorphic strain. It is usually difficult, if not impossible, to estimate precisely the absolute directions of maximum and minimum grain dimension of quartz or of calcite in a given rock. However, the ratio of the mean dimensions respectively parallel and normal to the trace of some prominent s-surface in a thin section may be estimated approximately by counting grains in corresponding traverses. Data so obtained should be interpreted with caution. It is tempting to regard the lensoid outlines of aligned quartz or calcite grains as reproducing the strain ellipsoid of at least the later phases of deformation. But this interpretation implies that the domain of each grain as it now exists was initially equant and that its volume has not substantially changed during deformation. How generally valid can such an assumption be in view of the important role of recrystallization in metamorphism? Experimental evidence suggests that some marbles with markedly elongated or lensoid grains may perhaps be so interpreted. And it is at least unlikely that the long dimensions of quartz lenses in tectonites are aligned parallel to a compressive force or to the short axes of the ellipsoid of finite strain.

More reliable indicators of strain are domains whose initial shapes are known and whose initial outlines though distorted by strain are still clearly recognizable. To this category belong pisolites and microfossils of recognizable identity. Because of their originally spherical shape both oolites and radiolarians[22] have been successfully used to compute strain respectively in marble and in jasper. Various other fossils, among them belemnites,[23] have been similarly employed.

MICROSCOPIC ANALYSIS OF PREFERRED ORIENTATION

Preferred Orientation in the Tectonite Microfabric. Long recognized as characteristic of foliated metamorphic rocks is the familiar tendency

[22] E. Cloos, Oolite deformation in the South Mountain fold, Maryland, *Geol. Soc. America Bull.*, vol. 58, pp. 843–918, 1947; M. P. Billings, Field and laboratory methods in the study of metamorphic rocks, *New York Acad. Sci. Trans.*, ser. 2, vol. 13, pp. 44–51, 1950; W. H. Bryan and O. A. Jones, Radiolaria as critical indicators of deformation, *Univ. Queensland Dept. Geology Papers*, vol. 4, no. 9 pp. 1–6, 1955.

[23] J. Ladurner, Zur Kenntnis des Gefüges "gestreckter" Belemniten, *Mineralog. petrog. Mitt.*, vol. 44, pp. 479–494, 1933; W. F. Brace, Analysis of large two dimensional strain in deformed rocks, *21st Internat. Geol. Cong. Rept.* (1960), pt. 18, pp. 261–269, 1960.

for dimensional alignment of mica tables subparallel to the foliation S and of hornblende prisms defining a lineation L in S. This is what Sander has called preferred orientation according to grain form. In Chap. 2 such phenomena were related to planar and linear fabric elements—discontinuities that are penetrative on a larger scale. Since mica and hornblende have pronounced crystal habits, this condition of orientation is necessarily accompanied by preferred orientation of lattice directions—{001} of mica parallel to S, [001] of hornblende parallel to S and to L. Quartz and calcite, as contrasted with mica and hornblende, lack any recognizable crystallographic habit in tectonites and very commonly occur as equant grains. If the grains are lensoid or elongate there is no regular correlation between their dimensions and optically measurable lattice directions. Yet, as first demonstrated by Sander and Schmidt, these minerals, too, almost invariably exhibit a state of preferred orientation in tectonites. This has been termed preferred orientation according to grain structure, or lattice orientation. It is manifested especially as preferred orientation of the readily measured direction [0001]. The condition of lattice orientation tends to be strongest and its pattern most sharply defined in monomineralic rocks or domains—in quartzites and marbles rather than in pelitic or calcareous schists.

Partially but not wholly dependent upon the pattern of preferred orientation of the lattice is a state of preferred orientation sometimes displayed by intracrystalline domains, notably twin lamellae (in calcite or dolomite) and "deformation lamellae" (in quartz or olivine). Such domains are of late origin. Their orientation patterns are to be correlated only with the latest phase of deformation. They tell us little or nothing of the means by which the pattern of lattice orientation of the host mineral has evolved. The pattern of preferred orientation of a given crystallographic form such as {01$\bar{1}$2} differs in both its nature and its significance from that of recognizable lamellae of the same form. For example, three planes per crystal must be plotted to bring out the state of preferred orientation of {01$\bar{1}$2} in calcite; but only one or two, or even none, of these may appear as recognizable twin lamellae. Orientation of the form {01$\bar{1}$2} reflects a property of the calcite lattice—its trigonal symmetry. Orientation of visible {01$\bar{1}$2} lamellae reflects only the stress system operating in the final stages of deformation.

Most of our information regarding preferred orientation in tectonites has been obtained through microscopic analysis using a univeral stage. X-ray techniques have been employed successfully to elucidate preferred orientation phenomena in artificial metallic aggregates[24] and in fine-grained rocks such as slates[25] not amenable to microscopic study.

[24] E.g., C. S. Barrett, *Structure of Metals*, 2d ed., pp. 170–195, McGraw-Hill, New York, 1952.

[25] B. Sander and G. Sachs, Zur röntgenoptischen Gefügeanalyse von Gesteine,

Recently developed methods, moreover, have proved to be rapid compared with microscopic methods and may be applied to coarse and even polymineralic tectonites.   While it is possible by such means to explore the preferred orientation of optically unrecognizable lattice directions—e.g., the *a* crystal axes of quartz[26]—orthodox microscopic examination has the great advantage of permitting recognition and separate analysis of grain categories and domains that can only be treated collectively by X-ray analysis.   It is no trouble to distinguish microscopically between large and small grains of quartz, between quartz-in-quartz and quartz-in-mica subfabrics, between undulatory and recrystallized quartz, between quartz aggregates in separate limbs of a microfold, and so on.   Indeed in attempting to fit the preferred orientation data into any kinematic interpretation of the total fabric such distinctions are vitally necessary.   For this reason, and because of the specialized nature of the technique, further discussion of X-ray analysis of rock fabrics is omitted from this book.

General Procedure.   *Measurement and Plotting.*   Sections of tectonites under low magnification may show obvious departures from homogeneity.   Microscopic domains such as laminae, folds, and porphyroblasts should be delineated on a photomicrograph or drawing, and preferred orientation data for each domain should be recorded separately.[27]   For a particularly significant analysis—e.g., of experimentally deformed material—it may even be advisable to number each measured grain and record its identity on the photograph.

Unless the rock is uniformly coarse in grain, only a fraction of the grains in a particular domain is measured.   The usual sampling procedure is to make a series of parallel traverses across the section, which is kept in constant orientation with its base against the horizontal arm of the guide sledge.   The site of each traverse is recorded, both by noting readings on the guide sledge and by marking the photomicrograph of the section.   If additional measurements are later required it is then possible to make additional intermediate traverses without fear of duplicating previous data.   Where there is a marked variation in grain size or in

---

Zeitschr. *Kristallographie*, vol. 75, no. 5/6, pp. 550–571, 1930; H. W. Fairbairn, *op. cit.*, pp. 270–274, 1949; H. W. Fairbairn, X-ray petrology of some fine grained foliated rocks, *Am. Mineralogist*, vol. 28, pp. 246–256, 1943.

[26] Sander and Sachs, *op. cit.*, H. Neff, Texturbestimmungen mit einem Zählrohrgoniometer, *Siemens-Zeitschr.*, vol. 31, no. 1, pp. 23–30, 1957; I. Pascal, Quantitative Mineralanalyse mit dem. Zählrohrgoniometer, *Silikattechnologie*, vol. 10, no. 8, pp. 409, 410, 1959; D. V. Higgs, M. Friedman, and J. E. Gebhart, Petrofabric analysis by means of the X-ray diffractometer, *Geol. Soc. America Mem. 79*, chap. 10, pp. 275–292, 1960.

[27] We recommend that all measurements and all work sheets and diagrams relating to any orientation analysis be kept permanently on file.   As ideas and techniques develop, records of old analyses may become most useful as a basis for more detailed work.

any obvious property of the mineral measured, it is advisable to record orientation data in several corresponding categories—large versus small grains, cloudy versus clear, and so on.   This involves no additional work, and orientation data recorded and plotted separately can be combined later if uniform in pattern.   Figure 6-13 shows one way in which the data may be recorded; the first reading in the left-hand column records a grain of quartz in which the optic axis plunges W at 14° when the inner rotation scale reads 216°.   In each traverse every grain passing across the cross-hair intersection must be included.

There is no fixed rule as to the optimum number of measurements in any analysis, for herein is a statistical problem to which little attention

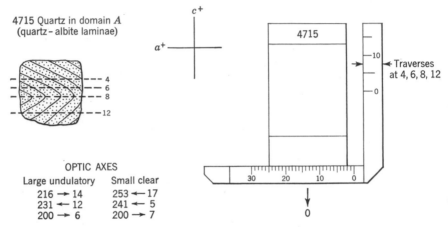

FIG. 6-13. Specimen of part of a work sheet recording orientation data.   At the left is a sketch of the measured domain as it appears under the microscope, inverted with respect to the fabric axes.

has been paid.   If too few grains are measured the full orientation pattern is not revealed, and the orientation diagram may be influenced unduly by local peculiarities of visible or unsuspected microscopic domains.   On the other hand to measure an excessive number of grains is to waste time that could be more profitably spent on an additional specimen.   For optic axes of quartz and {001} cleavages of mica, between 400 and 500 measurements may be made without undue expenditure of time.   For the three indicatrix axes of a biaxial mineral, or for optic axes and accompanying twin or cleavage planes in calcite, perhaps 100 to 200 grains is the optimum number—especially if the fabric is homogeneous and traverses are widely spaced.

The procedure for plotting the microscopically measured directions is the same as for mesoscopic data (cf. pages 52 to 58).   Points are always projected from the lower hemisphere.   Figure 6-14 illustrates a plot of the following data measured in a b section looking toward b^+:

a. [0001] of four quartz grains:

1. 60° ← 20°
2. 10° ← 70°
3. 285° → 15°
4. 310° → 30°

b. Measurements in one grain of calcite:

Cleavage r_1............ 351° − 40°↑
Twin lamellae e_1...... 99° − 6°↓
Twin lamellae e_2...... 145° − 10°↓
[0001]................ 32° → 22°

c. For zero reading of A_1, a^+a^- is aligned *EW*.

The procedure of contouring has already been described (cf. pages 58 to 64). The contour intervals should be approximately the same for all diagrams showing data of one type within a given mesoscopic domain. Thus the pattern of preferred orientation of quartz axes and the degree of homogeneity of preferred orientation of quartz in a large exposure can be evaluated most accurately by comparing similarly contoured diagrams based on the same number of measurements in each of several scattered hand specimens. For small domains, some of which may consist of only 50 or 100 grains, this may not be possible (e.g., see Fig. 6-15*c* and *e*).

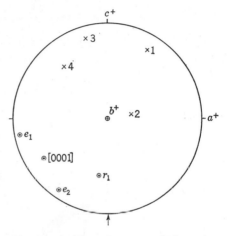

FIG. 6-14. Plot of measured data (see text): four quartz grains, crosses; one calcite grain, circled points.

Selective and Collective Diagrams. Where an orientation analysis of a microscopic domain includes several hundred measurements of one kind, it is advisable in the first instance to plot separate samples of about 50 to 100 grains each as selective diagrams. Each selective diagram can represent a separate traverse across the section; or it may include grains of some easily recognizable category—large as opposed to small, for example. There is usually no need to contour the selective diagrams individually. They should be scanned and compared with a view to estimating the homogeneity of the total sample. Features peculiar to one diagram probably are fortuitous or are due to some local unsuspected heterogeneity. Features common to all are those with respect to which the fabric of the measured domain is homogeneous.

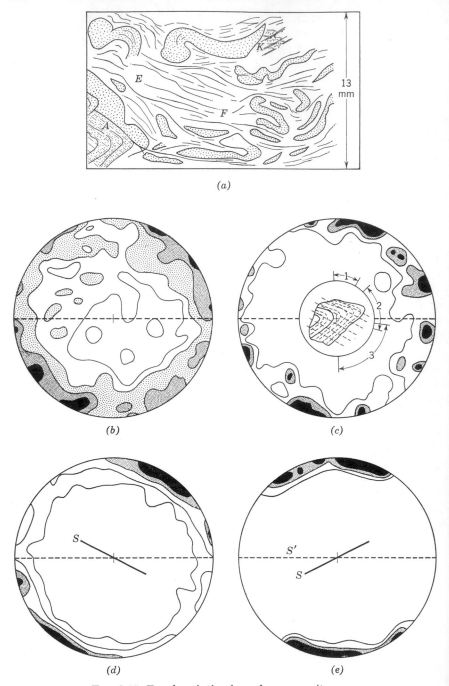

Fɪɢ. 6-15. For descriptive legend see opposite page.

A collective or synoptic diagram combines the plotted data of several selective diagrams for a single homogeneous domain. Commonly all the measurements refer to a single microsection. Where a subfabric is homogeneous throughout the domain of a hand specimen, data obtained in several differently oriented sections may be combined in one collective diagram. This involves rotating the plotted points onto a common plane of projection. The cases most frequently encountered are rotations of 90° and 180° respectively (cf. pages 70 to 75).

Statistical Significance of Orientation Diagrams. Figure 6-15a shows diagrammatically a section of a phyllonitic schist from eastern Otago, New Zealand,[28] cut normal to an axis of pronounced microfolding, *b*. Segments of folded and disrupted quartz-albite laminae (stippled) float in a micaceous matrix traversed by sinuous *s*-surfaces in which mica is especially concentrated. Muscovite and quartz were each measured separately within several of the domains so defined. The pattern of preferred orientation of quartz was found to be much the same in all the quartz-albite sectors, in spite of their obvious geometric individuality. Selective diagrams for quartz from several such domains were therefore combined into a single collective diagram (Fig. 6-15b) which depicts a quartz subfabric essentially homogeneous within the domain of the section (Fig. 6-15a). The orientation pattern of mica, on the other hand, varies notably from one domain to another. Selective diagrams have therefore been contoured and reproduced separately (Fig. 6-15c to e); each shows the influence of the local trend of visible *s*-surfaces upon parallel alignment of {001} planes. Common to all the mica diagrams is a marked tendency for {001} to lie parallel to *b*, the axis of microfolding. With respect to *b* the mica subfabric of the whole section (domain of Fig. 6-15a) is homogeneous, and the quartz and mica subfabrics homotactic.

Orientation diagrams such as those of Fig. 6-15 constitute a convenient, readily grasped graphic representation of data that have been subjected

---

[28] F. J. Turner, Structural petrology of the schists of eastern Otago, New Zealand, *Am. Jour. Sci.*, vol. 238, pp. 169–180, 1940; Mineralogical and structural evolution of the metamorphic rocks, *Geol. Soc. America Mem. 30*, pp. 211–214, 1948.

FIG. 6-15. Phyllonitic schist, eastern Otago, New Zealand. Horizontal broken lines of (*b–e*) are parallel to horizontal edge of (*a*). (*a*) Sketch of a thin section showing recognizable domains. Quartz-albite domains are stippled. Local trends of *s*-surfaces in intervening micaceous domains are indicated. (*b*) Quartz: collective orientation diagram for [0001] of 633 grains measured in six quartz-albite domains. Contours, 3%, 2%, 1%, 0.5%, per 1% area; maximum concentration 4%. (*c–e*) Muscovite: selective orientation diagrams for poles of {001} in different domains of (*a*). Insets show local trends of visible *s*-surfaces. (*c*) 73 crystals in quartz-albite domain *A*. Contours, 6%, 3%, 1.4%, per 1% area. (*d*) 300 crystals in micaceous layers of domain *E–F*. Contours, 6%, 4%, 2%, 0.3%, per 1% area. (*e*) 56 crystals in micaceous layers of domain *K*. Contours, 12%, 8%, 2%, per 1% area.

to a rather crude statistical analysis. Certain defects inherent in the microscopic method of sampling and analysis detract to some extent from the significance of the diagrams. The possible influence of sampling and contouring procedures and of unsuspected departures from homogeneity has already been noted. This last factor can best be brought out by contouring separate selective diagrams for minor domains, as has been done for mica in Fig. 6-15c to e. Tabular or prismatic habit may strongly influence selection of the grains comprising the analyzed sample. Measurement of planar crystallographic elements such as cleavages or twin lamellae is restricted to planes inclined at angles of 40° or more to the plane of the section, so that a vacant "blind spot" necessarily occupies the center of the diagram. These complications are serious. They will be discussed in greater detail in connection with the measurement of calcite and mica (see below, pages 225 to 230).

Recognizing that there are potential sources of considerable error in our statistical procedure we must ask to what extent the details and general pattern of an orientation diagram are likely to be statistically significant. Figure 6-15b seems to show a strong tendency for optic axes of quartz grains to be inclined at high angles to the mesoscopic lineation b. Is this tendency real? May it be fortuitous, or may it even reflect some consistent error in sampling or measurement?

Statistical tests have been devised to test the validity of preferred-orientation diagrams and the degree of preferredness that they represent.[29] Fortunately orientation patterns in tectonites usually are so strong that this question does not arise—important though it may be in the case of sedimentary fabrics with weak preferred orientation. In analysis of tectonite fabrics the all-important property of an orientation diagram is its symmetry. This can be evaluated without ambiguity only if the degree of preferred orientation is strong. For such diagrams the most satisfactory criterion of validity is reproducibility of the pattern in separately measured samples—especially if these are taken from sections of different orientation. Indeed to eliminate the possible influence of crystal habit on selection of grains and to minimize the effect of the "blind spot" in cleavage or lamella diagrams, analysis of differently oriented sections is essential (see below, pages 225 to 230). Figure 6-16 shows orientation diagrams for two samples of quartz axes separately measured in mutually perpendicular sections. Significant according to the criterion of reproducibility are (1) a girdle pattern with maximum

---

[29] H. Winchell, A new method of interpretation of petrofabric diagrams, *Am. Mineralogist*, vol. 22, pp. 15–36, 1937; F. Chayes, in H. W. Fairbairn, *op. cit.*, pp. 297–326, 1949; G. J. Pincus, The analysis of aggregates of orientation data in the earth sciences, *Jour. Geology*, vol. 61, pp. 482–509, 1953; D. Flinn, On tests of significance of preferred orientation in three-dimensional fabric diagrams. *Jour. Geology*, vol. 66, pp. 526–539, 1958.

concentrations distributed on a great circle; (2) a tendency for concentration of some [0001] axes near the fabric axis c, that is, at high angles to the mesoscopic schistosity plane; (3) monoclinic symmetry of the quartz fabric, with its symmetry plane (= the axes girdle) inclined to

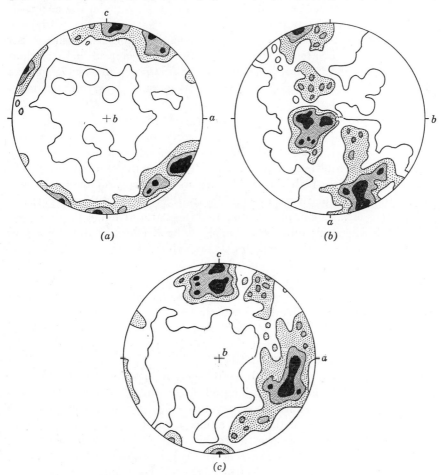

FIG. 6-16. Orientation diagrams for quartz [0001] in quartzose rods in quartz-albite-muscovite schist, eastern Otago, New Zealand.   Contours, 4%, 3%, 2%, 0.3%, per 1% area. (a) 400 grains in section perpendicular to mesoscopic lineation b; (b) 300 grains in section parallel to mesoscopic schistosity ab; (c) same data as diagram (b) rotated through 90° into the plane of diagram (a).

the mesoscopic lineation b at 10° to 25°. Obliquity of the symmetry plane of the quartz subfabric with reference to b is real, for it is reproduced in both samples. The angle of divergence, however, is greater in Fig. 6-16b and c than in Fig. 6-16a. The discrepancy between the two samples possibly reflects real heterogeneity of the fabric; or alternatively it may be due to difference in sampling or just conceivably to some consistent error in locating [0001] of quartz.

Finally it is emphasized that the presence of one or more obvious maxima in an orientation diagram is no certain criterion of significant preferred orientation—especially if the number of grains in the measured sample is small. A contoured diagram of 100 randomly distributed points cited by Flinn[30] has two strong concentrations exceeding 6 per cent per 1 per cent area of the projection. The diagram lacks obvious symmetry, however; and it is most unlikely that it would survive the test of reproducibility as judged from a second diagram based on 100 additional points similarly selected.

Detailed procedure. *Micas.* The only direction that can be measured readily in a mica crystal of any orientation is the normal to {001}. Most mica crystals have visible {001} cleavage cracks whose orientation is measured by rotation on A_1 to an *EW* alignment, and tilting on *EW* to the position in which the cracks are most sharply defined (cf. page 200). In this standard orientation the {001} plane is *EW* and vertical. Small flakes of mica completely enclosed in quartz or feldspar commonly lack visible cleavage; but their sharply defined external {001} surfaces may be measured by the same simple procedure. If the vibration direction of the polarizer is *NS*, biotite crystals in the standard position show minimum absorption, and this greatly facilitates measurement of {001}. If {001} is inclined to the section at an angle smaller than about 40° it cannot be measured directly. But the normal to {001} is *X* of the indicatrix; and this may be located by alternative procedures designed respectively for micas that have a moderate axial angle (e.g., muscovite) or are sensibly uniaxial (e.g., biotite):

In a muscovite crystal with {001} gently inclined to the section, *Y* and *Z* can be identified and located approximately by standard universal stage procedure for biaxial crystals (cf. page 200). The position of *X*—the intersection of the great circles respectively normal to *Y* and to *Z*—can be checked as the acute bisectrix of the axial angle (Fig. 6-17*a*); for both optic axes are accessible to measurement when *Y* has been aligned *EW* and rotated on A_5 to the 45° position.

When {001} cannot be measured directly, uniaxial micas such as biotite present a special problem. This is solved by locating a series of ordinary-ray directions *Z* (*Q* in Fig. 6-17*b*), which will be found to lie on a great circle, the pole of which is *X*. A complication is introduced by the strong absorption of biotite (for *Z* vibrations), which may hinder precise determination of extinction positions. To minimize this difficulty, proceed as follows: With the longest dimension of the crystal *EW*, tilt about 30° on *EW* in that sense which causes the absorption color to decrease. Tilt on *NS* to any angle, say 20°→. Now rotate on the inner-

[30] Flinn, *op. cit.*, p. 533.

most axis A_1 to extinction, such that the slow direction is EW and the absorption (with analyzer removed) is minimal. A Z direction is now EW; and its location is completed by reading the A_1 scale (say 280°),

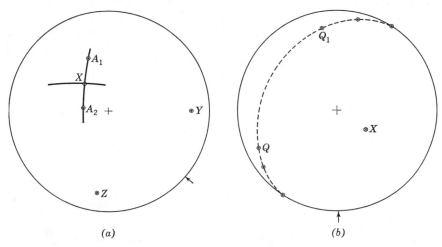

(a)   (b)

FIG. 6-17. Location of X in micas. (a) Muscovite, with $2V = 40°$. Stage readings: $Z = 33° \rightarrow 20°$; $Y = 310° \leftarrow 20°$, A_1—2°↑, A_2—42°↑. (b) Biotite. Circled points Q are optically measured ordinary-ray vibrations Z (for stage readings see text). To minimize absorption in locating Z directions (with index arrow on right), tilt on EW in the sense toward the observer, displacing X further from the center of the projection.

thus: $280° \rightarrow 20°$ (Q_1 in Fig. 6-17b). Repeat this procedure for a series of arbitrarily selected low tilts on NS, thus:

$$Q: 280° \rightarrow 20°$$
$$256° \rightarrow 10°$$
$$237° —\ \ 0°$$
$$217° \leftarrow 10°$$
$$205° \leftarrow 15°$$

If any point so determined and plotted is found to depart from the great circle connecting the others, it can be checked by a second measurement. Location of X by this method takes about five minutes.

For all the above measurements, whether of {001} cleavage or of X, we recommend using hemispheres with RI = 1.56. Correction of tilt is unnecessary except for biotite, for which angles greater than 30° should be reduced by 1°.

Analysis of mica subfabrics is complicated by the possibility of serious error arising from the widely prevalent tabular habit of mica crystals. The chance of a large mica crystal being intersected by a thin section is a function of the angle of inclination of {001} to the plane of the section.[31]   Any sample of a randomly oriented aggregate will include an unduly high proportion of grains with steeply inclined {001} and correspondingly fewer grains having {001} subparallel to the section.   The orientation diagram for {001} poles in a random or weakly oriented mica subfabric will therefore show an apparent girdle pattern which has no statistical significance—the "girdle" axis being normal to the plane of the section (Fig. 6-18a).   There are two ways of meeting this difficulty:

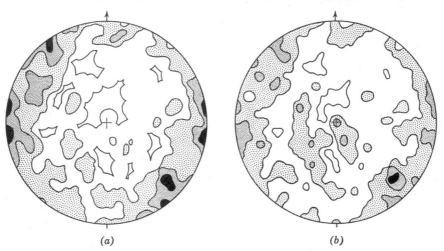

(a)   (b)

FIG. 6-18. Orientation diagrams for poles of {001} in biotite, measured in a section of granite.   (*After B. Sander.*)   Contours, 4%, 3%, 2%, 1%, 0.25%, per 1% area. (a) Uncorrected, 400 poles.   (b) Corrected, 476 poles.

1. If the preferred orientation of mica is weak, e.g., in a weakly foliated granite, the orientation diagram must be contoured by the grid method.   First, however, the pole count n at every point on the grid must be corrected to Fn, where the correction factor F depends on (a) the distance of the grid point from the center of the projection and (b) the ratio of the greatest to the smallest dimension of the average mica crystal. Little or no correction is required for points between the periphery and the small circle drawn at 50° from the center of the projection.   Table 6-2 gives values of F calculated by Billings and Sharpe[32] for grid points within the 50° circle (i.e., for crystals whose {001} planes are inclined

[31] M. P. Billings and R. P. Sharpe, Petrofabric study of a fossiliferous schist, Mt. Clough, New Hampshire, *Am. Jour. Sci.*, vol. 34, pp. 283–289, 1937; F. J. Turner and C. O. Hutton, Some porphyroblastic albite schists from Waikouaiti River (South Branch), Otago, *Royal Soc. New Zealand Trans.*, vol. 71, pt. 3, pp. 231, 232, 1941; B. Sander, D. Kastler, and J. Ladurner, Zur Korrektur des Schnitteffektes in Gefüge diagrammen heterometrischer Körner, *Österreich. Akad. Wiss. Sitzungsber., Math.- naturw. Kl.*, Abt. 1, vol. 163, no. 6–7, pp. 401–424, 1954.

[32] Billings and Sharpe, *op. cit.*, p. 286.   Note that corresponding values of F given by Sander, Kastler, and Ladurner (*op. cit.*, p. 409) are somewhat higher.

at less than 50° to the section). Figure 6-18a shows a weak apparent peripheral girdle, defining a plane of apparent symmetry (the plane of the page) in an uncorrected mica diagram.[33] These are eliminated from the corrected diagram (Fig. 6-18b) which reveals instead a nearly random distribution of poles.

TABLE 6-2. CORRECTION FACTOR F FOR TABULAR CRYSTALS

Distance from projection center	Values of F, $\dfrac{\text{Maximum crystal dimension}}{\text{Minimum dimension}} =$		
	10	5	3
5°	5.5	3.5	2.5
10°	3.8	2.7	2.0
15°	2.7	2.3	1.7
20°	2.4	1.8	1.6
30°	1.7	1.5	1.3
40°	1.4	1.3	1.1
50°	1.2	1.1	

2. For the typical strongly oriented mica fabrics of tectonites we recommend a different procedure with the dual aim of evaluating the symmetry of the total mica subfabric and correlating preferred orientation of {001} with s-surfaces and lineations of the mesoscopic fabric. Several sections must be examined; one should be cut parallel to the principal foliation (usually ab), and one transverse to each visible lineation. The ab section admittedly yields an imperfect sample of mica flakes. It is likely to cut fewer domains than a transverse section; and it includes disproportionately few crystals having what is actually the dominant orientation—{001} subparallel to ab. For this reason the mica data for the ab section should be plotted as a scatter diagram (Fig. 6-19a). To contour this would be misleading. However, the axis of the mica girdle, if such exists, is defined in Fig. 6-19a by those crystals—a minority, it is true—whose {001} planes depart most strongly from the prevalent ab orientation. It is precisely these grains that have the best chance of being intersected by the ab section. Once the axis of a mica girdle has been so identified, the mica subfabric may be fully sampled in a section cut more or less normal to the girdle axis (Fig. 6-19b). Since all grains have approximately equal chances of being cut by this section, the plotted points may be contoured in order to bring out a complete picture of the state of preferred orientation in the domain represented by the two sections.

[33] Sander, Kastler, and Ladurner, op. cit., pp. 410, 411.

Figure 6-19 illustrates the procedure just described. The rock is a quartz-albite-muscovite-chlorite schist with a strong foliation and lamination $S_1 = ab$, lineation and quartz rodding b, and local mica-rich s-surfaces S_2. Figure 6-19a is a plot of normals to $\{001\}$ in strongly tabular

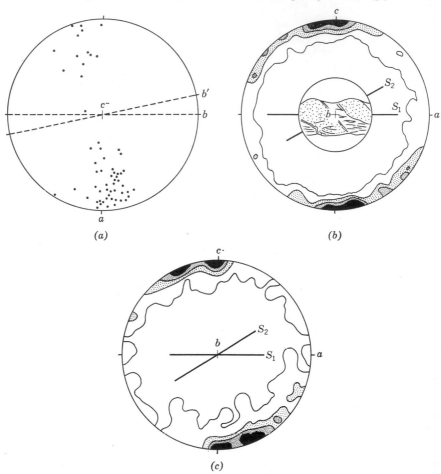

(a)

(b)

(c)

Fig. 6-19. Orientation diagrams for tabular muscovite in quartz-albite-muscovite-chlorite schist, Otago, New Zealand. (*After F. J. Turner and C. O. Hutton.*) (*a*) Poles of $\{001\}$ in 60 flakes, measured in ab section of a quartz-rich rod. (*b*) Poles of $\{001\}$ in 160 flakes, measured in section (normal to b) of two quartz-rich rods. Contours, 10%, 7%, 4%, 0.6%, per 1% area. (*c*) Poles of $\{001\}$ in 150 flakes measured in section (normal to b) of micaceous matrix. Contours, 10%, 8%, 4%, 0.7%, per 1% area.

flakes in a quartz-rich rod, measured in a section parallel to the foliation ab. It shows that the axis b' of the mica girdle is distinctly inclined to b; and this condition has been verified by additional measurements of $\{001\}$ of muscovite in a section parallel to S_2. So sections transverse to b or to b' can be expected to yield a sample of mica crystals representative of the whole fabric. Such samples are shown in Fig. 6-19b and c. These bring out clearly the tendency for {001} of muscovite to be aligned in S_1

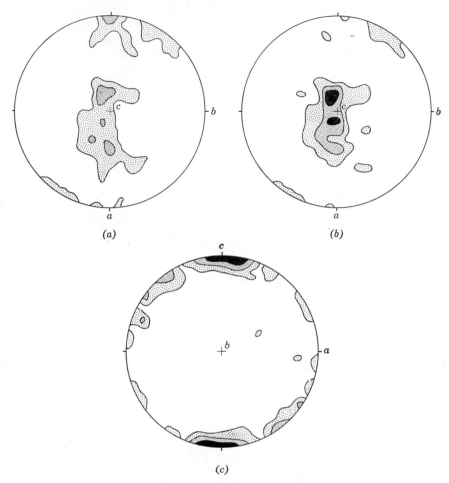

(a) (b)

(c)

FIG. 6-20. Orientation diagrams for tabulrr biotite in schist, New Hampshire. (*After M. P. Billings and R. P. Sharpe.*) (*a*) Poles of {001} in 200 flakes, measured in *ab* section (parallel to schistosity). Contours, 4%, 2%, per 1% area. (*b*) Same data as *a*, corrected to 231 effective poles. Contours, 6%, 4%, 2%, per 1% area. (*c*) Poles of {001} in 200 flakes, measured in *ac* section (normal to schistosity and to lineation). Contours, 6%, 4%, 2%, per 1% area.

and in S_2, and they confirm the existence of the mica girdle. Note, however, that they fail to bring out the slight but distinct departure of the girdle axis b' from the mesoscopic lineation b—a feature that renders triclinic an otherwise monoclinic total fabric. Possibly this condition is more generally prevalent than might be gathered from perusal of orthodox mica diagrams based on measurements in a section normal to b. It is clearly indicated in both uncorrected and corrected ab diagrams for Billings and Sharpe's New Hampshire mica schist (Fig. 6-20a and b).[34] Perhaps the axis of a mica girdle can be located with greater precision in a section parallel to the principal schistosity than in one normal to the lineation. The latter, however, shows the relation of {001} maxima to the various types of s-surfaces and to the laminar domains bounded by these.

Most published mica diagrams refer to {001}. In simply foliated schists the orientation pattern is commonly dominated by a single maximum—{001} subparallel to S—and so has axial symmetry. Additional information regarding symmetry may be obtained in the case of muscovite having a moderately large axial angle ($2V = 40° \pm$), for in sections more or less parallel to {001} Y and Z of the indicatrix are readily identified. Y approximates [100] and Z [010] of the muscovite lattice. Measurement of Y in appropriately oriented crystals in a section parallel to the foliation may reveal a state of preferred orientation with Y concentrated either normal or parallel to a mesoscopic lineation.[35] This then reduces the symmetry of the mica subfabric from axial to orthorhombic.

Mica crystals of deformed rocks may show indications of internal strain in the form of narrow kink bands steeply inclined to {001} and marked by sharp local deflection of the cleavage through 20° to 50°. Little attention has been paid to possible preferred orientation of these structures in micas of lavas and tectonites. However, kink bands induced in crystals of mica during experimental deformation of granites are geometrically related to the stress pattern.[36] Analysis of preferred orientation of natural kink bands might therefore be expected to throw some light on the dynamics of late strain of individual mica crystals and so of the rock as a whole.

Quartz. Because of its abundance in metamorphic rocks and the rapidity with which the optic axis [0001] may be measured and plotted, quartz has received more attention than any other mineral in the literature on preferred orientation of minerals in tectonites. Measurement of [0001] is a straightforward procedure that has already been described in detail (pages 202 and 203). Since there is little or no correlation between the external form and the lattice of quartz in most tectonites even when grains are elongated or lenticular,[37] a representative sample of grains is most likely to be furnished by a section normal to the foliation and to

[34] Billings and Sharpe, *op. cit.*, p. 282, figs. 8, 11.

[35] Sander, *op. cit.*, pp. 225, 326, D137, 1930; E. Ingerson, Fabric analysis of a coarsely crystalline polymetamorphic tectonite, *Am. Jour. Sci.*, vol. 31, pp. 183, 184, 1936; Turner and Hutton, *op. cit.*, p. 232, pl. 38.

[36] Griggs, Turner, and Heard, *op. cit.*, pp. 65, 66, 1960.

[37] This statement of course does not apply to vein quartz, which commonly tends to be elongate either parallel or normal to [0001].

the principal lineation—especially if the symmetry of the mesoscopic fabric is monoclinic. Normally about 400 grains—taking perhaps five hours to measure and plot—will yield a reproducible orientation diagram. To eliminate possible error in sampling we recommend strict adherence to widely separated traverses, care being taken not to omit grains that remain nearly dark between crossed nicols. For a grain with undulatory extinction only one measurement, representing the mean orientation, should be recorded. Where the grain size is variable as a result of late granulation or partial recrystallization of strained grains, measurements for large and for small grains should be recorded separately and plotted as selective diagrams. These can be combined as a collective diagram if similar in pattern. In rocks where quartz is closely associated with untwinned oligoclase of similar refractive index, the following rapid procedure will distinguish the quartz grains:[38] The problem is to distinguish a positive uniaxial mineral from a biaxial mineral with a large axial angle. With the tilting axes A_2 and A_4 approximately at zero rotate on the innermost axis A_1 to bring the grain into extinction with its slow direction Z' aligned NS. If the mineral is quartz, an ordinary-ray direction X is now aligned EW, and the grain remains in extinction for tilt through any angle on EW. If it is feldspar it will become illuminated, except for the rare case where X or Y happens to be in the plane of the section. This unlikely possibility may be neglected without statistical error. The Z direction of the grain identified as quartz is now measured in the usual way.

There is a wide range of pattern among recorded orientation diagrams for quartz axes in tectonites. Many conform to or approximate one or another of several recognized types, illustrated in Fig. 6-21 by examples chosen for perfection of symmetry and pattern. The general rule, however, is approximation rather than strict conformity to type; and it must be remembered that the quartz axes of some tectonites are weakly or randomly oriented. The quartz subfabrics of Fig. 6-21 are shown without reference to accompanying elements (s-surfaces, lineations) of the associated mesoscopic fabrics. Considered thus alone, most well-defined orientation patterns of quartz axes are seen to be strictly triclinic or monoclinic, but nevertheless not greatly departing from orthorhombic symmetry. Some few show perfect orthorhombic symmetry. Common quartz patterns classified according to symmetry are as follows (symmetry planes, m):

A. Orthorhombic quartz subfabrics
   1. A single maximum, typically elongated in the plane of a partial or complete girdle (Fig. 6-21a).

[38] C. M. Gilbert and F. J. Turner, Use of the universal stage in sedimentary petrography, *Am. Jour. Sci.*, vol. 247, pp. 22, 23, 1949.

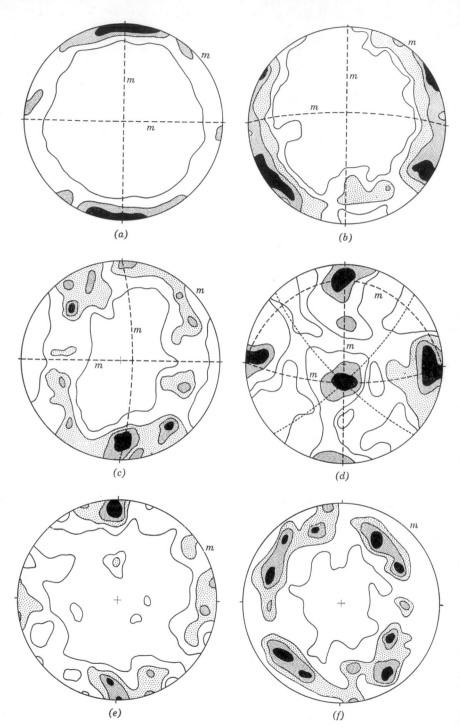

FIG. 6-21. For descriptive legend see opposite page.

2. Two maxima subtending an angle of about 70° to 90°, associated with a partial or complete girdle in the same plane (Fig. 6-21b). The sector of the girdle in the acute angle between the maxima is generally but not invariably more densely populated than the sector in the obtuse angle. Where the two sectors are equally populated and the maxima subtend an angle of 90°, the symmetry is tetragonal.

3. Two girdles, commonly mutually perpendicular (Fig. 6-21c). In strictly orthorhombic diagrams maxima are symmetrically paired across the symmetry planes.

4. Two mutually perpendicular girdles with three mutually perpendicular maxima (Fig. 6-21d). This may be considered a special case of 3; and the pattern approximates tetragonal symmetry (additional symmetry planes are given by dotted lines).

B. Monoclinic quartz subfabrics

1. A girdle pattern with somewhat asymmetrically distributed peripheral maxima (Fig. 6-21e). The plane of the girdle is the sole plane of perfect symmetry; note, however, the rather close approximation to orthorhombic symmetry.

2. A girdle pattern with maxima situated on a small circle around the girdle axis (Fig. 6-21f). This is sometimes termed a *cleft girdle*. For monoclinic symmetry the maxima must be paired about the girdle axis.

C. Triclinic quartz subfabrics

1. Very commonly a quartz-axis diagram approximates one of the orthorhombic or monoclinic patterns illustrated in Fig. 6-21, but because of asymmetric distribution of maxima or submaxima lacks any strict plane of symmetry, and so is triclinic. Such are Fig. 6-22a (cf. Fig. 6-21c) and b (cf. Fig. 6-21f). In the former strict symmetry is destroyed by the asymmetrically situated submaxima X and Y; in the latter, the maxima are not strictly paired about

---

Fig. 6-21. Orientation diagrams for [0001] in quartz, emphasizing symmetry properties. (a–d) Orthorhombic. Three mutually perpendicular symmetry planes (m). (a) Quartzite, Barstow, California; 300 grains. Contours, 8%, 4%, 1%, per 1% area. (b) Moine schist, Scotland; 250 grains. Contours, 5%, 4%, 2%, 1%, per 1% area. (After F. C. Phillips, Geol. Soc. London Quart. Jour., vol. 93, pl. 341, D2, 1937.) (c) Quartzite, Barstow, California; 300 grains. Contours, 4%, 3%, 2%, 1%, per 1% area. Two intersecting girdles. (d) Granulite, Finland; 176 grains. Contours, 3%, 2%, 1%, per 1% area. (After T. G. Sahama, Comm. géol. Finlande Bull. 113, p. 36, D41, 1936.) (e and f) Monoclinic; nearly orthorhombic. Symmetry plane (m) is plane of projection. (e) Quartzose layer in phyllite, Shikoku, Japan; 300 grains. Contours, 4%, 3%, 2%, 1%, per 1% area. (After G. Kojima and T. Suzuki, Hiroshima Univ. Jour. Sci., ser. C, vol. 2, p. 191, 1958.) (f) Quartzite, Brome County, Quebec. Contours, 5%, 4%, 3%, 1%, per 1% area. (After H. W. Fairbairn, Geol. Soc. America Bull., vol. 50, p. 1481, fig. 5c, 1939.)

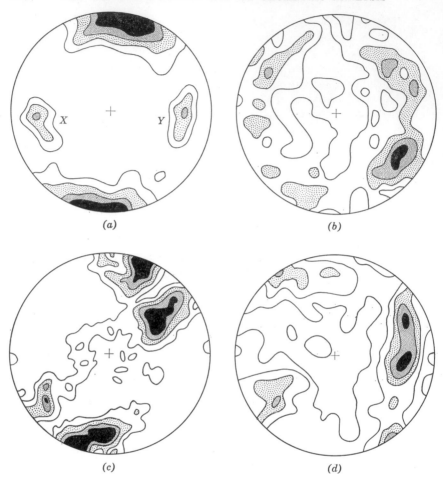

FIG. 6-22. Orientation diagrams for [0001] in quartz; triclinic symmetry. (*a*) Quartzite, Barstow, California; 300 grains. Contours, 8%, 6%, 4%, 2%, 1%, per 1% area. (*b*) Quartzite, Brome County, Quebec. Contours, 4%, 3%, 2%, 1%, per 1% area. (*After H. W. Fairbairn, Geol. Soc. America Bull., vol. 50, p. 1482, fig. 6b, 1939.*) (*c*) Granite mylonite, Sweden; 200 grains. Contours, 5%, 4%, 3%, 2%, 1%, per 1% area. (*After W. Larsson, Sveriges Geol. Undersökn., ser. C, vol. 32, p. 21, 1938.*) (*d*) Deformed quartzite pebble, Panamint Range, California; 416 grains. Contours, 5%, 4%, 3%, 2%, 1% per 1% area.

the center of the girdle. Other quartz diagrams (e.g., Fig. 6-22*c* and *d*) are more obviously triclinic and show little resemblance to any of the symmetric patterns of Fig. 6-21. Triclinicity may sometimes be correlated with inhomogeneity in the measured domain, e.g., where two monoclinic subdomains with different symmetry planes have been combined (Fig. 6-22*c*). But this is not always so. The slight triclinicity of the quartzite fabric illustrated in Fig. 6-22a is apparent in any selective diagram representing 100 grains measured in the same rock.

In homotactic fabrics the maxima and girdles of Fig. 6-21 are symmetrically related to mesoscopic fabric elements such as s-surfaces and lineations. For example, the maximum of Fig. 6-21a may lie in the principal foliation plane and normal to the lineation, or alternatively normal to the foliation of orthorhombic tectonites. This type of relation was the basis of Sander's classification of quartz-axis maxima of S-tectonites.[39] We prefer to consider only criteria inherent in the quartz subfabric itself; for in heterotactic fabrics the same patterns appear in the quartz diagrams but are not regularly related to s-surfaces or lineations of the mesoscopic fabric.[40]

Analysis of quartz orientation in some tectonites—especially in quartzites showing signs of postcrystalline strain—may be extended to cover swarms of parallel planar structures (deformation lamellae or Boehm lamellae) developed in the constituent quartz grains (see page 214).[41] The lamellae may be measured microscopically in ordinary light by aligning them EW and vertical, much as with cleavage of mica crystals. As with all diagrams for lamella poles, there must necessarily be a central blind spot, about 90° in diameter, corresponding to orientations inaccessible to measurement; indeed Boehm lamellae in quartz are difficult to measure if inclined to the section at angles of less than 60°. However, since the lamellae consistently tend to intersect [0001] at high angles, a fairly complete picture of their orientation usually may be obtained by selecting a section within which the [0001] axes themselves tend to be concentrated. A section parallel to the girdle axis of Fig. 6-21a, b, or e would serve this purpose. Failing this, the extent to which lamella poles possibly fall within the blind spot of one section may be explored by measuring lamellae in additional sections cut normal to the first.[42]

Preferred orientation of deformation lamellae in quartz is usually much stronger than that of quartz axes in the same domain (Fig. 6-23a, b, e, f).[43] In many rocks lamellae appear selectively in only a fraction of the quartz

[39] Sander, op. cit., pp. 182–183, D61, 1930; D. T. Griggs and J. F. Bell, Experiments bearing on the orientation of quartz in deformed rocks, Geol. Soc. America Bull., vol. 49, pp. 1741–1742, 1938; H. W. Fairbairn, Hypotheses of quartz orientation in tectonites, Geol. Soc. America Bull., vol. 50, pp. 1477–1479, 1939.

[40] Hietanen, op. cit., pl. 8, D.S. 1a, 9, 28, 30, 49; Sander, op. cit., D28, 35, 1930; R. Balk, Fabric of quartzites near thrust faults, Jour. Geol., vol. 60, pp. 415–435 (especially figs. 21, 22, 24, 29), 1952; L. E. Weiss, Structural analysis of the basement system at Turoka, Kenya, Overseas Geology and Mineral Resources, vol. 7, no. 2, pp. 142–145, London, 1959.

[41] Sander, op. cit., pp. 175–178, 1930; Christie and Raleigh, op. cit.

[42] Knopf and Ingerson, op. cit., p. 233, 1938; Christie and Raleigh, op. cit., p. 392.

[43] Fairbairn, op. cit., 1941; Riley, op. cit.; Christie and Raleigh, op. cit., p. 399.

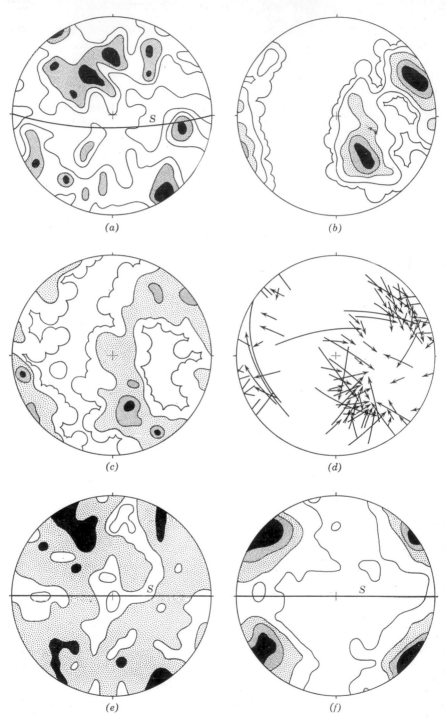

(a)

(b)

(c)

(d)

(e)

(f)

FIG. 6-23. For descriptive legend see opposite page.

236

grains.   These particular grains tend to have distinctly stronger preferred orientation of [0001] than that of the total quartz aggregate, and symmetry identical with that of the lamella pattern.[44]   It would seem that the lamellae are visible effects of late strain selectively developed in favorably oriented crystals—a conclusion supported by the occurrence of individual lamellae passing continuously across grain boundaries in some rocks.   The typical lamella-pole diagram is perfectly orthorhombic: strong paired maxima are situated in a small circle about 70° to 80° in diameter (Fig. 6-23b).[45]   Many published diagrams show only the pair of maxima (Fig. 6-23f), the small-circle girdle being weak or imperfectly revealed by analysis confined to a single section.   Great circles, each drawn through a lamella pole and [0001] of the host grain, tend to intersect in the center of the small circle of lamella poles (Fig. 6-23d).[46]

In some tectonites the lamella patterns conform in regard to symmetry to other elements in the fabric, notably foliation, lineation, and quartz-axis patterns (Fig. 6-23e and f).[47]   But there are also instances where there is no obvious relation between the symmetry of the quartz-lamella diagram and that of mesoscopic fabric elements.[48]

Calcite.   In a calcite tectonite subfabric the characteristic of greatest general significance is the pattern of preferred orientation of the c axis, [0001].   Twin lamellae $\{01\bar{1}2\}$ are additional elements that can give information relating to late minor strain.   Such lamellae, and also $\{10\bar{1}1\}$ cleavages, are useful in defining uniquely the orientation of the lattice— something that, by optical means alone, is impossible for quartz.   Because of difficulties connected with the extreme birefringence and commonly slightly biaxial condition of calcite, measurement of [0001] and identification of visible twin lamellae and cleavages in a single grain may occupy

[44] Christie and Raleigh, *op. cit.*

[45] *Ibid.*

[46] *Ibid.*

[47] E. Ingerson and O. F. Tuttle, Relations of lamellae and crystallography of quartz and fabric directions in some deformed rocks, *Am. Geophys. Union Trans.*, vol. 26, pp. 95–105, 1945.

[48] Riley, *op. cit.*

FIG. 6-23. Orientation diagrams for [0001] and deformation lamellae in quartz of quartzites.   (a–d) Cambrian quartzite below Moine Thrust, Scotland.   (*After J. M. Christie and C. B. Raleigh.*)   (a) [0001] of 607 grains.   Contours, 2%, 1½%, 1%, ½%, per 1% area.   S = foliation.   (b) Poles of deformation lamellae in 204 grains.   Contours, 7½%, 5%, 2½%, 1%, ½%, per 1% area.   (c) [0001] of 204 grains in which deformation lamellae were measured.   Contours, 3%, 1½%, ½%, per 1% area.   (d) Poles of deformation lamellae (arrow points) and arcs connecting each to [0001] of same grain, in representative grains of diagrams b and c.   (e and f) Ajibik quartzite, Michigan.   (*After H. W. Fairbairn.*)   (e) [0001] of 613 grains. Contours, 2%, 1%, 0.5%, per 1% area.   (f) Poles of deformation lamellae in 337 grains.   Contours, 6%, 4%, 2%, 1%, per 1% area.

ten or twenty minutes.   Analysis of a calcite fabric is thus a time-consuming procedure.   It should not be attempted unless the investigator is prepared to spend forty or fifty hours on a single specimen.

Crystallographic relations between c and a axes, $\{10\bar{1}1\}$ and $\{01\bar{1}2\}$ in calcite are shown in projection in Fig. 6-24.   It is convenient[49] to use the symbols e_1, e_2, and e_3 for the three planes of $\{01\bar{1}2\}$; r_1, r_2, and r_3 for $\{10\bar{1}1\}$; $[e_1{:}r_2]$ for the edge between e_1 and r_2, and so on.   Cozonal planes

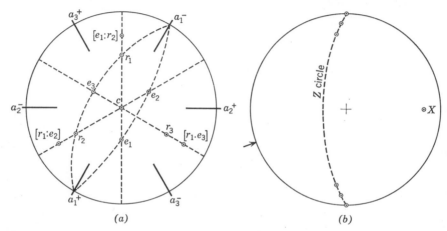

(a)   (b)

FIG. 6-24. (a) Calcite.   Commonly recorded crystallographic planes (poles, e_1, etc.), edges ($[e_1{:}r_1]$, etc.), and crystal axes; equal-area projection, lower hemisphere.   (b) Calcite.   Location of X as pole of great circle of measured Z directions.

whose poles lie on a great circle through [0001] are designated by the same subscript: thus, e_1, c, r_1 are cozonal.   Pertinent interfacial angles, used to identify lamellae and cleavages and to check the position of [0001], are as follows:

$$c \wedge r = 44\tfrac{1}{2}°$$
$$c \wedge e = 26°$$
$$e_1 \wedge e_2 = 45°$$
$$e_1 \wedge r_2 = 38°$$
$$e_1 \wedge r_1 = 71°$$
$$r_1 \wedge r_2 = 75°$$

Where calcite and dolomite are mutually associated they are readily distinguished by the crystallographic identity of visible lamellae:

Calcite, $\{01\bar{1}2\}$ = e lamellae   [0001] $\wedge$ e pole = $26°$
Dolomite, $\{02\bar{2}1\}$ = f lamellae   [0001] $\wedge$ f pole = $62\tfrac{1}{2}°$

[49] Cf. F. J. Turner, D. T. Griggs, H. Heard, Experimental deformation of calcite crystals, *Geol. Soc. America Bull.*, vol. 65, p. 886, 1954.

The first step in measuring [0001] in any grain is to identify the fast and the slow vibration directions X' and Z, respectively. (Since calcite is uniaxial and negative the slow direction in any grain is an ordinary ray and hence an axis Z of the indicatrix.) Because of the extreme birefringence of calcite it is difficult, except in very thin sections or in sections inclined at high angles to [0001], to identify the fast and slow directions directly by means of a quartz wedge. We recommend observing the change in relief when the section is rotated in polarized light without the analyzer. When X' is aligned EW, the section is in extinction, and on removal of the analyzer shows maximum relief (if the vibration direction of the polarizer is NS). Sections showing little change of relief on rotation are inclined at high angles to [0001]; for these a quartz wedge, or even a gypsum plate, may be used to identify Z. Once X' and Z have been identified, there are two ways in which to locate [0001] = X (cf. the opposite case, a uniaxial positive mineral, previously described on pages 202 and 203).

1. The direct but least accurate method is to bring X' EW, and then, by alternate tilting on NS and rotation on A_1, achieve permanent extinction for all angles of tilt on EW. X is now either EW or parallel to the axis of the microscope barrel A_5. The end point for tilting on NS to minimum illumination is usually far from sharp and may involve an uncertainty of $\pm 5°$.

2. The slower but more satisfactory procedure is to locate X as the normal to the great circle connecting four or five separately measured Z directions (dashed arc, Fig. 6-24b). Each Z is located by setting NS to some convenient tilt (between $25°\rightarrow$ and $25°\leftarrow$) and rotating to extinction on A_1, with the slow direction EW. Readings for the Z directions plotted in Fig. 6-24b are $349° \rightarrow 25°$; $343° \rightarrow 10°$; $339°—0°$; $335° \leftarrow -10°$; $331\frac{1}{2}° \leftarrow 20°$. The reading when [0001] is aligned EW is $69° \leftarrow 20°$.

Measured angles of tilt on the NS and EW axes of the stage may have to be corrected for error due to differences between refractive indices of calcite and of the hemisphere glass. Because of the high birefringence of calcite some care must be exercised in making this correction, which is at best only approximate. We recommend using hemispheres of refractive index 1.55 to 1.56. In locating [0001] directly by aligning X parallel to EW, low tilts need no correction (cf. Kamb's conclusions, page 205). The discrepancy in refractive index that arises when X is steeply inclined to the section is compensated for by the low range of tilt—not more than $10°$ to $15°$ on either side—then necessary to measure Z axes over a broad arc of the ordinary-ray great circle.

Calcite of tectonites occurs in equant or lensoid grains whose shape is largely independent of lattice structure; so that, in contrast with mica, any peripheral girdle that may appear in a c-axis orientation diagram may be accepted as real. Moreover, since [0001] of any homogeneous

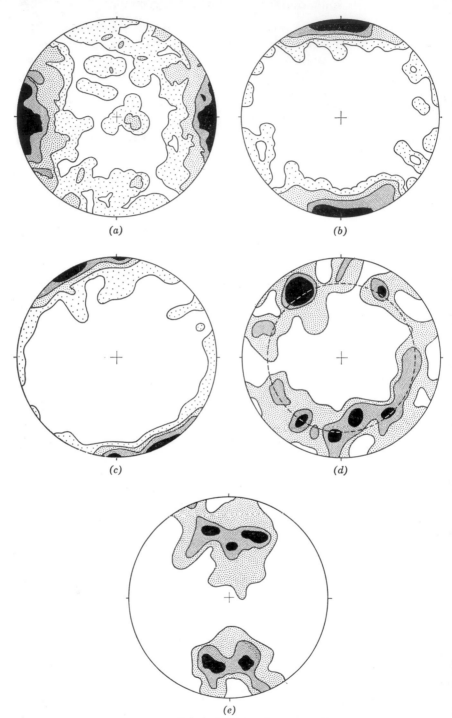

FIG. 6-25. For descriptive legend see opposite page.

grain, however oriented, is accessible to measurement, the orientation diagram for [0001] has no central blind spot.   Heavily twinned grains, however, present a special difficulty.   If they are oriented with [0001] steeply inclined to the section, overlap of e lamellae within the thickness of the section may make it impossible accurately to locate [0001].   The number of grains of this kind encountered during any analysis of a calcite fabric should be noted in the caption of the appropriate c-axis orientation diagram, thus: "Calcite, [0001] in 200 grains (inaccessible, because of overlapping e twins, in five other grains)."

Most [0001] diagrams for calcite of tectonites conform to or approximate one or another of several types each with its characteristic symmetry:

1. A single strong maximum (Fig. 6-25a); symmetry axial.

2. A single maximum, situated in a partial or complete girdle (Fig. 6-25b); symmetry orthorhombic.

3. A girdle with two or more unequal peripheral maxima (Fig. 6-25c); symmetry monoclinic, the sole symmetry plane being that of the girdle.

4. A girdle with maxima distributed through a small circle of large radius—cleft-girdle pattern; symmetry monoclinic if the maxima are paired symmetrically across the center of the diagram (Fig. 6-25d); otherwise triclinic.

5. A "ring maximum" (small-circle girdle of small radius), with internal concentrations, the distribution of which determines the symmetry— orthorhombic in Fig. 6-25e.   If the ring maximum is evenly filled, and so lacks internal concentrations, the symmetry is axial.

The orientation diagram for [0001] brings out the symmetry of the calcite subfabric.   If, as is often the case, this is the sole purpose of the microscopic analysis, there is no need to measure e lamellae.   On the other hand it may be desirable, in specimens showing a profuse development of e lamellae, to investigate these in some detail—at least in a few selected specimens.   Each set is measured in the usual way by rotating on the inner axis A_1 to an EW alignment and tilting on EW to maximum sharpness.[50]   Figure 6-26 shows two sets of conspicuous lamellae so measured: e_1, $359° - 4°\downarrow$; e_2, $314\frac{1}{2}° - 8°\downarrow$; [0001], $69° \leftarrow 20°$.   Some

[50] When $\{01\bar{1}2\}$ is so oriented the refractive index of calcite is only slightly less than that of the hemisphere glass, 1.55 to 1.56; no correction of tilt is necessary.

FIG. 6-25. Orientation diagrams for [0001] in calcite of calcite tectonites.   (a) Yule marble, Colorado; 300 contiguous grains.   Contours, 5%, 3%, 1%, 0.3%, per 1% area.   (b) Barstow, California; 100 grains.   Contours, 7%, 5%, 3%, 1%, per 1% area.   (c) Banded marble, Austria; 303 grains.   (After P. Paulitsch.)   Contours, 7%, 5%, 3%, 1%, per 1% area.   (d) Calc-phyllonite, Brenner, Tyrol; 263 grains. (After B. Sander.)   Contours, 3%, 2%, 1%, per 1% area.   (e) Calc-schist, near Mauls, Tyrol; 416 grains.   (After B. Sander.)   Contours, 3%, 2%, 1%, per 1% area.

lamellae are broad enough for their identity as twins to be established optically by symmetrical extinction behavior. Very commonly, on the contrary, the lamellae when tilted vertically appear as sharply ruled thin lines. For want of a better term, and not excluding the possibility of twinning on a very fine scale, these have been termed "nontwinned lamellae."[51] For each measured set of lamellae note whether lamellae are predominantly "twinned" or "nontwinned," closely or widely spaced, parallel-sided or lenticular. Check the identity as e by the angle [0001] $\wedge$ e, which because of error usually is between 25° and 29° rather than the ideal $26\frac{1}{4}°$. Check also the angle of 60° ($\pm 5°$) subtended by any pair of the three principal zone circles drawn through [0001] and the pole of an e plane (broken arcs in Fig. 6-26). Calcite grains of metamorphic rocks tend to have two or one well-developed sets of e lamellae. To decide whether the third set is lacking or merely is so obliquely inclined to the section that it is invisible (for example, e_3 in Fig. 6-26), determine its position graphically on the projection, set A_1 and NS axes at corresponding readings (341° $-$ 45°$\downarrow$), and scan the grain microscopically for visible e_3 lamellae.

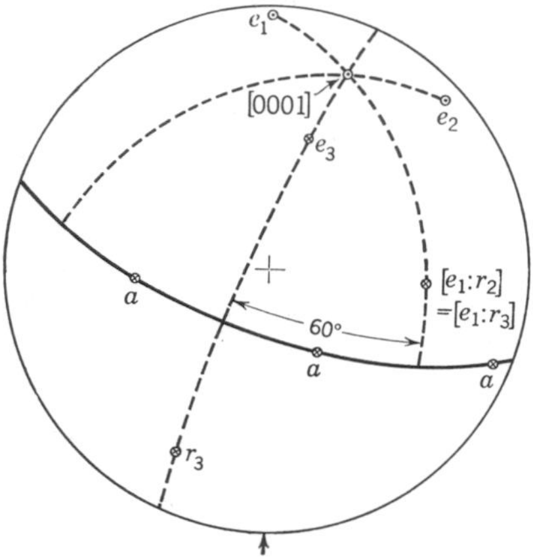

FIG. 6-26. Equal-area projection to illustrate plot of data measured for a calcite grain (see text).

Twinning on e in calcite has long been known to be a mechanically induced phenomenon. It is the result of twin gliding on e, the glide direction being the edge $[e_1:r_2]$ and the sense of shear positive—i.e., as illustrated by the arrows in Fig. 6-27. The unique compressive stress C that would most effectively initiate twin gliding on e_1 of a given grain is directed in the zone of e_1 and [0001] at 45° to e_1 and at 71° to [0001] (cf. Fig. 6-26). For this orientation the coefficient of resolved shear stress S_o of the e_1 glide system has the maximum possible value 0.5. The direction C so constructed individually for every grain of calcite showing broad optically recognizable e twins, commonly shows a high degree of preferred orientation throughout the domain of a thin section, a hand specimen, or even a large outcrop (Fig. 6-28).[52] The same thing applies

---

[51] I. Borg and F. J. Turner, Deformation of Yule marble, part VI, *Geol. Soc. America Bull.*, vol. 64, p. 1345, 1953; Turner, Griggs, and Heard, *op. cit.*, p. 897, 1954.

[52] E.g., D. B. McIntyre and F. J. Turner, Petrofabric analyses of marbles from Strathspey and Strathavon, *Geol. Mag.*, vol. 90, pp. 225–240, 1953; R. H. Clark, A study of calcite twinning in the Strathavon marble, Banffshire, *Geol. Mag.*, vol. 91, pp. 121–128, 1954; R. P. Nickelsen and G. W. Gross, Petrofabric study of Conestoga limestone from Hanover, Pennsylvania, *Am. Jour. Sci.*, vol. 257, pp. 276–286, 1959.

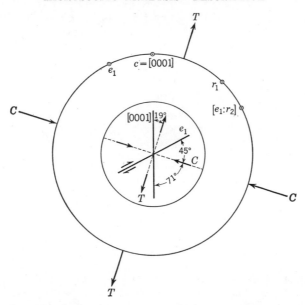

FIG. 6-27. Twin gliding on e_1 in calcite. C and T are the respective directions of compressive and tensional stress axes most effective in initiating twin gliding on e_1.

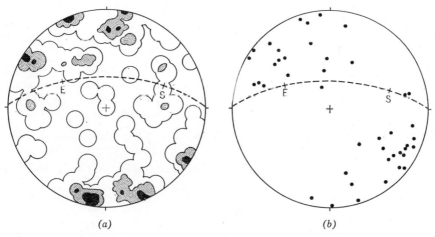

FIG. 6-28. "Compression axes" for calcite twins, Tomintoul marble, Strathavon, Scotland. (*After R. H. Clark.*) Projections are normal to the fold axis and foliation (horizontal). Broken arcs represent the geographic horizontal plane (east and south marked). (*a*) Calcite, [0001] in 100 grains. Contours, 5%, 3%, 1%, per 1% area. (*b*) "Compression axes" for 44 e twins measured in grains of diagram *a*.

to a complementary tensional stress T inclined at 19° to [0001]. From this it has been inferred that the observed twinning may be the visible expression of late strain induced by compression along an axis coinciding with the mean direction C. This interpretation is not always valid (see pages 414 to 419).

Preferred orientation of the *a* crystal axes in calcite of tectonites has received little attention to date.[53]   It would seem that in some, possibly in many, calcite tectonites, grains whose *c* axes are subparallel also show distinct preferred orientation of a_1, a_2, and a_3 in maxima 60° apart in the girdle normal to the mean orientation of *c*.   This fact has no obvious dynamic significance; for the trigonal symmetry so imparted to the partial fabric is merely an expression of the trigonal symmetry of calcite. The existence of preferred orientation of *a* may be tested, if it is thought

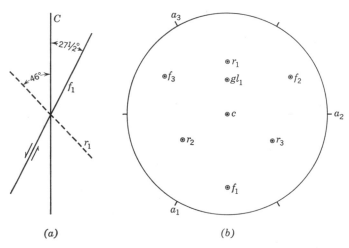

(a)   (b)

FIG. 6-29. Dolomite, commonly recorded planes and directions; equal-area projection, lower hemisphere. For explanation of symbols, see text; gl_1 = glide direction for twin gliding on f_1.

desirable, as follows: Select grains whose *c* axes fall within a conspicuous maximum of the *c*-axis diagram.   For each grain plot *c* and the great circle normal to it, construct the great circle through *c* and the pole of an accurately measured *e* lamella or *r* cleavage.   This cuts the zone circle of *c* at a point 30° distant from each of two *a* axes.   Plot all three *a* axes accordingly (cf. Fig. 6-26).

Dolomite.   Analysis of a dolomite fabric presents no difficulty to the student familiar with the procedure described for calcite.   Dolomite crystals commonly are untwinned.   Lamellar twinning, if present, is invariably parallel to the steep negative rhombohedron $\{02\bar{2}1\} = f$.   It may result from twin gliding on f_1 in a direction normal to the edge

[53] F. J. Turner and C. S. Ch'ih, Deformation of Yule marble, part III, *Geol. Soc. America Bull.*, vol 62, p. 895, 1951; P. Gilmour and M. F. Carman, Petrofabric analyses of the Loch Tay limestone from Strachur, Argyll, *Geol. Mag.*, vol. 91, p. 52, 1954.

[f_1:c], the sense of shear being negative (cf. Fig. 6-29a).[54] Though normally crystallized as a mosaic of xenoblastic grains, dolomite of some rocks tends to be idioblastic with well-developed {10$\bar{1}$1} faces. Useful interfacial angles for dolomite are as follows (cf. Fig. 6-29b):

$$c \wedge r = 44°$$
$$c \wedge f = 62\frac{1}{2}°$$
$$r_1 \wedge r_2 = 74°$$
$$r_1 \wedge f_1 = 73\frac{1}{2}°$$
$$r_1 \wedge f_2 = 50°$$
$$f_1 \wedge f_2 = 80°$$

It is easier to locate [0001] = X in dolomite than in calcite, since the position of extinction of dolomite during tilting on NS is relatively sharply defined. If hemispheres of refractive index 1.65 are used no correction of tilt angles is necessary either for alignment of [0001] parallel to EW, or for measuring {02$\bar{2}$1} lamellae in the standard EW orientation. If the only hemispheres available have refractive index 1.55 to 1.56, a small error arises; but in view of Kamb's analysis (page 205), the magnitude of the correction is uncertain.

Some patterns of preferred orientation of [0001] in dolomite of tectonites are illustrated in Fig. 6-30. Girdle patterns with one or more maxima are common.[55] Figure 6-30a is a triclinic small-circle or cleft-girdle pattern. Figure 6-30b shows a monoclinic girdle fabric with peripheral maxima; the same fabric shows distinct preferred orientation of a axes (Fig. 6-30c), which—if a slight eccentricity of the three maxima relatively to the center of the diagram is neglected—still retains the monoclinic character of the fabric.

Miscellaneous Biaxial Minerals, Exemplified by Olivine. Petrofabric investigation to date has been concentrated mainly on quartz, mica, and calcite. Other tectonite minerals, however, have been studied less extensively. Most of these are optically biaxial minerals commonly showing recognizable preferred orientation. Some, such as hornblende, kyanite, and epidote, have such a pronounced prismatic habit that their true orientation patterns tend to be obscured or even suppressed by artificial patterns reflecting the preferential selection and measurement of grains whose long axes happen to be inclined steeply to the plane of the

[54] H. W. Fairbairn and H. E. Hawkes, Dolomite orientation in deformed rocks, *Am. Jour. Sci.*, vol. 239, pp. 617–632, 1941; Turner, Griggs, Heard, and Weiss, *op. cit.*; D. V. Higgs and J. Handin, Experimental deformation of single dolomite crystals, *Geol. Soc. America Bull.*, vol. 70, pp. 250–251, 1959.

[55] J. Ladurner, Allgemeine Kennzeichnung und regionale Stellung alpiner Dolomittektonite, *Geol. Bundes. Vienna Jahrb.*, vol. 96, pp. 253–300, 1953; Turner, Griggs, Heard, and Weiss, *op. cit.*, pp. 478, 480.

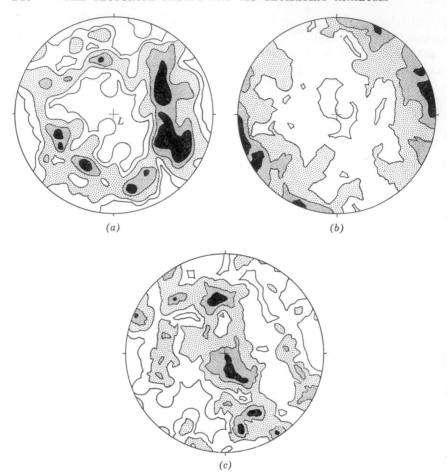

FIG. 6-30. Preferred orientation of dolomite in tectonites. (*a*) Dolomite tectonite in the Innsbruck quartz phyllonite, Austria. (*After J. Ladurner.*) [0001] in 200 grains. *L* = lineation, direction of elongation of dolomite grains. Contours, 3%, 2%, 1%, 0.5%, per 1% area; maximum concentration 6%. (*b*) Dolomite rock, Dover Plains, New York. (*After F. J. Turner, D. T. Griggs, H. Heard, and L. E. Weiss.*) [0001] in 300 grains. Contours, 3%, 2%, 1%, 0.2%, per 1% area. (*c*) Same rock as diagram *b*. 300 *a* axes in 100 grains selected at random. Contours, 3%, 2%, 1%, 0.3%, per 1% area.

section (cf. pages 225 to 230). Others like feldspars and olivines[56] tend to occur as equant xenoblastic grains, measurement of which brings out more clearly the symmetry of the tectonite fabric.

For this purpose the three indicatrix axes *X*, *Y*, and *Z* should be measured in a sample of 200 or 300 grains. To do this and to plot and contour

[56] W. Schmidt, Zur Regelung zweiachsiger Mineralien in kristallinen Schiefern, *Neues Jahrb. Mineralogie Beil.-Bd.*, vol. 57, A, pp. 203–222, 1928; Sander, *op. cit.*,

the three resulting orientation diagrams takes perhaps two full days' work. There is no blind spot in the diagram, for all three axes can be located in a grain of any orientation. Since each indicatrix axis is uniquely related to the crystal lattice the orientation diagram of each conforms solely to fabric symmetry and is uninfluenced by crystallographic symmetry. The three diagrams, considered collectively, bring out the symmetry of the subfabric.

Figure 6-31 shows the patterns of preferred orientation for $X = [010]$, $Y = [001]$, and $Z = [100]$, in olivine of two deformed lenses of periodotite intercalated with schists and gneisses of the Italian and Austrian Alps. In the first case only one symmetry plane—that of the girdles of Fig. 6-31b and c—is common to all three diagrams, so that the overall symmetry of the olivine orientation is monoclinic. Note, however, that only the imperfectly developed girdle of Fig. 6-31a detracts from orthorhombic symmetry. In the second case (Fig. 6-31d to f) each diagram is orthorhombic. Since the girdle of Fig. 6-31d is perpendicular to that of Fig. 6-31e and f, and since the respective maxima of all three diagrams are mutually perpendicular, the symmetry of the olivine subfabric as a whole is also orthorhombic.

In weakly defined orientation patterns for X, Y, and Z, it is a simple matter to test the significance of poorly developed individual maxima. Each of the three diagrams of Fig. 6-32a to c shows such a maximum (M), and the three are mutually perpendicular, and so possibly significant. X, Y, and Z have been replotted in Fig. 6-32d for those grains whose Y directions are clustered around M in Fig. 6-32b. A similar clustering of X and Z directions is thus demonstrated, so that the three maxima M, though faintly developed, are shown to be real.

Axial-distribution Analysis (A.V.A.).[57] Complex orientation patterns of some particular mineral direction—e.g., [0001] in quartz—commonly are associated with fabrics that seem to be microscopically homogeneous: microscopic scrutiny of the section reveals no recognizable domains defined by obvious textural characteristics or limited by visible s-surfaces. Are such fabrics truly homogeneous? Are the several orientations, cor-

---

pp. 216, 217, 1930; E. Wenk, Zur Genese der Bändergneise von Ornö Huvud, *Upsala Geol. Inst. Bull.*, vol. 26, pp. 53–89, 1936; Fairbairn, *op. cit.*, pp. 33–39, 1949; J. Ladurner, Der Verhalten des Olivins als Gefügekorn in einigen Olivingesteinen, *Tschermaks mineralog. petrog. Mitt.*, vol. 5, pp. 21–36, 1954; Untersuchungen am Interngefüge von Disthen, *Tschermaks mineralog. petrog. Mitt.*, vol. 5, pp. 380–393, 1956.

[57] H. Ramsauer, Achsensverteilungsanalysen an Quarztektoniten, *Dissert. Univ. Innsbruck*, Biblio. no. 304, 1941; Sander, *op. cit.*, pp. 161–217, 1950; J. Ladurner, Zur Kenntnis von Corundegefügen, *Neues Jahrb. Mineralogie Abh.*, vol. 84, pp. 1–42, 1952; Weiss, *op. cit.*, pp. 63-70, 1954; F. J. Turner, D. T. Griggs, R. H. Clark, and R. H. Dixon, Deformation of Yule marble, part VII, *Geol. Soc. America Bull.*, vol. 67, pp. 1264, 1265, 1956.

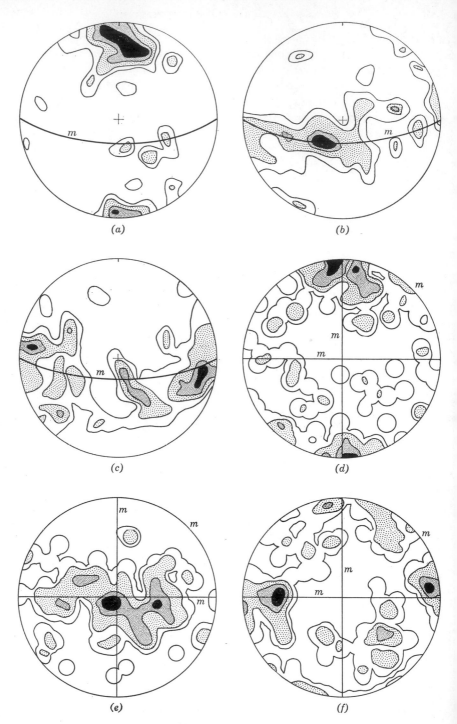

FIG. 6-31. For descriptive legend see opposite page.

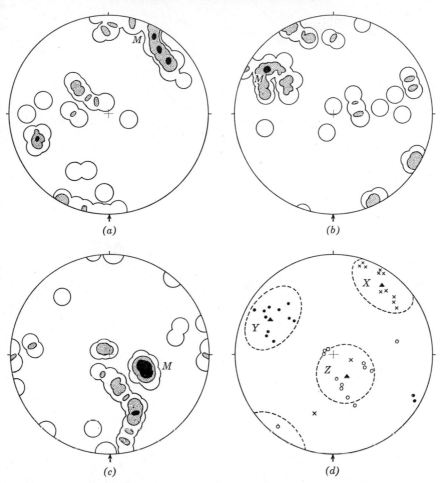

FIG. 6-32. Orientation diagrams for olivine of peridotite nodule in volcanic breccia, southern New Zealand. 50 grains. Contours, 8%, 4%, 2%, per 1% area. (a) X. (b) Y. (c) Z. (d) Plot of X (crosses), Y (full circles), and Z (open circles) for 13 grains having Y close to maximum of diagram b.

responding to individual maxima of the diagram, evenly distributed through the fabric, or are they localized in concealed domains defined solely by orientation criteria? Moreover, may there possibly be some correlation between particular orientations and peculiarities of grain size and shape? To answer such questions and to test the possible periodic

FIG. 6-31. Orientation diagrams for olivine in olivine tectonites, Alps. Symmetry planes are denoted m. (a–c) Ilmenspitz, Italy. (After C. Andreatta.) 120 grains. Contours, 6%, 4%, 2%, 1%, per 1% area. (a) X. (b) Y. (c) Z. (d–f) Clozner-Loch, Austria. (After J. Ladurner.) 100 grains. Contours, 6%, 4%, 2%, 1%, per 1% area. (d) X. (e) Y. (f) Z.

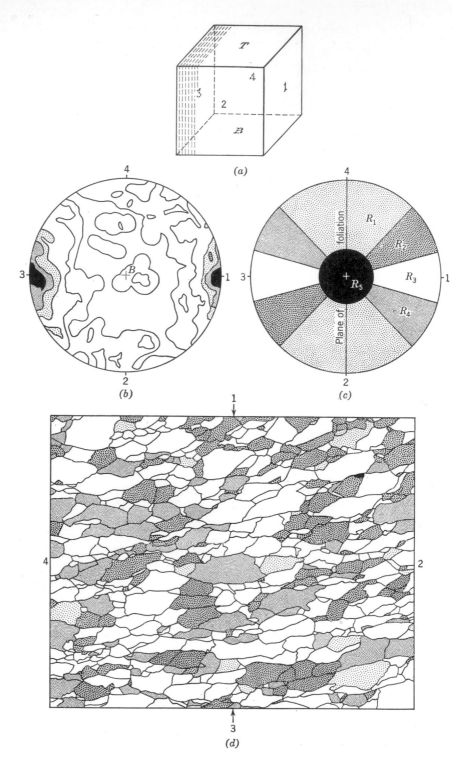

(a)

(b)   *(c)*

(d)

Fig. 6-33. For descriptive legend see opposite page.

distribution of differently oriented grains (cf. pages 376 to 378), Ramsauer and Sander developed the laborious technique of axial-distribution analysis (*Achsensverteilungsanalyse*, or A.V.A.). The essential procedure is outlined below; but the student who wishes to apply it in detail should consult the original sources.

The first step is a preliminary analysis of the orientation of a few hundred grains on widely separated traverses. The resulting orientation diagram (Figs. 6-33*b*, 6-34*a*) is arbitrarily divided into sectors representing *direction groups* R_1, R_2, etc., each of which corresponds to some restricted range of orientation (e.g., a maximum) of the diagram (Figs. 6-33*c*, 6-34*b*). The object of the analysis is to explore the distribution of the various direction groups within the domain of one or more sections. Accordingly the section or sections to be analyzed are photographed and enlargements prepared sufficient in scale to show the outlines of the smallest grains. To this is attached a transparent overlay on which the outline of every grain ultimately is traced. Every grain in the selected area is now measured, numbered, outlined on the overlay, and colored to correspond to the direction group in which it falls—red for R_1, blue for R_2, and so on. Two diagrams emerge from the analysis. The first is the conventional orientation diagram based on perhaps 1,000 to 5,000 plotted points. The second is the axial-distribution diagram (Figs. 6-33*d*, 6-34*c*) showing the distribution of the various direction groups in space.

Figure 6-33*d* suggests that in the compressed marble[58] there is a distinct tendency for grains of any main group (R_1, R_2, or R_3) to be mutually associated in irregularly bounded domains of between 5 and 30 grains. Moreover, reexamination of some of the larger domains shows a decided tendency for preferred orientation of *a* axes in the larger grains of any such domain.

Sander and others of the Innsbruck School have attempted to correlate individual direction groups with *s*-surfaces, discrete or penetrative, defined by other fabric criteria. In the striking examples figured by Sander[59] some such correlation seems obvious. None is obvious in Yule marble. Sander[60] advocates, as an elaboration of his A.V.A. technique,

[58] Turner, Griggs, Clark, and Dixon, *op. cit.*, pp. 1264–1265, 1956.
[59] Sander, *op. cit.*, pp. 403–405, 1950.
[60] Sander, *op. cit.*, pp. 182–185, 1950; Ladurner, *op. cit.*, pp. 28–31, 1952.

Fig. 6-33. Axial-distribution analysis of Yule marble shortened 19% normal to face 1. (*After R. H. Dixon.*) (*a*) Orientation of numbered faces of marble block in relation to foliation. (*b*) Orientation diagram for [0001] in calcite, 300 grains in undeformed marble. Contours, 7%, 5%, 3%, 1%, 0.3%, per 1% area. (*c*) Division of diagram *b* into direction groups. (*d*) Axial-distribution diagram for section of deformed marble. Each grain is shaded to correspond to one of the direction groups of diagram *c*. Note virtual elimination of grains oriented in direction group R_5.

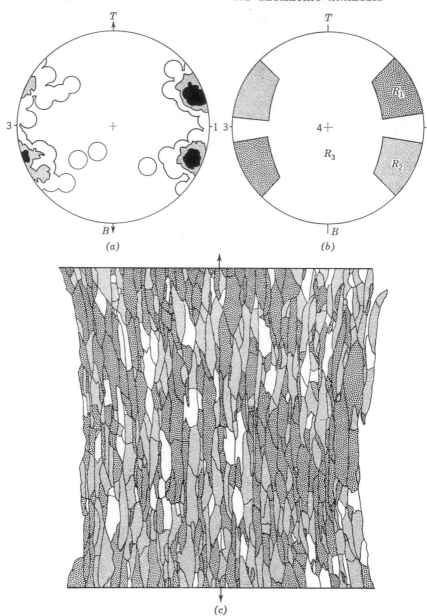

Fig. 6-34. Axial-distribution analysis of Yule marble elongated 118% normal to face T. (*After R. H. Dixon.*) (*a*) Orientation diagram for [0001] in calcite, 100 grains in neck. Contours, 10%, 5%, 1%, per 1% area. (*b*) Division of diagram *a* into direction groups. (*c*) Axial-distribution diagram, shaded to correspond to direction groups of diagram *b*.

plotting the center of each grain of some given direction group on a second transparent overlay, and contouring the density of the plotted points.   Where the maxima of the contoured diagram are elongated and aligned parallel to the trace of some otherwise recognizable s-surfaces of the fabric, it is concluded that the latter have in some manner influenced the orienting process.   We are not convinced of the soundness of this conclusion.   Certainly it should be applied with caution to direction groups characterized by variation in grain size, for the procedure is strictly democratic in that all grains regardless of size or color have equal value.

RELATION OF MICROSCOPIC TO MESOSCOPIC SUBFABRICS AND STRUCTURES

Microscopic analysis supplements information already obtained from analysis on the mesoscopic scale with respect to the nature, homogeneity, and symmetry of the total fabric.   The implications of microscopic data regarding the geometry and the time relations of structures visible on both scales are obvious.   More subtle and difficult to interpret, but clearly of great significance, are the geometric relations between microscopically determined patterns of mineral orientation and the principal structures—s-surfaces, lineations, and so on—of the mesoscopic fabric. Many published studies have overemphasized genetic interpretation of the observed preferred orientation patterns.   Hypothetical orienting mechanisms have been proposed on the basis of crystal gliding on systems for which experimental evidence is completely lacking; and there has been wide acceptance of the unwarranted idea that during "plastic deformation" active crystal glide planes become aligned in slip planes that permeate the rock fabric.   For example, alignment of [0001] axes of quartz grains parallel to an s-surface S—visible or invisible—has commonly been accepted as evidence that S is a slip plane of the tectonite fabric, the underlying assumption (still without experimental foundation) being that a prism such as $\{10\overline{1}0\}$ is a potential glide plane in quartz.

The prime criterion for comparison of microscopic and mesoscopic fabric data is symmetry.   Structural analysis can readily establish which of the microscopic subfabrics share a common symmetry with mesoscopic structures and which are discordant.   Some fabrics are ideally homotactic: all symmetry elements are shared by all subfabrics on both scales. For example in Fig. 6-35a the preferred orientation pattern of quartz has orthorhombic symmetry; its three symmetry planes m are shared also by the mesoscopic foliation S and lineation L.   Again in Fig. 6-35b a single symmetry plane m is common to the microscopic preferred orientation pattern and the combination of mesoscopic foliation and lineation defining a monoclinic fabric.   Most complex tectonite fabrics, however, are

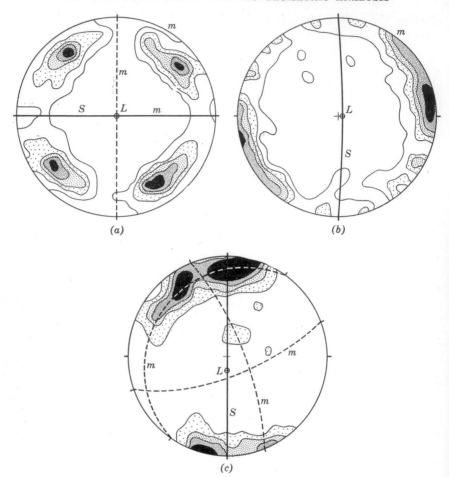

Fig. 6-35. Examples of homotactic and heterotactic fabrics (foliation, S; lineation, L; symmetry planes of microscopic subfabrics, m). (a) Orientation diagram for [0001] quartz in folded chert, 500 grains. Contours, 5%, 4%, 3%, 2%, 1% per 1% area. (*After T. Nureki, Hiroshima Univ. Jour. Sci., vol. 3, p. 118, fig. 35, 1960.*) (b) Orientation diagram for {001} of mica in granulitic gneiss, Kenya, 104 grains. Contours, 9%, 7%, 5%, 3%, 1% per 1% area. (c) Orientation diagram for [0001] of quartz in quartzite, Kenya, 250 grains. Contours, 7%, 5%, 3%, 1% per 1% area.

heterotactic, even though certain combinations of subfabric—e.g., mica pattern, foliation, and lineation—may be homotactic. In Fig. 6-35c the orthorhombic pattern of [0001] in quartz shares none of its three symmetry planes with the pattern of mesoscopic structures.

Of special interest is the geometric relation of microscopic subfabrics to mesoscopic folds. Here the main problem is to establish whether or not the structural heterogeneity implicit in a folded surface is accompanied by corresponding heterogeneity in microscopic subfabrics. The latter must be investigated in each of a suite of oriented thin sections cut from different domains within a single fold.[61] Three different kinds of relationship have been observed, and these must in some way reflect differences in the process of folding:

1. The microfabric is different in different domains and reflects precisely the mesoscopic heterogeneity of the individual fold.[62]

2. The microfabric is heterogeneous but does not exactly reflect the heterogeneity of the fold.[63]

3. The microfabric is homogeneous.[64]

GENERAL CONCLUSIONS

With study of microscopic structures and subfabrics the descriptive part of structural analysis of the tectonite body is completed. We now have a picture of the configuration and age relations of structures on all scales, and know something of the mutual relations of these structures and of the kinds and degrees of homogeneity and symmetry encountered in the internal order of natural tectonites. All the information contained in this picture is factual. Two competent investigators working on a given body should present essentially the same picture of its geometric properties.

Confronted with such a picture the curious geologist is impelled to attempt correlation of his findings with hypothetical but realistic interpretations of strains, differential movements, and even stresses connected with one or more episodes of natural deformation. Here he enters the realm of hypothesis and speculation, generally framed in terms of mathematical models of natural phenomena coupled with experimental investigation of deformation. Such is the subject matter of the chapters that now follow.

[61] Sander (*op. cit.*, pp. 286–295, 1950) combines this kind of analysis with interpretation. For other examples see L. E. Weiss, D. B. McIntyre, and M. Kürsten, Contrasted styles of folding in the rocks of Ord Ban, Mid-Strathspey, *Geol. Mag.*, vol. 92, pp. 21–36, 1955; I. Schäffler-Zozmann, Gefügeanalysen und Quartzfalten, *Neues Jahrb. Mineralogie*, vol. 87, pp. 321–350, 1955; Christie and Raleigh, *op. cit.*, pp. 385–407; T. K. Ball, A petrofabric analysis of a fold, *Am. Jour. Sci.*, vol. 258, pp. 274–281, 1960.

[62] Weiss, McIntyre, and Kürsten, *op. cit.*, pp. 29–32, fig. 5.

[63] Schäffler-Zozmann, *op. cit.*, pp. 337–339, fig. 7.

[64] Weiss, McIntyre, and Kürsten, *op. cit.*, pp. 25–27, fig. 4; Christie and Raleigh, *op. cit.*, pp. 390–392, fig. 1.

PART II

DEFORMATION OF ROCKS: THEORY AND EXPERIMENT

CHAPTER 7

STRESS AND STRAIN

INTRODUCTION

To discuss permanent deformation of rocks from almost any aspect the geologist must draw freely upon the notions of stress and strain as employed by physicists and engineers.   These notions are important, for instance, both in the theoretical explanations of problems of deformation and in the design and execution of experiments bearing upon the behavior of deformed rocks.   There has been some confusion among geologists as to concepts and terminology relating to stress and strain, with the result that application of theory to geological problems has not always been rigorous and at times has been misdirected.   A familiar illustration is the varied manner in which deformational structures such as foliation and jointing have been interpreted in terms of the "strain ellipsoid."

As a basis for discussing experimental results in Chaps. 8 and 9 and for later interpretation of natural tectonite fabrics, we now include a brief summary of fundamental concepts of stress and strain, and define the terms relating to these concepts as henceforth employed.   The theories of stress and of strain are branches of the mechanics of continua.   They deal mainly with the strictly continuous behavior of strictly homogeneous isotropic or anisotropic bodies under homogeneous or simply heterogeneous influences.   Only in the most general way can they be applied to crystalline aggregates such as rocks; for these are strictly neither homogeneous nor spatially continuous, and seldom are isotropic.

The topic of this chapter is treated in three parts.   The first concerns notions of stress and the terms used to define common states of stress.   Then follows a discussion of strain, with particular emphasis on the components of strain that can be specified with reference to internal coordinates—i.e., coordinates within the strained body.   The third section raises some problems concerning the relation of the stress field of a body to resultant strain.   Here we must consider the physical or rheologic state of the body.

STRESS

General Definitions.   A body in equilibrium under the action of a system of forces is said to be in a state of *stress*.   Conveniently the forces responsible for stress in a body are considered to be of two kinds:

1. Forces acting at every point in a body situated in a field of force such as a gravitational or electromagnetic field. These forces depend upon the location and orientation of the body within the field and are generally termed *body forces*.[1]

2. Forces acting across an external surface of the body as a result of action and reaction between the body and another body with which it is in contact. These forces are variously known as *surface forces*,[2] as *surface tractions*,[3] and as *external* or *impressed forces*. For example, in familiar laboratory experiments designed to test the behavior of rocks under stress, the *load* applied by a piston to the end of the specimen is a surface force—expressed in kilograms or in pounds.

In a general analysis of stress there is no need to distinguish the two kinds of forces responsible for the state of stress within the body. Stress is expressed as force per unit area (e.g., in pounds per square inch or bars) across any plane in the body. To specify the stress at a point it is necessary to determine the magnitude and direction of force per unit area across all planes through the point. The stress within a body is specified completely when the stress at every point is known. In some problems of mechanics of large bodies it is usual to consider only *homogeneous stress*, i.e., stress that is uniform at every point in a body; in other problems regular types of heterogeneous stress, such as that involved in simple bending of a beam, are considered.

From stress analysis[4] it is well known that the stress across a plane through any point in a body can be resolved into two components:

1. Acting normal to the plane is a *normal stress* (normal traction) σ. In classic mathematical and physical literature σ has a positive sign where tensional, a negative sign where compressional; in literature on experimental deformation of rocks (where all measured stresses are compressional) compressional stress is positive, tensional stress negative.[5] In Chaps. 8 and 9 we follow this latter convention.

2. Acting parallel to the plane is a *tangential stress* (tangential traction) τ. In geologic and engineering literature this is usually termed *shearing stress;* and this is the term henceforth used here.

[1] A. E. H. Love, *A Treatise on the Mathematical Theory of Elasticity*, p. 75, Dover, New York, 1944.

[2] M. Planck, The mechanics of deformable bodies, vol. II of *Introduction to Theoretical Physics*, p. 32, Macmillan, New York, 1949.

[3] J. C. Maxwell, *Matter and Motion*, p. 27, Dover, New York.

[4] A. Nádai, *Theory of Flow and Fracture of Solids*, vol. I, p. 89, McGraw-Hill, New York, 1950.

[5] Contrast Love, *op. cit.*, p. 77, 1944, and Nádai, *op. cit.*, p. 89, 1950, with J. Handin and R. V. Hager, Experimental deformation of sedimentary rocks under confining pressure, *Am. Assoc. Petroleum Geologists Bull.*, vol. 41, p. 4, 1957; D. T. Griggs, F. J. Turner, and H. C. Heard, Deformation of rocks at 500° to 800°C., *Geol. Soc. America Mem. 79*, p. 52, 1960.

It can be shown, too,[6] that at any point in a body three orthogonal planes exist upon which tangential stresses vanish and only normal stress is present. These planes are uniquely oriented throughout the body; the normal stresses across them are termed the *principal stresses* and designated σ_1, σ_2, and σ_3 (algebraically greatest, intermediate, and least, respectively[7]), and the planes are termed the *principal planes of stress.*

Types of Stress and Their Symmetry. A state of stress may be fully described by defining nine quantities—the normal stress acting on each of three faces of a cubic element, and the six components of shearing stress acting across the faces parallel to their edges.[8] It can be shown that stress is a symmetric tensor quantity[9] and that any state of stress has a symmetry which may be visualized in terms of the relative values of σ_1, σ_2, and σ_3.[10]

A state of stress can be resolved into two parts:

1. A hydrostatic part (which equals purely normal stress) such that across every plane through every point all stresses are normal stresses. For a given body these are equal in magnitude. The symmetry of all such states of stress is clearly spherical, $K_{\infty h}$. This is the state of stress termed simply *pressure* in thermodynamics. The hydrostatic pressure is the isotropic component of the stress tensor and is directly related to the dilatational component of strain (cf. page 266). In connection with experiments on the behavior of stressed rocks and minerals, hydrostatic pressure in a liquid completely surrounding the test specimen is termed *confining pressure* and is given a positive sign. This confining pressure must not be confused with the hydrostatic pressure *within* the test specimen.

2. A nonhydrostatic part generally termed a *shearing stress* or a *stress deviator.* The sum of the component stresses of a stress deviator equals zero.[11] Stress deviators, unlike hydrostatic pressures, do not all have the same symmetry. Four cases can be conveniently distinguished. Where the component stresses of the deviator are σ_1', σ_2', and σ_3' these cases are:

   a. Axial tension: $\sigma_2' = \sigma_1'$; $\sigma_3' = -2\sigma_1'$; symmetry of stress axial $D_{\infty h}$.
   b. Axial compression: $\sigma_2' = \sigma_3'$; $\sigma_1' = -2\sigma_2'$; symmetry of stress axial $D_{\infty h}$.

---

[6] Nádai, *op. cit.*, pp. 90, 91, 1950; Love, *op. cit.*, pp. 77–79, 1944.

[7] E.g., Nádai, *op. cit.*, p. 106, 1950.

[8] *Ibid.*, pp. 89, 90.

[9] J. F. Nye, *Physical Properties of Crystals*, pp. 87–89, Oxford, Fair Lawn, N.J., 1957.

[10] The *stress ellipsoid*, the derivation of which is described by Nádai (*op. cit.*, pp. 89–93, 1950), is a representation of a state of stress from which the symmetry is apparent.

[11] Nádai, *op. cit.*, p. 105, 1950.

   c. Pure shear:[12] $\sigma_2' = \sigma_1' + \sigma_3' = 0$; symmetry of stress orthorhombic D_{2h}.

   d. A general shearing stress: σ_1', σ_2', and σ_3' are unequal; none is zero; symmetry of stress orthorhombic D_{2h}.

Because the hydrostatic part of a state of stress always has spherical symmetry, the symmetry of any stress is the same as that of its deviatoric or shearing component.   The deviatoric component of stress is directly related to elastic distortion and it appears also to be the most important influence on permanent deformation during flow of real materials (page 277).

   If allowance is made for the inevitable departure from the ideal condition of homogeneous stress in a continuum, states of stress naturally or experimentally induced in rocks present analogies with some of the ideal states just discussed.   Consider for example a cylinder of marble immersed in a fluid in which the hydrostatic pressure is 5,000 bars, and carrying an axial stress, induced by pistons, of 6,900 bars.[13]   The state of stress within the marble approximates a general stress compounded of two elements: a hydrostatic pressure of 5,633 bars and an axial stress deviator such that $\sigma_1 = 1{,}267$ bars, $\sigma_2 = \sigma_3 = -633$ bars.   The confining pressure on the specimen is 5,000 bars; $\sigma_1 - \sigma_3$ equals the difference—1,900 bars—between the axial stress and the confining pressure (in experimental work commonly termed the *differential longitudinal stress* or *pressure*).

   Mohr's Stress Circles.   In problems relating to stress and strain, whether approached from the theoretical or the experimental standpoint, it is necessary to know the normal and the shearing stress on any plane in a homogeneously stressed body.   Mohr[14] devised a graphic solution which has been rather widely used in modern literature on structural geology.

   Consider a body in a state of stress such that $\sigma_3 = 0$.   On any plane P normal to the plane of σ_1 and σ_2, let the normal stress be σ and the shearing stress τ.   It can be shown[15] that

$$\left[\sigma - \left(\frac{\sigma_1 + \sigma_2}{2} \right) \right]^2 + \tau^2 = \left(\frac{\sigma_1 - \sigma_2}{2} \right)^2$$

[12] This is a particular case of *plane stress* (Love, *op. cit.*, pp. 82, 83, 1944) in that one principal stress is zero.   The same term has been used to describe a state of strain (p. 270).

[13] This is the condition represented at *b* in Fig. 8-22.

[14] O. Mohr, *Abhandlungen aus dem Gebiete der technischen Mechanik*, 2d ed., pp. 192–235, Ernst, Berlin, 1914.   See also, Nádai, *op. cit.*, pp. 94–108, 1950, for a comprehensive discussion in English.

[15] E.g., Nádai, *op. cit.*, p. 95, 1950.

This is the equation of a circle in the variables σ and τ, with radius $(\sigma_1 - \sigma_2)/2$ and center at $(\sigma_1 + \sigma_2)/2$ on the σ axis (Fig. 7-1). From this stress circle can be read (at point p, Fig. 7-1) the values of σ and τ on any plane P parallel to σ_3 and inclined to σ_1 at an angle α. The value of τ is

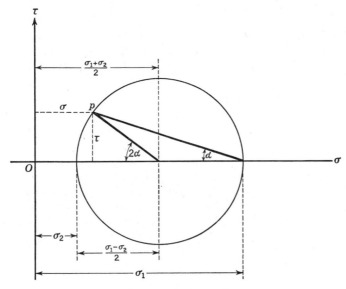

Fig. 7-1. Mohr diagram for plane stress.

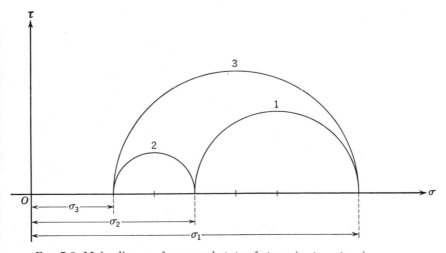

Fig. 7-2. Mohr diagram for general state of stress ($\sigma_1 > \sigma_2 > \sigma_3$).

maximal where $2\alpha = 90°$; i.e., the shearing stress has a maximum value for a plane inclined at 45° to σ_1.

A more general diagram (Fig. 7-2) represents stresses on the principal planes of stress—(1) $\sigma_1\sigma_2$, (2) $\sigma_2\sigma_3$, (3) $\sigma_3\sigma_1$—for the general state of stress

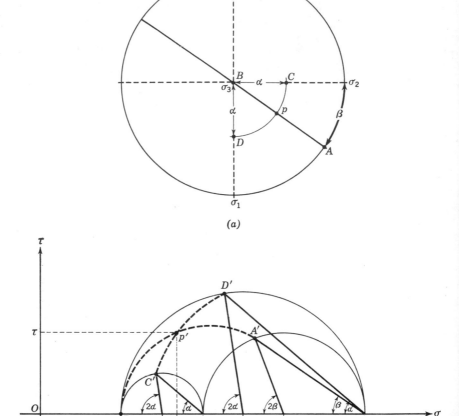

FIG. 7-3. Determination of shearing stress τ and normal stress σ on a plane P of known orientation in a general stress field. (*a*) Equal-area projection of σ_1, σ_2, σ_3, and p (pole of P). (*b*) Mohr construction to determine σ and τ.

where $\sigma_1 > \sigma_2 > \sigma_3$. From such a diagram by additional construction σ and τ can be obtained for a plane P of any orientation. Figure 7-3*a* is an equal-area projection showing the orientation of a plane P (pole p) in relation to σ_1, σ_2, and σ_3. The orientation of p is uniquely defined as the intersection of a great circle AB through σ_3 inclined to σ_2 at an angle β, and a small circle CD of angular radius α about σ_3. It can be shown[16]

[16] *Ibid.*, pp. 96–99; J. C. Jaeger, *Elasticity, Fracture and Flow*, pp. 18–20, Methuen, London, 1956.

that these circles can be represented on the general Mohr diagram by "images" ($A'B'$, $C'D'$ in Fig. 7-3b) that also are circles with centers on the σ axis. The image A' (Fig. 7-3b) of A (Fig. 7-3a) lies on the $\sigma_1\sigma_2$ circle and subtends an angle 2β to the σ axis at the center of the circle; and the image of the great circle AB is the circle passing through A' and B' (the σ_3 point). Similarly on the $\sigma_3\sigma_1$ circle D' (the image of D) is located by drawing a radius at an angle 2α to the σ axis; and C' is located on the $\sigma_2\sigma_3$ circle also at an angular distance of 2α from the σ axis. The intersection of the image circles $A'B'$ and $C'D'$ in Fig. 7-3b is p', the image of p; and from this the values of σ and τ for the plane P can be read directly.

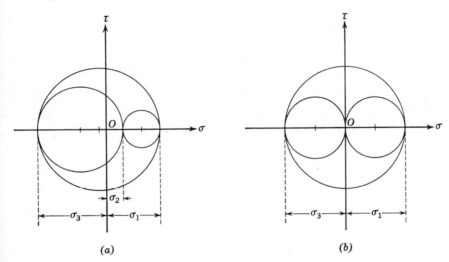

FIG. 7-4. Mohr diagrams for stress deviators. (*a*) General deviator (no principal stress = 0). (*b*) Pure shear ($\sigma_2 = 0$).

On a Mohr diagram the position of the origin of the σ and τ axes varies with change in the value of the hydrostatic pressure which is the isotropic component of a state of general stress; the radii of the three circles express the value differences of the $\sigma_1 - \sigma_2$, $\sigma_2 - \sigma_3$, and $\sigma_1 - \sigma_3$, regardless of variation in hydrostatic pressure. It is these differences regardless of sign, not the magnitudes of the principal stresses, that determine the value of the shearing stress τ on any plane. For a general stress deviator, the origin is situated between σ_1 and σ_3 (Fig. 7-4a); for pure shear, where $\sigma_2 = 0$, the origin coincides with σ_2 (Fig. 7-4b).

FINITE STRAIN

General. The changes in geometric properties such as volume and shape that are induced in a body in response to stress are known collectively as *strain*. The mathematical theory of strain[17] has been developed mainly in terms of small elastic deformations—i.e., infinitesimal reversible displacements in strictly homogeneous continua. For analysis of permanent deformation of a higher order of magnitude, it is still possible to treat strain in terms of strictly homogeneous continua; but we are here concerned with *finite strain*.

Geologic strain of tectonites is finite but on a small scale by no means homogeneous. It involves displacements of varying degree between crystalline aggregates as well as between individual crystals. Such displacements cannot correspond to a strictly homogeneous strain. Even microscopically homogeneous strain resulting from translation gliding in a single crystal is discontinuous on a submicroscopic scale. Nevertheless on the mesoscopic or the macroscopic scale it is possible to treat strain of tectonite bodies as continuous, with the proviso that continuity of strain is defined statistically in just the same fashion that homogeneity of fabric has been treated statistically in Chap. 2. For this reason the algebraic and geometric properties of homogeneous finite strain will be considered in further detail.

In order to specify the strain in a body it is necessary to know the positions of all material points in the body in the unstrained and in the strained states. Where strain is homogeneous the changes in positions of points result in effects that are uniform for the body as a whole. These strain effects can be resolved into four components:

1. Change in position: *translation*
2. Change in orientation: *rotation*
3. Change in volume: *dilatation*
4. Change in shape: *distortion*

Components 3 and 4 are generally combined to define the *pure strain* component of deformation. In analysis of homogeneous strain translation is almost universally neglected.

Mathematically, changes in positions of an aggregate of points are termed a *transformation:* any strictly homogeneous strain corresponds to a transformation of a regular kind now to be described.

Algebraic Treatment of Affine or Homogeneous Transformation.[18] Let (x_1, y_1, z_1) be the initial position of a point in a body referred to a right-handed Cartesian coordinate system (Fig. 7-5). And let (x_2, y_2, z_2) be the position of the same point after transformation. The component displacements of the point are

$$u = x_2 - x_1$$
$$v = y_2 - y_1 \qquad\qquad (7\text{-}1)$$
$$w = z_2 - z_1$$

[17] E.g., Love, *op. cit.*, pp. 32–73, 1944.
[18] E.g., Planck, *op. cit.*, pp. 5–8, 1949.

For a strain of any kind we may write

$$x_2 = f_1(x_1, y_1, z_1)$$
$$y_2 = f_2(x_1, y_1, z_1) \qquad (7\text{-}2)$$
$$z_2 = f_3(x_1, y_1, z_1)$$

These equations specify the changes in position of every point in the body during transition from an unstrained to a strained state. Where x_2, y_2,

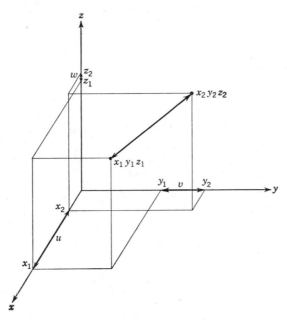

FIG. 7.5. Component displacements (u, v, and w) of a point displaced from (x_1, y_1, z_1) to (x_2, y_2, z_2), referred to right-handed Cartesian coordinates.

and z_2 are linear functions of x_1, y_1, and z_1, i.e., where

$$x_2 = a_1 x_1 + b_1 y_1 + c_1 z_1 + d_1$$
$$y_2 = a_2 x_1 + b_2 y_1 + c_2 z_1 + d_2 \qquad (7\text{-}3)$$
$$z_2 = a_3 x_1 + b_3 y_1 + c_3 z_1 + d_3$$

the transformation is *affine* or *homogeneous*. The coefficients d_1, d_2, and d_3 are component displacements of the whole system and represent the translational component of the transformation with reference to external coordinates. Neglecting such translation, Eq. (7-3) can be rewritten

$$x_2 = a_1 x_1 + b_1 y_1 + c_1 z_1$$
$$y_2 = a_2 x_1 + b_2 y_1 + c_2 z_1 \qquad (7\text{-}4)$$
$$z_2 = a_3 x_1 + b_3 y_1 + c_3 z_1$$

Where D is the determinant of the coefficients, i.e., where

$$D = \begin{vmatrix} a_1 & b_1 & c_1 \\ a_2 & b_2 & c_2 \\ a_3 & b_3 & c_3 \end{vmatrix}$$

and $D \neq 0$, it can be shown[19] that Eq. (7-4) has solutions for x_1, y_1, and z_1:

$$\begin{aligned} x_1 &= a_1' x_2 + b_1' y_2 + c_1' z_2 \\ y_1 &= a_2' x_2 + b_2' y_2 + c_2' z_2 \\ z_1 &= a_3' x_2 + b_3' y_2 + c_3' z_2 \end{aligned} \tag{7-5}$$

where $a_1' \cdots c_3'$ are minors of D divided by D.

Properties of Affine Transformation: The Strain Ellipsoid

1. Let a plane in the initial (untransformed) body be defined by the equation

$$P x_1 + Q y_1 + R z_1 = 0$$

Substituting the values of x_1, y_1, and z_1 from Eq. (7-5) we obtain for the same plane after transformation

$$P' x_2 + R' y_2 + Q' z_2 = 0$$

where P', Q', and R' are determined from P, Q, R and a', b', c'. This, too, is the equation of a plane. Thus, *an affine transformation transforms any plane into another plane.*

2. A straight line is specified as the intersection of two planes. Because planes are preserved in an affine transformation so is their line of intersection. Thus, *an affine transformation transforms any straight line into another straight line.*

3. From 1, above, it can be seen that substitution of values of x_1, y_1, and z_1 from Eq. (7-5) into equations in x_1, y_1, and z_1 for a surface of any degree will always result in a transformed surface of the same degree. Particularly important is the transformation of a spherical surface (second degree). For a general affine transformation the sphere becomes an ellipsoid, known in physics as a *strain ellipsoid*.[20] Con-

---

[19] *Ibid.*, pp. 5-10.

[20] The strain ellipsoid so defined, and as henceforth used in this book, is purely a geometric description of finite homogeneous strain (cf. F. J. Turner and J. Verhoogen, *Igneous and Metamorphic Petrology*, 2d ed., p. 605, McGraw-Hill, New York, 1960). The strain ellipsoid tells us nothing of the mechanism of strain—flow, rupture, and so on—and little regarding the orientation of the principal stresses σ_1, σ_2, and σ_3, although in geologic literature the strain ellipsoid has been widely correlated both with mechanisms of strain and with stress. For criticism of this approach see D. T. Griggs, The strain ellipsoid as a theory of rupture, *Am. Jour. Sci.*, vol. 30, pp. 121–137, 1935; F. J. Turner, Mineralogical and structural evolution of the metamorphic rocks, *Geol. Soc. America Mem. 30*, pp. 162, 163, 1948.

versely, to every sphere in the transformed state there corresponds an ellipsoid in the untransformed state, with radius vectors reciprocal to those of the strain ellipsoid. This is termed the *reciprocal strain ellipsoid.*[21] Each ellipsoid has three orthogonal principal axes. In the strain ellipsoid these are the directions of principal extensions or principal strain—ϵ_1, ϵ_2, and ϵ_3 (respectively greatest, intermediate, and least)—in the body, and are generally termed the *principal directions of strain.*[22] In geologic literature they are commonly termed the *A*, *B*, and *C* axes, such that $A > B > C$. The axes of the reciprocal strain ellipsoid define those directions in the unstrained body that become the principal directions of strain in the strained body;[23] i.e., the corresponding axes of both ellipsoids pass through the same lines of material particles. Where the orientation of the axes of the strain ellipsoid with reference to external coordinates differs from that of the axes of the reciprocal strain ellipsoid, the angle of rotation necessary to bring identity specifies the purely rotational component of the transformation.

4. The components of the most general kind of affine transformation are the same as those of a general strain, namely:

   a. A pure affine transformation made up of a distortion and a dilatation
   b. A pure rotation relative to external coordinates
   c. A translation of the system relative to external coordinates

   With reference to internal coordinates, only the first component is significant.

Types of Finite Homogeneous Strain and Their Symmetry. In physics the properties of affine transformations may be applied in all branches of the mechanics of continua. The geologist on the other hand is concerned only with their application to finite homogeneous strains, of which several kinds may be distinguished.[24] Each type has its characteristic symmetry, derived from the combined symmetries of the strain components. For simplicity the strains are specified in terms of component displacements of points (see Fig. 7-5).

1. *Uniform or Cubical Dilatation.* Displacements

$$u = cx_1$$
$$v = cy_1$$
$$w = cz_1$$

[21] Both ellipsoids refer to strain of a particular magnitude. In progressive strain each stage of strain is represented by a unique pair of ellipsoids. The axes of the strain ellipsoid at one stage do not necessarily coincide with those at another stage of progressive strain.

[22] E.g., Nádai, *op. cit.*, p. 119, 1950.

[23] Love (*op. cit.*, p. 62, 1944) terms these the "principal axes of the strain."

[24] Love, *op. cit.*, pp. 44–46, 1944; Nádai, *op. cit.*, pp. 109–110, 1950.

The strain ellipsoid is a sphere; and the strain is purely a volume change with spherical symmetry $K_{\infty h}$. Dilatation is a component of many of the more general types of strain listed below. It is the isotropic component of the symmetric tensor of strain. Dilatation plays a geologic role in compaction and lithification of sediments and in deformation accompanied by phase changes in metamorphism. But in evolution of tectonites other components of strain—constituting the deviator of the strain tensor—probably far outweigh accompanying dilatation; and in any case the symmetry of total strain cannot be affected by the spherical symmetry of the dilatational component. Symmetry of strain is, in fact, the symmetry of the deviator of the strain tensor.

2. *Simple or Pure Extension or Compression.* All points are displaced parallel to one coordinate axis. Where this is the x axis

$$u = cx$$
$$v = 0$$
$$w = 0$$

The strain ellipsoid is a prolate or an oblate spheroid, according to whether u is positive (extension) or negative (compression). Its unique axis, A for extension, C for compression, is parallel to x, and the symmetry of strain is axial nonpolar $D_{\infty h}$. This type of strain has a dilatational component and is approximated by symmetric compaction (u negative) under a vertical load. Note that in our usage, as contrasted with that of mathematics, the axis of negative strain here coincides with that of positive stress, σ_1.

3. *Pure Shear.* This is a combination of pure extension in direction x and pure compression in y, such that the volume is constant:

$$u = cx$$
$$v = \left(\frac{-c}{1 + c}\right) y$$
$$w = 0$$

Because dimensions parallel to one axis, z, are unchanged, such a strain belongs in the category of *plane strains;* and the xy plane is the *deformation plane.* The strain ellipsoid is triaxial; its intermediate principal axis B equals the diameter of the unstrained sphere. Symmetry is orthorhombic, D_{2h} (cf. Fig. 9-18b).

4. *Simple Shear.* All points are displaced parallel to x through distances proportional to y:

$$u = cy$$
$$v = 0$$
$$w = 0$$

In most respects simple shear is geometrically identical with pure shear: it is a plane strain (deformation plane equals xy), there is no volume change, and the strain ellipsoid is triaxial; its intermediate principal axis B equals the diameter of the unstrained sphere. But in simple shear there is in addition a pure rotational component about the intermediate axis of the ellipsoid. This reduces the total symmetry of strain to monoclinic C_{2h}—equivalent to symmetry of pure shear D_{2h} plus that of pure rotation $C_{\infty h}$.

5. *Pure Rotation.* Rotation as of a rigid body is a component of many general strains. Its symmetry is $C_{\infty h}$.

6. *Pure Strain.* Any general strain lacking a rotational component is termed a pure strain. It can be regarded as pure extension or compression of different magnitude in each of three mutually perpendicular directions that remain constant in orientation and become the principal axes of a triaxial strain ellipsoid. The intermediate (B) principal axis of the strain ellipsoid may be greater or less than the diameter of the unstrained sphere. The symmetry of strain is orthorhombic D_{2h}. *Axial strain* is a special case, where two axes of the ellipsoid are equal and there is no volume change.[25]

$$u = cx$$
$$v = -c'y$$
$$w = -c'z$$

$$c' = 1 - \frac{1}{\sqrt{1 + c}}$$

The symmetry of strain is then axial nonpolar $D_{\infty h}$, just as in pure extension or compression. It is closely approximated in experimental strain under axial load (σ_1 or σ_3) where the cross section of an initial cylinder remains circular (cf. Fig. 9-18a).

7. *General Strain.* The most general type of strain—specified by Eqs. (7-4) and (7-5)—can be described as a combination of a pure strain plus a pure rotation.[26] The magnitude of rotation is the angle through which the principal axes of the strain ellipsoid must be rotated to bring them into coincidence with the axes of the reciprocal ellipsoid. There is always a unique axis of rotation; and this need not necessarily be a principal axis of the strain ellipsoid. The symmetry of strain in the most general case is triclinic C_i; where the rotation axis coincides with a principal axis of the strain ellipsoid, there is a symmetry plane normal to that axis and the symmetry of strain is monoclinic C_{2h}.

Alternatively any general finite homogeneous strain not including dilatation can be regarded as composed of several simple operations:[27]

[25] Nádai, *op. cit.*, p. 110, 1950.
[26] Love, *op. cit.*, p. 69, 1944.
[27] *Ibid.*, p. 71.

either (*a*) a simple shear, a simple extension (or compression) normal to the deformation plane, and a rotation, or (*b*) three mutually perpendicular simple shears of different magnitudes plus a rotation. Nondilatational strains are deviators and are generally termed simply *shearing strains*.

The basic Mohr construction as outlined for stress can be used also as a geometric image of strain.[28] Mohr diagrams for strain contain ellipses instead of circles, but they may be used in much the same way as diagrams for stress to determine the corresponding components of a given strain. The use of these diagrams in strain analysis of deformed dimensional markers in tectonites has been recently discussed by Brace.[29]

Superposed Finite Homogeneous Strains. The properties of a compound deformation resulting from superposition of one finite homogeneous strain on another have been summarized thus by Love.[30]

After a body has been subjected to a homogeneous strain, it may again be subjected to a homogeneous strain; and the result is a displacement of the body, which, in general, could be effected by a single homogeneous strain. More generally, when any aggregate of points is transformed by two homogeneous linear transformations successively, the resulting displacement is equivalent to the effect of a single linear homogeneous transformation. This statement may be expressed by saying that linear homogeneous transformations form a *group*. The particular linear homogeneous transformations with which we are concerned . . . [i.e., that the transformations are *real* so that no component displacements are expressed by functions that become infinite, and no lines in the untransformed state reduce to zero in the strained state] form a *continuous group*. The transformations of rotation . . . also form a group; and this group is a *sub-group* included in the linear homogeneous group. The latter group also includes all homogeneous strains; but these do not themselves form a group, for two successive homogeneous strains may be equivalent to a rotation.

It follows from this statement that the commutative principle of addition does not hold in general for finite homogeneous strains:[31] if 1 and 2 denote two strains each of a given kind and magnitude, the strain resulting from superposing 2 on 1 is not necessarily the same as that where 1 is superposed on 2.

Strain in Tectonites. Table 7-1 summarizes the properties of the kinds of finite homogeneous strain discussed in the preceding pages—neglecting in all cases the translational component. In applying our knowledge of strain to tectonites we assume that the homogeneous deformation of crystalline aggregates over large domains approximates homogeneous

[28] Nádai, *op. cit.*, pp. 124–150, 1950.

[29] W. F. Brace, Mohr construction in the analysis of large geologic strain, *Geol. Soc. America Bull.*, vol. 72, pp. 1059–1080, 1961.

[30] Love, *op. cit.*, pp. 71–72, 1944.

[31] See also Nádai, *op. cit.*, p. 111, 1950.

TABLE 7-1. GEOMETRIC PROPERTIES OF FINITE HOMOGENEOUS STRAINS

Type of strain	Form of strain ellipsoid	Volume change	Rotation	Symmetry
1. Uniform dilatation	Sphere	Increase or decrease	None	Spherical $K_{\infty h}$
2. Simple extension (axial strain)	Spheroid	Increase or decrease	None	Axial $D_{\infty h}$
	Spheroid	None		
3. Pure shear (plane)	Triaxial ellipsoid	None	None	Orthorhombic D_{2h}
4. Simple shear (plane)	Triaxial ellipsoid	None	Rotation about intermediate axis of strain ellipsoid (normal to deformation plane)	Monoclinic C_{2h}
5. Pure rotation (rigid body)	Sphere equivalent to initial sphere	None	Rotation about an arbitrary axis	Axial rotational $C_{\infty h}$
6. Pure strain	Triaxial ellipsoid	Increase or decrease	None	Orthorhombic D_{2h}
	Triaxial ellipsoid	None		
7. General strain	Triaxial ellipsoid	Increase or decrease	Rotation about axis of ellipsoid	Monoclinic C_{2h}
		None	Rotation about arbitrary axis	Triclinic C_i
		None	Rotation about axis of ellipsoid	Monoclinic C_{2h}
		None	Rotation about arbitrary axis	Triclinic C_i

273

finite strain of continua.　However, by no means are all the strain types of Table 7-1 likely to have statistically defined counterparts in natural strains as exemplified in tectonites.　We can omit types 1 and 2 in which the sole or principal component of strain is dilatation, and type 5 which is ·pure rotation and so applies only to rigid bodies.　Plane strains (types 3 and 4) may be approximated in small domains of natural deformation—especially in single crystals—and are exemplified too in experimental strain (e.g., Fig. 9-18b).　But large-scale statistically homogeneous deformation of tectonite bodies must generally approximate one of the cases of nonplane strain (types 6 and 7, Table 7-1) elaborated in Table 7-2, with plane strain treated as special cases.　In Table 7-2 all strains are treated as nondilatational.

TABLE 7-2. TECTONICALLY SIGNIFICANT FINITE HOMOGENEOUS STRAINS

	Type of strain	Form of strain ellipsoid; $A > B > C$; D = diameter of unstrained sphere	Rotation	Symmetry
General cases (nonplane* strains)	Axial strain	Oblate or prolate spheroid $B = A > D$ $B = C < D$	None	Axial $D_{\infty h}$
	Pure strain	Triaxial ellipsoids $A > D$, $B >$ or $< D$, $C < D$	None	Orthorhombic D_{2h}
	General strain	As for pure strain	Rotation about A, B, or C	Monoclinic C_{2h}
			Rotation about axis inclined to A, B, and C	Triclinic C_i
Special cases (plane* strains)	Pure shear	Triaxial ellipsoid $A > D$, $B = D$, $C < D$	None	Orthorhombic D_{2h}
	Simple shear	Triaxial ellipsoid $A > D$, $B = D$, $C < D$	Rotation about B	Monoclinic C_{2h}

* Such strains are also termed respectively *three-dimensional* and *two-dimensional* strains (e.g., J. C. Jaeger, *Elasticity, Fracture and Flow*, pp. 23–24, Methuen, London, 1956).

A principal aim of structural analysis of tectonites is to deduce something of the nature, and especially the symmetry, of strain from the tectonite fabric.　Kinematic components referable to coordinates external to the body—namely, translation and rotation—leave no direct imprint on the fabric of the body.[32]　Translation has already been omitted from our general discussion of strain; in considering the natural

[32] M. S. Paterson and L. E. Weiss, Symmetry concepts in the structural analysis of deformed rocks, *Geol. Soc. America Bull.*, vol. 72, pp. 872, 873, 1961.

strain of tectonites as recorded in fabrics, rotation[33] must be omitted as well. With these omissions, tectonically significant strains that can be deduced from observations *within* a deformed body are reduced to three categories:

1. General strains with triaxial ellipsoids and orthorhombic symmetry D_{2h}

2. The special case of plane strains (simple shear and pure shear mutually indistinguishable), with orthorhombic symmetry D_{2h}

3. Axial strains with symmetry axial $D_{\infty h}$; likely to be encountered only in small domains and in laboratory experiments

Thus the pure strain components of all natural statistically homogeneous strains fall into two symmetry classes, axial $D_{\infty h}$ and orthorhombic D_{2h}, of which the second is by far the more important. Also important in tectonics are heterogeneous strains such as folding, but these can generally be treated in terms of homogeneous portions—localized in small domains such as a fold limb—or components (pages 470 to 490).

RELATIONS BETWEEN STRESS AND STRAIN: THE RHEOLOGIC STATE

General. The response of natural materials to stress—e.g., the rate, magnitude, and permanence of strain—varies widely. Even the strain behavior of a given material varies greatly with changes in such conditions as temperature, confining pressure, and duration of stress. Some materials, notably elastic solids, over a given range of stress develop small strains directly proportional to the magnitude of the stress; and on release of stress, strain is reversed to the point of full recovery. Other materials, notably viscous liquids, seem to flow continuously and irresistibly in response to even the smallest shearing stresses; and under hydrostatic pressure the same materials may develop small reversible strains (uniform dilatation). Between the two extremes is a wide spectrum of intermediate behavior. Our knowledge of such behavior comes from two sources: experimental observation of strain in stressed bodies, and analysis of mathematical models of ideal materials. These are respectively the experimental and theoretical approaches to rheology, the branch of physics dealing with flow and permanent continuous deformation of materials. The materials with which we are especially concerned are ductile solids. These respond to stress of sufficient magnitude by flow, i.e., permanent irreversible strain of large magnitude (cf. page 37).

In laboratory experiments on strain of rocks and minerals it is possible to vary temperature and confining pressure through ranges of magnitude

---

[33] This is "external rotation" in Sander's terminology as contrasted with "internal rotation" referred to markers within the strained body (cf. F. J. Turner, D. T. Griggs, and H. C. Heard, Experimental deformation of calcite crystals, *Geol. Soc. America Bull.*, vol. 65, pp. 898, 899, 1954).

comparable with those of metamorphism in the deeper levels of the earth's crust.   But in most experiments stress and resultant strain have a higher symmetry than the more general states of stress and strain believed to be typical in the evolution of most tectonites.   And a more serious limitation of experiment as applied to geologic problems is a great discrepancy relating to time.   Most experimentally observed strains have been accomplished within periods of time ranging between half an hour and a few weeks—rarely a few months.   Flow recorded in metamorphic rocks on the other hand has usually taken place more or less continuously over vastly greater periods of thousands or possibly millions of years.   Only recently, and for a limited range of materials, has the influence of this time factor been evaluated to a point where it is possible to predict the rheologic behavior of some rocks under stress of geologically long duration (cf. pages 308 to 314).   In spite of these limitations there is a mass of experimental data bearing on the relations between stress, strain, and fabric in geologically significant materials (see Chaps. 8, 9).   Some of these data seem to conflict with purely geologic observations; e.g., the brittle behavior of quartzite in a short-term compression test is at first sight hard to reconcile with the continuously folded and attenuated condition of quartzite beds in many metamorphic terranes.   Purely geologic observations indeed suggest that most rocks, brittle though they are in familiar laboratory experience, are endowed under geologic conditions with plastic or viscous properties usually regarded as characteristic of materials such as metals or liquids.

As a first step in reconciling the apparently conflicting data we must define more rigorously from a physical standpoint such terms as *solid* and *liquid, elastic, plastic,* and *viscous.*   Here we enter the field of theoretical rheology, which treats mathematical models of stress-strain relations in various types of ideal materials—all of them homogeneous continua. The remainder of this chapter is a discussion of the rheologic state of such ideal bodies, followed by extrapolation to statistically homogeneous bodies, i.e., to tectonites.

Rheologic State.   The rheologic state of a body undergoing continuous strain expresses the mathematical relation between the state of stress within the body and the magnitude and character of the resultant strain. A general equation relating these two quantities can be written in tensor form:[34]

$$R(\mathbf{e}, \mathbf{P}) = 0,$$

where $\mathbf{e}$ is the strain tensor, $\mathbf{P}$ is the stress tensor, and R is a *rheologic function* depending upon the rheologic characteristics of the body.   This relation is generally termed the *rheologic equation of state* of the body.

[34] M. Reiner, *Ten Lectures on Theoretical Rheology,* p. 33, Rubin Mass, Jerusalem, 1943.

Similar equations employing tensor notation are the simplest expressions relating stress, strain, and time in various kinds of rheologic bodies.

In deformation of tectonites volume changes (dilatation) and hydrostatic pressures are relatively unimportant components of the respective states of strain and stress. Moreover, volume changes resulting from changes in hydrostatic pressure almost always are completely reversible. So in the present discussion of relations between stress and strain it is permissible to neglect these isotropic components and to consider only the deviator components of the respective tensors.

In terms of the deviator components the rheologic equation becomes

$$R'(D_\epsilon, D_\sigma) = 0$$

where D_ϵ is the deviator of strain and D_σ is the deviator of stress. This equation states that the mathematical relation between the respective deviators of strain and stress is a function of the rheologic state of the body. Some ideal rheologic bodies will now be considered; equations relating parameters of stress, strain, and time for each type of body are appended in Table 7-3.

TABLE 7-3. CHARACTERISTIC EQUATIONS FOR IDEAL RHEOLOGIC BODIES[a]

Body	Equation
Elastic	$D_\epsilon = \dfrac{D_\sigma}{2G}$
Viscous	$D_\sigma = 2\mu D_{\dot\epsilon}$
Elasticoviscous	$D_{\dot\epsilon} = \dfrac{D_{\dot\sigma}}{2G} + \dfrac{D_\sigma}{2\mu}$
Firmoviscous	$D_\sigma = 2GD_\epsilon + 2\mu D_{\dot\epsilon}$
Plasticoviscous	$D_\sigma = \sigma^* + 2\mu D_{\dot\epsilon}$

D_σ = deviator of stress tensor
D_ϵ = deviator of strain tensor
$D_{\dot\epsilon}$ = deviator of rate-of-strain $(d\epsilon/dt)$ tensor
$D_{\dot\sigma}$ = deviator of rate-of-stress $(d\sigma/dt)$ tensor
G = shear modulus = modulus of rigidity
μ = coefficient of viscosity
σ^* = yield stress

[a] Cf. M. Reiner, *Ten Lectures on Theoretical Rheology*, p. 33, Rubin Mass, Jerusalem, 1943; A. Nádai, *Theory of Flow and Fracture of Solids*, vol. I, pp. 401–425, McGraw-Hill, New York, 1950.

Ideal Rheologic Bodies. *Ideally Elastic Body.* Strain is directly proportional to stress, is instantaneous, and is completely reversible. For a given body the relation of shear stress to shear strain is expressed by a constant G, known as the shear modulus or modulus of rigidity.[35] The familiar Young's modulus, determined in axial tensional or compressional tests, is a function of G. Many natural materials, such as quartz and

[35] E.g., Nádai, *op. cit.*, pp. 380–382, 1950.

olivine, when stressed for a short time duration below a limiting value (the elastic limit) at low temperature approximate ideally elastic bodies.

Viscous Liquid. At the opposite extreme of rheologic behavior from the elastic solid is the viscous liquid (which equals Newtonian liquid). Such a liquid when in equilibrium can support no shearing stress, so that the stress deviator is zero. When the liquid is in motion, however, stress deviators are generated which are proportional to the rate of flow (i.e., to the strain rate). Stress and rate of strain are related by a coefficient of viscosity μ.[36] In response to hydrostatic pressure the viscous liquid behaves like an elastic solid. The magnitude of strain at a given time is independent of the magnitude of stress generated by flow and depends more on the duration of flow. The rheologic behavior of many liquids approximates that of the ideal viscous liquid. However, experiment shows that the behavior of real liquids is generally nonlinear as contrasted with the linear behavior of the ideal Newtonian liquid. The viscosity of a real liquid, for example, varies as the stress deviator generated in flow changes in value. For this reason real liquids are sometimes designated non-Newtonian.

Elasticoviscous Body. Figure 7-6a is the strain-time curve for an elasticoviscous body. Instantaneous elastic strain, under stress below the elastic limit, is followed by continuously developed permanent strain under long-sustained stress of constant magnitude. The curve is compound: the first part corresponds to strain of an elastic solid (Fig. 7-6b), the second to strain of a viscous liquid (Fig. 7-6c). The ideal body behaving in this manner has been termed an *elasticoviscous solid* or a *Maxwell liquid.* Its viscous behavior under sustained stress is termed *creep.* If strain is kept constant at some point on the creep curve, the stress is reduced exponentially ("relaxation of stress") and cannot, therefore, be maintained at an appreciable value for an indefinite period.[37] Many natural solids, e.g., limestone, under geologic conditions of temperature and confining pressure, appear to exhibit elasticoviscous behavior over a range of stress apparently above a threshold value (creep strength) and below the elastic limit as determined in short-term tests (cf. pages 308 to 314).

Firmoviscous solid. Another combination of elastic and viscous properties is exhibited by the firmoviscous solid[38] (Kelvin body) as illustrated in Fig. 7-6d. In response to a given stress, elastic (reversible) strain is accomplished only over a finite period of time; and unloading (as shown on the right-hand part of the curve) also is not instantaneous. Such a body can support stress indefinitely at constant strain. Its "viscosity"

---

[36] E.g., Reiner, *op. cit.*, pp. 48, 49, 1943; Nádai, *op. cit.*, pp. 395–400, 1950.

[37] J. C. Maxwell, On the dynamical theory of gases, *Philos. Mag.*, ser. 4, vol. 35, p. 134, 1866; Reiner, *op. cit.*, pp. 80, 81, 1943.

[38] Nádai, *op. cit.*, pp. 421–424, 1950.

has been termed *solid viscosity,* and this property was proposed by Kelvin to account for damping of elastic oscillations. In ordinary tensional and compressional tests, rocks and minerals tend to show an appreciable though small time lag in the development and reversal of elastic strain.

Plastic Body. An ideally plastic body (St. Venant body)[39] is one which, when subjected to stress above a critical value (yield stress) flows continuously under constant stress (Fig. 7-7b). Strain is irreversible.

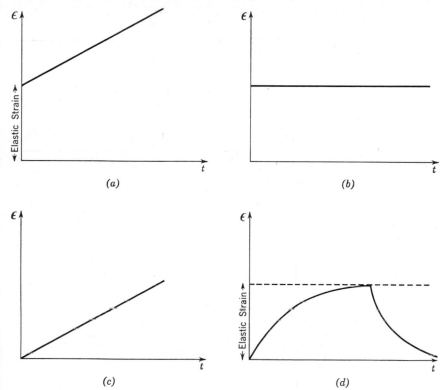

FIG. 7-6. Strain-time curves for ideal rheologic bodies. (a) Elasticoviscous body. (b) Elastic solid. (c) Viscous liquid. (d) Firmoviscous solid.

Below the yield stress the body is ideally rigid. The normal stress-strain curve for a ductile solid—such as copper, or calcite under high confining pressure (cf. Figs. 8-14 to 8-17)—shows elastic followed by plastic strain (Fig. 7-7a). At the elastic limit E there is a departure from the linear relation of strain to stress; and a somewhat higher stress Y (the yield stress) ushers in an almost steady state of strain under almost constant stress. The increase of stress beyond Y, known as strain hardening,[40] is a

[39] Reiner, *op. cit.,* pp. 109–111, 1943.
[40] E.g., J. M. Burgers, in *First Report on Viscosity and Plasticity,* vol. 15, chap. 2, pp. 105, 106, Academy of Sciences, Amsterdam, 1935.

departure from ideal plastic behavior.   Stress-strain behavior of single crystals deformed by twin and translation gliding closely approximates ideal plastic behavior (provided strain hardening is neglected).   A different model of a perfectly plastic body in which the behavior below the yield stress is elastic instead of rigid is favored by some rheologists.[41]

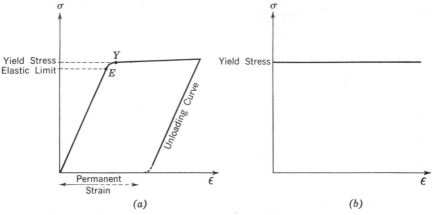

FIG. 7-7. Stress-strain curves for plastic bodies.   (a) Normal ductile solids.   (b) Ideally plastic (St. Venant) body.

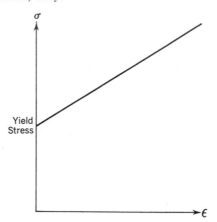

FIG. 7-8. Stress-strain curve for ideally plasticoviscous (Bingham) body.

Plasticoviscous Body.   This is an ideal body (Bingham body)[42] which, when subject to stress continuously increasing above a threshold value σ^* (yield stress), responds by continuous irreversible strain of an essentially viscous nature (Fig. 7-8).

Strain in Real Bodies.   A basic concept of rheology is that ". . . in all *real* materials, *all* material constants are present, differing only in

[41] Jaeger, *op. cit.*, p. 100, 1956.
[42] E.g., Reiner, *op. cit.*, p. 133, 1943; Jaeger, *op. cit.*, p. 104, 1956.

magnitude."[43]   In other words all real bodies combine to some degree elastic, viscous, and plastic properties.   Other combinations are possible than those exhibited by some of the ideal bodies discussed above.   Ingenious mechanical models—combinations of springs and pistons to denote elastic and irreversible flow respectively—have been invented by rheologists[44]—to illustrate behavior of real as well as ideal materials.   For further discussion of this topic the reader is referred to works on rheology.[45]

Speculations on the Rheologic Behavior of Tectonites. *Problem of the Rheologic State of Tectonites.*   Theories of stress and strain and the concepts of rheology apply essentially to homogeneous continua.   Tectonites, although statistically homogeneous, are structurally discontinuous; indeed discontinuity between component domains is the essence of the tectonite fabric.   In setting up a realistic model of rheologic behavior applicable to interpretation of tectonite fabrics we must take these discontinuities into account, and we must recognize that the rheologic states of the component domains may be very different.   For example, although a water-laden sediment may be statistically homogeneous, discontinuity between sand grains (rigid, elastic, or plastic) and water (viscous) plays an essential part in the mechanism of flow, and the rheologic properties of the mass clearly differ from those of either component.   The bulk rheologic properties of tectonites express a combination of such varied mechanisms of deformation as crystal gliding, microfracturing, slip on discrete surfaces of discontinuity, folding, recrystallization, and so on.   Models of deformation taking into account the small-scale *structure* of flow are the subject of *microrheology* and *structural analysis.*[46]

Experimental evidence, to be reviewed in Chap. 8, has provided a good deal of information as to strain behavior of simple rocks and minerals over a range of geologically significant temperatures and pressures.   The influence of the time factor, however, remains only partially explored. Such data as are available suggest that creep may play a highly significant role in metamorphic deformation of some, and perhaps most, rocks.

There can be little doubt that elastic, plastic, and viscous behavior all play some part in strain of tectonites; but their relative roles and the way in which the properties themselves may vary with temperature, pressure, and duration of stress have been only imperfectly evaluated.   The nature of the rheologic function for common rocks under metamorphic conditions is unknown.   It is small wonder, then, that dynamic and kinematic interpretation of common flow structures such as slaty cleavage is still confused.

[43] Reiner, *op. cit.,* p. 85, 1943.
[44] Burgers, *op. cit.,* pp. 21–37, 1935.
[45] E.g., Reiner, *op. cit.,* pp. 133–150, 1943.
[46] *Ibid.,* p. 96.

The Rheid Concept of Carey.   Carey[47] has discussed from a general geologic standpoint the rheologic properties of the earth's crust as inferred from present knowledge of permanent deformation of solids.   The rheologic properties of solids creeping under constant stress (load) are summarized as follows in terms of component strains:[48]

(*a*) a purely elastic component conforming closely to Hooke's Law;
(*b*) a time-independent non-elastic non-recoverable component (referred to as plasticity);
(*c*) an elastic and viscous afterworking and "transient creep," which diminishes with time, with or without some finite permanent strain or "set," and with or without some "work-hardening";
(*d*) a viscous component by which the strain increases at a slow but steady rate, so that this part of the strain is directly proportional to the duration of the loading.

The deformation (under constant shear stress, confining pressure and temperature) may be expressed by the following general equation (after Andrade):

$$S = \frac{P}{G} + f(P) + \beta t^{\frac{1}{3}} + \frac{Pt}{\mu}$$

Total strain = elastic + plastic + transient + viscous strain

where S = shear strain
$\quad P$ = shear stress
$\quad G$ = rigidity
$\quad \mu$ = "viscosity"
$\quad \beta$ = constant

The four terms on the right-hand side of Carey's equation correspond closely to properties that we have termed, respectively, elastic, plastic, firmoviscous, and viscous.   Carey goes on to point out that in geotectonic phenomena the duration of loading is great.   With increasing time the elastic, plastic, and transient components (initially much larger than the viscous) may become unimportant so that only the viscous property remains as a steady-state phenomenon.   Carey[49] further suggests that all but the viscous term can be neglected when considering deformations of duration longer than that required to allow the viscous term to become a thousand times as great as the elastic term.   This time can be shown to be $(\mu/G) \times 10^3$ seconds, and defines what Carey has termed the *rheidity* of the material—considered as the threshold of completely fluid behavior.

[47] S. W. Carey, The rheid concept in geotectonics, *Geol. Soc. Australia Jour.*, vol. 1, pp. 67–117, 1953.
[48] *Ibid.*, pp. 68, 69.
[49] *Ibid.*, p. 69.

A substance loaded for a time that exceeds its rheidity therefore behaves essentially as a viscous liquid. Carey[50] calls such a material a *rheid*.

General Conclusions. The theory of isostasy and current concepts relating to convection in the earth's mantle presuppose extensive continuous flow in the deep crust and the mantle under stress of long duration. Elastic waves, however, are universally transmitted through these zones, the rocks of which therefore seem to approximate the ideal elastico-viscous body. Some metamorphic rocks, at least, must have crystallized at temperatures and pressures high enough to indicate depths at which rheid behavior may be general. And there are some rocks, such as marble, which probably can deform extensively by creep even at relatively low temperatures of metamorphism (page 308). The very form of folded structures in many high-grade metamorphic rocks suggests viscous flow.[51] Moreover, many geologists believe that the intricate patterns of macroscopic folding in many regions of tectonic activity are best explained as the result of essentially viscous flow of rocks under stresses induced by gravitational body forces of long duration. Finally mathematical analysis, based on the assumption that the rate of solution on any intergranular surface of a fluid-saturated aggregate is proportional to the difference between the normal stress on that surface and the mean stress, leads to the conclusion that a stressed rock undergoing recrystallization in the deep levels of the crust may behave essentially as a viscous liquid.[52]

Yet schistosity and slaty cleavage—the hallmarks of the typical tectonite—are most regularly developed in the very rocks whose mineralogy indicates minimal metamorphic temperatures. So in the absence of experimental data relating to the origin of such structures it cannot be assumed—nor can it be disproved—that cleavage and schistosity are products of elasticoviscous flow.

[50] *Ibid.*, p. 70.

[51] E.g., *ibid.*, pp. 91–98.

[52] N. A. Haskell, On the possibility of viscous behavior in crystalline rocks under dynamometamorphic conditions, *Gerlands Beitrage Geophysik*, vol. 49, pp. 387–392, 1937.

CHAPTER 8

EXPERIMENTAL DEFORMATION OF
MINERALS AND ROCKS

STATEMENT OF THE PROBLEM

Part of the necessary background for interpreting tectonite fabrics is some understanding of the actual (as contrasted with ideal) strain behavior of common minerals and rocks in response to stresses that develop under metamorphic conditions—temperatures of perhaps 300° to 800°C—and confining pressures of a few kilobars. Within laboratory experience in tests of short duration conducted at room temperature and pressure such materials are essentially brittle. Even rocks such as marble fail suddenly by fracture after insignificant permanent strain (cf. Fig. 8-2c to e); the ultimate strength only slightly exceeds the yield strength. In tectonite fabrics evidence of brittle behavior is by no means lacking; the cataclastic textures of phyllonites and mylonites have generally, though probably incorrectly, been attributed to complete ruptural failure, whereas fracture cleavage and jointing may testify to less drastic fracture in the last stages of deformation. However, such widely prevalent structural features as continuous folded beds and laminae, and on a smaller scale elongated grains of quartz or calcite and smoothly bent crystals of many mineral species, show that throughout deformation at least the smaller domains of many tectonites have remained coherent. In other words, under most metamorphic conditions rocks are deformed by apparently continuous flow suggesting a rheologic state markedly different from that inferred from laboratory experiments of short duration at room temperature and pressure.

Laboratory experiments, however, have demonstrated that some rocks and minerals, under certain conditions, flow continuously—at least for strains of moderate magnitude—and even linearly. Material exhibiting permanent strain of this kind in laboratory testing experiments is termed *ductile* in contrast to those *brittle* materials that fail by rupture without significant permanent strain. The property of ductility as investigated in the laboratory can only in a general way be identified as the property responsible for continuous flow in tectonites. For instance, because some materials generally brittle can be made ductile by increasing

284

temperature of deformation, a geologist must not conclude that flow of tectonites is necessarily a high-temperature phenomenon; there is, in fact, little doubt that long duration of stress is more significant in natural deformation than is high temperature (pages 308 to 314).

Bearing in mind the difficulties involved in extrapolation from experimental to natural deformation, the geologist can, however, learn much about the flow properties of rocks from the results of laboratory investigation of ductility; at least he can be sure that ductile behavior has been a more significant influence in the evolution of most tectonite fabrics than has brittle behavior. Of particular importance, therefore, are the phenomena responsible for the transition from brittleness to ductility of minerals and rocks with passage from ordinary laboratory to geologic conditions, and the relative influence of pressure, magnitude and nature of shearing stress, temperature, and, particularly, duration of loading, upon the transition. In this chapter some of the findings bearing upon this problem are reviewed.

Within the experience of the engineering laboratory ductility is exemplified especially by metallic crystals and aggregates. It is crucial therefore to inquire whether the extensive available knowledge that relates to plastic deformation and recrystallization of metals in the laboratory[1] may perhaps be applied in elucidating the possible significance of tectonite fabrics. Are the processes operating in deformation of marble or granite at high temperature and pressure comparable to those familiar in experimental strain of zinc or copper aggregates under room conditions?,

Almost universally, metamorphism involves recrystallization of some or all of the component minerals of the rock affected. In consequence mineral grains individually lacking any evidence of internal strain are the main constituents of many highly strained tectonites. A distinction is drawn between syntectonic and post-tectonic crystallization according to whether crystallization was synchronous or subsequent to the processes responsible for the observed strain. And again it is pertinent to ask whether there may be some analogy between syntectonic and post-tectonic crystallization in tectonites and the familiar processes of hot-working and annealing in metals.

We also inquire as to the nature and especially the symmetry of other influences that may have played some part in molding the fabrics of deformed and recrystallized rock fabrics. What is the ultimate influence of initial anisotropy in the rock fabric, and can this influence persist and leave some imprint on the fabric of a strongly deformed tectonite? How closely does the symmetry of a tectonite fabric reflect the symmetry of accompanying strain and of such diverse influences as stress and internal displacements in the strained body?

[1] E.g., C. S. Barrett, *Structure of Metals*, 2d ed., McGraw-Hill, New York, 1952.

Answers to these and to similar questions must be sought in experimental data of two kinds: observations regarding bulk behavior (e.g., stress-strain relations) of minerals and rocks under controlled conditions, and microscopic observations on the experimentally induced tectonite fabrics. This chapter concerns data of the first category.

TECHNIQUE OF GRIGGS, HANDIN, AND ASSOCIATES

Much of the experimental data discussed in this chapter has been drawn from the work of Griggs, Handin, and associates,[2] who since the Second World War have successfully investigated the ductile behavior of several minerals and simple rocks at temperatures and pressures likely to be encountered at depths of a dozen miles or less within the earth's crust. The experimental technique developed by Griggs and Handin permits a continuous accurate record of temperature, confining pressure, stress, and strain throughout each experiment. Their results are therefore preferable to those of earlier workers such as Adams[3] and Von Kármán[4] whose pioneer studies on the ductility of marble and limestone were conducted under imperfectly controlled conditions.

In the procedure first developed by Griggs[5] and subsequently employed also with various modifications by Handin and by Heard, a small solid cylinder (e.g., 1 by 0.5 in.) of the test material is subjected to a controlled confining pressure of a few kilobars exerted on all sides by an enclosing fluid such as kerosene or carbon dioxide. Pistons in contact with the ends of the cylinder maintain a longitudinal pressure either greater or less than the confining pressure. Accordingly, if a homogeneous state of stress is assumed, the specimen becomes deformed respectively by compression ($\sigma_1 > \sigma_2 = \sigma_3$) or by extension ($\sigma_1 = \sigma_2 > \sigma_3$). Temperature is maintained at some constant value between 25° and 800°C. The strain

[2] D. T. Griggs and J. Handin, Rock deformation, *Geol. Soc. America Mem. 79*, 1960, and papers cited therein.

[3] F. D. Adams and J. T. Nicholson, An experimental investigation into the flow of marble, *Royal Soc. London Philos. Trans.*, Ser. A, v. 195, pp. 363–401, 1901; F. D. Adams and J. A. Bancroft, Internal friction during deformation and relative plasticity of rocks, *Jour. Geology*, vol. 25, pp. 597–637, 1917; J. Goguel, Introduction à l'étude méchanique des déformations de l'écorce terrestre, *Carte géol. France Mem.*, 2d ed., Paris, pp. 145–149, 1948.

[4] T. von Kármán, Festigkeitsversuche unter allseitigem Druck, *Zeitschr. Ver. Deutsche Ingenieure*, vol. 55, pp. 1749–1757, 1911; D. T. Griggs, in F. Birch, J. F. Schairer, and H. C. Spicer, Handbook of physical constants, *Geol. Soc. America Spec. Paper 36*, pp. 110, 124, 1942; Goguel, *op. cit.*, pp. 150–153.

[5] D. T. Griggs, Deformation of rocks under high confining pressures, *Jour. Geology*, vol. 44, pp. 545–550, 1936; D. T. Griggs and W. B. Miller, Deformation of Yule marble, part I, *Geol. Soc. America Bull.*, vol. 62, pp. 853–862, 1951; D. T. Griggs, F. J. Turner, and H. Heard, Deformation of rocks at 500° to 800°C., *Geol. Soc. America Mem. 79*, pp. 41–48, 1960.

rate—e.g., 100 per cent elongation (in a few experiments as little as 10 per cent) per hour—is very high compared with rates considered likely under most geologic conditions. In many experiments the test cylinder is sealed from contact with the enclosing fluid by a thin copper jacket, and strain is achieved in the dry material (Fig. 8-1). In others the cylinder is in direct contact with water, carbon dioxide, or some other geologically significant fluid throughout strain.

The longitudinally directed differential stress (load) operating on the ends of the cylinder is the difference $(\sigma_1 - \sigma_3)$ between the stress operating on the pistons and the confining pressure measured in the enclosing fluid; it is positive for compression, negative for extension experiments. Strain ϵ is recorded as percentage shortening or elongation of the cylinder, shown by relative displacement of the two pistons. Several corrections are necessary, notably that for change in cross section of the cylinder on the assumption that strain is homogeneous. The behavior of the test material in any experiment is most conveniently demonstrated—following conventional engineering procedure—by plotting longitudinal differential stress per unit of cross section [in bars, $= (\sigma_1 - \sigma_3)$ per cm²] against strain ϵ.

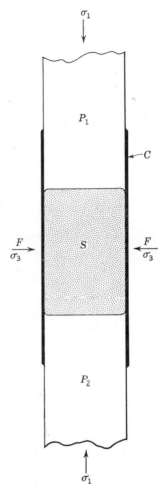

Fig. 8-1. Assembly for compression experiment, much simplified. (*After D. T. Griggs.*) S = specimen; P_1, P_2 = pistons exerting longitudinal pressure σ_1; C = copper seal; F = enclosing fluid at confining pressure σ_3.

BRITTLE FRACTURE OF ROCKS AND MINERALS

Character of Brittle Behavior. At atmospheric pressure and temperatures of a few hundred degrees common rocks are brittle. Figure 8-2a and b shows stress-strain curves for compression experiments carried out on cylinders of Solenhofen limestone at 400° and 480°C, respectively.[6] At the lower temperature (curve a) elastic, i.e., reversible, strain, conforming closely to Hooke's law, is terminated by brittle fracture at a stress

[6] H. Heard, Transition from brittle fracture to ductile flow in Solenhofen limestone, *Geol. Soc. America Mem. 79*, p. 201, fig. 4A, 1960.

of 3,200 bars.   At 480°C (curve *b*) the limestone is slightly ductile; elastic strain is succeeded, at stresses exceeding 3,000 bars, by limited permanent strain which terminates in brittle fracture.   This permanent mesoscopically homogeneous irreversible strain, the result of flow, is the essential criterion of ductility.   Marble (Fig. 8-2*c* to *e*) is notably weaker than the fine-grained limestone; at room temperature elastic strain terminates in brittle fracture with only slight intervening ductile behavior.[7]

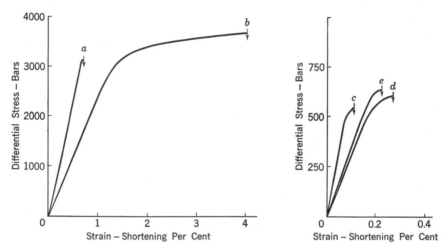

Fig. 8-2. Stress-strain curves for limestone and marble in compression.   Confining pressure = 1 bar.   The arrows denote failure by fracture.   *a* = Solenhofen limestone, 400°C.   (*After H. C. Heard.*)   *b* = Solenhofen limestone, 480°C.   (*After H. C. Heard.*) *c* = Yule marble compressed parallel to foliation, 25°C.   (*After H. A. Lepper.*) *d* = Yule marble compressed normal to foliation, 25°C.   (*After H. A. Lepper.*) *e* = Wombeyan marble, 25°C.   (*After M. S. Paterson.*)

Limestone and marble are among the few common rocks that show any recognizable tendency toward ductility at low pressures.   Even anhydrite and dolomite are essentially brittle at atmospheric pressure.[8] Silicate rocks such as granite and quartzite are almost ideally brittle in standard engineering tests of breaking strength at room temperature and pressure.

Two kinds of fracture characterize brittle failure:[9] extension joints exemplified by longitudinal fractures in compression or by transverse

[7] H. A. Lepper, Compression tests on oriented specimens of Yule marble, *Am. Jour. Sci.*, vol. 247, pp. 570–574, 1949; M. S. Paterson, Experimental deformation and faulting in Wombeyan marble, *Geol. Soc. America Bull.*, vol. 69, pp. 467, 468, fig. 3, 1958.

[8] J. Handin and R. V. Hager, Experimental deformation of sedimentary rocks under confining pressure: tests at room temperature on dry samples, *Am. Assoc. Petroleum Geologists Bull.*, vol. 41, pp. 1–50, 1957.

[9] Griggs, *op. cit.*, p. 552, 1936; Paterson, *op. cit.*, p. 468, pl. 1 (fig. 1).

fractures in extension tests, and shear fractures inclined obliquely to the axis of the test cylinder. For strictly brittle behavior of Solenhofen limestone Heard[10] records both types of fracture in compression, but only tension joints in typical extension experiments.

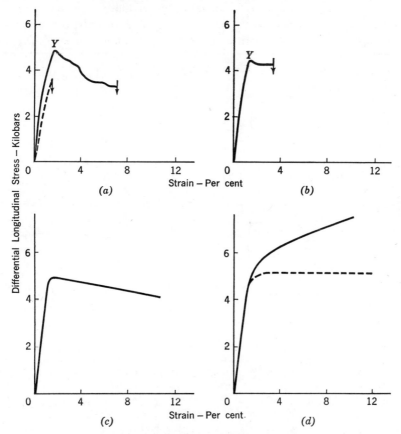

FIG. 8-3. Stress-strain curves characteristic of brittle, transitional, and ductile behavior of Solenhofen limestone compressed below 300°C. (*After H. C. Heard.*) Arrows denote fracture and loss of cohesion. Y = yield point. (*a*) Brittle; 25°C, 750 bars (broken curve, 1 bar). (*b*) Transitional; 150°C, 800 bars. (*c*) Transitional; 25°C, 1,000 bars. (*d*) Ductile; 25°C, 5,000 bars (broken curve, 1,500 bars).

Transition from Brittle to Ductile Behavior. *Criteria of Transition.* Brittleness and ductility are converse properties. With changing physical conditions, e.g., as temperature or confining pressure increases, a given material may become less brittle and correspondingly more ductile. No unequivocal line of demarcation may be drawn between the two states, which are separated rather by a range of transitional behavior. For marble and limestone at room temperature the distinction has been

[10] Heard, *op. cit.*, pp. 210–212.

drawn in terms of the shape of the stress-strain curve:[11] For brittle behavior " . . . the load passes through a maximum at a relatively small strain and thereafter falls steadily so that the larger the strain the less the load needed for further straining" (Figs. 8-3a, 8-5a).   The yield point is relatively sharp.   Beyond it the curve falls gradually, indicating steady diminution in strength preceding complete loss of cohesion.   The criterion of ductility on the other hand is that " . . . the load continues to rise with increasing strain [the phenomenon of strain hardening] and does not show a maximum, that is, the greater the strain the greater the load

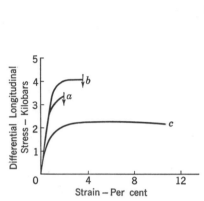

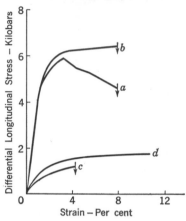

Fig. 8-4. Stress-strain curves characteristic of brittle, transitional, and ductile behavior of dry Solenhofen limestone compressed above 300°C. (*After H. C. Heard.*)   Arrows denote fracture and loss of cohesion.   a = brittle; 450°C, 1 bar. b = transitional; 300°C, 400 bars.   c = ductile; 600°C, 400 bars.

Fig. 8-5. Stress-strain curves characteristic of brittle, transitional, and ductile behavior of dry Solenhofen limestone in extension. (*After H. C. Heard.*)   Arrows denote fracture and loss of cohesion. a = brittle; 25°C, 7,000 bars.   b = ductile; 25°C, 7,500 bars.   c = transitional; 600°C, 2,000 bars.   d = ductile; 600°C, 3,000 bars.

needed for further straining" (Figs. 8-3d and 8-5b).   Transitional behavior is illustrated by Fig. 8-3b and c.

Heard found this criterion inapplicable to Solenhofen limestone strained at temperatures of 300°C or higher.   The shape of the stress-strain curve prior to rupture is the same for brittle as for ductile behavior—beyond a rather vaguely defined yield point the stress rises slightly before final rupture of the specimen.   What distinguishes ductile behavior is a high degree of permanent strain prior to rupture.   Heard arbitrarily defined the brittle-ductile transition above 300°C as the range of conditions over which failure with notable loss of cohesion is preceded by strain of more than 3 but less than 5 per cent (Figs. 8-4b, 8-5c, as contrasted with Figs. 8-4a and c, and 8-5d).

[11] Paterson, *op. cit.*, p. 470; cf. also Heard, *op. cit.*, p. 206.

Influence of Physical Variables. The brittle-ductile transition of a given material is a function of several geologically significant conditions, notably confining pressure, temperature, presence of pore fluids, and probably rate of strain. The influences of the first three of these have been explored only for the simplest of rocks—limestone and marble.[12] The conclusions summarized below refer specifically to these materials; but they probably apply at least qualitatively to other monomineralic aggregates and even to rocks composed of several mineral phases. We still have no adequate information, however, as to how the brittle-ductile

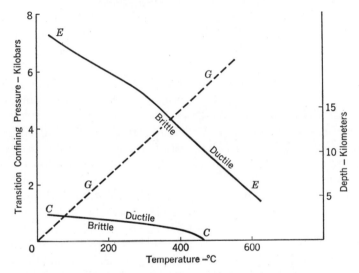

Fig. 8-6. Brittle-ductile transition for dry Solenhofen limestone as a function of temperature and confining pressure. (*After H. C. Heard.*) *C* = compression experiments; *E* = extension experiments; *G* = assumed geothermal gradient correlated with depth (right-hand scale).

transition may be affected by two potentially influential factors of the geologic environment—exceedingly slow strain rates and syntectonic chemical reactions.

Figure 8-6 shows the brittle-ductile transition for dry Solenhofen limestone expressed as a function of confining pressure and of temperature—increase in either of which favors ductility. Because of the influence of internal friction ductility is favored by compression as contrasted with extension, so that there is a broad range of conditions over which limestone is brittle in extension but ductile under compression. From this (cf. Fig. 8-7) it has been inferred that normal faulting (cf. experimental extension) can occur down to depths at which reverse faulting (cf. experi-

[12] Paterson, *op. cit.*; Heard, *op. cit.*

mental compression) is prohibited. Assuming, for lack of pertinent data, that strain rate has no influence on faulting, Heard[13] gives 15 and 3.5 km as critical values of the maximum possible depths respectively for normal and reverse faulting in dry fine-grained limestone. Paterson[14] fixes the brittle-ductile transition of dry coarse-grained marble in compression at only 300 bars at room temperature; and from this he infers that the limiting depth for reverse faulting of marble may conceivably be as low as 1 km.

The presence of an interstitial fluid such as water or carbon dioxide favors brittle rather than ductile behavior of experimentally deformed rocks;[15] i.e., it extends the brittle at the expense of the ductile region of Fig. 8-6. Taking this factor into account Heard extends the maximum depth for reverse faulting in fine-grained limestone saturated in an interstitial fluid at a pressure approaching that of the overburden to 5.5 km.

Ductility is also affected greatly by grain size. Under similar physical conditions, fine-grained limestones not only are stronger, but also are more brittle than coarse marbles.[16]

Faults, Shear Fractures, and Slickensides.[17] Following Griggs and Handin[18] we recognize two categories of mesoscopic surfaces of failure, namely, extension fractures and faults. Extension fractures form by clean, sudden separation of the specimen along planes normal to the direction of least principal stress σ_3. They are typical products of strictly brittle failure. Faults are localized offsets parallel to more or less plane surfaces of fairly high shear stress. They have the same dynamic significance as geologic faults on the macroscopic scale. Faults resulting from brittle failure are commonly sharply defined shear fractures (Fig. 8-7a). But faults characteristic of the brittle-ductile transition tend to be slickensided or mylonitized zones whose development is accompanied by neither loss of cohesion nor sudden release of energy such as attends brittle failure on extension or shear fractures.

The angle of inclination of experimentally induced faults to the axis of maximum principal stress σ_1 may be anywhere between a few degrees and 45°, with 20° to 30° perhaps the commonest values.[19] For Solenhofen limestone Heard[20] records 17° to 32° for compression, 9° to 22° for exten-

[13] Heard, *op. cit.*, p. 226.

[14] Paterson, *op. cit.*, pp. 473, 474.

[15] Griggs, *op. cit.*, pp. 566, 567, 1936; Heard, *op. cit.*, pp. 216–223, 226.

[16] Goguel, *op. cit.*, pp. 180, 204; Paterson, *op. cit.*, p. 474.

[17] Paterson, *op. cit.*, pp. 468, 469, pls. 1, 2; Heard, *op. cit.*, pp. 210–212, 221; D. T. Griggs and J. Handin, Observations on fracture and a hypothesis of earthquakes, *Geol. Soc. America Mem. 79*, pp. 347–350, 364, 1960; J. C. Jaeger, Shear failure of anisotropic rocks, *Geol. Mag.*, vol. 97, pp. 65–72, 1960.

[18] Griggs and Handin, *op. cit.*, pp. 347, 364, 1960.

[19] Griggs and Handin, *Ibid.*, pp. 347, 352–353.

[20] Heard, *op. cit.*, pp. 212, 221.

sion experiments; for marble compressed at 25°C, Paterson[21] records 25° to 32°.   For coarse-grained dolomite rock deformed at 20° and 300°C under a confining pressure of 500 bars, Handin and Fairbairn[22] found that compression and extension tests invariably terminate by shear fracture on surfaces inclined at about 30° to the σ_1 axis.   Failure of limestone and marble in extension typically ends in rupture along a single oblique fault (Fig. 8-7d).   In compression tests, especially within the

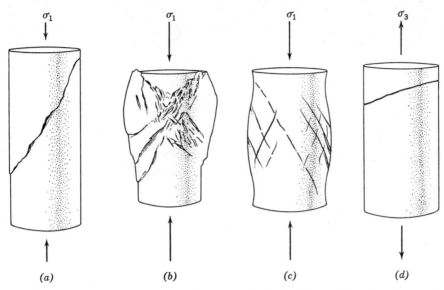

FIG. 8-7. Shear fractures and faults characteristic of failure of dry limestone and marble.   (After H. C. Heard and M. S. Paterson.)   (a) Marble, brittle failure; 25°C, 35 bars, 1 per cent strain.   (b) Marble, transitional failure; 25°C, 280 bars, 20 per cent strain.   (c) Solenhofen limestone, almost ductile failure; 25°C, 1,000 bars, 11.2 per cent strain.   (d) Solenhofen limestone, ductile behavior followed by rupture; 150°C, 6,500 bars, 9.1 per cent strain.

range of the brittle-ductile transition, faults tend to be more numerous (Fig. 8-7b) and they commonly develop on two sets symmetrically inclined to the σ_1 axis.   With increasingly ductile behavior they become more closely spaced until, as ductility is achieved, they appear on the surface of the bulging cylinder as the *Lüders' lines* (Fig. 8-7c) familiar to the metallurgist.[23]

Little information is available as to how a strong anisotropy of initial fabric may affect the development of faults during brittle and transitional

[21] Paterson, *op. cit.*, p. 470, fig. 5.

[22] J. Handin and H. W. Fairbairn, Experimental deformation of Hasmark dolomite, *Geol. Soc. America Bull.*, vol. 66, pp. 1262–1264, 1955.

[23] E. B. Knopf and E. Ingerson, Structural petrology, *Geol. Soc. America Mem. 6*, pp. 182–185, pls. 14, 15, 1938; Paterson, *op. cit.*, p. 469; Heard, *op. cit.*, p. 211.

failure.   The problem has been analyzed mathematically by Jaeger[24] for the geologically common case of a rock having a single plane of weakness such as slaty cleavage or some similar set of s-planes S.   On the not unreasonable assumption that the shear strength of such a system varies continuously from a maximum in planes normal to S to a minimum value in planes parallel to S, Jaeger predicts failure on a single set of faults F obliquely intersecting S, not by slip on S itself. F will always be between S and the nearest of the planes predicted by the Coloumb-Navier theory.   So, if F and S make respective angles α and β with the axis of

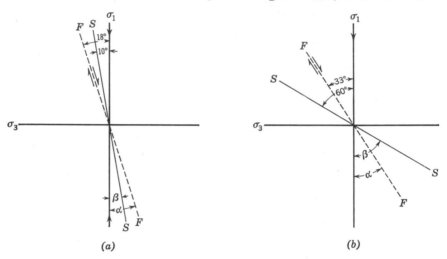

(a)   (b)

FIG. 8-8. Schematic diagram of failure on faults F in an anisotropic system in which the shear strength varies from a minimum value parallel to s-planes S.   (Compatible with predictions of J. C. Jaeger, Shear failure of anisotropic rocks, *Geol. Mag.*, vol. 97, *p.* 71, *fig.* 5, 1960.)

maximum principal stress σ_1, then for small values of β the angle α will be smaller than in a corresponding isotropic system (Fig. 8-8a); for large values of β the angle α will be somewhat larger than if the system were isotropic (Fig. 8-8b).   Experimental results obtained by Donath on slate compressed at low confining pressures confirm this last prediction.[25]   And the common occurrence of strain-slip structures and "kink bands" in slaty rocks shows that in natural deformation such rocks commonly fail by faulting oblique to the cleavage.   According to Jaeger's conclusions, slip in S is likely only in a system such as a jointed rock which is weak parallel to the plane of jointing S, but otherwise more or less equally strong in all directions.   Even here failure on S rather than on some intersecting plane would be confined to a limited range of orientation, e.g., where S

[24] J. C. Jaeger, Shear failure of anisotropic rocks, *Geol. Mag.*, vol. 97, pp. 65–72, 1960.
[25] F. A. Donath, Experimental study of shear failure in anisotropic rocks, *Geol. Soc. America Bull.*, vol. 72, pp. 985–990, 1961.

intersects the axis σ_1 at angles between about 10° and 40°.   Donath found that, at 30 to 500 bars confining pressure, failure parallel to S occurs in slate where the angle between S and σ_1 is less than 45° to 60°.

Strength of Relatively Brittle Minerals and Rocks.   The strength[26] of any material, determined under some given physical conditions, is the stress necessary to produce some kind of measurable mechanical response such as permanent strain (yield strength) or fracture (breaking strength); the ultimate strength is the maximum stress on the stress-strain curve. For ideally brittle materials, such as quartz or granite at room temperature and pressure, strength is unambiguous and is readily measured: in experiments such as those of Griggs and Handin it is the stress necessary to induce rupture, e.g., a differential longitudinal stress $(\sigma_1 - \sigma_3)$ of 3,200 bars in Fig. 8-2a.   For somewhat less brittle materials, such as limestone at 25° and confining pressures of a few hundred bars (Fig. 8-3a and b), there is a sharply defined yield point Y at which reversible gives way to irreversible strain; and the corresponding yield strength is the stress at the yield point.   The breaking strength at the point of final rupture is commonly less than the yield strength.   For stress-strain curves representing behavior in the brittle-ductile transition (e.g., Fig. 8-4b) the yield point tends to be less sharply defined, and the breaking strength may be either somewhat higher or somewhat lower than the yield strength.   To evaluate the influence of physical variables on strength of such materials—or of ductile materials too—the yield stress must be arbitrarily defined as the stress at some constant small strain beyond the limit of elastic strain.   Thus Griggs and Miller[27] fixed the "yield point" of Yule marble for this purpose at 3 per cent longitudinal strain.

Strength of relatively brittle materials is found to vary notably with confining pressure, temperature, time (i.e., duration of stress), grain size, and presence of pore fluids.   Table 8-1 illustrates the influence of confining pressure at constant temperature.   With increasing confining pressure, yield strength markedly increases, though at the same time rocks become more ductile.   Note also that coarse-grained rocks (e.g., marble) are notably weaker than fine-grained rocks of the same mineral composition (e.g., limestone).   Temperature, which in the earth's crust tends to increase sympathetically with confining pressure, normally has the opposite effect on strength.   Granite, dunite, and pyroxenite,[28] at 5,000 bars confining pressure and a strain rate of 3 per cent per minute,

---

[26] For discussion of the geologic significance of experimentally measured values of strength, see D. T. Griggs, *op. cit.*, pp. 557–566, 1936; Experimental flow of rocks, *Geol. Soc. America Bull.*, vol. 51, pp. 1018–1020, 1940; R. W. Goranson, Flow in stressed solids, *Geol. Soc. America Bull.*, vol. 51, pp. 1023–1034, 1940.

[27] Griggs and Miller, *op. cit.*, p. 861.

[28] Griggs, Turner, and Heard, *op. cit.*, p. 102.

TABLE 8-1. INFLUENCE OF CONFINING PRESSURE ON STRENGTH

Material	Reference	Confining pressure, bars	Yield strength, bars	Breaking strength, bars	Behavior
Quartz compressed parallel to [0001] at 25°C	Griggs and Heard*	1	25,000		Brittle
		2,500	45,000		Brittle
		5,000	53,000		Brittle
Solenhofen limestone compressed at 25°C	Heard†	1	3,450	3,450	Brittle
		750	4,680	3,300	Brittle
		1,500	5,150		Ductile
Solenhofen limestone in extension at 25°C	Heard‡	4,000	4,100	3,800	Transitional
		5,000	4,800	4,500	Transitional
		7,500	6,100	6,400	Ductile
Wombeyan marble in compression at 25°C	Paterson§	1	700	700	Brittle
		100	1,000	700	Transitional
		700	1,500		Ductile

* D. T. Griggs, F. J. Turner, and H. Heard, Deformation of rocks at 500° to 800° C., *Geol. Soc. America Mem.* 79, p. 69, 1960.

† H. Heard, Transition from brittle fracture to ductile flow in Solenhofen limestone, *Geol. Soc. America Mem.* 79, pp. 200, 202, 203, 1960.

‡ *Ibid.*, p. 207, 1960.

§ M. S. Paterson, Experimental deformation and faulting in Wombeyan marble, *Geol. Soc. America Bull.*, vol. 69, p. 468, 1958.

have a compressive strength of about 20,000 bars at 25°C; about 10,000 bars at 500°C; and about 7,000 bars at 800°C. Some crystalline dolomite rocks behave exceptionally in this respect.[29] Thus Handin and Fairbairn reported Hasmark dolomite rock, compressed at 5,000 bars, to be somewhat stronger at 300°C than at 25°C. Dover Plains dolomite rock on the other hand is weaker at 500°C than at room temperature; but the decrease in strength is not nearly so great as for dunite or granite over the same temperature interval.

The effect of pore fluids and of time upon strength of rocks will be discussed later with reference to ductile materials.

DUCTILE BEHAVIOR OF MINERALS AND ROCKS

Criteria of Ductile Behavior. The essence of ductility is that the test material, stressed beyond the elastic limit (i.e., the yield point), deforms continuously and permanently—by a process known as flow—without loss of cohesion or of strength. Indeed the stress-strain curve typically rises gently beyond the yield point (e.g., Figs. 8-14, 8-15b and d) showing

[29] Handin and Fairbairn, *op. cit.*, pp. 1263, 1264; Griggs, Turner, and Heard, *op. cit.*, pp. 80, 81, 102.

that as strain proceeds the test material becomes progressively stronger—a phenomenon called *strain hardening*. Ductile strain ends eventually in fracture. Highly as contrasted with less ductile materials can sustain very high strain before the onset of fracture. Thus Yule marble, strained rapidly at 5,000 bars and 800°C, has been elongated locally by 1,000 per cent.[30] Many minerals and rocks show at least some degree of ductility at geologically likely temperatures and pressures. Our illustrations are drawn chiefly from calcite and marble, which are among the most ductile of common rock-forming minerals and rocks and for this reason have been most fully investigated experimentally. But at temperatures of 500° to 800°C and a few thousand bars pressure, less spectacular ductility has also been demonstrated for a variety of other metamorphic and igneous minerals, such as dolomite, micas, pyroxenes, and olivine.

Gliding in Crystals.[31] Ductile strain of a single crystal is the result of gliding (or in the terminology of the metallurgist, slip) on one or more glide systems. Each system comprises a glide plane T and within it a glide direction t, both of some simple rational crystallographic orientation. With regard to the geometry of gliding, no specific assumption need here be made regarding relative motion of ions during gliding. Whether this involves the generation and migration of lattice defects (dislocations) along fixed paths in the lattice or some other mechanism, the ultimate result of gliding is as if successive thin layers parallel to the glide plane were relatively displaced along the glide line in a uniform sense. In translation gliding each such displacement is through an integral number of interionic distances, so that the configuration of the lattice is unchanged even though the crystal as a whole is strained as regard dimensions and shape. In twin gliding each layer has moved through a constant appropriate fraction of an interionic distance, so that the lattice of the strained (twinned) sector is homogeneous though in twinned relation to the initial lattice. It follows that whereas shear s ($= \tan \theta$ in Figs. 8-9 and 8-10) is variable in translation gliding, its value in twin gliding is rigidly fixed by the geometric requirements of twinning.

Today it is generally agreed that crystal gliding, though conventionally described in terms of simple shear on glide planes, is really achieved through generation, and migration along glide planes, of lattice imperfec-

[30] Griggs, Turner, and Heard, *op. cit.*, p. 91, pl. 10.

[31] O. Mügge, Ueber Translationen und verwandte Erscheinungen in Krystallen, *Neues Jahrb. Mineralogie, Geologie, u. Paläontologie*, vol. 1, pp. 71–158, 1898; M. J. Buerger, Translation gliding in crystals, *Am. Mineralogist*, vol. 15, pp. 1–20, 1930; Barrett, *op. cit.*, pp. 336–352, 1952; W. G. Burgers, Plasticity of crystals, in R. Houwink, *Plasticity, Elasticity and Structure of Matter*, pp. 73–127, Harren Press, Washington, 1953; M. S. Paterson, The plastic deformation of single crystals, *Australian Inst. Metals Jour.*, vol. 1, no. 2, pp. 112–124, 1956; D. V. Higgs and J. Handin, Experimental deformation of dolomite single crystals, *Geol. Soc. America Bull.*, vol. 70, pp. 250–253, 1959.

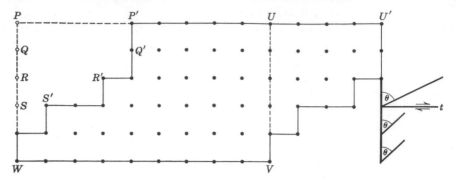

FIG. 8-9. Diagrammatic illustration of translation gliding parallel to glide direction t through a variable angle of shear θ ($s = \tan \theta$). The rectangle $PUVW$ represents the initial array of points (centers of ions). During translation P becomes displaced to P', Q to Q', R to R', and so on.

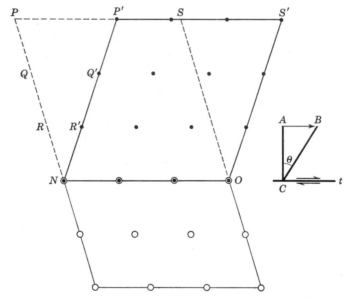

FIG. 8-10. Diagrammatic illustration of twin gliding parallel to glide direction t through a constant angle of shear θ. Initial lattice is represented by open circles, twinned lattice by solid circles. The area $PNOS$ becomes displaced to $P'NOS'$; A is displaced to B in relation to C.

tions known as *dislocations*.[32] These tend to pile up and accumulate along surfaces of discontinuity in the lattice—cracks, lamella boundaries,

[32] E.g., Barrett, *op. cit.*, pp. 393–413, 1952; W. T. Read and W. Shockley, *Imperfections in Nearly Perfect Crystals*, pp. 77–94, Wiley, New York, 1952; W. T. Read, Jr., *Dislocations in Crystals*, McGraw-Hill, New York, 1953; N. F. Mott, Dislocations and the theory of solids, *Nature*, vol. 171, pp. 234–237, 1953; Paterson, *op. cit.*, pp. 119–121, 1956.

grain boundaries, and so on.   Resistance of a given material to gliding, and hence its brittleness and strength, depend partly on the density of distribution of dislocations in the lattice.   Strain hardening—increase of strength and brittleness with strain—is correlated with storing of dislocations and corresponding increase of strain energy in the progressively strained lattice.

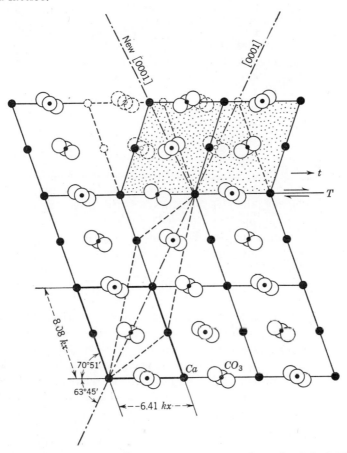

FIG. 8-11. Section, parallel to $(1\bar{2}10)$, i.e., normal to a_2, through calcite lattice, illustrating (at top right, stippled area) twin gliding on $(\bar{1}012) = e_1 = T$.   (*After A. Pabst.*) Note (1) the positive sense of shear and (2) reorientation of the c axis in the opposite sense to that of gliding.

Translation and twin gliding are illustrated schematically in Figs. 8-9 and 8-10, which show one plane (normal to T and parallel to t) in a regular array of similar points.   This kind of representation grossly oversimplifies any but the simplest crystal lattices.   Gliding—especially twin gliding—in ionic crystals must commonly give rise to lattice imperfections in the vicinity of the glide plane.   Note, for example, that in twinning of calcite (Fig. 8-11) the CO_3 groups are rotated as well as displaced. So that there must be a discrepancy in their orientation across the twin plane T. Figures 8-9 and 8-10 also ignore the existence of dislocations, all-important though they are in the gliding mechanism.

The experience of metallurgists shows that the glide direction t is the direction of closest packing of atoms in the crystal lattice, while the glide plane also is a plane of high density of packing. From the meager available data the same generalization would seem to apply, too, to ionic crystals, with the stipulation that density of packing applies only to ions of the same size and electric charge.

It is generally thought that ductile strain of a crystal begins when the shear stress on a glide system exceeds some critical value—the shear strength of the system in question. With the onset of strain hardening, or if the crystal changes its orientation in the stress field, gliding on a second system may set in, and so on. One of the problems arising from experimental strain of crystals concerns identification of the active glide systems and assessment of their appropriate shear strengths. There are several independent lines of evidence bearing on this problem: the nature of the crystal lattice, the stress-strain data, the geometry of strain, the development of striations (microscopic offsets) on the surface of the test specimen, and certain microscopically observable rotational effects must all be taken into account and correlated. Discussion of this aspect of gliding will be included in Chap. 9.

The term plastic flow strictly should be reserved for gliding (by twinning or by translation) in single crystals.

Ductile Strain of Rocks. Undoubtedly gliding within the individual component crystals plays a dominant role in ductile strain of a polycrystalline aggregate. For this reason even a monomineralic rock (e.g., marble or dunite) composed of anisotropic crystals having some degree of preferred orientation will itself be anisotropic as regards ductile response to stress. Other possible elements in the mechanism of ductile flow are rotation and relative displacement of grains or grain segments, and even recrystallization from newly formed nuclei. Such aspects of experimentally induced strain will also be discussed after the microscopic character of deformed aggregates has been considered in Chap. 9.

Ductile Strain of Calcite.[33] Figure 8-12 is an equal-area projection showing the relative positions of the crystal axes $c = [0001]$, a_1, a_2, and a_3, and of poles of some simple crystallographic forms $c = \{0001\}$, $m = \{10\bar{1}0\}$, $r = \{10\bar{1}1\}$, $e = \{01\bar{1}2\}$, and $f = \{02\bar{2}1\}$ in calcite. The three planes of each rhombohedral or prismatic form are distinguished by

[33] D. T. Griggs, Deformation of single calcite crystals under high confining pressures. *Am. Mineralogist*, vol. 23, pp. 28–33, 1938; F. J. Turner, D. T. Griggs, and H. Heard, Experimental deformation of calcite crystals, *Geol. Soc. America Bull.*, vol. 65, pp. 883–934, 1954; Griggs, Turner, and Heard, *op. cit.*, pp. 81–87, 1960.

subscripts—thus r_1, r_2, r_3—and planes cozonal with each other and with {0001} are designated by the same subscript—thus r_1, e_1, f_1.

It has long been known that even at room temperature and pressure, a calcite crystal compressed normal to the c axis is highly ductile (Fig. 8-14a).   Moreover, the mechanism of gliding is well known: it consists of twin gliding on {01$\bar{1}$2} $= e$, the glide line being the edge $[e_1:r_2]$ (the zone axis of r_2, e_1, and r_3), and the sense of gliding being such that upper layers are displaced toward the positive end of the c axis in relation to underlying layers (Fig. 8-13).   This sense of slip has been designated positive.[34]   For other orientations favoring positive slip on {01$\bar{1}$2}—e.g.,

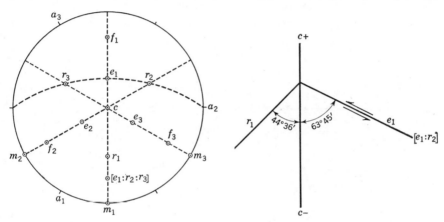

FIG. 8-12. Equal-area projection (upper hemisphere) of calcite crystal showing crystal axes c, a_1, a_2, and a_3, and poles of simple planes.

FIG. 8-13. Section normal to a_2 through calcite showing sense of shear for twin gliding on e_1 (plane normal to diagram) in the glide direction $[e_1:r_2]$.

extension parallel to the c axis [0001]—calcite crystals are equally ductile (Fig. 8-14b) and respond to stress by twin gliding on e.   Twin gliding if carried to completion yields a new, homogeneous, apparently untwinned lattice in which, under favorable stress conditions, twinning might be initiated afresh on one of the three e planes.   For twin gliding on a given e plane there is of course an upper limit to strain, corresponding to complete twinning.[35]   Thus for extension parallel to [0001] the maximum possible elongation is 36 per cent; for compression parallel to [0001] the maximum shortening is 26 per cent.   At confining pressures of a few thousand bars, which favor ductility, complete twinning is readily achieved in Griggs's apparatus over a temperature range of 25° to 800°C.

At high confining pressures calcite crystals are also highly ductile, even when so oriented in the stress field that the sense of slip on all three

[34] Turner, Griggs, and Heard, *op. cit.*, p. 887, 1954.
[35] J. W. Handin and D. T. Griggs, Deformation of Yule marble, part II, *Geol. Soc America Bull.*, vol. 62, pp. 868–871, figs. 5, 6, 1951.

e planes is negative, thus precluding the possibility of twin gliding on *e*. Compression parallel to [0001] (Fig. 8-14*c*) and extension normal to [0001] exemplify this condition.   Evidently some alternative mechanism —one of translation gliding—then operates.   And from Fig. 8-14 it is clear that at low temperatures calcite is much stronger for this translation mechanism than for twin gliding.

The strength of calcite so oriented that *e* twinning is impossible decreases greatly with increasing temperature over the interval 20° to

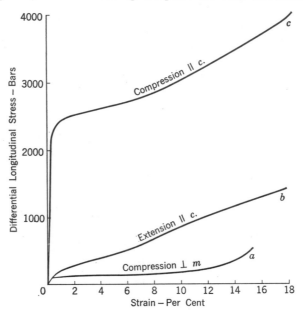

FIG. 8-14. Stress-strain curves for calcite, 20°C, 10,000 bars.   (*After F. J. Turner, D. T. Griggs, and H. C. Heard.*)   *a* = compression perpendicular to {10$\bar{1}$0} = *m* (twin gliding on *e*).   *b* = extension parallel to [0001] (twin gliding on *e*).   *c* = compression parallel to [0001] (*e* twinning impossible).

800°C (Figs. 8-15, 8-16).   The shape of the stress-strain curve changes in the vicinity of 400° to 500°C.   At 500°C and higher temperatures a sharp yield point, such as characterizes curves for 400°C and lower temperatures, is lacking (Fig. 8-16).   Possibly a new translation mechanism becomes effective at about 400° to 500°C.   The strength of calcite oriented for *e* twinning also diminishes somewhat as temperature increases up to 300°C.   Thus the yield stress (shear stress on the active *e* gliding system at 3 per cent elongation) at 5,000 bars confining pressure drops from 155 ± 20 bars at 25°C to 90 ± 5 bars at 300°C; at 800°C it has much the same value.[36]   The discrepancy in strength of calcite for twin

[36] Griggs, Turner, and Heard, *op. cit.*, pp. 83–85, 1960.

gliding on e as contrasted with the alternative mechanism of translation tends to vanish with rising temperatures.   At room temperature cylinders of a given orientation are 10 or 20 times stronger when stressed so that twinning is impossible (cf. Fig. 8-14); at 800°C they are only about twice as strong.

Figure 8-17 shows how, at a given temperature and confining pressure, the strength of calcite varies with orientation even though in all cases twinning on e is impossible. Either more than one glide mechanism is effective, or else variation in strength reflects variation in resolved shear stress on a single glide system differently oriented in different experiments.

If τ is the resolved shear stress on a plane T in a direction t, $\sigma_1 - \sigma_3 =$ longitudinal stress parallel to cylinder axis, $S_o =$ coefficient of resolved shear stress such that $\tau = S_o(\sigma_1 - \sigma_3)$, $\chi_0 =$ angle between T and cylinder axis, and $\lambda_0 =$ angle between t and cylinder axis, then

$$S_o = \sin \chi_0 \cos \lambda_0$$

and $\qquad \tau = \sin \chi_0 \cos \lambda_0 (\sigma_1 - \sigma_3)$

S_o has a maximum value of 0.5 when both χ_0 and $\lambda_0 = 45°$.   This is possible only when σ_1, σ_3, t, and the normal to T are coplanar—illustrated for a compression experiment by the solid arc of Fig. 8-18. In Fig. 8-18 the broken arcs illustrate two other cases for which S_o necessarily is less than 45°:

For glide system Tt'

$$S_o = \sin 45° \cos 70° = 0.24$$

For glide system $T't'$

$$S_o = \sin 70° \cos 70° = 0.32$$

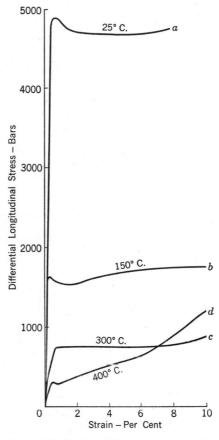

FIG. 8-15. Stress-strain curves for calcite compressed at 30° to [0001] and 75° to r_1 (e twinning impossible); confining pressure 5,000 bars. (*After F. J. Turner, D. T. Griggs, and H. C. Heard.*)

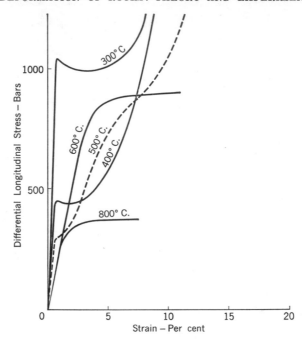

FIG. 8-16. Stress-strain curves for calcite compressed at 30° to [0001] and 75° to r_1 (e twinning impossible); confining pressure 5,000 bars. Different material from calcite of Fig. 8-15. (*After D. T. Griggs, F. J. Turner, and H. C. Heard.*)

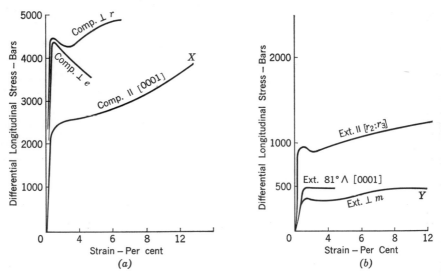

FIG. 8-17. Stress-strain curves for calcite for different orientations (e twinning impossible). (*a*) At 25°C, 5,000 bars. (*b*) At 300°C, 5,000 bars. (*After F. J. Turner. D. T. Griggs, and H. C. Heard.*)

At 25° and 300°C (Fig. 8-17) the longitudinal stress at the yield point of calcite is minimal for compression parallel to [0001] and for extension normal to [0001] (curves X, Y). Assuming that a single glide system is effective this suggests that the angle of inclination of the glide plane to [0001] is in the vicinity of 45°. So much may be inferred from stress-strain data. Identification of the system of translation gliding is possible only in the light of data drawn from analysis of microscopic structures in the deformed crystals (pages 336 to 344).

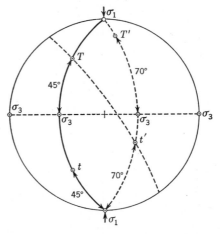

FIG. 8-18. Equal-area projection illustrating variation in coefficient of resolved shear stress S_o with orientation of glide systems in relation to axial compression σ_1 (see text).

Ductile Strain of Marble and Limestone.[37] We have seen already that ductility of marble and of limestone is a function of temperature and pressure. Even in extension experiments both rocks are thoroughly ductile at room and higher temperatures at 8,000 bars confining pressure, and at temperatures of 300°C or higher at 5,000 bars pressure.

Yule marble, the subject of many experiments by Griggs and his associates, has a remarkably homogeneous anisotropic fabric on both the mesoscopic and the microscopic scale. There is a simple foliation S marked by parallel alignment of somewhat lenticular grains; and the [0001] axes of the calcite grains are significantly concentrated at high angles to S. Correlated with anisotropy of fabric is a marked mechanical anisotropy: a cylinder cut normal to the foliation (so that [0001] of calcite tends to be inclined at low angles to the cylinder axis) is much stronger in compression than in extension (Fig. 8-19). The reverse is true for cylinders cut parallel to the foliation. In other words the marble is relatively weak when stressed so that most grains can twin on one or more e planes.

Under given physical conditions the yield strength (at 3 per cent strain) is higher for marble of any orientation than for single crystals of calcite of most orientations (broken curves in Fig. 8-19). Relatively coarse-grained marbles are much weaker than fine-grained limestones

[37] Griggs and Miller, *op. cit.*, pp. 853–862, 1951; D. T. Griggs, F. J. Turner, I. Borg, and J. Sosoka, Deformation of Yule marble, part V, *Geol. Soc. America Bull.*, vol. 64, pp. 1328–1334, 1953; F. J. Turner, D. T. Griggs, R. H. Clark, and R. Dixon, Deformation of Yule marble, part VII, *Geol. Soc. America Bull.*, vol. 67, pp. 1259–1264, 1956; Heard, *op. cit.*, pp. 199–210; Griggs, Turner, and Heard, *op. cit.*, pp. 87–89, 1960.

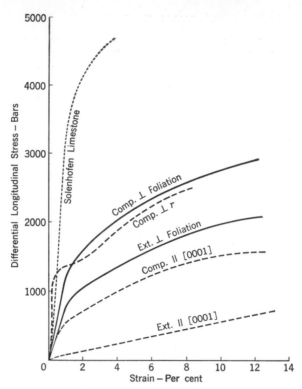

FIG. 8-19. Stress-strain curves for Yule marble (full lines) at 300°C and 5,000 bars confining pressure. (*After D. T. Griggs and colleagues.*) Broken curves are for calcite at 300°C and 5,000 bars. (*After F. J. Turner, D. T. Griggs, and H. C. Heard.*) Dotted curve is for Solenhofen limestone at 300°C and 3,000 bars. (*After H. C. Heard.*)

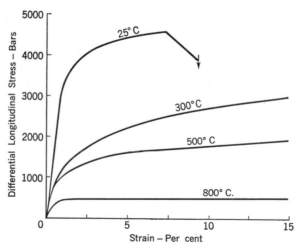

FIG. 8-20. Stress-strain curves for cylinders of Yule marble cut parallel to the foliation and deformed by extension at various temperatures. Confining pressure 5,000 bars; strain rate 3 per cent elongation per min. (*After D. T. Griggs, F. J. Turner, and H. C. Heard.*)

(dotted curve in Fig. 8-19).   Both rocks, like metallic aggregates, show notable strain hardening as evidenced by steady rise of the stress-strain curve beyond the yield point.   This effect is more marked for limestone than for marble.

Figure 8-20 shows the effect of temperature, at constant pressure and strain rate, on the stress-strain curve.   Increasing temperature markedly lowers both yield strength and strain hardening.   In Fig. 8-21 the yield stress (at 3 per cent strain) is plotted (log scale) against temperature for extension experiments on cylinders cut parallel to the foliation.   The

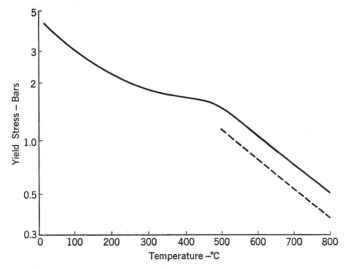

FIG. 8-21. Yield stress (at ϵ = 3 per cent) of Yule marble (on a log scale) as a function of temperature.   Extension of cylinders cut parallel to foliation; 5,000 bars.   Full curve, strain rate 3 per cent per min; broken curve, strain rate 0.2 per cent per min. (*After D. T. Griggs, F. J. Turner, and H. C. Heard.*)

change in slope in the 300° to 500°C interval seems to correspond with the change in shape of stress-strain curves of calcite crystals about 400° to 500°C (cf. page 302) and probably is due to some change in the glide mechanism over this range of temperature.

Ductile behavior of marble is also a function of strain rate—a fact of potentially great geologic significance when it is remembered that natural metamorphic deformation may be perhaps 10^{-10} times the normal experimental rate.   Decrease in the strain rate by a factor of 15—from the normal rate of 5×10^{-2} to a slow rate of 3×10^{-3} per sec—lowers the strength of Yule marble for a given strain at all temperatures, without changing the general shape of the stress-strain curve.[38]   At 500°C the strength of Yule marble at 5 per cent strain is decreased by 20 per cent at the slow strain rate.

[38] Griggs, Turner, and Heard, *op. cit.*, p. 88, 1960.

CREEP

The Problem of Creep.[39]   Elastic strain of any substance ideally is instantaneous, depending under given conditions solely on the magnitude of applied stress.   By contrast, as we have just seen, the element of time influences ductile strain and even affects the yield stress itself.   A characteristic of ductile behavior, related to the phenomenon of strain hardening, is that continued *rapid* strain beyond the yield point demands ever-increasing stress.   If, however, the stress is held constant for a comparatively long period (e.g., for many hours or days) some continuous flow may still ensue.   This is termed *creep* (cf. pages 278 to 283).

Because of the immensity of available time for natural metamorphic deformation creep is clearly a process of great possible geologic significance.   We must ask ourselves such questions as these: What is the nature and mechanism of creep?   What magnitude of strain is likely to develop from creep under geologically possible conditions?   Is creep possible in any stressed solid or only in solids stressed above some critical value?   How is the process influenced by temperature, pressure, and the presence of chemically active fluids?

Experiments have been devised to provide partial answers to some of these questions.   It is now possible in the laboratory[40] to vary strain rates by a factor of 10^{-6} over a temperature range of 500°C; but the lowest experimental strain rate—about 10^{-8} per sec (as compared with normal rates of 3 to 5×10^{-4}) still falls far short of geologically possible rates of the order of 10^{-12} to 10^{-14} per sec.   A general idea of the potentiality of rocks to creep at rates of this order may be gained by direct observation of creep at relatively high temperatures.   Temperature and time possibly exert a generally similar influence on the strain process.   So perhaps what is observed at 500° to 700°C indicates what might happen, if the rate of strain were slowed down by several orders of magnitude, at 300° to 400°C.   Moreover, allowing qualitatively for the great differences in ductility that are involved, much that is known about creep in metals may be applied in a general way to monomineralic rocks.

Laboratory Demonstration of Creep.   Figure 8-22 is the stress-strain curve for an experiment in which a cylinder of Yule marble was shortened by 37 per cent under variable stress over a 48-hr period.[41]   In the first

[39] D. T. Griggs, Creep of rocks, *Jour. Geology*, vol. 47, pp. 225–251, 1939; Barrett, *op. cit.*, pp. 365–369, 1952; J. Handin, Experimental deformation of rocks and minerals, *Colorado School of Mines Quart.*, vol. 52, pp. 75–98, 1957; E. Orowan, Mechanism of seismic faulting, *Geol. Soc. America Mem. 79*, pp. 335–339, 1960; E. C. Robertson, Creep of Solenhofen limestone under moderate hydrostatic pressure, *Geol. Soc. America Mem. 79*, pp. 229–230, 1960.

[40] H. C. Heard, The effect of time on the experimental deformation of rocks (abstract), *Jour. Geophys. Research*, vol. 66, p. 2534, 1961.

[41] Griggs, Turner, Borg, and Sosoka, *op. cit.*, pp. 1330–1331.

3 min (*a* to *b*) rapid increase of stress from zero to 1,900 bars was accompanied by strain of about 3 per cent.   The stress was now held constant for 30 min and slight creep (*b* to *c*) ensued.   The load was rapidly increased once more and again held constant, this time for 800 min at 2,600 bars; creep again set in, at an appreciably higher rate, and a strain of about 5 per cent (*d* to *e*) resulted.   Now the stress was temporarily relaxed to zero (*f*) with slight resultant reverse elastic (recoverable) flow. On resumption of rapid loading to 2,800 bars the response was purely

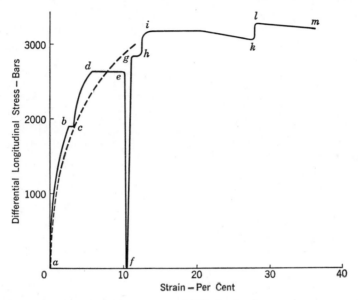

F<small>IG</small>. 8-22. Stress-strain curve for Yule marble (cylinder normal to foliation) in compression at varying strain rates, dry, 300°C, 5,000 bars confining pressure (see text). (*Simplified, after D. T. Griggs and J. Sosoka.*)   Broken curve is for an experiment (Fig. 8-19*b*) at normal strain rate.

elastic (*f* to *g*).   Then followed further creep *g* to *h*, (200 min) at 2,800 bars, *i* to *k*, (1,344 min) at about 3,000 bars, and *l* to *m*, (350 min) at about 3,200 bars.   At these higher pressures creep was initially rapid and then gradually slowed down pending renewed increase of stress (Fig. 8-23).

From this and similar experiments[42] it appears that for a given material under otherwise constant physical conditions there is a threshold value of stress—the *creep strength*—below which creep is inappreciable (cf. page 278).   Thus creep strength is virtually synonymous with *fundamental strength*[43]—the maximum differential stress that a body can withstand under given conditions of temperature and confining pressure without

[42] Griggs, *op. cit.*, pp. 560–564, 1936; Heard, *op. cit.*, 1961.
[43] Griggs, *op. cit.*, p. 564, 1936.

rupture or permanent flow.   The creep strength of Yule marble at a strain rate of 10^{-14} per sec—extrapolated from data at rates down to 10^{-8} per sec—varies from 500 bars at 300°C to 10^{-3} bar at 500°C.   Subjected to stress below the fundamental strength even for geologically long periods of time a rock body would respond only by elastic strain.   As

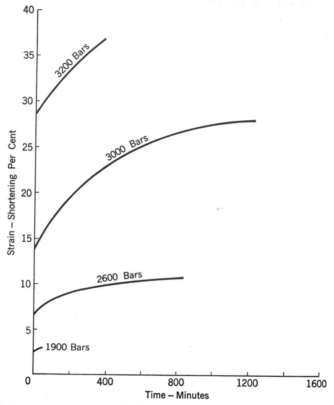

FIG. 8-23. Strain-time curve for Yule marble, same experiment as Fig. 8-22.   (*After D. T. Griggs and J. Sosoka.*)

stress is increased above the creep strength the rheologic state of the material changes: the rate of strain, and hence the effectiveness of creep, increase rapidly (Fig. 8-23).[44]

Griggs[45] found that the creep strength of alabaster at room temperature is greatly lowered by the presence of dilute hydrochloric acid or even water, in which gypsum is relatively soluble (Fig. 8-24).   In a normal rapid compression test at room temperature and pressure alabaster is essentially brittle: it fails by rupture under stress of about 500 bars after shortening only 0.3 per cent.   Loaded dry at 420 bars for 40 days a small additional reversible strain (0.07 per cent) was achieved by creep.   But

[44] Cf. Orowan, *op. cit.*, p. 336.
[45] Griggs, *op. cit.*, pp. 1010–1013, 1940.

in the presence of distilled water under a compressive stress of only 205 bars the rheologic properties were greatly affected: creep was much more effective, giving a strain of 1.5 per cent after 35 days, without rupture. In dilute hydrochloric acid under the same stress creep was more still rapid (2.7 per cent strain in 21 days) but ended in rupture.

The creep strength of a material is a function of temperature. As the melting point is approached, but while the rock is still strong with regard to stress of short duration, the creep strength becomes very low indeed, probably of the order of 10 or 100 bars.[46] "Hot creep" of this kind is doubtless the principal mechanism of deformation in a number of geologic environments, e.g., in glacial ice at subzero temperatures (stresses of only a few bars), in migmatite complexes, and in convecting sectors of the earth's mantle. Environments of low-grade regional metamorphism— the situations in which slaty cleavage and regular schistosity develop with greatest perfection—do not, however, fall within this category.

The Strain-Time Curve of Creep.   In any individual creep experiment under constant conditions the rate of creep changes with time. This behavior, well known for metals and rocks alike,[47] is illustrated in Fig. 8-25 by creep of alabaster in contact with distilled water at room temperature and pressure under different stresses (all well below the normal breaking strength).[48] The typical strain-time curve (Fig. 8-25b) shows three successive stages of behavior marked by changes of slope at x and y:

1. *Primary creep* from o to x is characterized by a decreasing strain rate such that log ϵ bears a linear relation to log t (Fig. 8-26b). Its total magnitude is small. Strain by primary creep is slowly reversed by recovery on relaxation of stress and for this reason this first stage is sometimes termed *transient* or *elastic flow* (firmoviscous strain of rheologists; see page 278). At low stresses not greatly above the creep strength, primary creep is commonly the only stage represented in a laboratory test (e.g., Fig. 8-26).[49] The strain rate of primary creep decreases notably with increase in confining pressure.

2. *Secondary creep* occurs at a constant minimum velocity between x and y and results in irreversible strain. By analogy with a viscous liquid, a coefficient of equivalent or apparent viscosity μ can be calculated thus:[50]

$$\mu = \frac{\sigma_1 - \sigma_3}{3(d\epsilon/dt)}$$

where $\sigma_1 - \sigma_3$ = differential stress (compression)

$d\epsilon/dt$ = strain rate (slope of the strain-time curve)

[46] Orowan, *op. cit.*, pp. 336, 338.

[47] E.g., D. T. Griggs, *op. cit.*, p. 562, 1936; *op. cit.*, pp. 234–245, 1939; J. Goguel, *op. cit.*, pp. 194–195; A. Nádai, *Theory of Flow and Fracture in Solids*, vol. I, p. 416, McGraw-Hill, New York, 1950; Barrett, *op. cit.*, pp. 365–369, 1952.

[48] Griggs, *op. cit.*, pp. 1010–1015, 1940.

[49] For discussion of primary creep in Solenhofen limestone see Robertson, *op. cit.*

[50] Cf. Griggs, *op. cit.*, pp. 229, 230, 1939; *op. cit.*, p. 1017, table 1, 1940.

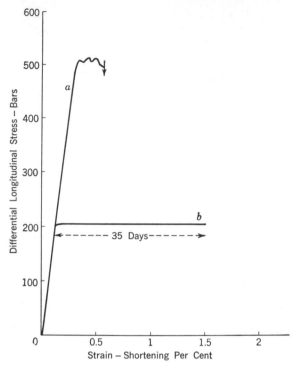

FIG. 8-24. Stress-strain curves for Ohio alabaster. a = normal rapid compressive test. b = loaded at 205 bars in water (creep). (*Data from D. T. Griggs.*)

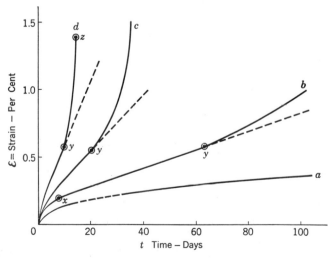

FIG. 8-25. Creep curves for alabaster in water at room temperature and pressure. Steady-state secondary creep rate is projected beyond y as broken lines. (*After D. T. Griggs.*) Longitudinal differential stresses: a = 103 bars; b = 150 bars; c = 205 bars; d = 250 bars, rupture at z.

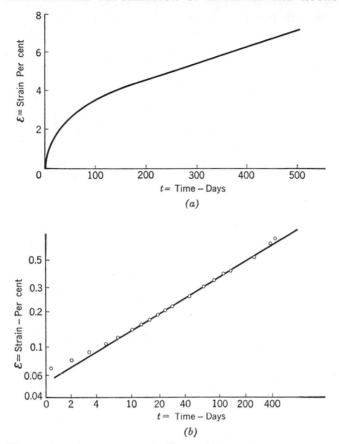

FIG. 8-26. Curves for primary creep of albaster in water at room temperature and pressure under longitudinal differential stress of 103 bars (Fig. 8-25a). (*After D. T. Griggs.*) (*a*) Normal coordinates. (*b*) Double log coordinates.

the rate of flow at this stage of creep is correlated with stress. The value of μ, too, depends on stress. Thus for the segment xy of curve b (Fig. 8-25) $\mu = 6.36 \times 10^{16}$ poises; for curve d, 1.60×10^{16} poises. For this reason secondary creep is sometimes called *steady-state* or *pseudo-viscous flow*.

3. *Tertiary creep* at an accelerating strain rate characterizes the third stage of the creep curve beyond y, and ultimately leads to rupture at z.

Mechanism of Creep: Implications Regarding Tectonites. "The mechanisms of creep include fracturing, twin gliding, translation gliding, recrystallization (including grain growth, diffusion and phase changes) and intergranular slip"[51]—in fact in Sander's terminology all types of componental movement, direct and indirect (cf. pages 37 and 38). Some

[51] Robertson, *op. cit.*, p. 234.

writers believe that primary creep is due principally to microfracturing and complementary rehealing; others assign an important role to intracrystalline gliding and limited displacement of grain boundaries. Intergranular movements of this latter kind and accompanying boundary adjustment by local recrystallization are generally thought to dominate secondary creep. In the tertiary stage, it is agreed, unhealed fractures develop progressively as microfracturing outstrips recrystallization, and finally fracture ensues on the mesoscopic scale.

Whatever its mechanism, it is clear that creep is a process of great potential in the evolution of tectonites, especially within the higher range of metamorphic temperatures. Experimental demonstration that creep ultimately leads to fracture on the mesoscopic scale in no way invalidates this conclusion. We envisage natural creep as a cyclic process many times repeated in a single metamorphic deformation; rupture terminating the tertiary stage of one creep cycle in a given domain with local release of stress would be followed by healing of fractures (recrystallization) and initiation of a new creep cycle beginning once more with primary creep. The view that under stress of long duration the rocks of the deep crust react to orogeny as relatively weak materials of low equivalent viscosity[52] receives general support from experimental data discussed in this chapter. It is further strengthened when it is remembered that complete recrystallization and chemical reaction play an all-important role in the evolution of most tectonites, and that a gas phase, maintained at pressures not greatly different from prevailing load pressures, commonly participates. Such chemical processes—whose influence on creep so far has not been systematically explored in the laboratory—must surely increase the effectiveness of creep as a mechanism of metamorphic deformation.

EXPERIMENTAL BEHAVIOR OF MISCELLANEOUS MINERALS AND ROCKS

Dolomite and Dolomite Rock.[53]   Two glide mechanisms are known for single crystals of dolomite:[54] (1) translation on $\{0001\} = c$ with an

---

[52] Cf. M. K. Hubbert, Strength of the earth, *Am. Assoc. Petroleum Geologists Bull.*, vol. 29, pp. 1630–1653, 1945; S. W. Carey, The rheid concept in geotectonics, *Geol. Soc. Australia Jour.*, vol. 1, pp. 67–117, 1954.

[53] F. J. Turner, D. T. Griggs, H. Heard, and L. E. Weiss, Plastic deformation of dolomite rock at 380°C., *Am. Jour. Sci.*, vol. 252, pp. 477–488, 1954; J. Handin and H. W. Fairbairn, Experimental deformation of Hasmark dolomite, *Geol. Soc. America Bull.*, vol. 66, pp. 1257–1273, 1955; Higgs and Handin, *op. cit.*, pp. 245–278; Griggs, Turner, and Heard, *op. cit.*, pp. 79–81, 1960; D. T. Griggs and J. Handin, Observations on fracture and a hypothesis of earthquakes, *Geol. Soc. America Mem. 79*, pp. 356, 357, 1960.

[54] A. Johnsen, Biegungen und Translationen, *Neues Jahrb. Mineralogie, Geologie, u. Paläontologie*, 1902, pt. 2, pp. 133–153, 1902; Higgs and Handin, *op. cit.*, pp. 250–253.

a axis as glide direction; (2) twin gliding on $\{02\bar{2}1\}$ = f with the edge $[f:a]$ = $[(02\bar{2}1):(2\bar{1}\bar{1}0)]$ as glide line, sense of slip negative (Fig. 8-27). Under a confining pressure of 5,000 bars dolomite crystals are ductile at all temperatures provided they are so oriented that the resolved shear stress on the basal translation system is high.   A favorable orientation is compression or extension normal to $\{10\bar{1}1\}$ = r (S_o on the [0001] translation system = 0.43).   At room temperature the critical resolved shear stress on $\{0001\}$ for yield by translation is 900 bars—about the same as

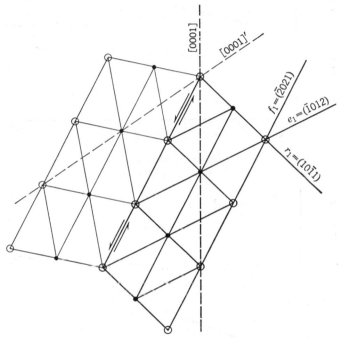

FIG. 8-27. Twinning of dolomite (diagrammatic) as seen in plane $\{1\bar{2}10\}$—normal to a_2 axis. CO_3 groups omitted; Ca^{++} and Mg^{++} ions represented by open and solid circles respectively.   Dark lines initial lattice, light lines twinned lattice.   For spatial relations of r_1, e_1, f_1, and a_2 compare Fig. 8-12.

for translation in calcite.   A most unusual feature is that, at least from room temperature to 400°C, the strength increases with temperature (Fig. 8-28).

Below 400°C dolomite crystals, if oriented so that the resolved shear stress on $\{0001\}$ is inappreciable, are strong and brittle (curve a, Fig. 8-29).   Compression or extension normal or parallel to [0001] exemplifies this behavior.   At 400°C, however, crystals in extension parallel to an a axis or compressed parallel to [0001] become markedly ductile (Fig. 8-29, curve b) and become strained by twin gliding on $\{02\bar{2}1\}$ = f.   The critical resolved shear stress at the yield point is 1,160 bars at 400°C—

about 60 times that necessary for e twinning in calcite under the same conditions. It drops rapidly to 500 bars at 500°C. Dolomite is then significantly weaker for twin gliding than for basal translation. Consequently a crystal at 500°C oriented for extension normal to r_1 (for which

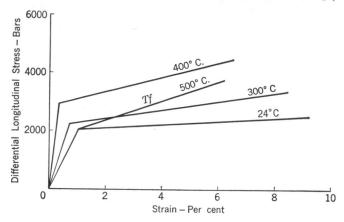

FIG. 8-28. Average stress-strain curves for dolomite crystals in extension normal to r_1. T_f indicates failure by twin gliding on f_1.   (*After D. V. Higgs and J. Handin.*)

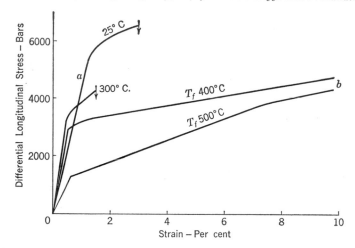

FIG. 8-29. Average stress-strain curves for dolomite crystals compressed parallel to [0001] at 5,000 bars confining pressure.   Arrows indicate failure by rupture; T_f indicates twin gliding on f.   (*After D. V. Higgs and J. Handin.*)

S_o on f_1 is 0.27, sense negative, while S_o on {0001} is 0.43) fails preferentially by twin gliding and is sensibly weaker than a similarly oriented crystal at 400°C (Fig. 8-28).

Just as in the case of marble and calcite, dolomite rock under given conditions is much stronger than a single crystal and shows more pronounced strain hardening. Strength decreases with temperature (cf.

Fig. 8-30), but not nearly to such a marked extent as with marble—a type of behavior which doubtless reflects the anomalous increase in resistance to translation in single crystals as the temperature rises from 20° to 400°C. Strength also increases with confining pressure; at 500°C and 5,000 bars the rock is significantly stronger than at 380°C and 3,000 bars (broken curve, Fig. 8-30). The strength of dolomite rock is almost independent of the pattern of preferred orientation of its component crystals.[55]

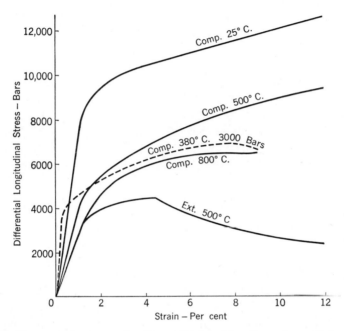

FIG. 8-30. Stress-strain curves for Dover Plains dolomite rock; confining pressure 5,000 bars, except broken curve at 3,000 bars. (*After D. T. Griggs, F. J. Turner, and H. C. Heard.*)

As might be expected from the recorded behavior of single crystals, crystalline dolomite rock is stronger and less ductile than marble under the same conditions. This property under natural conditions might be inferred from the common occurrence of fractured blocks and boudins of dolomite in plastically deformed marbles of metamorphic terranes. Griggs and Handin[56] have simulated development of boudinage by experimental elongation, at 5,000 bars, of composite cylinders consisting of a dolomite core sheathed in marble. At room temperature the dolomite core is brittle and fails by diagonal fracturing; but at 500°C the dolomite

[55] Handin and H. W. Fairbairn, *op. cit.*, p. 1264, 1955.
[56] Griggs and Handin, *op. cit.*, pp. 356–357, 1960.

is sufficiently ductile to develop local necks (incipient boudinage) into which the surrounding marble flowed readily.

Quartz.[57]   At room temperature and pressure quartz is brittle and very strong, the breaking strength of a crystal compressed parallel to [0001] being about 25,000 bars.   In normal rapid compressive tests it remains essentially brittle even at pressures up to 10,000 bars and temperatures as high as 800°C—a range which spans the α- $\rightleftarrows$ β-quartz transition (704°C at 5,000 bars).   Slight ductility (permanent strain of less than 1 per cent) is indicated for slower strain in the higher range of temperature, e.g., a crystal compressed for 30 min under a constant differential pressure of 22,000 bars at 500°C and 5,000 bars confining pressure.[58]

Strength of quartz at room temperature is roughly doubled by raising the confining pressure to 5,000 bars.   At this pressure increase in temperature from 20° to 800°C lowers the strength from about 50,000 to about 25,000 bars.   At 800°C the quartz must be the β phase.

The strength of quartz under given conditions seems to be sensitive to the condition of the surface of the test cylinder.   This perhaps accounts for the marked discrepancies between strength data recorded by different workers using a diversity of confining media—kerosene, copper, bismuth, etc.   Great reduction in strength was observed in crystals held in contact with a mildly alkaline solvent.   Thus at 400°C and 300 bars confining pressure the breaking strength of quartz in a dilute solution of sodium carbonate is only about 4,000 bars—a sixfold reduction compared with dry quartz at room temperature and pressure.   Unpublished experimental data of Christie and Heard show that ductility of quartz is increased and its strength greatly lowered if the strain rate is reduced by several orders of magnitude.

Silicate Rocks—Granite, Dunite, Pyroxenite.[59]   At 5,000 bars confining pressure and a normal rapid strain rate (5×10^{-4} per sec) the respective strengths of granite, dunite, and enstatite pyroxenite at any given temperature are mutually similar.   Average values of compressive strength are 20,000 bars at 25°C, 10,000 bars at 500°C, 7,000 bars at 800°C.   These values are for yield strength at 3 per cent strain and also are maximum strengths (cf. Fig. 8-31).

The shape of the stress-strain curves, and especially the high stress continuously sustained up to strains of 10 or 15 per cent, suggest failure by some form of flow.   There is little indication, however, of strain hardening such as characterizes truly ductile strain of marble and

---

[57] D. T. Griggs and J. F. Bell, Experiments bearing on the orientation of quartz in deformed rocks, *Geol. Soc. America Bull.*, vol. 49, pp. 1723–1746, 1938; Griggs, Turner, and Heard, *op. cit.*, pp. 65–72, 100, fig. 30, 1960.

[58] Griggs, Turner, and Heard, *op. cit.*, pp. 71, 72, 1960.

[59] *Ibid.*, pp. 50–65, 102.

dolomite rock. Indeed the curves for granite tend to fall continuously with increasing strain in the manner typical of curves for Solenhofen limestone in the brittle-ductile transition (cf. page 290). Moreover, failure of granite specimens at all temperatures is due to development of a single diagonal shear zone inclined at between 28° and 41° to the axis of maximum stress σ_1. Similar shear zones develop in dunite and pyroxenite except in the higher temperature range—500° to 800°C—where, especially in pyroxenite, strain is more evenly distributed. We conclude that failure—except in dunite and pyroxenite at high temperature—is essentially brittle, and that the fractured specimen remains coherent by virtue

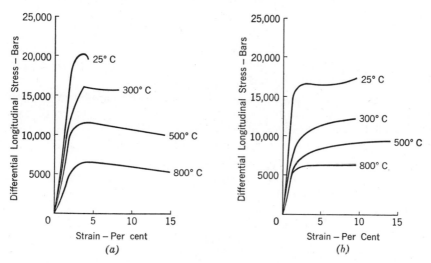

FIG. 8-31. Stress-strain curves, 5,000 bars confining pressure for (a) granite, (b) pyroxenite. (*After D. T. Griggs, F. J. Turner, and H. C. Heard.*)

of internal friction on the microscopic fracture surfaces. This view is substantiated by the microscopic character of the fabric (typically mylonitic) in the shear zones.

Experimental data on creep of granitic rocks have been recorded by Lomnitz.[60] Specimens were tested in a torsion apparatus, under very low shear stress (less than 140 bars) of about one week's duration. As might be expected only transient creep of small magnitude, at the usual logarithmically decreasing rate, was observed. And the strain rate is directly proportional to the magnitude of stress. Lomnitz concludes that it is not impossible that, even under small stress, very slow steady-state creep might ensue within a geologically possible span of time and might ultimately result in considerable deformation.

[60] C. Lomnitz, Creep measurements in igneous rocks, *Jour. Geology*, vol. 64, pp. 473–479, 1956.

APPLICATION OF EXPERIMENTAL DATA TO TECTONITES

Locally, in slickenside films, mylonite zones, and limited zones of dislocation, tectonites may form at low temperatures and at pressures consistent with depths of a few kilometers. But information on the stability ranges of common mineral assemblages of regional metamorphism indicates that regional development of tectonites is virtually restricted to temperatures of about 300° to 800°C and confining pressures ranging from a few thousand to perhaps 10,000 bars.[61] Slaty cleavage, a characteristic feature of tectonites in lower metamorphic grades of the greenschist facies, must develop at 300° to 400°C and pressures upward of 4,000 bars.[62] The regular almost planar foliation of quartzo-feldspathic granulites must be assigned to temperatures of the order of 700° to 800°C and a wide range of pressures whose upper limit may be around 10,000 bars.[63] Moreover, many tectonites of high metamorphic grade crystallized close to or within their melting range.

Stress-strain and strain-time data discussed in this chapter give a good deal of general information as to the behavior to be expected of rocks subjected to long-continued stress in such environments. Most rocks under rapidly applied stress at room temperature and pressure are strong and brittle. Strength increases with confining pressure but in most instances decreases with rising temperature. Ductility—the ability of the rock to flow continuously and homogeneously without great decrease in strength—increases markedly with both confining pressure and temperature. Under rapidly applied stress of short duration most rocks in the metamorphic environment—except where fusion is actually in progress—should behave as strong but appreciably ductile materials. An exception is dry quartzite; for quartz shows little if any sign of ductility and remains very strong under the conditions stated. This picture changes with consideration of the time factor in the light of experiments on creep. Under relatively low stress of long duration compatible with the duration of an orogeny, alternating creep, fracture, and rehealing by crystallization might accomplish strains of the order inferred from the fabrics of tectonites. Creep would be especially effective where recrystallization, rapid diffusion of gas, or incipient fusion were taking place. In environments favorable to creep the response of a rock to long-sustained stress could be more like that of a weak, viscous, ductile material under familiar laboratory conditions. Marble at 500°C and 5,000 bars certainly would behave thus; but we still have no knowledge

[61] Cf. W. S. Fyfe, F. J. Turner, and J. Verhoogen, Metamorphic reactions and metamorphic facies, *Geol. Soc. America Mem. 73*, p. 237, fig. 107, 1958.

[62] F. J. Turner and J. Verhoogen, *Igneous and Metamorphic Petrology*, 2d ed., McGraw-Hill, New York, p. 534, 1960.

[63] *Ibid.*, p. 557.

of the threshold conditions beyond which rocks such as granite and schist assume such properties and can be regarded as rheids.

Experimental data also yield information as to the geometry of strain under given conditions. A cylinder of ductile marble, strongly elongated at say 700°C, may become elliptical in section; and the principal axes of the ellipse are regularly oriented with respect to the directions of the principal stresses σ_1 and σ_3 and to directions of anisotropy in the initial marble fabric. Herein are valuable data for testing hypotheses relating to symmetry of stress, strain, and fabrics—a topic to be discussed in the next chapter.

Finally it is found that over the whole range of experimental conditions stress-strain and strain-time curves closely resemble in form the corresponding curves for metallic aggregates of varying strength and ductility. We may infer a general parallel between strain of rocks and strain of metals. This strengthens cautious interpretation of tectonite evolution in terms of processes familiar to the metallurgist—crystal gliding, hot- and cold-working, annealing, and so on. Discussion of this topic must await examination of the crystal and rock fabrics resulting from experimental deformation. To this we turn in the ensuing chapter.

CHAPTER 9

MICROSCOPIC FABRICS OF EXPERIMENTALLY DEFORMED ROCKS AND MINERALS: PREDICTION, OBSERVATIONS, AND INFERENCES

INTRODUCTION

The experimental programs of Griggs and Handin have yielded much needed information as to the nature and evolution of microscopic fabrics resulting from deformation under controlled conditions compatible with some geologic environments. Of special importance are patterns of preferred orientation of grains in crystalline aggregates, notably in marble and dolomite rock. The symmetry of these has been compared with that of stress and of observed strain. Observations have been made on such structural characteristics as grain shape, twin lamellae, and grain boundaries and in some rocks newly crystallized grains have been noted and measured. The main purpose of this chapter is to review the microscopic data with special emphasis on preferred orientation of crystals in the deformed aggregates. These are artificially formed tectonites of limited diversity. They supply evidence that may be applied to the broad problems of genesis and interpretation of natural tectonite fabrics. Moreover, since the artificial rock fabrics evolved under specific controlled conditions, it is possible to speculate on orienting mechanisms against a background compounded of mathematical prediction and of technological theory based on extensive and diversified experimental experience in the fields of metallurgy and ceramics. This background is briefly set out in the sections that now follow.

GENERAL THEORETICAL PREDICTIONS

Symmetry of Preferred Orientation. As first recognized and repeatedly emphasized by Sander, the most important general clue to the kinematics and dynamics of deformation is the symmetry of the resultant tectonite fabric.[1] Paterson and Weiss[2] have reviewed and reassessed the

[1] E.g., F. J. Turner, Lineation, symmetry and internal movement in monoclinic tectonite fabrics, *Geol. Soc. America Bull.*, vol. 68, pp. 1–18, 1957.

[2] M. S. Paterson and L. E. Weiss, Symmetry concepts in the structural analysis of deformed rocks, *Geol. Soc. America Bull.*, vol. 72, pp. 841–882, 1961.

kinematic and dynamic implications of fabric symmetry in tectonites; and their conclusions are summarized later in this book (pages 385 to 391). Here it is sufficient to predict, on the basis of symmetry theory, that the symmetry elements common to (1) the system of externally applied forces (load) and (2) the initial anisotropic fabric of the test material (e.g., Yule marble) will appear also in (3) the geometry of homogeneous strain (including rotation as well as change of shape) and in (4) the final deformed fabric (notably in the pattern of preferred orientation of the component crystals). In the type of experiment conducted by Griggs and Handin it is possible to observe independently all four of these systems. So the experimental data provide an adequate test of the symmetry principle as applied to tectonite fabrics.

Preferred Orientation of Plates and Rods in a Flowing Medium.[3] Predictions of a completely different kind relate to the behavior of plates and rods rotating in space during flow of an otherwise homogeneous medium. Mathematical analysis so far has been restricted to simple idealized models somewhat remote from geologic reality.

March considered the special case where initially randomly oriented rods and platelets become oriented through "affine deformation of the medium."[4] His mathematical analysis concerns an affine transformation. Two cases are treated. The first postulates rods and particles having the composition of the medium itself; they would necessarily change shape during the transformation (homogeneous strain) process, but their boundary surfaces would have no mechanical significance and so would behave in an ideally passive manner. The second case treats small rigid particles incapable of change in shape or size. March found that in both cases the same patterns of preferred orientation of particles according to grain shape would develop: (1) rods would tend to align themselves with their long axes parallel to the longest axis A of the strain ellipsoid of the enclosing medium; (2) normals to platelets would tend to approximate the shortest axis C of the strain ellipsoid.

From March's analysis Sander[5] deduced the development of girdle patterns in special cases where the strain ellipsoid is a spheroid: (1) For a prolate spheroid of strain the poles of plates occupy a girdle whose axis is A, the principal symmetry axis (∞-fold) of strain. (2) For an oblate

[3] G. B. Jeffrey, The motion of ellipsoidal particles immersed in a viscous fluid, *Royal Soc. London Proc.*, vol. 102, A, pp. 161–179, 1922; A. March, Mathematische Theorie der Regelung nach der Korngestalt bei affiner Deformation, *Zeitschr. Kristallographie*, vol. 81, pp. 285–298, 1932; E. B. Knopf and E. Ingerson, Structural petrology, *Geol. Soc. America Mem. 6*, pp. 133–136, 1938; B. Sander, *Einführung in die Gefügekunde der Geologischen Körper*, Pt. II, pp. 107–110, Springer, Berlin, Vienna, 1950.

[4] March, *op. cit.*, p. 285.

[5] B. Sander, Zur Kinematik passiver Gefügeregelungen, *Zeitschr. Kristallographie*, vol. 81, pp. 298–308 (especially pp. 301, 302), 1932.

spheroid the long axes of rods would fall in a girdle normal to the C axis of strain.   Note that in Sander's model the symmetry of the final fabric is identical with that of strain (Fig. 9-1).

Jeffrey calculated that small elongated or flattened spheroidal particles immersed in a slowly flowing highly viscous fluid would ultimately tend toward stable orientations as follows: (1) elongated bodies, with their long axes normal to the plane of undisturbed motion of fluid (equivalent

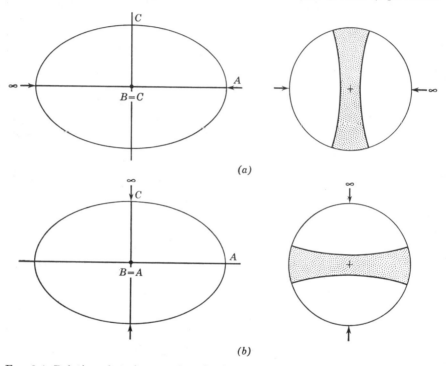

(a)

(b)

Fig. 9-1. Relation of strain to preferred orientation in Sander's extension of March's analysis. (a) Prolate spheroid of strain (left), girdle of poles of plates (right). (b) Oblate spheroid of strain (left), girdle of rod axes (right).   Arrows indicate axis of ∞-fold symmetry.

to the deformation plane) and thus normal to the direction of flow; (2) flattened bodies with one diameter normal to the deformation plane so that the poles of the planes of flattening (e.g., the poles of disks) would occupy a girdle coinciding with the deformation plane.   The axis of the girdle coincides with the axis of vortices in flow.   Here there is a correlation between symmetry of fabric and symmetry of movement.

The above mathematical treatments are mentioned here mainly because since the earliest days of petrography the well-known preferred orientation of mica crystals in slates and schists has been widely attributed to passive rotation of the mica in an enclosing flowing matrix.   In the absence of reliable information as to the mechanical behavior of mica and its associated minerals (such as quartz and feldspar) under metamorphic conditions we do not subscribe to this general interpretation of mica patterns in tectonites. However, some such type of behavior in a more complex model might play a part in orienting clay particles during compaction of shale, or even in orienting mica particles in some tectonites—perhaps, for example, in the conversion of shale to slate where a penetrative pore fluid at pressures comparable with the load pressure is continuously present. Moreover, the mathematical treatments of March and Jeffrey perhaps give some indication of the behavior to be expected on a much larger scale where fabric elements such as bedding or other s-surfaces become passively rotated during essentially homogeneous strain of the enclosing rock.

Preferred Orientation in Syntectonically Crystallized Aggregates. In the evolution of many tectonite fabrics deformation and recrystallization are broadly synchronous. Even in the simplest case of a monomineralic aggregate stressed homogeneously on the mesoscopic scale, stress on the scale of a few grains is likely to be heterogeneously distributed. There must be local fluctuations in free energy corresponding to stress fluctuations from grain to grain or even within the domain of a single grain, so that there must be a tendency for some grains to grow at the expense of others, or even for new phases to nucleate preferentially at points of maximum or minimum local stress. Recrystallization so induced would reduce the total free energy of the stressed system and tend toward a state such that stress throughout the rock would be minimal.[6] Accordingly a preexisting pattern of preferred orientation could be modified or obliterated, or an entirely new state of preferred orientation could develop. Such effects are in fact well known in experimentally strained materials such as metals and marble.

If syntectonic recrystallization involves evolution of a more from a less stable pattern of preferred orientation, and relative stability of the system under given conditions is determined primarily by energy factors, the problem is open to a thermodynamic solution. Riecke[7] discussed from this standpoint the lowering of melting point of an elastic body under homogeneous nonhydrostatic stress. His analysis has been widely, though incorrectly, invoked to explain parallel alignment of elongate or tabular mineral grains in schists: it has been said, for example, that according to "Riecke's principle" grains tend to dissolve at stressed faces and grow at free faces and in this manner develop a flattened or elongated habit in the plane normal to an axial compression. No such conclusion

---

[6] F. J. Turner and J. Verhoogen, *Igneous and Metamorphic Petrology*, 2d ed., p. 476, McGraw-Hill, New York, 1960.

[7] E. Riecke, Ueber das Gleichgewicht zwischen einem festen homogen deformierten Koerper und einer flussigen Phase, *Annalen der Physik*, vol. 54, pp. 731–738, 1895.

follows directly from Riecke's analysis, although comparable behavior is likely[8]—and indeed has been experimentally induced—in nonhomogeneously stressed solids in contact with a saturated solution.

In recent years several writers[9] have treated rigorously the problem of orientation by recrystallization from the thermodynamic standpoint. Unfortunately no general agreement has been reached as to either thermodynamic theory or predicted states of orientation. For a critical discussion of the various current theories—which the reader must evaluate for himself—reference should be made to an essay by Kamb, and critical comments thereon.[10] In a theory of equilibrium under nonhydrostatic stress as applied to linearly elastic crystals under infinitesimal strain, Kamb[11] predicts stable patterns of preferred orientation in situations of uniaxial stress, e.g., [0001] of calcite parallel to the axis of greatest compressive stress σ_1; [0001] of α-quartz in a girdle normal to σ_1. The theory of MacDonald[12] extends a treatment of materials obeying a linear elastic stress-strain law to cover also systems in which strain is the result of an irreversible process such as plastic flow; and he predicts a stable orientation such that strain energy is maximized. On this basis Brace[13] calculates stable orientations under axial compression as follows: calcite, $\{10\bar{1}1\}$ approximately normal to σ_1, [0001] in a small-circle girdle 49° from σ_1; α-quartz, $\{02\bar{2}1\}$ normal to σ_1, [0001] in a small-circle girdle 71° from σ_1.

Comparison of predicted with natural and experimentally induced fabrics is not enough to test the validity of rival theories nor to permit dynamic interpretation of natural preferred orientation patterns. The writers cited above agree that the differences in chemical potential that constitute the driving force of recrystallization of elastic solids under nonhydrostatic stress are very small, of the order of a fraction of a calorie per mole for stress differences of 1,000 bars. Surface tension effects, which are probably considerable, are perforce neglected in theoretical treatments for lack of adequate data.[14] Likewise excluded is annealing

[8] Turner and Verhoogen, op. cit., p. 476, 1960.

[9] J. Verhoogen, The chemical potential of a stressed solid, Am. Geophys. Union Trans., vol. 32, pp. 251–258, 1951; W. B. Kamb, Theory of preferred crystal orientation developed by crystallization under stress, Jour. Geology, vol. 67, pp. 153–170, 1959; The thermodynamic theory of nonhydrostatically stressed solids, Jour. Geophys. Research, vol. 66, pp. 259–271, 1961; G. F. J. MacDonald, Orientation of anisotropic minerals in a stress field, Geol. Soc. America Mem. 79, pp. 1–8, 1960; W. F. Brace, Orientation of anisotropic minerals in a stress field: discussion, Geol. Soc. America Mem. 79, pp. 9–20, 1960.

[10] Kamb, op. cit., 1961; discussion by G. J. F. MacDonald and by A. Hoffer, Jour. Geophys. Research, vol. 66, pp. 2599, 2600, 1961.

[11] Kamb, op. cit., 1959.

[12] MacDonald, op. cit.

[13] Brace, op. cit.

[14] MacDonald, op. cit., p. 5; Brace, op. cit., p. 9.

recrystallization of previously deformed crystal aggregates—post-tectonic recrystallization involving release of stored energy of considerable magnitude.[15]   Experiment shows that this latter can be a powerful orienting or deorienting mechanism; and metamorphic recrystallization of monomineralic rocks such as quartzite and marble may in fact commonly be an annealing process.[16]   As the situation now stands experiment rather than thermodynamic prediction seems more likely to provide information relating preferred orientation patterns of syntectonic recrystallization to simple stress systems—especially since the "stable" patterns in tectonites and worked metals probably reflect a steady state controlled by flow rather than a stable condition.

DEFORMATION, RECRYSTALLIZATION, AND PREFERRED ORIENTATION OF METALS[17]

Cold- and Hot-working.   At room temperature, permanent deformation of metals is accomplished mainly through flow of individual grains by intragranular translation or twin gliding.   At the same time each grain rotates in space in the sense opposite to that of internal gliding.   Progressive strain is accompanied by *strain hardening*, now generally attributed to development and storing of lattice defects—especially dislocations—within the strained crystals.   By virtue of the energy so stored, the free energy of the strain-hardened metal is higher than that of unstrained metal under the same conditions.   After release of stress, strain hardening—as evidenced by increased hardness and a higher yield point on the stress-strain curve—tends slowly to diminish.   This is the process known as *recovery*.   It involves no recrystallization about new nuclei.   At low temperatures recovery may be slow or even imperceptible; but with rising temperature the rate and degree of recovery increase, and above some critical temperature recovery is so effective that strain hardening even fails to develop.   Deformation at temperatures low enough to permit appreciable strain hardening is termed *cold-working* as contrasted with

[15] E.g., L. M. Clarebrough, M. E. Hargreaves, D. Mitchell, and G. W. West (The determination of the energy stored in a metal during plastic deformation, *Royal Soc. London Proc.*, vol. 215, A, pp. 518, 519, 1952) record release of 6 to 20 calories per mole during annealing of cold-worked copper.

[16] M. J. Buerger and E. Washken, Metamorphism of minerals, *Am. Mineralogist*, vol. 32, pp. 296–308, 1947; D. T. Griggs, M. S. Paterson, H. C. Heard, and F. J. Turner, Annealing recrystallization in calcite crystals and aggregates, *Geol. Soc. America Mem. 79*, pp. 21–23, 1960.

[17] Parts of this section are quoted with slight modification from F. J. Turner, D. T. Griggs, and H. C. Heard, Experimental deformation of calcite crystals, *Geol. Soc. America Bull.*, vol. 65, pp. 893–897, 1954; Griggs, Paterson, Heard, and Turner, *op. cit.*, pp. 23, 24.   See also C. S. Barrett, *Structure of Metals*, 2d ed., pp. 336–508, McGraw-Hill, New York, 1952.

hot-working at temperatures too high for strain hardening to occur.   We have already seen that in experimental deformation of calcite and marble strain hardening, as shown by stress-strain curves, ceases to be appreciable at 500°C.   Above this temperature deformation of marble falls in the category of hot-working.

Microscopic Character of Strained Metal.   In the fabric of a cold-worked metal grain outlines are characterized by distortion, elongation, flattening, bending, marginal granulation, and so on.   Within individual grains microscopic strain effects such as the following are visible in polished sections: *twin lamellae*, rendered visible by differential etching of the polished surface with acid; *deformation bands*, which are narrow more or less rationally oriented lamellae within which the orientation of the lattice progressively departs from that of the host crystal as deformation proceeds, and within which gliding is localized—usually on planes transverse to the trend of the band; *kink bands*, which are simple deformation bands, sometimes microscopic but commonly mesoscopic in scale.   Kink bands have a special significance in elucidation of the active glide mechanism in experiments on single crystals.   They are bounded by surfaces of bend gliding transverse to the glide plane, and with progressive strain the material in the kink band rotates (with reference to external coordinates) about an axis which initially lies in the glide plane T, normal to the glide direction t.   Kinking is a consequence of the usual experimental condition that the undeformed ends of the specimen are constrained to remain coaxial (cf. Fig. 9-2).   In the usual situation of axial stress the glide plane progressively approaches the extension axis (the axis of minimal stress σ_3) or departs from the axis of principal compressive stress σ_1.   The use of experimentally observed kinking in elucidating an unknown glide mechanism will be elaborated later in connection with translation gliding in calcite (pages 336 to 344).

In experimentally deformed metals microscopic lamellae and lines also appear on the previously polished surface of the specimen; and these too give some indication of the mechanism of gliding.   To this category belong *slip lines*, representing displacements of the order of 1μ where active glide planes cut the surface of an individual crystal.   *Slip bands*, commonly about 1μ apart, are closely spaced clusters of slip lines.   Where twinning occurs in deformation of single crystals of metal, corresponding lamellae appear on the surface of the specimen.[18]   Lüders' lines are the outcrops of closely spaced shear surfaces or thin layers on the external surface of a strained metallic aggregate.

Preferred Orientation in Cold-worked Metals.   In a cold-worked metallic aggregate the crystals assume a high degree of preferred orientation, the symmetry of which precisely duplicates that of the working

[18] E.g., E. B. Knopf and E. Ingerson, Structural petrology, *Geol. Soc. America Mem. 6*, p. 90, pl. 10, 1938.

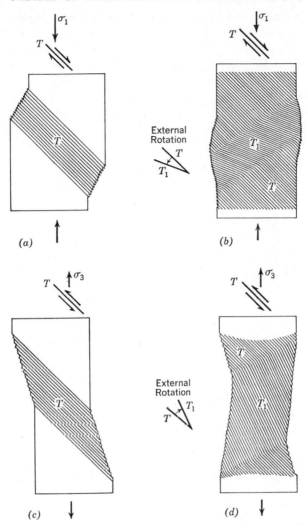

FIG. 9-2. Development of kink bands in axial compression (a, b) and extension (c, d). External rotation is shown by change of orientation of active glide plane from T to T_1 in b and d. In a and c the ends of the specimen are free to move laterally. In b and d the ends are constrained to remain coaxial. (*After D. V. Higgs and J. Handin.*)

process.[19]   Figure 9-3a is an orientation diagram for {111}—the plane of readiest gliding—in a strip of cold-rolled aluminum.   The strip was reversed between passes so that the symmetry of the working process was orthorhombic; and this is reflected in almost perfect orthorhombic symmetry of fabric.   The fabric of a second strip rolled in one sense only—a monoclinic working process—is shown in Fig. 9-3b whose symmetry likewise is monoclinic.   Strain in both cases involves shortening normal to the plane of rolling and elongation in the rolling direction RD, the dimension in the axis of rolling being almost unchanged;[20] its symmetry is of course orthorhombic.   The ideal orientation corresponding to the maxima of Fig. 9-3a is one in which {123} is parallel to the plane of rolling and [1$\bar{2}$1] coincides with the rolling direction.   The plane {123} and direction [1$\bar{2}$1] do not constitute a glide system.

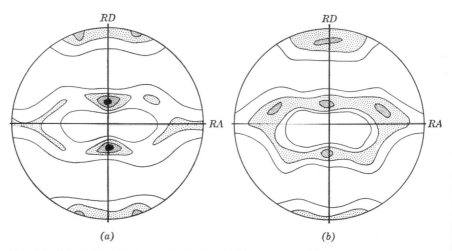

(a)   (b)

FIG. 9-3. Orientation diagrams ("pole figures," in stereographic projection) for {111} in cold-rolled aluminum strip.   (*After C. S. Barrett.*)   (*a*) Rolled in alternating senses in direction *RD* about an axis *RA*.   (*b*) Rolled in a constant sense in direction *RD* about an axis *RA*.   Contours on an arbitrary scale showing relative intensities determined by Geiger counter.

The Orienting Process in Cold-working of Metals.[21]   It is generally thought that the fabric of cold-worked metallic aggregates is the product of a complex process of crystal gliding and accompanying rotation of the individual grains.   Knowing the mechanism of gliding it should be possible to predict both the stress-strain curve and the manner in which preferred orientation will develop in a polycrystalline aggregate.   Outstanding among the attempts to do this in the field of metallurgy is Taylor's treatment of aluminum aggregates.[22]   Aluminum has face-centered cubic symmetry and can glide with equal ease on each of 24 glide systems of the type $T = (111)$ $t = [10\bar{1}]$; so the angles between glide systems for which the resolved shear stress is maximal in each of two adjacent

[20] *Ibid.*, p. 469.
[21] *Ibid.*, pp. 448–457, 469–480, 484.
[22] G. I. Taylor, Plastic strain in metals, *Inst. Metals Jour.*, vol. 62, pp. 307–324, 1938.

crystals must always be small. This is one reason why there is little difference between the respective stress-strain curves for an aggregate and for a single crystal of aluminum.

Taylor assumed that the strain in each grain of an aggregate is identical with that of the aggregate as a whole—a condition possible only if five glide systems can operate simultaneously in each grain. From the principle of least work he deduced which systems would function in a grain of any given orientation. The stress-strain curve which he so predicted for an aluminum aggregate agreed closely with experimental curves. Moreover, he predicted changes in grain orientation qualitatively agreeing with those observed experimentally. It was shown, however, by Barrett and Levenson[23] that in about one-third of the grains the paths of rotation are not those predicted by Taylor. There is abundant microscopic evidence that strain in metallic grains of an aggregate is not strictly homogeneous.[24] For this reason there is still a wide range of individual views between Taylor's hypothesis of homogeneous strain and other hypotheses which assume that the strain of each grain is in no way restricted by the behavior of neighboring grains. Strict homogeneity, in the sense that the strain at all points in the aggregate is identical, is incompatible with the concept of the movement picture of strain as developed on pages 370 to 378.

Whether strain of an aggregate is approximately homogeneous or essentially heterogeneous, it is generally agreed that cold-working leads toward "stable" orientations of the lattice (more properly termed steady-state orientations) which persist unchanged as strain becomes extreme. In these "stable" orientations two or more glide systems can function simultaneously. A glance at the stable patterns recorded in "pole diagrams" of standard metallurgical works shows that these are characterized above all by their symmetry; and this symmetry faithfully duplicates that of the working process.

Preferred Orientation in Hot-worked Metals.[25] Hot-working commonly produces an orientation pattern similar to that of the corresponding cold-worked aggregate but with a much greater degree of scatter for the same degree of strain. Where the metal is worked above the temperature of a polymorphic inversion, nearly random orientation may result.

---

[23] C. S. Barrett and L. H. Levenson, The structure of aluminum after compression, *Am. Inst. Mining Metall. Engineers Trans.*, vol. 137, pp. 112–126, 1940.

[24] E.g., W. Boas and M. E. Hargreaves, On the inhomogeneity of plastic deformation in the crystals of an aggregate, *Royal Soc. London Proc.*, A, vol. 193, pp. 89–97, 1948; W. Boas and G. W. Ogilvie, The plastic deformation of a crystal in a polycrystalline aggregate, *Acta Metallurgica*, vol. 2, pp. 655–659, 1954.

[25] E.g., R. K. McGeary and B. Lustman, Preferred orientation in zirconium, *Jour. Metals*, vol. 3, p. 994, 1951; Barrett, *op. cit.*, p. 480, 1952.

Recrystallization of Cold-worked Metal.[26]   A cold-worked aggregate heated to temperatures high enough to cause substantial recovery from strain hardening still retains its essential microscopic fabric, including its state of preferred orientation.   A minor obvious effect is *polygonization* whereby a single strained grain becomes resolved into several sharply bounded homogeneous strain-free sectors differing slightly in orientation —a condition that has a petrographic analogy in strained quartz and olivine of some plutonic rocks and tectonites.[27]   This is believed to

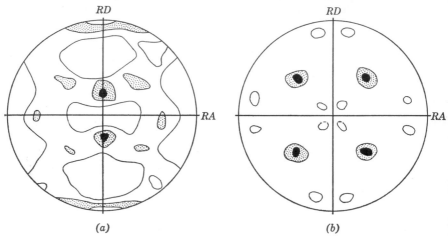

(a)   *(b)*

FIG. 9-4. Orientation diagrams ("pole figures" in stereographic projection) for {111} in annealed cold-rolled metals.   (*After C. S. Barrett.*)   (*a*) aluminum.   (*b*) copper. Contours on an arbitrary scale showing relative intensities determined by Geiger counter.

originate by migration of dislocations from an initially random distribution in the gradationally strained grain, into planar arrays at subgrain boundaries in the polygonized grain.   Such boundaries are transverse to the active glide planes of the lattice.

At higher temperatures, approximating half the melting temperature on the absolute scale, *annealing recrystallization* sets in.   Unstrained crystals growing from new nuclei completely replace the strained crystals of the cold-worked aggregate.   At the same time stored strain energy is released and recovery from strain hardening becomes complete.   With prolonged annealing at high temperature, recrystallization enters a second phase termed *grain growth*.   Certain grains in the now strain-free aggregate slowly grow at the expense of less favored grains, and a general

[26] Barrett, *op. cit.*, pp. 485–509, 1952; P. A. Beck, Annealing of cold worked metals, *Philos. Mag. Supp.* (*Advances in Physics*), vol. 3, pp. 245–324, 1954; W. Boas, Stored energy and lattice defects in cold-worked metals, *Phys. Soc. Conf. Defects in Crystalline Solids, Bristol 1954, Rept.*, pp. 212–221, 1954.

[27] S. W. Bailey, R. A. Bell, and C. J. Peng, Plastic deformation of quartz in nature, *Geol. Soc. America Bull.*, vol. 69, pp. 1452–1454, 1958.

coarsening of fabric results.   Grain growth reduces surface energy at the crystal interfaces to a minimum.

Annealing crystallization changes the pattern of preferred orientation of the original cold-worked aggregate.   It may cause almost complete deorienting toward random orientation; but if the degree of initial cold strain is high a regular and characteristic pattern of preferred orientation may develop in the annealed fabric.   Thus cold-rolled copper with an oriented fabric close to that of Fig. 9-3a ({123} in the plane of rolling, [1$\bar{2}$1] in the rolling direction) develops an essentially isometric annealing texture in which {100} coincides with the plane, and the edge [001] with the direction of rolling (Fig. 9-4b).   Annealing of the aluminum strip illustrated in Fig. 9-3a, for 5 min at 300°C, yields a pattern (Fig. 9-4a) which is still orthorhombic but combines the pattern of Fig. 9-3a with a growth orientation of the "cube texture" type just described for copper (Fig. 9-4b).   Apparently the symmetry of an annealing fabric may reflect two influences: first that of the preexisting fabric due to cold-working, and secondly the symmetry of the crystal lattice in question. Highly developed preferred orientation in the cold-worked aggregate seems to be a prerequisite for the evolution of a well-defined annealing fabric.

EXPERIMENTS ON ORIENTATION OF RIGID PARTICLES IN A FLOWING MATRIX

For over a century and in a variety of fields experiments have been conducted to investigate the states of preferred orientation assumed by rigid tabular or prismatic bodies immersed in a flowing viscous or plastic matrix.   Some of these specifically refer to the possible role played by some such process in the evolution of tectonite fabrics.[28]   Other experiments have been designed to investigate preferred orientation of clay particles, quartz fragments, prisms of rutile, and so on in worked ceramic bodies.[29]   Others again are experiments relating to problems in hydrodynamics.[30]   The experimental results are mutually compatible and collectively confirm predictions based on mathematical analysis (cf. pages 323 to 325).   They may be summarized as follows:

[28] E.g., H. C. Sorby, On the origin of slaty cleavage, *Edinburgh New Philos. Jour.*, vol. 10, pp. 137–147, 1853; B. Sander, *Gefügekunde der Gesteine*, pp. 149–150, Springer, Berlin, Vienna, 1930; W. O. Williamson, Lineations in three artificial tectonites, *Geol. Mag.*, vol. 92, pp. 53–62, 1955.

[29] W. O. Williamson, Some structures of unfired pottery bodies revealed by a new technique, *British Ceramic Soc. Trans.*, vol. 40, pp. 275–294, 1941; The effects of rotational rolling on the fabric and drying shrinkage of clay, *Am. Jour. Sci.*, vol. 252, pp. 129–143, 1954; *op. cit.*, 1955.

[30] G. I. Taylor, The motion of ellipsoidal particles in a viscous fluid, *Royal Soc. London Proc.*, vol. 103, A, pp. 58–61, 1923.

1. Axial compression of clay or plasticine induces preferred orientation of enclosed plates and rods with their maximum dimensions approaching the AB plane of the strain ellipsoid, i.e., the plane normal to the axis of compression (σ_1). Symmetry of orientation—which has been only roughly estimated—apparently is identical with that of strain in the matrix.

2. In Taylor's experiments prolate and oblate spheroids of aluminum (about 0.1×0.25 cm) became oriented by very slow laminar flow of an exceedingly viscous liquid (water glass). The movement picture of flow was monoclinic, with vortex axes normal to a plane of undisturbed motion which is a plane of symmetry. The particles became aligned—as predicted by Jeffrey (see page 324)—with their longest axes normal to the

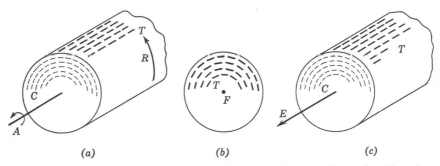

(a)   (b)   (c)

FIG. 9-5. Diagrammatic representation of alignment of tourmaline and rutile prisms (T) and aggregates of clay particles with subparallel {001} (C) in worked ceramic clays. (*After W. O. Williamson.*) (a) During rolling in direction and sense R about axis A. (b) During flattening of a sphere to a disk normal to axis F. (c) During extrusion of a cylinder parallel to axis E.

symmetry plane of movement, which thus is also the principal symmetry plane of the orientation pattern.

3. In Williamson's experiments on extrusion, rolling, and flattening of clay containing minute prisms of rutile and tourmaline, a correlation may be made between the clay particle and the tourmaline subfabrics and the symmetry of the working process (rather than that of the induced internal movements which comprise the movement picture).

a. In rolling experiments (Fig. 9-5a) the symmetry of the working process is monoclinic, with a symmetry plane normal to the axis of rolling, which was carried out in one sense only. Tourmaline prisms and tabular clay particles both become aligned parallel to the axis of rolling; the symmetry of orientation is axial, $D_{\infty h}$, with the principal symmetry axis normal to the symmetry plane of the process. The tourmaline pattern is linear while the clay subfabric has a girdle pattern.

b. Deformation of a clay sphere (Fig. 9-5b) to a thin disk by repeated dropping, in alternating senses, onto a flat plate produced a pattern of tourmaline orientation in which the long axes were tangentially aligned;

tabular clay crystals tend to be oriented parallel to the plane of the disk. The symmetry of the working process is identical with that of strain and with that of orientation (within the domain of the whole disk); it is axial, with the principal symmetry axis normal to the disk surface, which is also a girdle of c axes for tourmaline.

c. Compression of clay in a cylinder and extrusion through a terminal narrow circular die is a complex working process with a principal polar symmetry axis parallel to the length of the cylinder. In the resulting narrow cylinder of extruded clay (Fig. 9-5c) both the tourmaline prisms and the tabular crystals of clay are aligned parallel to this symmetry axis, i.e., to the direction of extrusion.

Whether or not the experiments just described have any direct bearing on the orienting of micas in tectonites—as has been claimed by a number of writers—they collectively confirm one of the fundamental tenets in the interpretation of tectonite fabrics: there is a consistent and precise correlation of fabric symmetry with symmetry of movement and of strain as set forth on pages 385 to 391.

MICROSCOPIC CHARACTER OF EXPERIMENTALLY DEFORMED CALCITE AND MARBLE

The Problem. Calcite and marble are not only highly ductile under experimentally accessible temperatures and pressures within the geologically significant range, but they are also amenable to standard metallurgical treatments such as cold- and hot-working and annealing. Microscopic study of the fabric of calcite and marble so treated can be expected to throw light upon problems that center around questions such as the following:

1. What are the effective glide mechanisms in calcite? Particularly what translation mechanisms are there alternative to the well-known twin gliding (in the positive sense only) on $\{01\bar{1}2\} = e$? Does translation gliding in calcite leave any microscopically visible trace? And does the translation mechanism vary within the broad range of metamorphic temperatures—say 200° to 800°C?

2. What is the significance of visible e lamellae in the evolution of natural tectonite fabrics? For example, what correlation exists between the respective patterns of preferred orientation of [0001] and of associated visible e lamellae, and what significance is to be attached to such correlation?

3. What inferences may be drawn from preferred orientation patterns observed in marble tectonites regarding stress, strain, and movement in their tectonic history? In particular are the symmetry principles discussed on pages 385 and 386 borne out by experimental findings on marble fabrics?

4. What is the mechanism of orienting during strain of an initially randomly oriented aggregate of calcite grains? Does the preferred orientation pattern in a highly strained tectonite still show features inherited from a condition of anisotropy in the parent fabric?

5. How is a marble fabric affected by annealing recrystallization? What are the effects of syntectonic recrystallization?

6. To what degree is development of marble fabrics by cold- and by hot-working comparable with evolution of fabrics in cold- and hot-worked metallic aggregates?

At least partial answers—some of them admittedly tentative—can now be supplied to all these questions. In the absence of evidence relating to other minerals it seems permissible in the mean time to extrapolate some of these answers to cover similar questions regarding tectonite fabrics in general.

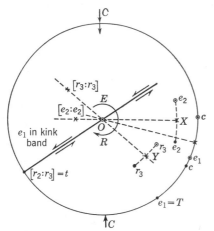

FIG. 9-6. External rotation of lattice of kink band (solid circles) with reference to lattice in undeformed end of specimen (circled dots) by twin gliding on e_1 in calcite. $[r_3:r_3]$ is intersection of r_3 in kink band with r_3 in end; broken lines XO, YO are planes bisecting angles between corresponding lattice planes (for example, r_3) in kink band and in end sector. O is axis of external rotation (sense shown by circular arrow ER). CC is the axis of compression. c, e_1, e_2, r_3 refer to the initial lattice (prior to twinning) in both sectors.

Rotation, Strain, and Gliding in Crystals. In experimental deformation of a single crystal there are three independent criteria by which collectively a single active glide system may be identified:[31]

1. First, where glide is confined to one system $T:t$, there are two independently observable components of strain—change of shape, and rotation of the strained mass in space:

a. The initially circular cross section of the test cylinder becomes transformed into an ellipse, one diameter of which remains unchanged and is perpendicular to the glide direction t. On a stereographic or equal-area projection the direction t and the pole of the glide plane T lie on a great circle normal to the unchanged diameter of the elliptical section. This great circle represents the deformation plane of strain—AC of the strain ellipsoid.

b. The strained sector of the specimen—usually a kink band—rotates bodily in space with reference to external coordinates such as the com-

[31] Turner, Griggs, and Heard, *op. cit.*, pp. 897–901, 1954; D. V. Higgs and J. W. Handin, Experimental deformation of single dolomite crystals, *Geol. Soc. America Bull.*, vol. 70, pp. 247–250, 1959.

pression or extension axis. This is an *external rotation* in Sander's terminology. In an axial compression experiment, for example, the ends of the specimen are constrained to remain coaxial, so that the kink band rotates in the sense opposite to that of shear on the active glide plane (Fig. 9-6; cf. also pages 328 and 329, Fig. 9-2), and the angle between the axis of compression (stress σ_1) and the glide plane progressively increases. The axis of external rotation is normal to the deformation plane, and so lies in the glide plane T at right angles to t. It may be located graphically, using the construction described on page 57, by bisecting the angles between corresponding crystallographic planes measured in the kink band and in the undeformed end of the specimen; the bisecting planes (arcs in the projection XO, YO in Fig. 9-6) intersect in the rotation axis O. The magnitude of the angle of external rotation depends upon the magnitude of strain as follows:[32]

$$\frac{D_0{}^2}{D_1 D_1''} = \frac{l_1}{l_0} = 1 - \epsilon \qquad \text{in compression experiments}$$

or $\qquad\qquad\qquad = 1 + \epsilon \qquad \text{in extension experiments}$

where D_0 = initial diameter
D_1 and D_1' = diameters of strained sector
l_0 and l_1 = initial and final lengths in strained sector
ϵ = strain expressed as decimal fraction of initial length

In compression experiments

$$\frac{l_1}{l_0} = \frac{\cos \chi_1}{\cos \chi_0}$$

In extension experiments

$$\frac{l_1}{l_0} = \frac{\sin \chi_0}{\sin \chi_1}$$

where χ_0 and χ_1 are the angles between the glide plane T and the axis of compression or extension in the unstrained and strained sectors respectively. The difference $\chi_0 - \chi_1$ is the angle of external rotation. These equations refer to particular experimental conditions relating to dimensions and mode of constraint of the test cylinder. They are at best only approximate for kink bands in crystals strained according to the technique of Griggs and Handin. A more satisfactory relation for compression is

$$\tan \omega = s \qquad \text{or} \qquad \omega = \theta$$

---

[32] Cf. J. W. Handin and D. T. Griggs, Deformation of Yule marble, part II, *Geol. Soc. America Bull.*, vol. 62, pp. 866–869, 1951; F. J. Turner, Rotation of the crystal lattice in kinkbands, deformation bands, and twin lamellae of strained crystals, *Natl. Acad. Sci. Proc.*, vol. 48, pp. 955–963, 1962.

where ω = angle of external rotation

s = shear

= $\tan \theta$

θ = the angle of shear on T

2. Any preexisting planar structure such as a thin twin lamella e_2 or a cleavage fracture r_1 becomes rotated passively through the strained sector as a result of gliding on an intersecting plane such as e_1 in the enclosing crystal. This is an *internal rotation* measured with respect to coordinates within the strained sector. These coordinates provided by the glide system itself (for this survives strain) remain rational and unchanged even when the glide mechanism is one of twinning. In translation gliding any measurable crystallographic or optical plane or direction in the strained mass is a suitable coordinate for estimating internal rotation, for the lattice itself is geometrically the same before and after strain. The rotated lamella is recognizable as such by its irrational orientation—except, as will be explained later, in the case of twin gliding carried to completion. The geometry of internal rotation is that of slip folding (cf. pages 482 to 486). The axis of rotation is the intersection of the glide plane and the rotated plane. The angle of rotation depends upon the degree of strain according to the expression

$$\cot \alpha - \cot \beta = s \sin \gamma = \frac{\epsilon}{S_o} \sin \gamma \text{ (where } \epsilon \text{ and } s \text{ are small)}$$

where α and β = respective angles between the rotated plane and glide plane before and after rotation $(\alpha < \beta)$

s = shear (= $\tan \theta$, the angle of shear) on glide system

γ = angle between t and rotation axis

S_o = coefficient of resolved shear stress on glide system

Figure 9-7 illustrates internal rotation of a cleavage r_1 and a twin lamella f_2 during translation gliding on $\{0001\}$ = c with the crystal axis a_1 as glide direction in dolomite. Following a convention in which the glide plane is shown as a superscript and the rotated plane as a subscript, the rotated plane r_1 is denoted $L_{r_1}^c$, and the rotated f_2 lamella $L_{f_2}^c$.

The identity of a glide system, deduced from strain and rotation data as just described, may be further tested by comparing observed lengthening or shortening (ϵ) with strain calculated from formulae based on a given glide system:[33]

For extension,

$$1 + \epsilon = \frac{l_1}{l_0} = \sqrt{1 + 2sS_o + s^2 \sin^2 \chi_0}$$

For compression,

$$\frac{1}{1 - \epsilon} = \frac{l_0}{l_1} = \sqrt{1 + 2sS_o + s^2 \cos^2 \lambda_0}$$

[33] E. Schmid and W. Boas, *Crystal Plasticity*, pp. 57–63, Hughes, London, 1950; Handin and Griggs, *op. cit.*, p. 867, 1951.

where l_0 and l_1 = respective lengths before and after strain

s = shear (tan θ, angle of shear) on active glide system

S_o = coefficient of resolved shear stress on glide system

χ_0 and λ_0 = angles which axis of compression or extension makes initially with glide plane T and glide line t, respectively

Experimentally Deformed Calcite Crystals.[34] *Microscopic Effects of Twin Gliding on* $\{01\bar{1}2\}$. It has long been known that, even at room temperature and pressure, calcite may readily be made to twin by gliding on $\{01\bar{1}2\}$ by applying a small stress so directed that the sense of shear on e is positive.[35] This behavior is easily demonstrated by squeezing a cleavage rhomb along a diagonal between opposite acute solid angles in a small vise. Observations on oriented crystals deformed by twinning under controlled conditions provide data for testing the validity of the relations between gliding, rotation, and strain set out in the previous section.

Figures 9-6, 9-8, and 9-9 show the effects observed when a cylinder of calcite whose axis is normal to $\{10\bar{1}0\} = m_1$ is compressed at 300°C and 5,000 bars confining pressure (see Fig. 8-12 for projection of axes and planes in calcite). The value of S_o on e_1 is 0.4, that on e_2 and e_3, 0.1, sense of shear on all three being positive. The specimen is deformed by

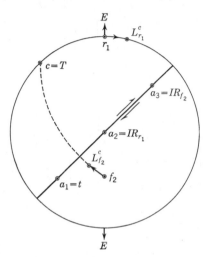

FIG. 9-7. Hypothetical illustration of internal rotation during translation gliding on $c = \{0001\}$ with glide direction a_1 in dolomite. r_1 is rotated to $L_{r_1}^c$; f_2 is rotated to $L_{f_2}^c$. Axes of internal rotation are IR. Crystal is deformed by extension parallel to EE.

twin gliding on e_1, which is carried to completion in a diagonal kink band $UVWZ$ in Fig. 9-8. The cross section of the central portion of the cylinder is now elliptical with one diameter (normal to the plane of Fig. 9-8) unchanged, the other elongated; the deformation plane is normal to the crystal axis a_2—the zone axis of m_1, r_1, and e_1 (the active glide plane). The axis of external rotation of the kink band (cf. Fig. 9-6) also is a_2. The sense of external rotation, shown by deflection of the active glide plane e_1 to e_1' in the kink band, is clockwise. Lamellae e_2 developed prior to e_1 twinning have been internally rotated counterclockwise to a new

[34] Turner, Griggs, and Heard, *op. cit.*, pp. 883–934, 1954; D. T. Griggs, F. J. Turner, and H. C. Heard, Deformation of rocks at 500° to 800°C., *Geol. Soc. America Mem. 79*, pp. 81–87, 1960.

[35] For a modern account see J. F. Bell, Morphology of mechanical twinning in crystals, *Am. Mineralogist*, vol. 26, pp. 247–261, 1941.

position $L_{e_2}{}^{e_1}$ in the kink band.   This rotation is estimated by comparing $L_{e_2}{}^{e_1}$ with the rational e_2 plane within the kink band; and the axis of internal rotation—the normal to the arc $e_2 L_{e_2}{}^{e_1}$ in Fig. 9-9—lies as predicted in e_1; it is in fact the edge $[e_1 : e_2]$.

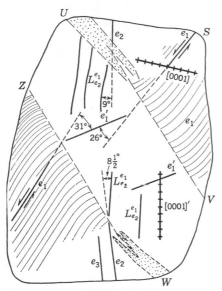

FIG. 9-8. Single crystal of calcite compressed normal to $\{10\bar{1}0\}$, i.e., normal to [0001]; longitudinal section parallel to deformation plane. (*After F. J. Turner, D. T. Griggs, and H. C. Heard.*) *UVWZ* is a kink band completely twinned on e_1; adjoining diagonally striated areas are heavily twinned on e_1; stippled areas are complex secondary kink bands heavily twinned on e_1.

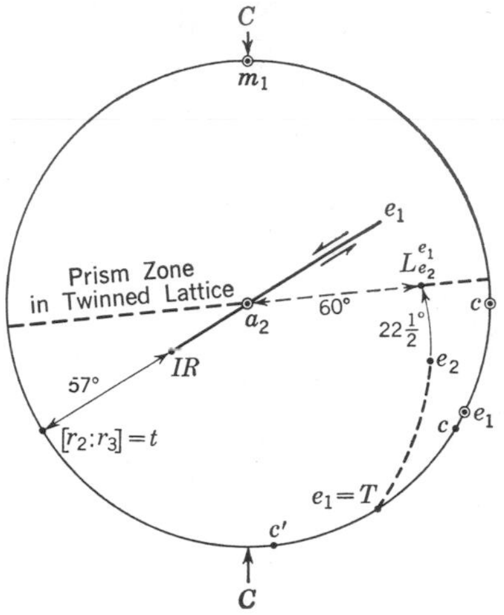

FIG. 9-9. Internal rotation of e_2 lamella to $L_{e_2}{}^{e_1}$ during twin gliding to completion on e_1 in kink band of Fig. 9-8. Measured planes and axes in kink band are solid circles; in undeformed ends, circled dots. c' is [0001] in the twinned lattice of the kink band. *IR* is axis of internal rotation of e_2. *CC* is axis of compression.

The linear strain for complete twinning in calcite may be calculated by substituting in the formula[36]

$$\frac{l_0}{l_1} = \sqrt{1 + 2sS_o + s^2 \cos^2 \lambda_0}$$

the values for e twinning in calcite[37]

$$s = 0.694 \qquad S_o = 0.4 \qquad \lambda_0 = 26\tfrac{1}{4}° \qquad \chi_0 = 26\tfrac{1}{4}$$

From these data, $l_0/l_1 = 1.394$, and $\epsilon = 0.394$.

From the equation $\tan(\chi_1 - \chi_0) = s = 0.694$ the angle of external rotation $(\chi_1 - \chi_0)$ equals 35°.   The observed angle is 31° to 37°.

[36] Schmid and Boas, *op. cit.*, p. 60, 1950.
[37] Handin and Griggs, *op. cit.*, p. 868.

The observed angle of internal rotation of e_2 to $L_{e_2}{}^{e_1}$ in the kink band (cf. Fig. 9-9) is $22\frac{1}{2}°$, in agreement with the angle predicted by the formula

$$\cot \alpha - \cot \beta = s \sin \gamma$$

from which

$$\cot \beta = \cot 45° - 0.694 \sin 57°$$
$$= \cot 67\frac{1}{2}°$$

and   Angle of internal rotation $= 67\frac{1}{2}° - 45° = 22\frac{1}{2}°$

Note that the observed clockwise deflection of e_2 in the bottom sector of Fig. 9-8, through $8\frac{1}{2}°$ to $L_{e_2}{}^{e_1}$ in the adjoining kink band, is the difference between (1) clockwise external rotation of the kink band as a whole and (2) counterclockwise internal rotation of e_2 within the kink band.

A general consequence of the geometry of twin gliding is that any rational discrete surface in the initial crystal on internal rotation assumes a rational orientation with respect to the twinned lattice.[38] By internal rotation accompanying e_1 twinning in calcite, an initial e_2 lamella is brought to coincide with $\{11\bar{2}0\}$ of the twinned lattice. This is the actual position occupied by $L_{e_2}{}^{e_1}$ in the case just described (cf. Fig. 9-9).

From the above and other experiments on e_1 twin gliding in single crystals of calcite it is concluded that strain and external rotation effects are approximate criteria, and internal rotation effects precise criteria of the active glide mechanism.

Demonstration of Translation on $\{10\bar{1}1\}$. Figures 9-10 and 9-11 illustrate strain and microscopic effects in a calcite crystal deformed in extension normal to $\{10\bar{1}0\} = m_1$ at 300°C and 5,000 bars confining pressure.[39] In this orientation the negative sense of shear on all three e planes precludes the possibility of twin gliding.

The overall elongation of the specimen is 16 per cent; but strain is concentrated in a centrally situated kink band ($UVZY$, Fig. 9-10) whose elliptical cross section (0.4927×0.3813 in. compared with the diameter 0.4916 in. of the initial circular section) indicates approximately plane strain with a local elongation of 29 per cent. The deformation plane is normal to a_2 which is also the axis of external rotation of the kink band. Assuming that gliding is restricted to a single system, the geometry of strain and of external rotation restricts the glide plane to the zone of the a_2 axis (i.e., to planes whose poles lie on the circumference of Fig. 9-11). The glide direction t must also lie on the same circle.

Of the simple crystal planes in the zone of a_2, e_1 and f_1 are ruled out by the sense of shear which is the same as that of observed external rotation (see inset circle, Fig. 9-11); m_1 and c have zero resolved shear stress in

[38] A. Pabst, Transformation of indices in twin gliding, *Geol. Soc. America Bull.*, vol. 66, pp. 897–912, 1955.

[39] Turner, Griggs, and Heard, *op. cit.*, pp. 910–912, 1954.

the initial orientation and so are also excluded. The only simple plane for which the sense of shear is opposite to that of external rotation is r_1. The glide system therefore is tentatively identified as $T = r_1$, $t = [f_2:f_3]$ (cf. Fig. 9-11). The resolved shear stress on this system, moreover, is

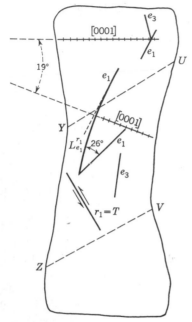

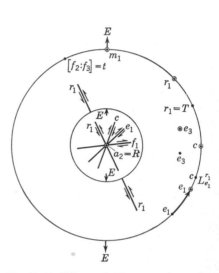

FIG. 9-10. Single crystal of calcite in extension normal to $\{10\overline{1}0\} = m_1$; longitudinal section through the deformation plane. (*After F. J. Turner, D. T. Griggs, and H. C. Heard.*) $UVZY$ is a kink band, the active glide plane is r_1. Angle of clockwise external rotation (19°) is given by relative positions of [0001] in end and in kink band. Angle of counterclockwise internal rotation of e_1 to $L_{e_1}{}^{r_1}$ is 26°.

FIG. 9-11. Effects of (1) external rotation of kink band and (2) internal rotation of e_1 to $L_{e_1}{}^{r_1}$ in calcite crystal elongated normal to m_1 (cf. Fig. 9-10). Measured planes and axes in kink band are solid circles; in undeformed ends, circled dots. R is axis of internal rotation of e_1 and external rotation of kink band. Inset shows sense of shear on various planes in the zone r_1 and e_1 within the kink band.

maximal—$S_o = 0.5$. Identification of the glide system may now be tested by criteria of internal rotation:

In the kink band, early formed rotated e_1 lamellae, continuous with lamellae present in the ends, now intersect late-formed rational e_1 lamellae at 26° and thus happen to lie normal to c. They are tentatively identified as $L_{e_1}{}^{r_1}$. The axis of internal rotation, a_2, and the counterclockwise sense of rotation are consistent with translation gliding on the assumed system $r_1:[f_2:f_3]$. Substituting $\epsilon = 0.29$, $S_o = 0.5$, $\chi_0 = 44\frac{1}{2}°$ in the equation for extension

$$1 + \epsilon = \sqrt{1 + 2sS_o + s^2 \sin^2 \chi_0}$$
$$s = 0.65$$

From the equation of internal rotation

$$\cot \alpha - \cot \beta = s \sin \gamma$$

where $\beta = e_1 \wedge r_1 = 71°$

$\gamma = 90°$

$s = 0.65$

α is found to be $45°$.

The angle of internal rotation of e_1 is $\beta - \alpha = 26°$. This is precisely the observed angle $e_1 \wedge L_{e_1}{}^{r_1}$ in the kink band.

Other experiments at $300°C$ and $5,000$ bars confirm the conclusion that under these conditions calcite, so stressed as not to permit e twinning, glides by translation on the most highly stressed of the three r planes. Similar experiments in the range $500°$ to $800°C$ show that in the higher temperature range the glide mechanism is translation on $\{02\bar{2}1\} = f$ parallel to the same glide direction $[f_1:f_2]$.

Thin sections of crystals deformed by r translation typically show no visible lamellar structure parallel to the glide plane. Some crystals show microscopic deformation bands visible in polarized light by virtue of differences in extinction of $5°$ or $10°$. These usually trend transversely to the active glide plane.

Summary of Gliding Mechanisms in Calcite. Cursory examination of the calcite lattice shows that there are three kinds of direction along which the ions are closely spaced and which therefore merit consideration as possible glide directions:

1. Three edges of the type $[e_1:r_2] = [e_1:r_3] = [r_2:r_3]$, on which alternating Ca^{++} and C^{4+} ions are spaced at intervals of 3.21 Å. This is the observed direction of twin gliding on e; but the alternating arrangement of ions makes it improbable as a direction of translation.

2. Three edges of the type $[r_1:f_2] = [r_1:f_3] = [f_2:f_3]$ on which ions of one type—either Ca^{++} or C^{4+}—are spaced at intervals of 4.04 Å.

3. Three crystal axes of the type a_1, on which ions of one type are spaced at intervals of 4.99 Å.

By analogy with experience in the field of metal deformation, translation is most likely to occur parallel to edges of type 2, i.e., to $[f_2:f_3]$. Theoretically possible glide planes containing $[f_2:f_3]$ are $\{10\bar{1}1\} = r$, $\{02\bar{2}1\} = f$, and $\{11\bar{2}0\} = a$.

Three glide systems have been deduced from strain and rotation effects such as those described in the preceding sections:

1. Twin gliding on e_1 parallel to $[e_1:r_2]$, sense positive. This mechanism is effective over the complete range of investigated conditions $20°$ to $800°C$, 1 to $10,000$ bars.

2. Translation on r_1 parallel to $[f_2:f_3]$, sense negative (when stress favors positive r translation it also favors e twinning, which occurs in preference). At 5,000 bars pressure, r translation is the dominant mechanism of translation at 20°C, the sole mechanism at 300° to 400°C, and a possible mechanism at higher temperatures.

3. Translation on f_1 parallel to the same direction $[f_1:f_2]$ has been observed in a few experiments at 20°C and 5,000 bars. At the same pressure it becomes dominant at between 500° and 600°C and continues so to 800°C.[40]   Note that the shape of the stress-strain curves for calcite indicates a change in the mechanism of translation in the interval 400° to 500°C (page 302).

Gliding in Calcite—a Guide to Interpreting Tectonite Fabrics.   Extensive gliding on r or on f in calcite commonly leaves no microscopically visible trace except an irrational orientation of internally rotated preexisting twin lamellae.   In some crystals deformation bands more or less transverse to the active glide plane may appear.   In most naturally deformed marble neither rotated lamellae nor deformation bands survive minor post-tectonic adjustments; indeed in calcite experimentally strained at high temperatures or slow strain rates $L_{e_1}{}^{r_1}$ lamellae seldom survive even the duration of the experiment.   Rationally oriented e twin lamellae are more durable structures and persist abundantly in many tectonites; but in most rocks they correspond collectively to only minor total strain imposed in the last stage of deformation.

Literature on the fabric of tectonites abounds in discussion of supposed glide mechanisms that have been invoked to explain established patterns of preferred orientation of various common minerals—among them calcite.   Merely because of their visibility microscopic lamellae—such as Boehm lamellae in quartz, thin $\{01\bar{1}2\}$ lamellae in calcite, and $\{100\}$ extinction lamellae in olivine—have been identified without any justification as "translation lamellae."   Gliding on such visible planes, moreover, has been widely accepted as playing a significant role in orienting processes.   Other supposed glide mechanisms have been inferred, again totally without justification, from recurrent patterns of preferred orientation of simple crystallographic directions such as [0001] in quartz and in calcite.   Possibly the most significant outcome of experimental studies of strain and gliding in calcite is the discounting of such speculations as these.   It was not possible either from perusal of fabric diagrams or from accurate identification of visible microscopic structures in marble tectonites to deduce the experimentally established mechanisms of r and f gliding.   Indeed the principal outcome of speculations concerning natural marble fabrics was a widespread belief (now disproved) that e translation was an alternative glide mechanism to e twinning.   By analogy it would

---

[40] Griggs, Turner, and Heard, *op. cit.*, p. 87, 1960.

seem that, in the absence of experimental data, the multifarious theories of quartz orienting[41] based on imaginary translation mechanisms invoked to explain established patterns of preferred orientation of c axes and of Boehm lamellae are equally without foundation.

Experimentally Deformed Marble.   *The Initial Marble and Conditions of Experiments.*   Most of what is known regarding the fabric of marble strained under accurately controlled conditions comes from the experiments of Griggs and coworkers.[42]   The starting material is Yule marble—

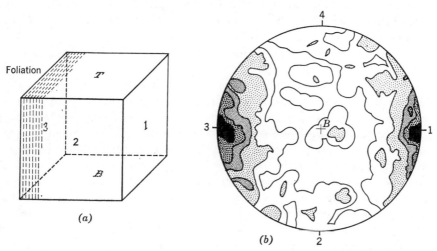

(a)

(b)

Fig. 9-12. Initial fabric of Yule marble.   (a) Reference block showing faces numbered with reference to foliation.   The back face is 4.   (b) Orientation diagram for c axes in 300 grains of calcite.   Contours, 7%, 5%, 3%, 1%, 0.3%, per 1% area.

an even-grained pure calcite marble with a remarkably homogeneous fabric.   A single distinct plane of foliation (parallel to faces 1 and 3 in Fig. 9-12a) is defined by parallel alignment of somewhat lensoid grains. Correlated with this dimensional anisotropy of fabric is a simple pattern of preferred orientation such that 60 per cent of the grains have c axes inclined at between 55° and 90° to the foliation (Fig. 9-12b).   Most test cylinders (cf. Fig. 9-12a) are cut normal (*1* cylinders) or parallel to the foliation (*T* cylinders); some (*d* cylinders) are inclined at 45° to the foliation.   Most grains in Yule marble show a few thin e lamellae—typically

[41] Cf. F. J. Turner, Mineralogical and structural evolution of the metamorphic rocks, *Geol. Soc. America Mem. 30*, pp. 264–266, 1948.

[42] E.g., F. J. Turner and C. S. Ch'ih, Deformation of Yule marble, part III, *Geol. Soc. America Bull.*, vol. 62, pp. 887–906, 1951; D. T. Griggs, F. J. Turner, I. Borg, and J. Sosoka, Deformation of Yule marble, part V, *Geol. Soc. America Bull.*, vol. 64, pp. 1327–1342, 1953; F. J. Turner, D. T. Griggs, R. H. Clark, and R. Dixon, Deformation of Yule marble, part VIII, *Geol. Soc. America Bull.*, vol. 67, pp. 1259–1294, 1956; Griggs, Turner, and Heard, *op. cit.*, pp. 87–97, 1960.

two sets per grain.   Their mean spacing index (the number of lamellae in any set per millimeter normal to the lamella plane) is 11.

The range of experimental conditions is 20° to 150°C, 10,000 bars; 150° to 800°C, 5,000 bars.   In most experiments the marble cylinder was dry; in some it was in contact with water, a condition that has no effect on the final fabric.   Although some of the low-temperature experiments were conducted at temperatures and pressures well within the stability field of aragonite, no inversion to aragonite occurred during the short time available.   The most striking changes in fabric occur in highly strained material—e.g., in specimens locally elongated by 100 to 1,000 per cent in the necked region.   Much of what follows regarding preferred orientation refers to such material strained in the high-temperature range (300° to 800°C) which favors ductility.

General Microscopic Strain Effects.   The rather small strains ($\epsilon = 5$ to 20 per cent) achieved at 20° and 150°C are accompanied by slight elongation or flattening of grains, marked intragranular clouding, some marginal granulation, and profuse internal development of swarms of new e lamellae.   Undulatory extinction is widespread and testifies to inhomogeneity of strain within the domain of the individual grain.   Lamellae inherited from the initial stage become internally rotated to irrational $L_e{}^r$ and $L_e{}^e$ orientations.   In grains so oriented as to permit e twinning, narrow e lamellae—many of them optically recognizable as twins— develop in increasing profusion with progressive strain.   Ultimately, at strains of 15 or 20 per cent, they become so numerous as to coalesce to give almost completely twinned grains in which dark relict $L_e{}^e$ lamellae are readily identified.   In every such grain e twinning occurs most profusely—as shown by a high spacing index—on that e plane for which the sense of slip is positive and S_o is highest; and from this it seems that the stress pattern throughout the aggregate is not far from homogeneous. Grains so stressed that e twinning is impossible have a different appearance.   Gliding on r (that r plane for which S_o is highest) is shown by rotated $L_e{}^r$ planes inherited from the initial fabric.   But these grains also show a profuse development of extremely thin e lamellae parallel to that e plane for which, in any grain, S_o is minimal.   These lamellae are too thin for twinning to be optically recognizable, and the total strain represented by a swarm—even where the spacing index exceeds 100— must be small.   Their rational orientation, by contrast with associated $L_e{}^r$ lamellae, indicates late origin, possibly connected with recovery during and after unloading.

The microscopic effects of strain at 300° to 600°C are somewhat different.[43]   At high strains (e.g., elongation of 100 per cent or more) the individual grains are greatly elongated and commonly show undulatory

---

[43] Turner, Griggs, Clark, and Dixon, *op. cit.*, pp. 1271, 1272, 1285.

extinction; but there is no marginal granulation or internal clouding. Appropriately oriented grains become completely twinned and retain dark $L_e{}^e$ lamellae. In grains deformed principally by translation recognizably twinned e lamellae develop late on planes of low resolved shear stress statistically normal to the σ_1 stress axis (Fig. 9-13a).

The textural features that develop at 700° to 800°C are different again.[44] Specimens favorably oriented for twinning (*1* cylinders in extension) indeed show conspicuous e lamellae in most grains. But in spite of the high strains attained at these temperatures, grains are seldom more than half twinned; and the lamellae—numbering two to six per grain—are

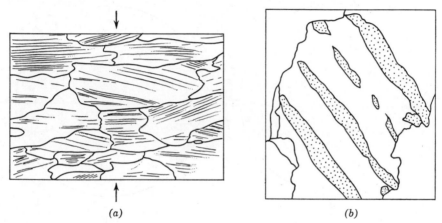

(a)   *(b)*

Fig. 9-13. Development of e lamellae in calcite of experimentally deformed Yule marble. (*a*) *1* cylinder, shortened 39.9 per cent at 400°C, 3,000 bars; e lamellae, approximately normal to σ_1 (arrows), are of late origin; grains initially oriented unfavorably for e twinning. Magnification × 50. (*b*) *1* cylinder elongated 80 per cent at 800°C, 5,000 bars. Lensoid and irregular e lamellae (stippled) in grain oriented favorably for twinning. Magnification × 88.

thick, lensoid, and irregular in outline (Fig. 9-13b). In grains oriented unfavorably for twinning late e lamellae normal to the axis of the σ_1 stress are lacking.

Preferred Orientation Data. Even for low strains of the order of 10 or 20 per cent, any grain initially oriented favorably for e twinning becomes strikingly twinned, the c axis changing its orientation through 52°. Consequently c axes inclined at high angles to σ_1 are soon eliminated; and this is the main respect in which orientation diagrams for c (Fig. 9-14) differ from that representing the undeformed marble. Reorientation of grains responding to stress by translation is due solely to external rotation, and for small strains this amounts to only a few degrees.

For high strains—shortening of 50 per cent, elongation of 100 per cent or more—the orientation patterns have changed completely; for even

[44] Griggs, Turner, and Heard, *op. cit.*, pp. 93, 94, 1960.

external rotation accompanying translation is now sufficiently large to be an effective reorienting mechanism. The c axes in the newly developed fabric (Figs. 9-15a, 9-16a and b) are inclined at 20° to 30° to σ_1 and at 60° to 70° to the σ_3 axis. This seems to be a steady-state orientation; for the c axis pattern of an elongated T cylinder is almost the same (Fig. 9-16b) in sectors where the local strains are respectively 85 and 120 per cent. Virtually the same pattern (Fig. 9-16a), but with sharpened maxima is developed in a similarly oriented cylinder elongated 590 per cent at 600°C. At 800°C reorienting seems to be less effective. The

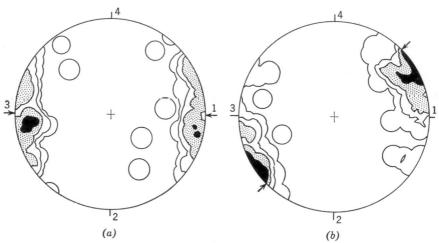

(a)   (b)

FIG. 9-14. Orientation diagrams for calcite in Yule marble, shortened 19 per cent at 300°C and 5,000 bars. Contours, 10%, 5%, 3%, 1%, per 1% area. (a) 100 c axes in 1 cylinder. (b) 100 c axes in d cylinder. Arrows indicate compression axis σ_1. Note absence of c axes normal to σ_1.

c-axis pattern for elongation of 1,000 per cent[45] is almost identical with that in a similarly oriented specimen elongated 85 per cent at 500°C.

At high strains, too, there is significant preferred orientation of a axes in grains whose c axes have approximately the same orientation (Figs. 9-15c, 9-16c).[46] There are three maxima 60° apart (X, Y, Z, Fig. 9-16c).

For high strains at 300° to 600°C there is very strong orientation of conspicuous e twin lamellae, even though these are believed to form at the latest stage and to represent a minor component of the total strain. Diagrams are simple, each having a strong pole maximum coinciding with the C axis of the strain ellipsoid (Figs. 9-15b, 9-16d).

Symmetry of Fabric.[47] The orientation patterns for c axes of calcite in any highly strained marble cylinder are characterized by two consistently

[45] *Ibid.*, p. 92, fig. 26B.

[46] E.g., Turner, Griggs, Clark, and Dixon, *op. cit.*, pp. 1271, 1272; Griggs, Turner, and Heard, *op. cit.*, pp. 92, 93, fig. 26E, 1960.

[47] Turner, Griggs, Clark, and Dixon, *op. cit.*, p. 1269.

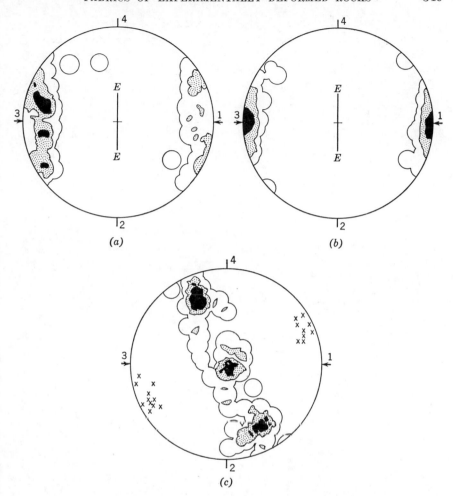

Fig. 9-15. Orientation diagrams for calcite in Yule marble, *1* cylinder, shortened 39.9 per cent at 400°C, 3,000 bars in 400 min.   *EE* mean elongation of grains $= A$ of strain ellipsoid.   Arrows indicate σ_1.   (*a*) 100 *c* axes.   Contours, 10%, 5%, 1%, per 1% area.   (*b*) 100 *e* lamellae, most conspicuous in each grain.   Contours, 20%, 5%, 1%, per 1% area.   (*c*) 60 *a* axes in 20 grains whose *c* axes are shown by crosses.   Contours, 12%, 9%, 5%, 1.7%, per 1% area.

reproducible features: constant location of maxima at 20° to 30° to the σ_1 axis, and an overall symmetry which for different conditions may be axial, orthorhombic, or monoclinic (Fig. 9-18, line 3).   The observed symmetry of fabric is identical with that of strain; and this in turn reflects the superposed individually axial symmetries of the external stress (load) system and the initial marble fabric.   Three cases are illustrated in Fig. 9-18:

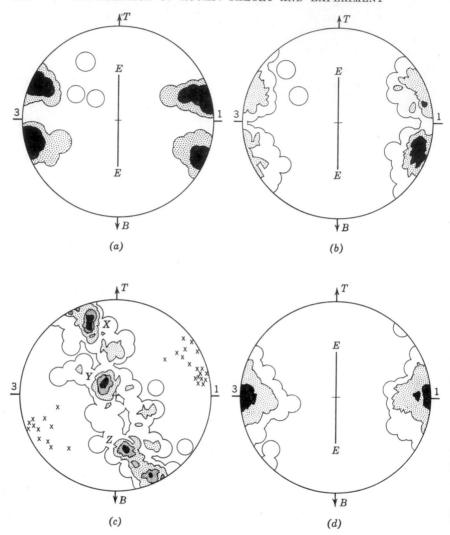

Fig. 9-16. Orientation diagrams for calcite in Yule marble, T cylinders in extension EE mean elongation of grains = A of strain ellipsoid. Arrows indicate σ_3. (a) Elongation 590 per cent at 600°C, 3,000 bars. 38 c axes (all grains of necked region). Contours, 8%, 3%, per 1% area. (b–d) Elongation 90 to 120 per cent at 500°C, 5,000 bars. (b) 100 c axes. Contours, 10%, 5%, 1%, per 1% area. (c) 90 a axes in 30 grains whose c axes are shown by crosses. Contours, 9%, 5½%, 3%, 1%, per 1% area. (d) 152 most conspicuous e lamellae in 100 grains. Contours, 13%, 3%, 0.7%, per 1% area.

a. The principal symmetry axis of load coincides with that of the initial fabric. The strained cylinder is circular in section; i.e., the symmetry of strain is also axial. So, too, is symmetry of fabric. The symmetry axes of load, initial fabric, strain, and strained fabric coincide.

b. The principal symmetry axes of load and initial fabric are mutually perpendicular, so that their combined symmetry is orthorhombic. The strained cylinder is elliptical in sections; i.e., its symmetry is orthorhombic. So, too, is symmetry of fabric.

c. The principal symmetry axes of load and initial fabric are mutually inclined at 45°, so that their combined symmetry is monoclinic. The

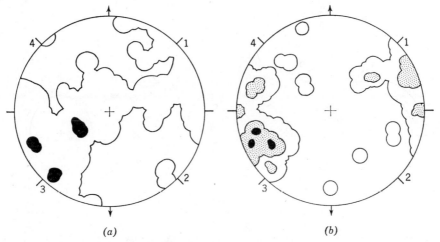

(a)   (b)

Fɪɢ. 9-17. Orientation diagrams for calcite in Yule marble, *d* cylinders (cut at 45° to foliation) in extension. Arrows indicate σ_3. (*a*) Elongated 20 per cent at 300°C, 5,000 bars. 114 *c* axes in 100 grains. Contours, 5%, 1%, per 1% area. (*b*) Elongated 250 per cent at 500°C, 5,000 bars. 80 *c* axes in 80 grains. Contours, 10%, 5%, 1%, per 1% area.

transverse section of the strained cylinder is elliptical, but the longitudinal section parallel to the deformation plane is asymmetric (Fig. 9-18*c*, 1), so that symmetry of strain, including its rotational component, is monoclinic. So, too, is symmetry of fabric (Fig. 9-17*c*, 3).

The Orienting Process.[48] Handin and Griggs showed that a modified form of Taylor's hypothesis of homogeneous deformation of metals (page 331) can explain the evolution of a state of preferred orientation of calcite crystals in cold-strained marble. Strain in the temperature range 20° to 500°C is now known to involve twin gliding on *e* or translation gliding on *r*, depending on the initial orientation of the individual grain. It is assumed that strain is approximately homogeneous in any grain, and that

[48] Turner, Griggs, Clark, and Dixon, *op. cit.*, pp. 1273–1290.

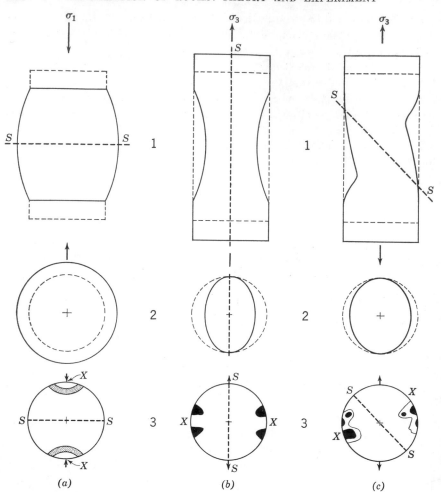

FIG. 9-18. Preferred orientation of c axes in relation to strain in deformed Yule marble. (a) Compression (parallel to arrows) normal to initial foliation SS. (b) Extension (parallel to arrows) parallel to initial foliation SS. (c) Extension (parallel to arrows) at 45° to initial foliation SS. (1 and 2) Longitudinal and transverse sections of strained cylinders; initial shape in broken lines. (3) c-axis diagrams on plane of longitudinal section. $X = c$-axis maximum of initial fabric.

all grains become equally strained in any particular experiment. Reorienting is the result of two processes: e twinning of favorably stressed grains (a powerful reorienting mechanism), and external rotation of all grains in the sense opposite to that of internal gliding on the active e or r system.

It can be shown that once a grain becomes completely twinned on e it will continue to deform by translation on the most highly stressed of the three r glide systems of the new lattice. Thenceforth it behaves like other grains whose initial orientation compels r translation from the beginning. Just as with metallic aggregates, steady-state end orientations may be predicted for calcite, such that two or more active glide systems are symmetrically oriented in the stress field. The effects of external rotation for the glide systems then nullify each other. The predicted end orientations for calcite in simple axial compression and extension experiments are as follows:

1. For axial compression an e plane is approximately normal to σ_1, and on it appreciable twinning should occur. The c axis of the principal lattice is inclined at 26° to σ_1; one of the a axes is normal to σ_1. Most grains should attain this orientation in specimens shortened by 50 per cent. Measured fabrics of strongly compressed specimens (Fig. 9-15) agree strikingly with the predicted patterns.

2. For axial elongation an e plane is parallel to σ_3, and on this plane, too, appreciable twinning should occur. The c axis of the principal lattice is inclined at 72° to σ_3; the three a axes are inclined to σ_3 at about 25°, 45°, and 80°, respectively.[49] This predicted orientation also is confirmed by orientation diagrams for calcite in marble elongated by 100 per cent or more (Fig. 9-16).

Further confirmation of the hypothesis of broadly homogeneous deformation and of the predicted orienting mechanism is given by the behavior and computed strain of individual grains as reconstructed from microscopic observations on still internally recognizable lamellae $L_e{}^e$ and $L_e{}^r$.

Syntectonic Recrystallization.[50] Recrystallization of calcite during experimental deformation is equivalent to syntectonic recrystallization in geology and to hot-working in metallurgy. In rapidly strained (normally strained) specimens of marble there is no sign of recrystallization about new nuclei below 400°C. In specimens slowly strained at 400°C, and in marble normally strained over the range 500° to 800°C, many grains show internally one or two new granules—ragged in outline—whose orientation differs sharply from that of the host. Their growth seems to be favored by moderate rather than by extreme strain, for they are inconspicuous in the necks of highly elongated specimens. Some cylinders highly strained at 600°C show notable intergranular recrystallization to a mosaic of small grains along boundaries between highly elongated primary grains.

The pattern of preferred orientation of syntectonically recrystallized grains is very sharp: the c axes are concentrated subparallel to the σ_1 axis.

Recrystallization is increasingly effective over the interval 400° to

[49] Incorrectly recorded by Turner, Griggs, Clark, and Dixon (*op. cit.*, p. 1272) as 65°, 45°, and 10°.

[50] Griggs, Turner, and Heard, *op. cit.*, pp. 94–97, 1960.

600°C, but is much less conspicuous in specimens strained at higher temperatures. It is influenced, too, by strain rate. When this is diminished by a factor of 10 the maximum recrystallization effect is seen at 550°C instead of 600°C. Possibly under geologic conditions of exceedingly slow prolonged strain syntectonic recrystallization may be effective at much lower temperatures, say 300°C.

Like all processes involving nucleation and diffusion recrystallization must be accelerated by rising temperature. But the driving force of syntectonic recrystallization is the augmented free energy due to strain in the lattice; and diffusion, moreover, seems to be facilitated by accumulated lattice defects. As the temperature rises (e.g., from 600° to 800°C in the case of calcite), or as the rate of strain at constant temperature decreases, strength and strain hardening decrease, and internal lattice strain presumably diminishes accordingly. Recrystallization, in spite of advancing temperature, then becomes ineffective.

Microscopic Fabric of Annealed Calcite and Marble.[51] Because of its somewhat higher free energy (stored strain energy) a cold-worked material tends to recrystallize to a strain-free state. However, the rate of recrystallization (annealing recrystallization) becomes appreciable only when the temperature is raised above some critical value at which an appropriate activation energy is attained. Cold-worked calcite, marble, and compressed ground calcite anneal rapidly and completely when heated for short periods at 700° to 800°C and 5,000 bars pressure.

Yule marble elongated 20 per cent at 20°C and subsequently annealed for 30 min at 500°C shows incipient recrystallization; annealed for the same time at 800°C it recrystallizes completely. For small cold strains (e.g., 6 per cent elongation) annealing recrystallization is ineffective at 500°C and only partially complete at 800°C.

A single crystal of calcite, shortened 31 per cent by compression parallel to [0001] at 25°C, completely recrystallized to an aggregate of a dozen grains when annealed at 800°C. Cold strain in this specimen was the result of r translation. A crystal comparably deformed in an orientation permitting e twinning showed only incipient recrystallization about many centers of local strain when annealed at 800°C.

Undeformed Solenhofen limestone was found to recrystallize at 800°C and 5,000 bars. The driving force of recrystallization in this case was high surface energy connected with initial very small grain size.

Annealing of calcite crystals and of marble affects the fabric markedly in two ways: the grain size is notably reduced, and the initial pattern of preferred orientation is virtually destroyed. The aggregate of six or a dozen new grains crystallizing from a single parent grain may have some crystallographic direction such as an a axis or the $[f_1:f_2]$ edge of close ionic packing in common. But the c axes become dispersed so that their

[51] Griggs, Paterson, Heard, and Turner, *op. cit.*, pp. 21–36.

preferred orientation in the annealed aggregate is nearly random.   The deoriented fabric resulting from annealing contrasts sharply with the very strong patterns of preferred orientation resulting from syntectonic crystallization (hot-working) of marble.

Finely ground marble (average grain diameter 2 μ) compressed at room temperature and annealed for 30 min at 1,000°C and 4,000 bars recrystallizes as a granoblastic aggregate of polygonal grains whose average diameters are 10 times that of the initial material.   In some annealed samples large porphyroblasts several millimeters in diameter appear in a recrystallized coarsened groundmass whose grain size averages 20 μ.

MICROSCOPIC FABRIC OF MISCELLANEOUS EXPERIMENTALLY DEFORMED ROCKS

Dolomite.[52]   At temperatures between 25° and 400°C flow in single crystals of dolomite under high confining pressure is due solely to translation gliding on {0001} with an a axis as glide direction.   At 400° to 500°C twin gliding on $\{02\overline{2}1\} = f$ in a negative sense becomes the preferred mechanism of flow.

At temperatures below 300°C at 5,000 bars pressure, the fabric of dolomite rock strained 5 to 10 per cent is not appreciably changed.   At 300°C, however, there is a profuse development of f lamellae in suitably oriented grains.   A plot of spacing indices for all three sets of f lamellae in each grain shows a strong correlation between closeness of spacing of lamellae and the value of the resolved shear stress on f (sense negative). For dolomite rock strained 10 per cent at 300°C, the c-axis orientation diagram shows incipient development of a girdle normal to the axis of compression σ_1.   This agrees with patterns predicted on the assumption that the effective mechanism of flow is twin gliding in the negative sense on f.   Dolomite shortened 9 per cent by compression at 380°C and 3,000 bars shows only slight changes in the pattern of preferred orientation of c; new f lamellae develop profusely in grains whose c axes are subparallel to σ_1; in other grains inherited f lamellae are internally rotated to an irrational orientation $L_f{}^c$, such that $L_f{}^c \wedge c = 52°$ to $56°$ compared with $f \wedge c = 62\frac{1}{2}°$.

Quartz Aggregates.   In spite of widespread petrographic evidence that under metamorphic conditions quartz commonly is ductile, laboratory experiments on single crystals at temperatures up to 800°C and 5,000 to 10,000 bars pressure and at ordinary rapid strain rates have produced

[52] F. J. Turner, D. T. Griggs, H. C. Heard, and L. E. Weiss, Plastic deformation of dolomite rock at 380°C., *Am. Jour. Sci.*, vol. 252, pp. 477–488, 1954; J. W. Handin and H. W. Fairbairn, Experimental deformation of Hasmark dolomite, *Geol. Soc. America Bull.*, vol. 66, pp. 1257–1273, 1955; Higgs and Handin, *op. cit.*, pp. 245–278.

only very limited effects of flow—permanent strains of less than 1 per cent at 500°C to 800°C.[53] Notable plastic flow has recently been achieved, however, in quartz crystals deformed within the range 300°C to 1,300°C at extreme pressures—14,000 to 40,000 bars.[54] There is strong evidence to show that the principal mechanism of flow involves translation gliding on {0001}. Boehm lamellae, mainly inclined at low angles to [0001], and deformation bands parallel to [0001] are profusely developed in the strained quartz. The coefficient of resolved shear stress for the planes on which the lamellae appear is always high.

Although preferred orientation of c axes is strongly developed in quartz of many tectonites, experimental attempts to produce similar orientation patterns by deformation of quartz aggregates have been singularly unfruitful. The only recognizable patterns so far produced experimentally by Griggs are those resulting from shearing of wet quartz aggregates at 400°C under high confining pressures, and from crystallization of fine-grained quartz from amorphous silicic acid or flint similarly sheared at 200° to 400°C. The predominant orientation so developed seems to be an alignment of c axes more or less transversely to the direction of shear; some alignment of c parallel to the direction of shear has also been noted. The relative roles of syntectonic crystallization versus rotation of quartz needles in the orienting process have not been clarified.

Compaction of angular quartz sand by axial compression in the presence of sodium carbonate solution at 300° to 435°C and confining pressures of 2,000 to 7,000 bars yields a synthetic quartzite whose fabric is characterized by alignment of somewhat elongated grains with their greatest dimensions normal to the compression axis.[55] This is believed to be the result of slight elongation of grains normal to σ_1 in accordance with "Riecke's principle." Even for compaction involving an overall reduction in volume by 50 per cent the orientation of c axes remains random.

Aggregates of uniform-sized round sand grains (St. Peter sand) have been deformed at high confining pressures under a variety of conditions. In jacketed cylindrical specimens axially compressed or elongated at room temperature under pressures of 500 to 2,000 bars, the principal microscopic effect is the development of intragranular fractures symmetrically related to the external load system: shear fractures inclined at low angles to σ_1 in compression experiments, tensile fractures approxi-

[53] Griggs, Turner, and Heard, op. cit., pp. 65–72, 75–79, 102, 1960.

[54] J. M. Christie, N. L. Carter, and D. T. Griggs, Experimental evidence for a basal slip mechanism in quartz (Abstract, National Academy of Sciences Autumn meeting 1961), Science, vol. 3, p. 3, November, 1961.

[55] H. W. Fairbairn, Synthetic quartzite, Am. Mineralogist, vol. 35, pp. 735–748, 1950.

mately normal to σ_3 in extension experiments.[56] The orientation pattern of c axes remains virtually unchanged. Sand of the same kind, deformed in a squeezer at 25° to 700°C under pressures of 12,000 to 100,000 bars,[57] develops two kinds of structure that commonly appear in quartz of natural tectonites affected by postcrystalline strain: undulatory extinction, mainly in zones parallel to the c axis, and deformation lamellae (= Boehm lamellae) inclined at high angles to [0001] on planes of high shearing stress. Experiments on single crystals of quartz at 15,000 bars and above 300°C yield evidence of basal and possibly rhombohedral gliding. Heard has produced similar effects under geologically possible conditions—500°C, 5,000 bars, and slow strain rates (of the order of 10^{-7} per sec). Long-sustained stress may prove to be the essential condition for flow of quartz rocks in nature; for in Heard's experiments the otherwise very great yield strength of quartz was notably lowered by reducing the strain rate by half a dozen orders of magnitude.

Silicate Rocks: Granite, Dunite, Pyroxenite.[58] *Mylonitic Structure.* In experiments of short duration at 5,000 bars pressure and temperatures ranging up to 500°C silicate rocks, though capable of flow while maintaining considerable shear stress (cf. pages 318 and 319), are essentially brittle. Granite remains brittle up to 800°C, but above 500°C dunite and enstatite-pyroxenite show some degree of ductility. Brittle failure is characterized by development of a diagonal shear zone crossing the specimen at an angle of 25° to 40° to σ_1. Within the shear zone the structure tends to become mylonitic; the grain size is greatly reduced by crushing, and undulatory extinction in the larger remnant grains indicates widespread internal strain. No pattern of preferred orientation could be recognized in the mylonitized material. Strain effects peculiar to individual minerals are noted below.

Quartz and Feldspars. The only strain effects are undulatory extinction and fragmentation of grains.

Biotite is clearly susceptible to plastic deformation by some form of translation gliding. Within individual crystals appear multiple kink bands, narrow and sharply bounded by plane surfaces trending at high angles to {001} (Fig. 9-19). Within each band the {001} cleavage is sharply deflected through an angle of between 20° and 50°—an effect of external rotation. Chevron-like pairs of kink bands symmetrically

[56] I. Borg, M. Friedman, J. Handin, and D. V. Higgs, Experimental deformation of St. Peter sand: a study of cataclastic flow, *Geol. Soc. America Mem. 79*, pp. 133–191, 1960.

[57] N. L. Carter, J. M. Christie, and D. T. Griggs, Experimentally produced deformation lamellae and other structures in quartz sand, *Jour. Geophys. Research*, vol. 66, pp. 2518, 2519, 1961. See also J. M. Christie, N. L. Carter, and D. T. Griggs, Plastic deformation of single crystals of quartz, *Jour. Geophys. Research*, vol. 67, pp. 3549, 3550, 1962.

[58] Griggs, Turner, and Heard, *op. cit.*, pp. 50–65, 1960.

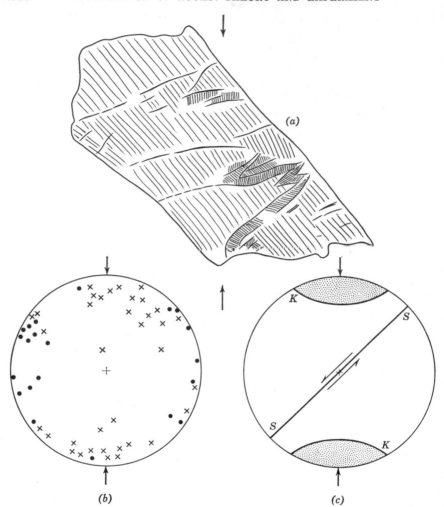

FIG. 9-19. Kink banding in biotite of granite compressed 20 per cent (in direction of arrows) at 500°C, 5,000 bars. (*After D. T. Griggs, F. J. Turner, and H. C. Heard.*) (*a*) A typical biotite crystal showing kink bands. (*b*) Poles to {001} of biotites with kink bands (solid circles) and lacking kink bands (crosses) in the same traverses. (*c*) Relation of maximum concentration of kink-band poles (*K*) to compression axis and to mesoscopic shear zone *SS*.

inclined to {001} of the host grain are not uncommon. Kink bands appear only in grains oriented with {001} inclined at low angles to σ_1. Poles of the kink bands themselves are clustered around σ_1. In all respects the experimentally produced structures resemble the familiar kink bands of strained biotite and muscovite in natural tectonites.

Olivine. In some specimens undulatory extinction in bands parallel to {100} is strengthened in the deformed sector. The spread of the indicatrix axes in a strained grain is usually between 5° and 35°— somewhat less for Y than for X and Z.

Diopside at 500°C and 5,000 bars shows two mechanisms of gliding: (1) translation with $T = \{100\}$ and $t = [001]$; (2) twinning with $T = \{001\}$ and $t = [100]$.

Enstatite at 500° to 800°C and 5,000 bars is notably ductile. Grains bend through 90° around $X = [010]$ without appreciable fracture; kink bands develop readily and are sharply bounded by planes inclined to [001] at high angles. The glide mechanism is translation on $\{100\}$ with $t = [001]$ just as in diopside. Gliding is accompanied by widespread inversion of enstatite to clinoenstatite.[59]

APPLICATION OF EXPERIMENTAL DATA TO NATURAL TECTONITES

From the microscopic study of experimentally deformed minerals and rocks emerge a number of generalizations bearing on the genetic interpretation of tectonite fabrics in general:

1. Ionic crystals and aggregates react to stress in much the same way as do metallic crystals and aggregates. So the mass of information relating to strain of metals may be applied qualitatively, if due caution is exercised, to natural deformation of rocks. It must be remembered that on the whole most rocks, even at high confining pressures, are much less ductile than metals; and annealing temperatures and the critical temperature separating cold- from hot-working are substantially lower for most metals than for rocks.

2. Preferred orientation of crystal lattices may arise from any of a number of processes: twin gliding; external rotation of grains accompanying intracrystalline twin or translation gliding; passive external rotation of rigid rods or plates in a flowing matrix; syntectonic (hot-working) or post-tectonic (annealing) recrystallization.

   a. For small strains twin gliding is a more effective orienting mechanism than translation. But a high degree of preferred orientation may result purely from translation during strains of the order of 50 per cent shortening or 100 per cent elongation.

   b. Preferred orientation of rigid inequidimensional grains during flow of an enclosing matrix is consistent with hydrodynamic prediction and experiment.

   c. Syntectonic crystallization about new nuclei may lead to a very high degree of preferred orientation of the crystal lattice. Thermodynamic predictions in this connection currently are far from unanimous; thermodynamic models possibly are too simple to provide a safe guide to the

[59] F. J. Turner, H. Heard, and D. T. Griggs, Experimental deformation of enstatite and accompanying inversion to clinoenstatite, *21st Internat. Geol. Congr. Rept.* (1960), pt. 18, pp. 399–408, 1960.

development of a steady-state pattern of preferred orientation in a flowing body. Syntectonic preferential growth of some grains and suppression of others through the activity of a pore solution, according to "Riecke's principle," may give rise to significant dimensional orientation but not to preferred orientation of the crystal lattice.

d. Annealing recrystallization can be an extremely effective deorienting process.

3. Certain natural strain effects may be interpreted dynamically by analogy with identical effects resulting from experimental strain: twin lamellae (orientation and spacing index) (*a*) in calcite and (*b*) in dolomite; rotated lamellae $L_f{}^c$ in dolomite; deformation lamellae (Boehm lamellae) and fractures in quartz; kink bands in micas and in orthopyroxene. These are all effects of postcrystalline strain; and this is commonly only a minor component of the total deformation. Possibly some natural orientation patterns for *c* axes of calcite may be correlated with patterns identified in experimentally strained marble.

4. Glide mechanisms of common tectonite minerals cannot safely be deduced—though this has commonly been done without any justification —from preferred orientation patterns of natural tectonites. The only safe guide is to be found in experimental data—observations on strain and accompanying rotational effects produced under known conditions of stress.

5. The ultimate steady-state pattern of preferred orientation resulting from flow in a crystalline aggregate (such as marble or metal) is geometrically related to the stress system. There is no evidence whatever for existence of "slip planes in the fabric" in which the active glide planes of individual grains are supposed to have become aligned. This concept, which has played a large part in discussion of the genetic significance of preferred orientation of crystals in tectonites, must be abandoned.

6. The symmetry of the orienting process and of its contributory influences, whatever their nature, is faithfully reflected in the symmetry of the resulting microscopic fabric. Even though the evolution of a natural tectonite fabric may be imperfectly understood, the symmetry of the orienting mechanism of the forces which governed it and of the strain accruing from it must be consistent with the observed symmetry of the fabric itself (see also, pages 385 to 391).

PART III

INTERPRETATION OF TECTONITE FABRICS

CHAPTER 10

INTERPRETATION OF TECTONITE FABRICS—PRINCIPLES

INTRODUCTION

In Chaps. 10 to 14 structural properties of tectonites will be used as a basis for reconstructing the kinematic and where possible the dynamic factors concerned in the evolution of tectonite fabrics. Interpretation of this kind is more speculative than the essentially descriptive materials of preceding chapters. The ideas expressed are tentative. Some no doubt will later be modified or rejected as the dynamics, kinetics, and kinematics of rock flow become more fully understood. But some ideas first proposed half a century ago by Sander have stood up remarkably well to repeated testing in the light of steadily increasing data relating to the fabric of tectonites.

The structures and fabrics of tectonites are direct records of the kinematics of deformation, i.e., of rock flow. Inherited structures record the magnitude and nature of distortion and dilatation; they tell us something of the dimensions of strain. Imposed structures express the appearance of new discontinuities in the flowing rock mass. But as yet no satisfactory rheologic model has been proposed for deformation recorded in tectonite fabrics; and without such a model discussion of possible stress conditions may be sterile. For this reason the structures and fabrics of tectonites are generally interpreted, not in terms of stress, but rather in terms of strain and displacements. In special circumstances, e.g., in analysis of $\{01\bar{1}2\}$ twinning in calcite (pages 413 to 421), it may be possible to make inferences regarding stress.

One basis for kinematic analysis of tectonites is the theory of finite homogeneous strain (pages 265 to 272). This has proved useful more particularly where the form of inherited structures provides evidence for analysis of bulk strain;[1] but so far it has not proved broadly applicable to analysis of fabrics. This is only to be expected. The concept of fabric is based on the existence of local structural discontinuities within a statistically homogeneous domain, whereas the theory of finite homogeneous strain is a simplification dealing only with strictly continuous homogeneous strain of strictly homogeneous isotropic continua. In other words,

---

[1] E.g., W. F. Brace, Mohr construction in the analysis of large geologic strain, *Geol. Soc. America Bull.*, vol. 72, pp. 1059–1080, 1961.

the theory of finite homogeneous strain is not directly applicable to the development of fabric, because a realistic kinematic model of homogeneous deformation in a crystal aggregate must take into account the fine structure of flow itself. Observations on naturally and experimentally deformed aggregates show that the essence of this fine structure is a systematic array of local adjustments to stress, controlled either by pre-existing local mechanical or rheologic weaknesses or by discontinuities induced by the stresses themselves.

On a small scale stress differences become adjusted by local relative movements of component parts within the strained body. The moving parts range in size from ions and groups of ions (moving in solutions or diffusing through crystals) to single crystals and crystal aggregates. Such movements, controlled by a stress pattern, and cumulatively resulting in strain of a tectonite domain, Sander has termed componental movements (*Teilbewegungen*).[2] It was Sander's realization of the correlation between componental movement and fabric of tectonites that ushered in the modern approach to structural analysis of tectonite fabrics.

DIRECT AND INDIRECT COMPONENTAL MOVEMENTS

Sander has distinguished two limiting kinds of componental movements (pages 37 and 38):

1. Indirect componental movements: adjustments on a molecular or ionic scale by means of imperfectly coordinated movements of ions or small groups of ions in solution or by diffusion. Deformation proceeds by recrystallization and neomineralization—crystalloblastic processes in the terminology of other European writers.[3]

2. Direct componental movements: systematic adjustments of discrete portions of a body by differential displacement across surfaces, or families of surfaces, of slip, fracture, or kinking on the scales of both crystals and aggregates of crystals. Such movements correspond to what other writers have termed cataclastic and plastic processes of deformation.

That direct componental movements play an important role in the evolution of tectonites is proved by widespread occurrence of corresponding visible discontinuities in structure. Twin lamellae in calcite, Boehm lamellae in quartz, kink bands in mica crystals, slip foliations, and fracture cleavage, kink surfaces, and folds on all scales are visible structures

[2] B. Sander, Über Zusammenhänge zwischen Teilbewegung und Gefüge in Gesteine, *Tschermaks mineralog. petrog. Mitt.*, vol. 30, pp. 281–283, 1911; *Gefügekunde der Gesteine*, pp. 115–118, Springer, Berlin, Vienna, 1930; E. B. Knopf, The record of deformational movements shown by petrofabric analysis, *Am. Jour. Sci.*, vol. 241, pp. 337–342, 1943; F. J. Turner and J. Verhoogen, *Igneous and Metamorphic Petrology*, 2d ed., pp. 611–612, McGraw-Hill, New York, 1960.

[3] E.g., U. Grubenmann and P. Niggli, *Die Gesteinsmetamorphose*, pp. 234, 235, Borntraeger, Berlin, 1924.

admitting no other explanation.   Preferred orientation of mineral crystals, almost universal in tectonites, has been widely attributed by some
to orienting processes involving direct componental movement alone.
Some such patterns indeed have been produced experimentally by such
means.   But metamorphism as a whole is a process of crystallization.
Preexisting minerals recrystallize, usually with notable increase in grain
size; so that some of the original grains are enlarged, some are eliminated,
and new grains grow about new nuclei.   Many of the principal minerals
of metamorphic tectonites are products of neomineralization in which
the initial mineral assemblage is replaced by a new assemblage.   At some
time during the crystallization process the state of preferred orientation
develops.   Most mineral orientation patterns that figure so conspicuously in the literature on structural analysis of tectonites must be regarded
as expressions of indirect componental movements.   Where crystallization was syntectonic such movements were directly influenced by stress.
And although post-tectonic crystallization—a common metamorphic
process—is not directly influenced by stress it nevertheless may involve
molecular and ionic movements controlled by existing structures such as
foliations and lineations whose configuration and orientation directly
express the stress system of deformation.

The concept of autocorrelation of displacements, so important in
analysis of fluid flow, can be applied in a general way to flow of rocks.[4]
In rapid turbulent shear flow of a fluid, the velocities of particles within
the same eddy are well correlated, whereas the velocities of particles in
different eddies are uncorrelated except with respect to the mean shearing
motion of the fluid which may be effectively homogeneous in large
domains.

It is possible to make a distinction between Sander's direct and indirect componental movements in terms of the range of correlation [of local displacements].
If these are uncorrelated for pairs of points at all spacings larger than those
comparable with ionic or molecular dimensions, we are dealing with indirect
componental movements.   However, if the [local displacements] are well correlated we are dealing with direct componental movements as in translation
gliding or local folding.[5]

Most of the visible structures of tectonites, as contrasted with mineral
orientation patterns, seem to be products of direct componental movements.   For the present, therefore, we shall confine our attention to displacements of this kind.   Instead of considering strain of a continuum
we shall attempt—following Sander—to develop a more realistic model of
deformation involving direct componental movements of discrete domains

---

[4] M. S. Paterson and L. E. Weiss, Symmetry concepts in the structural analysis of
deformed rocks, *Geol. Soc. America Bull.*, vol. 72, p. 874, 1961.

[5] Paterson and Weiss, *op. cit.*, p. 874.

in a tectonite fabric. In this discussion only homogeneous deformation is considered.

HOMOGENEOUS DEFORMATION OF TECTONITE FABRICS

Statistically Homogeneous Deformation. A force applied to an elastic body induces small changes in the mean positions of atoms and ions. If the body is homogeneous—e.g., a single crystal or a homogeneous aggregate or fabric—the distribution of displacements of ions throughout the body likewise is homogeneous. When the forces are removed the atoms and ions ideally take up their initial positions without permanent displacement and without the appearance of larger-scale structural discontinuities such as fracture on slip surfaces. Thus the crystal or crystalline aggregate can be viewed as a structural continuum and its deformation as strictly homogeneous, because local discontinuities in displacement are on the smallest possible scale and are fully recovered on unloading. Hence the model of a strictly homogeneous deformation, familiar in classic strain theory of continua, is totally adequate as a model of elastic deformation; and the kinds of homogeneous elastic deformations encountered in nature correspond closely in their geometric properties with those listed previously as tectonically significant strains (Table 7-2).

The characteristic criterion of permanent as contrasted with elastic deformation is that on removal of external forces some ions and atoms remain permanently displaced. The stresses have exceeded some threshold value sufficient to cause generation and movement of lattice dislocations,[6] gliding in individual crystals, and development of surfaces of displacement on a larger scale—slip surfaces, kink surfaces, ruptures, and so on. Permanent deformation of a single crystal " . . . can only be understood by taking account of the fine details in the structure of crystals, details that can be ignored when considering elastic properties."[7] The same restriction applies, too, to permanent deformation of rock fabrics. We must take into account the local discontinuities in deformation that have no part in classic strain theory. However, provided the nature and distribution of local discontinuities in deformation are statistically the same in all representative samples of the body, deformation of a fabric may be regarded as *statistically homogeneous* and *statistically continuous*. Henceforth we shall term such deformations *homogeneous* as distinct from *strictly homogeneous* strain of classic theory.

Where the scale of discontinuity in deformation is very small as compared with the scale of the body as a whole, the broad geometric proper-

[6] E.g., A. H. Cottrell, *Dislocations and Plastic Flow in Crystals*, Oxford, Fair Lawn, N.J., 1953; W. T. Read, Jr., *Dislocations in Crystals*, McGraw-Hill, New York, 1953.

[7] Cottrell, *op. cit.*, p. 1, 1953.

ties of a homogeneous deformation closely approximate those of strictly homogeneous deformation. However, to any one strictly homogeneous deformation there can correspond an infinite number of homogeneous deformations differing among one another in the nature and pattern of the small-scale discontinuities. Thus identical strain ellipsoids can develop in a single calcite crystal as a result of any of three mechanically possible processes: translation gliding on $\{10\bar{1}1\}$ or on $\{02\bar{2}1\}$ or twin gliding on $\{01\bar{1}2\}$. Classic theory of strictly homogeneous continua cannot distinguish between the three mechanisms. Only because of fine-scale discontinuities in deformation related to inhomogeneity of the calcite lattice on the ionic scale is the distinction real and the mechanism of deformation capable of identification. The kinematic model of tectonite deformation that we seek must be able to differentiate between alternative patterns of discontinuity in deformation in a way that cannot be done by considering the gross geometry of strain alone. This model Sander has termed the *movement picture (Bewegungsbild)*.

The Movement Picture of Deformation.[8] *Discontinuities in Deformation.* A strictly homogeneous deformation can be specified in terms of a displacement field, such that all points initially on any straight line remain on a straight line (the "affine transformation" discussed on pages 266 to 269). In a homogeneous deformation this condition is fulfilled only statistically because of local discontinuities of movement. These are on many different scales. In a crystallographic domain they range from discrete ionic jumps involved in displacement of dislocations, through displacements on glide and twin lamellae, to relative movement of kink-band boundaries. In larger domains there are displacements on grain boundaries or on surfaces of slip and fracture defined by arrays of grain boundaries. The discontinuities in movement are in fact the kinematic equivalents of some of the structures that we have termed fabric elements (page 32).

In a hypothetical model of fabric deformation it is convenient to distinguish two limiting kinds of discontinuity:

1. Displacement discontinuities. These are surfaces of discontinuity in the displacement field without necessary discontinuity in strain (except for the translational component). Geologists commonly term them *slip surfaces*. In Fig. 10-1b a displacement discontinuity (slip surface) DD' has developed during strain of the initial body (Fig. 10-1a). In this example there is no strain within the two displaced domains; the surface of displacement is a discrete discontinuity such as separates cards in a deformed deck. Figure 10-1c shows a situation commonly encountered in tectonites: the displaced domains are separated by a very narrow domain of intense deformation (cf. a "surface" of strain-slip cleavage).

[8] This section is based on the ideas of Sander. The development is drawn in simplified form from Paterson and Weiss, *op. cit.*

Although not a discrete surface it can be treated as such if small compared with the undistorted mutually displaced domains on either side.

2. Strain "discontinuities." These are separate domains that are homogeneously deformed to different degrees (DD' in Fig. 10-1d). Again the discontinuity may be a narrow zone of intense strain rather than a simple discrete discontinuity. Among tectonites this is exemplified in the axial regions of kink folds. Figure 10-1e shows a composite discontinuity combining displacement with difference in strain.

All natural homogeneous deformations are statistically homogeneous arrays of local discontinuities in deformation on various scales.

Shear Domains. For deformation to be homogeneous the discontinuities must mirror the geometric properties of the fabric elements. They

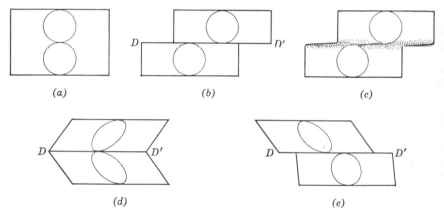

FIG. 10-1. Types of displacement and strain discontinuity in deformation.

must be present in parallel penetrative families, planar or nonplanar; and where two or more such families intersect they define a linear discontinuity in deformation. In all representative samples of a domain of homogeneous deformation the geometric array of discontinuities must be statistically the same. On a sufficiently small scale the discontinuities, now few in number and significantly large, divide the body into small domains in which deformation is homogeneous on a scale smaller than that of the whole body. Such domains of locally homogeneous deformation are here termed *shear domains*. Their nature and kinematic significance are illustrated by two simple examples:

1. Figure 10-2a to c represents diagrammatically the existence of shear domains in a homogeneously deformed crystalline aggregate such as marble. The initial aggregate a becomes deformed homogeneously so that the mean strain is represented by the ellipse (a section through the strain ellipsoid) in b. We have previously referred to Taylor's model of strictly homogeneous strain of crystalline aggregates (page 331)—a

model theoretically possible where the individual crystals have at least five potential glide systems.[9]   And we saw that while Taylor's hypothesis explains many experimental observations, other data show that local fluctuations and discontinuities in strain are widely prevalent even in a monomineralic aggregate such as marble.   In Fig. 10-2c each grain is shown as a shear domain homogeneously strained to a degree that varies slightly from grain to grain.[10]   This variation could arise from differences

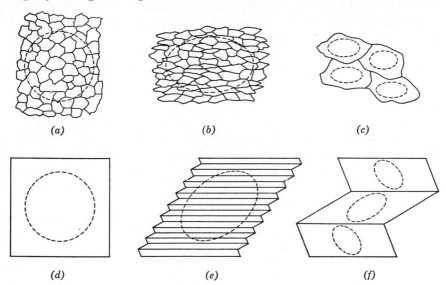

(a)   (b)   (c)

(d)   (e)   (f)

Fig. 10-2. Small-scale features of statistically homogeneous deformations.   (a) Undeformed homogeneous aggregate of grains.   (b) Deformed homogeneous aggregate. Ellipse indicates mean strain.   (c) Local strains within grains.   (d) Undeformed homogeneous body.   (e) Arrangement of shear domains.   Ellipse indicates mean strain.   (f) Local strains within shear domains.

in orientation of the active glide systems from grain to grain, even where stress is strictly homogeneous.   On an even smaller scale deformation within the individual grain will not be strictly homogeneous; the grain may be subdivided into even smaller shear domains such as twin lamellae, kink bands, and so on.   Clearly the ellipse of Fig. 10-2b, which would completely define the deformation of a strictly homogeneous continuum, is inadequate as a description of deformation in the crystal aggregate. A more adequate picture would be obtained by supplementing Fig. 10-2b with a three-dimensional array of local strains and deformation discontinuities.

2. In Fig. 10-2d to f the shear domains are rhythmically arranged parallel layers such as are exemplified in nature by regular cylindrical

[9] G. I. Taylor, Plastic strain in metals, *Inst. Metals Jour.*, vol. 62, pp. 307–324, 1938.
[10] The grain boundaries are strain discontinuities.

kink folds.   The complete picture of deformation is given by the mean strain (ellipse of Fig. 10-2e) supplemented by the array of local strains and strain discontinuities shown in part in Fig. 10-2f.

From these and other examples certain generalizations concerning the kinematics of statistically homogeneous deformation emerge.   In a homogeneously deformed body there are shear domains separated by deformation discontinuities.   The local homogeneous strain in the individual shear domain generally departs from the mean strain of the whole body and this departure is termed the *local strain perturbation*.[11]   The local strain perturbation, since it is a difference between two strains, can also be represented as a strain ellipsoid (page 268).   The sum of local perturbations for the whole body must be zero; for on that scale there is no departure from mean strain.

Concept of the Movement Picture.   A simple kinematic model for homogeneous deformation involving direct componental movements is the three-dimensional array of shear domains and deformation discontinuities discussed above.   In many tectonites shear domains of active deformation survive as recognizable fabric domains, and deformation discontinuities remain after cessation of movement as visible fabric elements (s-surfaces, lineations, and so on).   The pattern of movements in a homogeneous deformation thus is closely related to the resultant tectonite fabric.   It is what Sander[12] has called the *movement picture* of deformation.   Where local perturbations are on an infinitesimal scale, shear domains, deformation discontinuities, and fabric elements all disappear and the movement picture degenerates into strictly homogeneous strain of a continuum.   In real bodies, however, the scale of perturbations in strain and of related heterogeneities in movement and structure is significantly large where concern is with fabric.   They must figure in any attempt to correlate fabric with deformation.   In fact it is not the mean strain that is most closely relevant to the structural properties of a tectonite fabric, but the movement picture.[13]

It is difficult to envisage directly the nature and degree of perturbation and discontinuity inherent in indirect componental movements.   The scale of such phenomena must in many cases be small.   Yet the symmetry of mineral orientation patterns of recrystallized tectonite minerals very commonly is related to or identical with that of the mesoscopic fabric.   It would seem, therefore, that the broad pattern of fluid migration and ionic diffusion may be closely related to the movement picture framed in terms of direct componental movements on a larger scale.

[11] Paterson and Weiss, *op. cit.*, p. 873

[12] B. Sander, *Einführung in die Gefügekunde der Geologischen Körper*, Pt. I, p. 39, Springer, Berlin, Vienna, 1948; Turner and Verhoogen, *op. cit.*, p. 606, 1960   *Bewegungsbild* has also been translated as "movement plan."

[13] Cf. Paterson and Weiss, *op. cit.*, pp. 873–874.

Conversely where, as has often been observed in the case of quartz, the symmetry of the mineral orientation pattern departs radically from that of the mesoscopic fabric, the movement pictures of direct and of indirect componental movement may have been independent.

Relation of the Movement Picture to Strain. The movement picture is a complex vector field which corresponds only in its broad features with the simple vector field of strictly homogeneous strain.[14] A strictly homogeneous strain has three components: a pure strain, a rotation, and

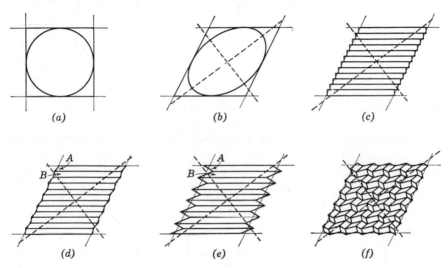

Fig. 10-3. Geometric examples of movement picture. (a) Undeformed body. (b) Strictly homogeneous strain. (c–f) Four types of movement picture with periodic shear domains.

a translation (page 266). The last two are defined with reference to external coordinates and are indeterminate in geologic situations where the initial orientation and position of the body are unknown. Only the component of pure strain—which is referred to coordinates within the deformed body—need be considered in analysis of mean strain in tectonites.

Figure 10-3 illustrates something of the infinite variety of movement pictures corresponding to a single pure strain. The diagrams are sections through a body initially square in cross section (a). Figure 10-3b represents the product of strictly homogeneous plane strain, corresponding to a simple shear (it could equally well have been drawn, without a rotational component, as a pure shear). Figure 10-3c to f shows four distinct arrangements of deformation discontinuities and shear domains, i.e., four movement pictures—each corresponding to the same mean

[14] Paterson and Weiss (*op. cit.*, pp. 870–876) treat this topic more rigorously and in greater detail.

strain (Fig. 10-3b). If the local heterogeneities so depicted are significantly large they will be reflected in the corresponding tectonite fabrics; and the evolution of any fabric will be fully understood only by taking into account the corresponding movement picture. But if the heterogeneities are infinitesimal all four cases become indistinguishable and each is in fact identical with the same strictly homogeneous strain.

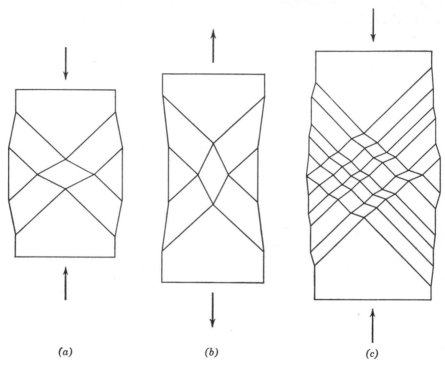

(a)   (b)   (c)

FIG. 10-4. Shear domains in test specimens. (*After A. Nádai.*)

Relations between the movement picture and strain are clearly illustrated on the mesoscopic scale by the development of recognizable slip layers in experimentally deformed test specimens (Fig. 10-4).[15] "Two such layers or several parallel strips may cross each other, in which the material is distorted by simple shear of variable or uniform intensity, and these layers may be separated by domains of the body which remain undistorted and are merely displaced . . . as rigid bodies."[16] The slip layers correspond precisely to our shear domains, and their boundaries are strain discontinuities. "States of strain may occur in which *only one layer of slip will form*. This is the case, for example, if one portion of the

[15] A. Nádai, *Theory of Flow and Fracture of Solids*, vol. I, pp. 527–559, McGraw-Hill, New York, 1950.
[16] *Ibid.*, p. 550.

body is fixed in space while the other part remaining rigid beyond the slip layer is allowed to move as a rigid body according to the motion prescribed through the layer of shear. Thus we see that *slip along a single family of characteristics is also a possible case of distortion* and that the requirements of the *Mohr theory claiming the formation of two symmetrical systems of surfaces of slip* is not a necessary attribute of their formation."[17] This last observation is significant with regard to dynamic interpretation of shear foliation (cf. pages 450 to 468). Clearly this need not be symmetrically related to the stress system, nor yet, as shown in Fig. 10-3c to f, to the axes of mean strain.

A geometric image of the movement picture is presented by the array of local strain ellipsoids for the individual shear domains. Simple ideal cases corresponding to Fig. 10-3d and e are shown in two dimensions in Fig. 10-5. Here there are only two kinds of shear domain, A and B. The perturbations (departure from the mean strain) in A and B must be equal and opposite since their sum must be zero. In tectonites the array of shear domains is three-dimensional and will usually be much more varied and complex than those of our simple illustrations. But for the movement picture to be statistically homogeneous the same two conditions must hold in every case: the strain in each shear domain must be homogeneous on the scale of the domain, and the sum of the local departures from mean strain must be zero.

Symmetry of the Movement Picture.[18] Consider now the symmetry of statistically homogeneous deformation as exemplified in a tectonite body. On the scale of the whole body only one component of the mean strain, namely, that of pure strain, is significant. We can have no information as to mean translation or mean rotation. So the symmetry of recorded mean strain for the body as a whole must be either axial $D_{\infty h}$ or orthorhombic D_{2h}.

The movement picture on the other hand represents not only mean strain but also the spatial distribution and magnitudes of all three components (pure, translational, and rotational) of local deformations throughout the body. The symmetry of the movement picture is the space symmetry of the array of local rotations of the local strain ellipsoids relative to the mean strain ellipsoid (exemplified in a very simple form in the second and third columns of Fig. 10-5). For the movement picture, then, five classes of symmetry are possible:

1. Spherical $K_{\infty h}$—random distribution of local rotations symmetrically across planes of all orientations
2. Axial $D_{\infty h}$—local rotations distributed symmetrically across all planes intersecting in one line and across the plane normal to it

[17] *Ibid.*, pp. 550, 551.
[18] Paterson and Weiss, *op. cit.*, pp. 874, 875.

3. Orthorhombic D_{2h}—local rotations distributed symmetrically across three orthogonal planes

4. Monoclinic C_{2h}—local rotations distributed symmetrically across a single plane

5. Triclinic C_i—local rotations distributed asymmetrically across planes of all orientations

The first of these classes corresponds to pure dilatation. The remaining four are the common classes of symmetry represented among tectonite fabrics (cf. Table 7-2).

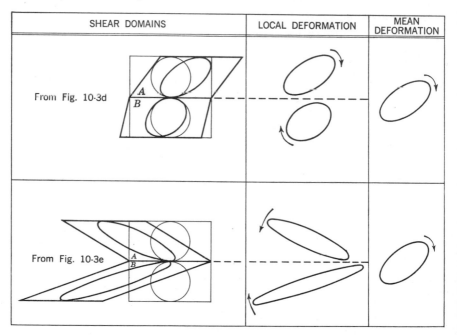

SHEAR DOMAINS	LOCAL DEFORMATION	MEAN DEFORMATION
From Fig. 10-3d		
From Fig. 10-3e		

FIG. 10-5. Analysis of local strains in shear domains: Upper, in Fig. 10-3d. Lower, in Fig. 10-3e.

Whereas the symmetry of the movement picture is subject to wider variation than that of associated mean strain, the two kinds of symmetry must nevertheless be closely related. There are three possible cases:

1. Orthorhombic movement picture: Three orthogonal symmetry planes coincide with three symmetry planes of pure strain.

2. Monoclinic movement picture: The single symmetry plane is also a symmetry plane of pure strain (Fig. 10-3c to f).

3. Triclinic movement picture: No symmetry planes.

In Fig. 10-6 an initial body (a) undergoes a statistically homogeneous plane strain (pure shear) whose mean dimensions are shown in b. Diagram c is the corresponding array of shear domains and strain discontinuities. The array, which is the graphic expression of the movement picture, is represented as ideally periodic. In a real tectonite body there will be departures from periodicity. In fact the tendency toward periodic arrangement of domains may be relatively slight; but in samples of adequate size the array must be statistically homogeneous.

The mean strain represented in Fig. 10-6 is nonrotational (pure shear). If a rotational component were added to the mean strain, as in the case of simple shear, the symmetry of the movement picture (Fig. 10-6c) would still be orthorhombic provided the array of shear domains were

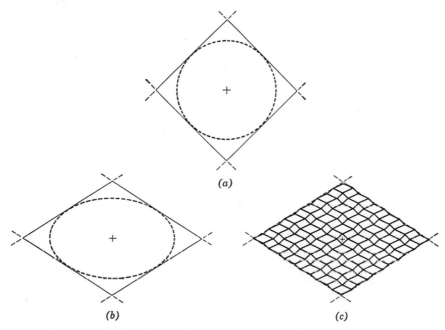

(a)

(b)   *(c)*

Fig. 10-6. Orthorhombic movement picture. (*a*) Undeformed body. (*b*) Strictly homogeneous strain. (*c*) Possible orthorhombic arrangement of shear domains in mean strain corresponding to strictly homogeneous strain of *b*.

not changed. Figure 10-3*f* on the other hand shows a monoclinic movement picture corresponding to a similar mean pure strain. A triclinic movement picture can be represented only in three dimensions.

Deformations of the kinds shown in Figs. 10-3*f* and 10-6*c* have sometimes been considered as products of displacement upon intersecting "slip surfaces." Note, however, that on the scale of the whole body there are no continuous slip surfaces, but only a rhomboid array of strain discontinuities. Note, too, that there is no direct relation between strictly homogeneous "simple shear" and "monoclinic movement," or between "pure shear" and "orthorhombic movement" as many geologists, ourselves included, have suggested. The array of local rotations in a statistically homogeneous deformation field defines a space symmetry which need not be related to the corresponding mean strain and its rotational component (an external rotation of the mean strain ellipsoid).

Periodicity in Movement Picture and Fabric. Figure 10-6c is a diagrammatic periodic repetition of the shear domains and strain discontinuities that actually appeared in the test specimen figured in Fig. 10-4a and b. The movement picture in Fig. 10-6c, by virtue of periodicity, has space symmetry like that of a crystal lattice. For periodic arrangements of domains in a movement picture the only possible symmetry types are those of crystal classes. Consequently no axis can have ∞-fold symmetry. The closest approach would be a 4-fold symmetry axis in an array such that two mutually perpendicular sections would show an identical distribution of domains (e.g., the distribution represented in Fig. 10-6c). Thus tetragonal symmetry is theoretically possible in tectonite fabrics and in movement pictures, provided periodic arrangement of fabric and shear domains is permissible.[19]

The arrangement of some structures highly characteristic of tectonites —folds, kink bands, strain-slip cleavages, s-surfaces defined by mineral lamination—typically tends to be approximately periodic.[20] Again in an experimentally deformed single crystal of calcite there commonly develops a mosaic of periodically repeated microscopic shear domains (deformation bands) in which different glide mechanisms—e.g., translation on r and twinning on e—have alternately been active.[21] Figure 10-7a shows part of such a mosaic in a crystal compressed parallel to the c axis (arrows). Broad NW-SE deformation bands trending approximately parallel to f_1 of the lattice are of three kinds, differing mutually in the present orientation of the c axis, and in the particular glide systems that were effective both in the main phase of deformation (probably r_1, r_2, and r_3) and in late minor strain (e_1, e_2, and e_3). They are usually differentiated by three different patterns of late e twin lamellae, and by the appearance in bands 2 and 3 of secondary, periodically repeated, transverse deformation bands trending parallel to r_2.

There is evidence, too, that periodicity enters into the spatial distribution of mineral grains belonging to different individual direction groups of some mineral orientation patterns. This is clearly brought out in some of Ramsauer's A.V.A. diagrams for quartzite,[22] and is illustrated also in Fig. 10-8. Something of periodicity, too, appears in some speci-

---

[19] This possibility was noted by E. B. Knopf and E. Ingerson, Structural petrology, *Geol. Soc. America Mem. 6*, p. 43, 1938.

[20] Sander, *op. cit.*, pp. 109–111, 1930; *op. cit.*, pp. 31–33, 1948.

[21] F. J. Turner, D. T. Griggs, and H. Heard, Experimental deformation of calcite crystals, *Geol. Soc. America Bull.*, vol. 65, pp. 914–915, 921, pl. 5, fig. 23, 1954.

[22] Sander, *op. cit.*, pp. 404, 405, 408, 409, 1950.

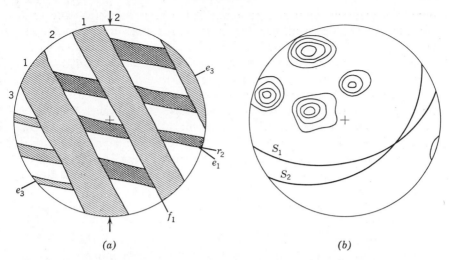

FIG. 10-7. (a) Microscopic shear domains in single crystal of calcite compressed parallel to [0001] (arrows). Width of field, 6 mm. (*After F. J. Turner, D. T. Griggs, and H. C. Heard.*) (b) Preferred orientation pattern for [0001] in ice of glacier ice. Contours, 15%, 10%, 5%, 1%, per 1% area. (*After G. P. Rigsby.*)

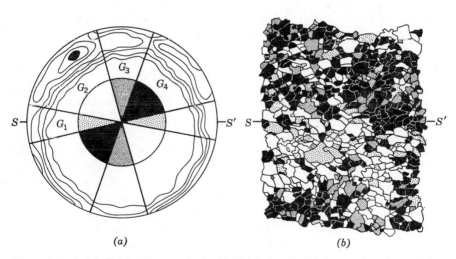

FIG. 10-8. Axial distribution analysis (A.V.A.) for [0001] in quartz of quartzite. (*After H. J. Koark, Gefügeregel und Gefügegenität in einem Quarz in Quarz-B-Tektonit, Upsala Geol. Inst. Bull., vol. 37, pp. 55, 57, 1956.*) (a) Orientation diagram for 750 c axes. Contours, 10%, 8%, 6%, 4%, 2%, 1%, ½%, per 1% area. Direction groups shown G_1, G_2, etc. SS' is trace of foliation (normal to plane of diagram). (b) Distribution of direction groups G_1–G_4 in a thin section normal to foliation SS'.

mens of very highly deformed Yule marble,[23] where there is a tendency for elongate grains of two distinct orientations to alternate symmetrically with respect to the axis of extension.

Finally evidence of a more tenuous kind appears in the approximately tetragonal symmetry of some mineral orientation patterns,[24] notably for [0001] of ice crystals in glacier ice (Fig. 10-7b) and for [0001] of quartz in some quartzites (Fig. 6-21d). In both cases the aggregate is mono-mineralic and has been strongly deformed. We have seen earlier that tetragonal symmetry is to be expected in tectonite fabrics only if the disposition of the shear domains—here grains or grain groups of some definite orientation—is periodic. This has not yet been verified by A.V.A.

In the face of the cumulative evidence cited above we put forward the conjecture that periodicity may be an essential characteristic of steady-state homogeneous deformation of solids—with regard to the disposition both of shear domains and strain discontinuities of the movement picture and of oriented elements of the tectonite fabric. As periodicity becomes more perfect the fabric becomes statistically homogeneous on an increasingly small scale.

ANALYSIS OF DEFORMATION

Factors in Deformation and in Evolution of Tectonite Fabrics. The tectonite fabric is the product of physical influences acting upon a pre-existing rock. Evolution of the fabric and synchronous development of strain have been viewed in terms of several different models shown diagrammatically in Fig. 10-9:

1. Figure 10-9a shows the classic relation between stress and strain where the rock body is treated as an isotropic continuum. This sequence is adequate for small reversible (elastic) strains in strictly homogeneous deformation but cannot be applied to the evolution of tectonites.

2. Figure 10-9b represents a sequence which treats heterogeneous phenomena in terms of statistical means. It is adequate for representing permanent bulk strain of rocks but takes no account of the evolution of rock fabrics.

3. The significance of tectonite fabrics is demonstrated only in the third sequence, Fig. 10-9c, for this is concerned not only with mean stress and strain but with perturbations in stress, strain, and displacements within the strained body. Consequently it serves as an adequate basis

[23] D. T. Griggs, F. J. Turner, and H. C. Heard, Deformation of rocks at 500° to 800°C., *Geol. Soc. America Mem. 79*, p. 91, pl. 10, fig. 1, pl. 12, fig. 2, 1960.

[24] G. P. Rigsby, Crystal fabric studies on Emmons Glacier, Mount Rainier, Washington, *Jour. Geol.*, vol. 59, p. 594, fig. 2, 1951; T. G. Sahama, Die Regelung von Quarz und Glimmer in den Gesteinen der Finnisch-Lappländischen Granulitformation, *Comm. géol. Finlande Bull. 113*, D26, 29, 41, 44, etc., 1936.

for interpreting the resultant array of structural discontinuities that defines the tectonite fabric.

In each of the three sequences of Fig. 10-9 the symmetry of what may be regarded as resultant phenomena at any stage will reflect the super-

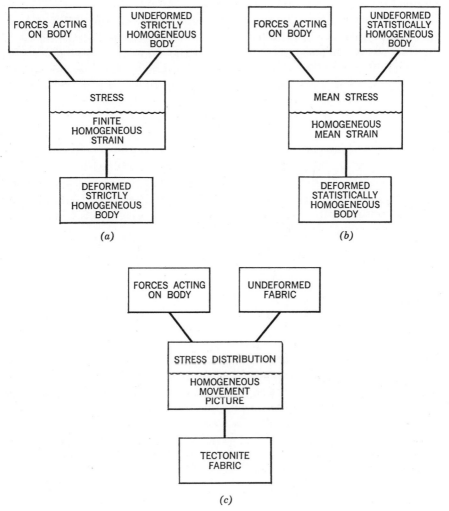

FIG. 10-9. Factors in evolution of tectonites. (*a*) Viewed on scale of strict homogeneity. (*b*) Viewed on scale of statistical homogeneity. (*c*) Viewed on scale of local discontinuity.

posed symmetries of the primary influences—the initial body and the external forces acting upon it. Consequently there will be some relation as regards symmetry between the tectonite fabric and all the phenomena tabulated in Fig. 10-9. But the closest correlation will be between the tectonite fabric and the corresponding movement picture.

Strain Analysis and Fabric Analysis.   The aim of strain analysis is to estimate mean strain of tectonites in statistically homogeneous domains. In a quantitative analysis the dimensions and orientation of geometric markers within the tectonite must be compared for the initial and the strained states.   Such markers are provided by inherited structures such as pebbles, concretions, fossils, oolites, and cross-bedding.   Because of the general difficulty of establishing an initial orientation of the marker, analysis is for the most part limited to the pure-strain component of deformation, i.e., to the form of the strain ellipsoid.   Since strain analysis treats tectonites as statistical continua (cf. Fig. 10-9b), it is not concerned with the movement picture of deformation nor with the nature of the tectonite fabric.   It will be possible, however, to correlate the mean pure strain so determined with the associated fabric revealed by fabric analysis. For example, Fairbairn has found that in quartzite a well-developed girdle pattern of [0001] in quartz may be correlated with only insignificant strain as recorded in cross-bedding.[25]   In experimentally deformed materials it is of course a simple matter, since initial and final dimensions are both known, to correlate development of fabric with progressive strain.

Attempts have also been made to correlate mean pure strain, determined by strain analysis, with stress.   Usually it has been assumed that the three axes of the strain ellipsoid are also the axes of principal stress, so that the C axis of the ellipsoid can be equated with the direction of σ_1. Such correlations require large assumptions—e.g., that the rotational component of mean strain is zero—and consequently are of uncertain value.

The purpose of fabric analysis is to interpret tectonite fabrics in terms of the movement picture and even where possible in terms of stress distribution.   Interpretation may be made on two different scales: Individual fabric elements such as twin lamellae, foliations and folds may be viewed as evidences of displacement and local strain.   On the larger scale arrays of such elements in homogeneous domains—patterns of preferred orientation of s-surfaces, lineations, crystal axes, etc.—are interpreted in reconstructing the movement picture of deformation.

Both types of structural analysis are important.   But to date more attention has been given to fabric analysis because most tectonites lack inherited structures permitting unequivocal estimation of mean pure strain.   There are some notable exceptions in the case of deformed conglomerates and oolitic limestones (pages 520 and 521), for which the mean strain ellipsoid as well as local perturbations in strain may be reconstructed within reasonable limits of error.

[25] H. W. Fairbairn, The stress-sensitivity of quartz in tectonites, *Tschermaks Mineralog. Petrog. Mitt.*, vol. 4, pp. 75–80, 1954.

INTERPRETATION OF TECTONITE FABRICS

Fabric Elements in Relation to Strain.   In homogeneous deformation of real bodies discontinuities in displacement and strain must be related in some way to structural discontinuities.   The simplest case is a single crystal in which gliding is controlled by lattice structure.   It is usually

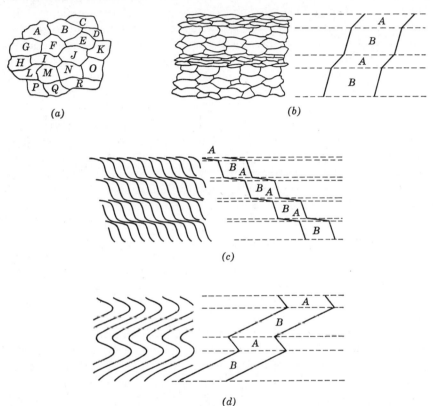

      (a)   (b)

                                    (c)

                                    (d)

Fig. 10-10. Some arrangements of shear domains in tectonite fabrics.   (*a*) Grain fabric.   (*b*) Laminar domains deduced from A.V.A.   (*c*) Strain-slip cleavage.   (*d*) Similar folding.

concentrated in microscopic domains such as twin lamellae and deformation bands, and so both the fabric and the movement picture in the domain of a single crystal are likely to be heterogeneous.   The controlling structure—that of the lattice—is homogeneous down to a very much smaller scale.

In noncrystallographic domains of tectonites the shear domains and displacement discontinuities are generally clearly defined by visible discontinuities in structure (Fig. 10-10), commonly on the mesoscopic scale. The domains *A* to *R* in Fig. 10*a* are individual grains whose boundaries constitute strain discontinuities; strain, which may be homogeneous within each grain, varies slightly from grain to grain. Figure 10-10*b* represents ideally a situation that may be approximated in laminated tectonites. Each polycrystalline lamina is shown as a homogeneous shear domain and the degree of strain varies between periodically alternating laminae (cf. Fig. 10-3*d*). Possibly the domains of constant preferred orientation of crystals revealed by A.V.A. of a monomineralic aggregate are also shear domains of the movement picture of deformation. Arrangements of laminar shear domains on a larger scale are characteristic of strain-slip foliation (Fig. 10-10*c*) and some patterns of crenulation (Fig. 10-10*d*), both common in tectonites. Note that the horizontal strain-slip foliation of Fig. 10-10*c* is an array, not of strict displacement discontinuities, but of narrow domains (*A*) of intense strain.

The structures thus defined by these and other domains and discontinuities of tectonites are fabric elements (cf. page 32). Clearly there is a close geometric similarity between the respective concepts of a fabric and of a movement picture. Both are homogeneous three-dimensional arrays of discontinuities separating locally homogeneous domains: in a fabric these phenomena are structurally defined; in a movement picture, kinematically. Fabric elements that correspond to discontinuities in movement have therefore a spatial array in a deformed fabric that is some kind of geometric image of the corresponding movement picture.

Two inferences may be drawn from observed relations between the tectonite fabric and the fabric of the initial body:

1. If the tectonite fabric contains recognizable inherited subfabrics— i.e., if the effects of overprinting (*Überprägung*) are discernible—then all the factors contributing to the development of the tectonite fabric (cf. Fig. 10-7*c*) must have been homogeneous. Otherwise the deformed rock could not be structurally homogeneous (i.e., possess a fabric) in the domain under consideration.

2. If the tectonite fabric is a product of complete obliteration (*Umprägung*) of the initial fabric, so that only imposed subfabrics are now present, then the initial body may have been heterogeneous, but other factors must have been homogeneous within the given domain. Although theoretically it is impossible to eliminate all traces of initial heterogeneity, extreme deformation commonly renders them illegible.

Influence of the Initial Fabric on the Tectonite Fabric. In deformation of an initially homogeneous body under homogeneous stress, both the strain and the resulting tectonite fabric depend upon the combined properties of (1) the stress system and (2) the initial fabric.

The relation between strain and stress depends upon the rheologic properties of the body (pages 276 to 283); and in this respect multiphase aggregates such as most rocks are not strictly homogeneous. They consist of small monomineralic domains having different rheologic properties.

And if these are penetrative in their distribution they may build up a statistically homogeneous array which may be considered as a rheologic fabric. Elastic grains of quartz distributed through a plastic matrix of marble exemplify this condition, or again "competent" beds of quartzite interstratified with "incompetent" beds of shale. The bulk rheologic behavior of such a body may depart widely from that of its individual components, or it may approximate the behavior of a single dominant component.

The mechanical properties of a rock likewise are influenced by structural anisotropy on the mesoscopic scale. For example, Sander[26] recognized a prevalent tendency for slip surfaces (or in our terminology laminar

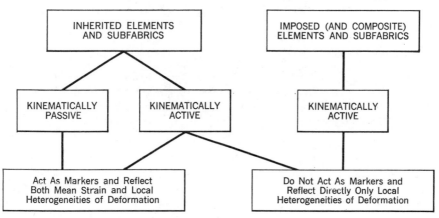

Fig. 10-11. Functions of noncrystallographic fabric elements. (*After M. S. Paterson and L. E. Weiss.*)

shear domains) to develop parallel to preexisting mechanically significant s-surfaces of any origin—bedding presumably included. In some rocks, on the other hand, the strength anisotropy may be scarcely influenced by bedding—a "mechanically inconsequential s-surface"—which then, in the course of strain, becomes geometrically transformed in a completely passive manner.[27] In general two limiting classes of structure may be distinguished in the initial fabric:[28]

1. Mechanically effective structures endowed with significant mechanical or rheologic properties. They control the development of shear domains and strain discontinuities, thus shaping directly the movement picture and the ultimate tectonite fabric.

2. Mechanically ineffective structures which merely transform passively as geometric markers. They may survive as inherited structures

[26] Sander, *op. cit.*, p. 103, 1930; F. J. Turner, Mineralogical and structural evolution of the metamorphic rocks, *Geol. Soc. America Mem. 30*, p. 176, 1948.

[27] Sander, *op. cit.*, pp. 98, 243–244, 1930.

[28] Sander, *op. cit.*, p. 173, 1948.

in the tectonite fabric, but they are not directly related to shear domains and strain discontinuities and so have no direct influence on the movement picture.

Accordingly we may distinguish in the tectonite fabric two corresponding classes of noncrystallographic elements and subfabrics: kinematically active (type 1 above) and kinematically passive (type 2).[29]   Inherited elements and subfabrics may be of either class; but imposed elements and subfabrics can only be kinematically active (Fig. 10-11).

Symmetry of Initial Fabric.   Table 10-1 summarizes the noncrystallographic elements commonly occurring in a rock fabric prior to deformation.   There may or may not be associated patterns of preferred orientation of the component minerals.

TABLE 10-1. NONCRYSTALLOGRAPHIC FABRIC ELEMENTS*

Rock type	Fabric elements	
	Planar	Linear
Sedimentary.........	Bedding Cross-bedding Planar dimensional preferred orientation of grains	Ripple marks Groove casts Flute casts, etc. Intersections of normal and cross-bedding Linear dimensional preferred orientation of grains or microfossils
Igneous.............	Bedding or compositional layering Flow layering Planar dimensional preferred orientation of grains	Flow lineation Linear dimensional preferred orientation of grains
Metamorphic (including tectonites)	Foliation (cleavage, schistosity, etc.) Axial planes of folds Planar dimensional preferred orientation of grains Inherited earlier planar structures	Lineation Fold axes Other linear structures (boudins, mullions, elongated pebbles, fossils, etc.) Inherited earlier linear structure

* After M. S. Paterson and L. E. Weiss.

The symmetry types exemplified by initial fabric elements are summarized in Table 10-2.   Most are centrosymmetric.   But in sedimentary and perhaps in some igneous rocks there are noncentrosymmetric structures reflecting a noncentrosymmetric influence such as the force field of gravity.   Such are graded bedding and comparable structures commonly employed to distinguish "tops" from "bottoms" in stratified sediments.

[29] Paterson and Weiss, *op. cit.*, p. 878.

TABLE 10-2. SYMMETRY OF INITIAL SEDIMENTARY AND IGNEOUS FABRICS*

Symmetry	Examples	
	Sedimentary rocks	Igneous rocks
Spherical, $K_{\infty h}$.	Aggregates of equant grains, e.g., massive sandstones with spherical quartz grains lacking preferred orientation of crystallographic directions	Aggregates with randomly oriented grains, e.g., some granites and basalts (a hornfels is a metamorphic rock that can have this symmetry)
Axial, $D_{\infty h}$.....	Bedded sediments of equant and inequant grains, e.g., shales and limestones	Aggregates with bedding or nonlinear flow layering or purely linear flow structures, e.g., some lava flows, minor and major intrusive rocks
Axial-polar, $C_{\infty v}$	Bedded sediments with regular rhythmic small-scale graded bedding	
Orthorhombic, D_{2h} or C_{2v}	Possibly some bedded and lineated sediments lacking grain imbrication	Possibly some aggregates with layering and lineation
Monoclinic, C_{2h} or C_{1h}	Bedded sediments containing linear structures, e.g., graywackes with sole markings (groove and flute casts), imbrication, grain lineation, cross-bedding	Aggregates containing laminar and linear flow structures of certain kinds
Triclinic, $S_2 = C_i$ or C_1	Bedded sediments containing nonparallel linear flow structures, convolute bedding, etc.	Aggregates containing irregular and convolute flow structures, e.g., swirls and "magmatic rolls" in rhyolites

* Modified from M. S. Paterson and L. E. Weiss.

Symmetry Principles in Interpretation of Tectonite Fabrics. *Symmetry Principles.*

The possible relations between a physical system and the various interacting factors within or contributing to the system are governed by symmetry principles. And throughout the whole of Sander's work runs the idea that symmetry principles form the soundest basis for correlating tectonite fabrics with the physical factors—stress, strain, movement picture, and so on—concerned in their evolution.[30] A symmetry principle relates empirically the symmetries of physically interdependent phenomena. Two principles pertinent to the interpretation of tectonite fabrics are as follows:

[30] Sander, *op. cit.*, e.g., pp. 21–32, 53–73, 145–147, 1930; *op. cit.*, pp. 66–83, 1948; F. J. Turner, Lineation, symmetry, and internal movement in monoclinic tectonite fabrics, *Geol. Soc. America Bull.*, vol. 68, pp. 1–18, 1957; Paterson and Weiss, *op. cit.*, pp. 841–859.

1. In general

. . . a medium under an external influence will exhibit only those symmetry elements that are common to the influence without the medium and the medium without the influence.   For example, if a crystal of halite is subjected to a simple compressive stress parallel to the three-fold axis, the resultant point symmetry of the [elastically strained] halite is D_{3d}, a subgroup common to both the symmetry of the unstressed halite (O_h) and the symmetry of the stress ($D_{\infty h}$). . . . [And again] if a homogeneous triaxial stress, having the point symmetry D_{2h} of a general ellipsoid is applied to an isotropic medium, it gives rise to a uniform strain which also has the point symmetry D_{2h} of a general ellipsoid; the absence of particular symmetry elements (such as infinite-fold axes) in the ellipsoid representing the strain necessarily implies the absence of such elements in the ellipsoid representing the stress.[31]

It should be noted that a symmetry element is common to two phenomena only where it is the same element in the same orientation.   In the above example of stressed halite the single 3-fold axis and 2-fold axes normal to it are identically oriented in both the unstressed crystal and the stress system.

2. A more general principle states that

. . . the symmetry of any physical system must include those symmetry elements that are common to all the independent factors (physical fields and physical properties of the medium) that contribute to the system and it may include additional symmetry elements; however, any symmetry element absent in the system must also be absent in at least one of the independent contributing factors.[32]

Symmetry of the Initial Fabric.   The only elements and subfabrics of the initial fabric that can influence deformation are those that are kinematically active.   On this basis three ideal cases are distinguished:

1. All elements and subfabrics of the initial fabric are kinematically passive.   From the mechanical standpoint the symmetry of the initial fabric is spherical, $K_{\infty h}$.

2. All elements and subfabrics are kinematically active.   Mechanically the symmetry of the initial fabric is identical with its geometric symmetry.

3. Some elements and subfabrics are kinematically active, some passive.   If the initial fabric is homotactic its mechanical symmetry is identical with its geometric symmetry.   If the initial fabric is heterotactic its mechanical symmetry is the geometric symmetry common to all the kinematically active subfabrics.

[31] Paterson and Weiss, *op. cit.*, pp. 858, 859.
[32] *Ibid.*, p. 859.

The above generalizations apply specifically to the influence of the initial fabric upon the movement picture. The corresponding tectonite fabric may be more complex, including inherited passive as well as kinematically active subfabrics. This is the interpretation placed upon a not uncommon type of heterotactic fabric in which the quartz subfabric is markedly discordant with regard to a prominent foliation and to the related mica fabric. It is suggested that the quartz fabric was kinematically active (imposed) and that its symmetry reflects that of the movement picture; while the foliation, mimetically emphasized by late recrystallization of mica, was mechanically passive (perhaps inherited bedding) and has acted purely as a geometric marker.[33]

In the case of tectonites, the respective symmetries of initial fabric, stress, strain (including mean strain and movement picture), and final tectonite fabric (cf. Fig. 10-7) must be related according to the superposition principle (principle 2, page 386). If all elements of the tectonite fabric were kinematically active, symmetry elements not common to all the above factors would normally be absent from the tectonite fabric. However, application of the symmetry principle is more complex and more equivocal where the initial fabric is thought to have included both active and passive subfabrics. It is then not sufficient to equate the symmetry of deformation with that of the tectonite fabric. In the hypothetical illustrations that follow, we make these assumptions: (1) all phenomena are homogeneous; (2) inherited subfabrics may be either active or passive; (3) the tectonite fabric includes both inherited and imposed (active) elements; (4) the stress system has orthorhombic symmetry D_{2h}.

Case 1. All Inherited Subfabrics Passive (Fig. 10-12a to c). Figure 10-12a: Let the symmetry of the initial fabric be spherical, $K_{\infty h}$. The symmetry of stress D_{2h} shares all its planes with the initial fabric symmetry. The respective symmetries of mean strain (pure strain without rotation), movement picture, and final tectonic fabric are identical—D_{2h}. The final fabric is homotactic and all its subfabrics are imposed. A possible example is an initially isotropic granite which has become foliated and lineated under a general state of stress.

Figure 10-12b: Let the initial fabric be axial, $D_{\infty h}$, and let the ∞-fold axis be normal to only one of the axes of principal stress. Because the fabric is completely passive its effective symmetry is spherical, $K_{\infty h}$. The mean strain and the movement picture are orthorhombic, D_{2h}, as in a. But the transformed initial fabric, as an inherited subfabric, reduces the symmetry of the final fabric from D_{2h} (the symmetry of the combined

---

[33] We now prefer this general type of explanation based purely on symmetry to more detailed explanations, involving supposed orienting mechanisms, advanced in earlier publications (e.g., Turner, *op. cit.*, pp. 211–214, 1948; L. E. Weiss, Fabric analysis of a triclinic tectonite, *Am. Jour. Sci.*, vol. 253, pp. 225–236, 1955).

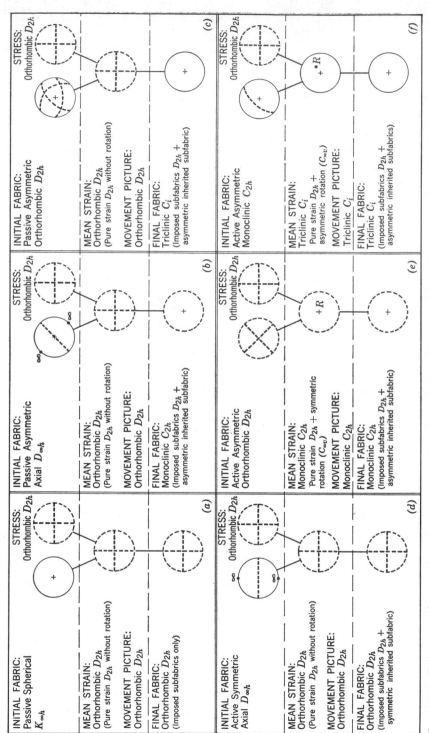

Fig. 10-12. Diagrammatic examples of symmetry relations in evolution of tectonite fabrics (explanation in text). Broken lines = symmetry planes; R = rotation axis.

imposed subfabrics) to monoclinic C_{2h}. A general example is a tectonite formed by deformation of a sedimentary rock with passive bedding S, under general stress whose principal axes σ_1 and σ_3 were inclined to S while σ_2 was parallel to S.

In portions of a metaconglomerate from the Shetland Islands,[34] the pebbles are strongly triaxial ellipsoids (presumably strain ellipsoids) which define a mesoscopic subfabric with orthorhombic symmetry D_{2h}. Other subfabrics—notably (1) a foliation and (2) a lineation, both defined by mica orientation, and (3) the c-axis pattern of quartz within the pebbles—have identical orthorhombic symmetry. But the intersection of foliation and bedding is inclined both to the lineation and to all three symmetry planes of the other subfabrics. It is concluded that the bedding is an inherited passive element of the conglomerate fabric.[35] A further inference is that the remaining fabric elements, with their common symmetry D_{2h}, reflect the symmetry of stress, strain, and movement picture.

Figure 10-12c: Let the initial fabric be orthorhombic, D_{2h}, and let none of its symmetry planes coincide with a symmetry plane of the stress system. In contrast with the strain and the movement picture, both of which reflect the symmetry D_{2h} of the stress system, the final heterotactic fabric must also reflect the symmetry of the transformed passive initial fabric, and so has triclinic symmetry C_i. The imposed subfabrics, considered alone, have the same symmetry D_{2h} as that of stress, strain, and movement picture. An example would be a tectonite formed by oblique deformation of a bedded sediment with primary linear current structure, provided both bedding and lineation were passive.

Case 2. All Inherited Subfabrics Active (Fig. 10-12d–f). Figure 10-12d: Let the initial fabric be axial $D_{\infty h}$, and let the ∞-fold axis coincide with one of the axes of principal stress. Stress, strain, movement picture, and final fabric have identical symmetry D_{2h}. An example is a sedimentary rock thrown into a system of symmetric isoclinal folds (with possible extension parallel to the fold axes) under orthorhombic stress with the maximum compressive stress σ_1 parallel to the bedding. An analogous example is the orthorhombic fabric of Yule marble, experimentally deformed so that the stress system and the initial fabric have three planes of symmetry in common (Fig. 9-18b).

Figure 10-12e: Let the initial fabric be orthorhombic D_{2h} and let it have only one symmetry plane in common with the stress system. The mean strain and the movement picture are both monoclinic C_{2h}, for the kinematically active initial fabric induces a rotational component of both strain and movement about R, the normal to the common symmetry plane of stress and initial fabric. The final fabric, with its active

[34] D. Flinn, Deformation of the Funzie conglomerate, Fetlar, Shetland, *Jour. Geology*, vol. 64, pp. 480–505, 1956.
[35] *Ibid.*, p. 491.

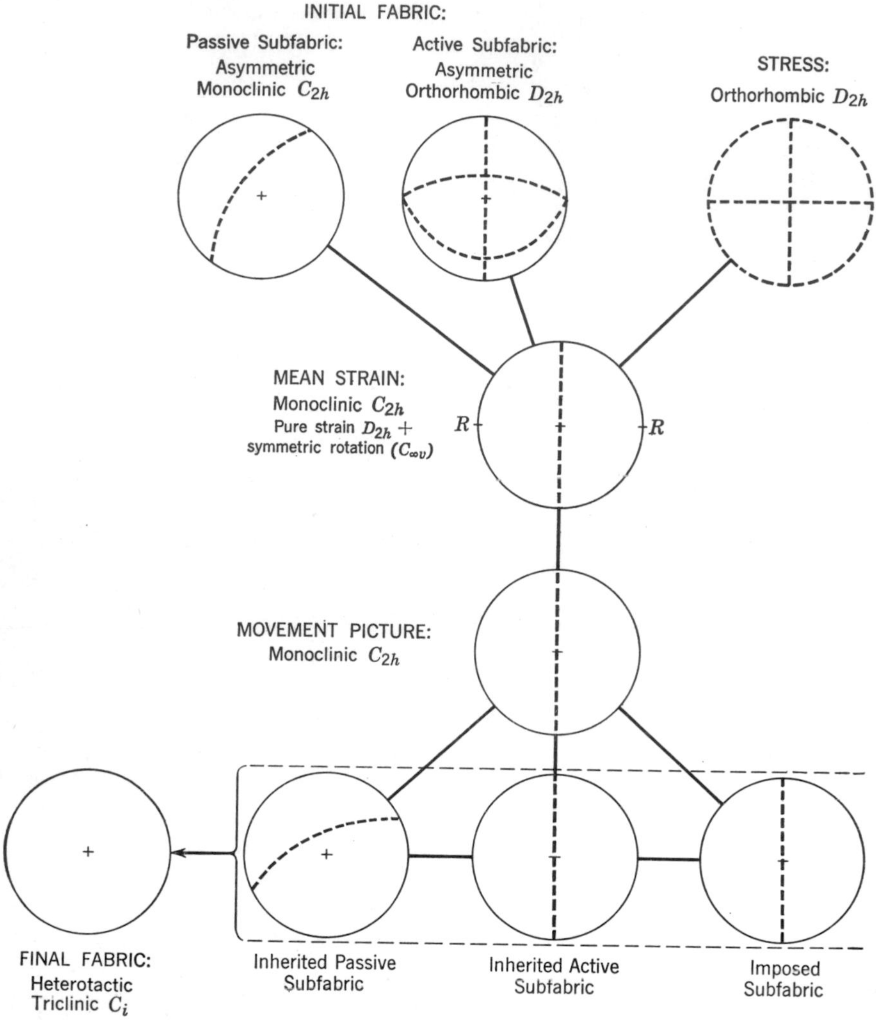

FIG. 10-13. General symmetry relations in evolution of a complex heterotactic tectonite fabric (explanation in text).

inherited and imposed subfabrics, is homotactic and also has monoclinic symmetry.[36] A familiar example is deformation of a tectonite, originally containing a foliation S and a lineation L, by compression oblique to S and normal to L, both elements being active.

Figure 10-12f: Let the initial fabric be monoclinic C_{2h}, and let its symmetry plane be inclined to all three symmetry planes of the stress system.

[36] An analogous case, in which, however, the stress system and the initial fabric both have axial symmetry $D_{\infty h}$, is the monoclinic fabric of Yule marble resulting from experimental deformation of a cylinder so oriented that the initial fabric and the stress system have a single symmetry plane in common (fig. 9-18c).

Here R, the axis of the rotational component of strain and movement, is inclined to all three symmetry planes of the orthorhombic pure-strain component. Consequently the symmetry of strain, movement picture, and final fabric is triclinic.

Case 3. Inherited Subfabrics both Active and Passive (Fig. 10-13). Let an initial heterotactic fabric have (1) kinematically active subfabrics, orthorhombic D_{2h}, having one symmetry plane in common with the stress system, and (2) a kinematically passive subfabric with monoclinic symmetry C_{2h}. Just as in Fig. 10-12e, the mean strain—including a component of pure strain and a component of rotation about R—and the movement picture both have monoclinic symmetry C_{2h}. The final fabric is heterotactic and has triclinic symmetry. It consists of three kinds of subfabric:

a. Imposed; symmetry C_{2h}, the same as that of the movement picture.

b. Inherited active; symmetry C_{2h}, the same as that of the movement picture and of type *a*.

c. Inherited passive; either symmetry C_{2h}, but with symmetry plane inclined to that of subfabrics *a* and *b*; or symmetry triclinic.

It is commonly not possible to determine whether the behavior of an inherited subfabric has been active. So in analysis of heterotactic tectonite fabrics—especially those with triclinic symmetry—the most reliable guide to the symmetry of deformation is given by subfabrics known to be imposed and therefore certainly active. These generally have a symmetry that is higher than or the same as that of strain and movement; it cannot be lower. Herein lies the special value of [0001] orientation patterns of syntectonically recrystallized quartz and calcite, for these must be imposed subfabrics. Orientation patterns of mica on the other hand commonly preserve mimetically s-surfaces and lineations which may possibly belong to the category of inherited passive fabrics.

TRANSFORMATION OF PASSIVE MARKERS BY HOMOGENEOUS DEFORMATION

General. Reconstruction of the movement picture (gliding mechanism) of experimentally induced deformation of calcite crystals (cf. pages 339 to 344) was based largely on observed passive rotation of inherited twin lamellae with respect to internal coordinates (the axes of the crystal lattice).[37] On a larger scale the same kind of evidence relating to tectonites is provided by passive markers—inherited s-surfaces and lineations—internally rotated on similar geometric principle with regard to

[37] I. Borg and F. J. Turner, Deformation of Yule marble, part VI, *Geol. Soc. America Bull.*, vol. 64, pp. 1348, 1952; F. J. Turner, D. T. Griggs, and H. Heard, *op. cit.*, pp. 898–901, 1954.

some suitable frame of reference.[38]   The geometric transformations in question may be treated mathematically as affine transformations in a strictly continuous body undergoing strictly homogeneous deformation (pages 266 to 269).

More practically the motions of passive markers during any progressive deformation may be expressed on an equal-area projection.   On this are plotted the paths traced by the poles of rotated planes or the impingement points of rotated lines.   Two alternative planes of projection have been employed for this purpose in analysis of tectonites.   For strains of orthorhombic symmetry where the strain ellipsoid may be identified from fabric criteria, the AB plane has been used.   For strains of lower symmetry, however, it is more convenient to use some other plane known to contain the same material points (e.g., a surface of structural discontinuity), for this can be identified even though the principal axes of the ellipsoid cannot be located.   Obviously the respective paths of any rotated plane or line plotted on different planes of projection will not be geometrically identical.

Paths of Rotation Referred to the AB Plane of the Strain Ellipsoid. Flinn[39] has derived trigonometric equations for paths (termed by him "structural movement paths") of this kind, which he also has plotted geometrically.   His plane of projection is AB[40] of a series of strain ellipsoids corresponding to progressive chronologic stages of deformation. This plane maintains a constant orientation in space only if the rotational component of deformation is zero.   Otherwise Flinn's analysis applies only to the pure-strain component of deformation (pure affine transformation of page 269).   His conclusions for strictly continuous and homogeneous transformations are as follows:

1. On progressive deformation the pole of a plane always moves away from the longest axis (A) toward the shortest axis (C) of the strain ellipsoid, but not necessarily by the shortest path.   For axial deformations the shortest path is taken, so that a pole moves along a great circle of the projection.   The axis of this great circle is given by the intersection of the passive plane with the plane normal to the axis of compression (C) or extension (A).   For a triaxial ellipsoid (plane or nonplane deformations) the path is neither a great circle nor a small circle of the projection.

2. The impingement point of any rotated line moves away from C and toward A.   The path followed is identical with that of the pole of a plane, but the sense of motion is reversed.

---

[38] Cf. Weiss, *op. cit.*, p. 228, fig. 1; J. G. Ramsay, The effects of folding upon the orientation of sedimentation structures, *Jour. Geology*, vol. 69, pp. 84–99, 1961.

[39] We thank Dr. Flinn for permitting us to cite from an advance copy (in manuscript) of his paper, "On folding during three-dimensional progressive deformation" (abstract in *Geol. Soc. London Circ. 94*, November, 1961).

[40] By analogy with standard procedure in optics, Flinn uses X, Y, and Z for what we term the A, B, and C axes.

3. Poles and lines lying in any symmetry plane of the ellipsoid remain in that plane.

4. Planes and lines rotate without becoming curved (i.e., transformations are affine).

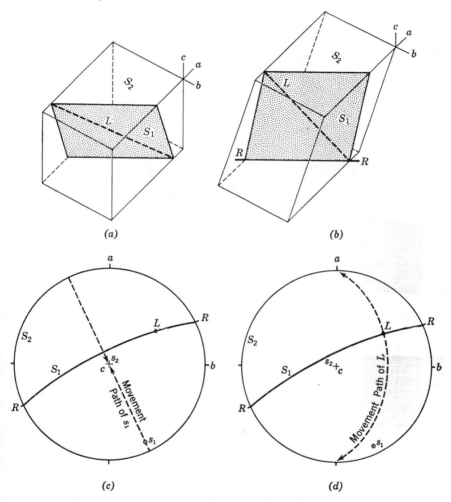

FIG. 10-14. Deformation of passive planar marker (S_1) and linear marker (L) by simple shear. s_1 and s_2 are poles of S_1 and S_2; a, b, and c are reference axes (kinematic axes); (a) Undeformed body. (b) Body deformed by simple shear on S_2. (c) Movement path (broken line) of s_1 projected on S_2. R = axis of internal rotation of S_1. (d) Movement path (broken line) of L projected on S_2.

Paths of Rotation Referred to a Circular Section of the Strain Ellipsoid. Figure 10-14 shows paths of rotation for simple shear, plotted on the shear plane. Within the deformed body is an inherited passive marker plane S_1 containing a lineation L (Fig. 10-14a). Figure 10-14b shows the same body after deformation by simple shear, with S_2 as the shear plane (a circular section of the strain ellipsoid and a plane of no distortion and no rotation). During deformation the marker plane S_1 becomes rotated about R, its intersection with S_2; and L rotates within a unique plane

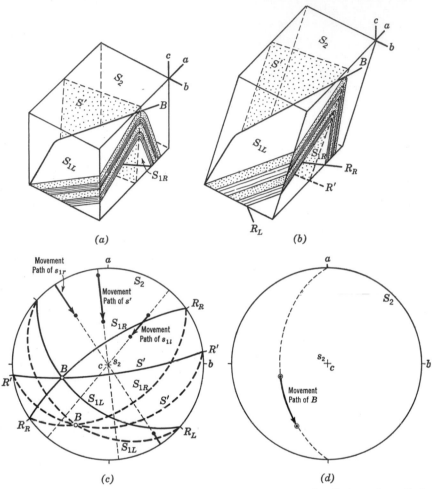

Fig. 10-15. Internal rotation of a plane cylindrical fold in passive S_1 (two planar limbs S_{1R} and S_{1L}, axis B, axial plane S') by simple shear on S_2 in direction a. (a) Undeformed body. (b) Body after simple shear on S_2 in direction a. Axis of rotation of $S_{1R} = R_R$, of $S_{1L} = R_L$, of $S' = R'$. (c) Movement paths of poles s_{1r}, s_{1l}, and s'. Full lines, positions before deformation; broken lines, positions after deformation. (d) Movement path of B.

toward a, the direction of displacement of all particles in the body. The deformation plane ac and the plane of no distortion S_2 ($= ab$) intersect in a. Figure 10-14c and d shows the respective movement paths of the pole of S_1 and the impingement point of L, projected on S_2—a convenient projection plane since it maintains a constant orientation in space. Both paths are arcs of great circles. This would not be so if the plane of projection were AB of the strain ellipsoid; for as deformation proceeds the circular section S_2 rotates with reference to AB about the B axis of the ellipsoid (b of Fig. 10-14).

Strain of the above kind has been illustrated by affine gliding of a deck of cards.[41] It is approximated, too, by a crystal glide system in which the glide plane T corresponds to S_2 and the glide direction t to a of Fig. 10-14. In neither case, however, is deformation strictly homogeneous. But on a sufficiently large scale it may be treated as statistically homogeneous.

Figure 10-15 illustrates internal rotation of a passive s-surface initially having the configuration of a plane cylindrical fold. The geometry of rotation of the axial plane and the fold axis is identical with that of S_2 and L in Fig. 10-14. After deformation the structure is still a plane cylindrical fold; but it has become more tightly appressed or more open, depending upon its initial orientation with respect to S_1.

The deformations pictured in Figs. 10-14 and 10-15 have practical importance since any homogeneous deformation can be expressed in terms of simple shear together with a simple extension (or compression) normal to the deformation plane, a uniform dilatation, and a rotation.[42] We return to this topic in discussing the relation of kinematic axes to strain (pages 398 to 400). And in Chaps. 13 and 14 we discuss the deformation paths for shear domains of simple movement pictures, where the condition of strict homogeneity of strain is relaxed sufficiently to permit nonaffine transformation (bending and folding) of markers on a small scale.[43]

KINEMATIC AXES OF MOVEMENT PICTURES

General. The concept of the movement picture has been illustrated repeatedly in geologic literature by reference to simple models such as gliding and flexural slip in a deck of cards, or laminar flow of a fluid in a trough.[44] For any such model it is possible to define three mutually perpendicular axes (a, b, and c) which facilitate description of the movement picture and the resultant homogeneous or heterogeneous strain. For

[41] A. E. H. Love, *A Treatise on the Mathematical Theory of Elasticity*, p. 71, Dover, New York, 1944.

[42] *Ibid.*

[43] Flinn, *op. cit.*, also treats the existence of folds within the framework of an otherwise homogeneous deformation and reaches some conclusions with which we disagree (cf. pp. 490–491).

[44] E.g., Sander, *op. cit.*, pp. 57, 58, 62–73, 1930; Knopf and Ingerson, *op. cit.*, pp. 40–47; Turner, *op. cit.*, p. 3, 1957.

movement pictures of plane deformation involving gliding on a family of displacement discontinuities—as in a card deck—a is the glide direction, b the normal to a in the glide plane, and c the normal to the glide plane ab; ac is the deformation plane. If bending (external rotation) accompany gliding in a heterogeneous strain of this type, the axis of bending is b. There is an exact analogy with the simple picture of translation gliding in crystals:[45] ab is the equivalent of the glide plane T; a and b are identical respectively with the glide direction t and the axis of bend gliding f.

The movement picture of gliding corresponds to a plane deformation with monoclinic symmetry C_{2h} or C_{1h}; and the deformation plane is also the plane of symmetry of movement. Most natural deformation as exemplified in tectonites is nonplane; but within the total tectonite fabric there are common heterogeneous structures, notably folds, that can be described in terms of plane deformation involving gliding parallel to an a kinematic axis (see pages 473 to 487). Gliding and folding, however, then make up only one component of the movement picture. That other components have participated in development of the tectonite fabric may be indicated by other structures such as boudinage or deformed pebbles or by discordant patterns of mineral orientation. This situation was appreciated by Sander,[46] who distinguished between two "plans" of movement picture: (1) a monoclinic picture corresponding approximately to plane strain involving gliding on one or more planes and referred to kinematic axes as just defined; (2) a more complex picture that can be resolved into two such plane strains with mutually perpendicular b axes.

Use of kinematic axes to describe the movement picture and fabric of tectonites has led to widespread confusion in several aspects of structural analysis:

1. In the first place there is confusion between movement and the distortional component of strain. Some geologists have correlated evidence of elongation—stretched pebbles and crystals, flattened oolites, boudinage, and so on—with "movement" or "flow" parallel to the axis of elongation, which on these grounds has been designated an a kinematic axis. But in homogeneous nonplane deformation it is impossible to define precisely any single direction of "movement" or relative displacement within the strained body. Terms such as "movement," "flow," and "tectonic transport" cannot be precisely referred to kinematic axes except for very simple movement pictures of plane deformation. Although we have used them widely in the past,[47] they will not be used henceforth in this book in reference to kinematic axes.

[45] M. J. Buerger, Translation gliding in crystals, *Am. Mineralogist*, vol. 15, pp. 45–64, 1930; Knopf and Ingerson, *op. cit.*, p. 92.

[46] Sander, *op. cit.*, pp. 56–58, 1930.

[47] E.g., L. E. Weiss, A study in tectonic style, *Univ. California Geol. Sci. Pub.*, vol. 30, pp. 43, 76, 1954; Turner and Verhoogen, *op. cit.*, p. 628, 1960.

2. There has been confusion, too, between relative displacement of opposite boundaries of a strained domain and the system of small-scale penetrative movements that constitute the movement picture within the domain itself. Under slightly eccentric loading, strain in a test specimen tends to be concentrated in a diagonal domain whose opposite boundaries are mutually displaced in the opposite sense to that of gliding within the strained domain; and the internal glide planes that define the movement picture are oriented transversely with reference to the external boundaries of the large-scale displacement zone (Fig. 10-16). In the field of tectonics, the movement picture within a mylonite zone may be radically different from the large-scale displacement of the overlying thrust plate relative to the underlying basement. Herein is one of the reasons for the long-sustained controversy regarding the relation of large-scale displacements on the Moine Thrust of northwest Scotland to the lineated structures of associated mylonites and of the Moine schists of the overriding plate.[48]

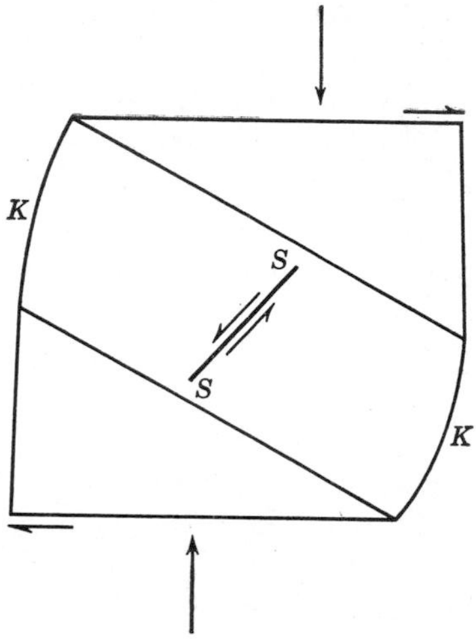

3. It has not always been realized that there is not necessarily any regular geometric relation between the translational component of strain —which affects the strained domain bodily and in no way affects its fabric—and the movement picture, which is an internal feature reflected in the fabric of the strained body. For example the direction of bodily movement (translation) of the metal sheet during the manufacture of corrugated iron is parallel to the corrugations;[49] but the internal movement picture of buckling and associated small-scale componental movements has a symmetry plane normal to that of accompanying translation of the strained sheet. Again the relative movements of particles within

FIG. 10-16. Displacement of opposite undeformed ends A and B of a marble cylinder under eccentric loading. Within the diagonal region of strain KK, there has been intragranular translation gliding on crystallographic planes r whose mean orientation and sense of glide are shown as SS. (After F. J. Turner, D. T. Griggs, R. H. Clark, and R. H. Dixon, Geol. Soc. America Bull., pp. 1285, 1286, fig. 9E, 1956.)

---

[48] For a summary of conflicting ideas on the tectonic significance of the Moine Thrust see the following and papers referred to therein: D. B. McIntyre, The Moine Thrust: its discovery, age, and tectonic significance, Geologists' Assoc. Proc., vol. 65, pp. 203–223 (especially pp. 208–212, 219–223), 1954.

[49] Cf. E. Cloos, Lineation, Geol. Soc. America Mem. 18, p. 28, 1946.

expanding cork are unrelated to the bodily motion of the cork as it is drawn from a bottle.

4. Finally there is the difficulty that inevitably attends any attempt to describe the movement picture of nonplane deformation in terms of a uniform system of kinematic axes designed to treat plane deformation by gliding. It is tempting to interpret homotactic monoclinic fabrics as products of plane deformation involving gliding in the symmetry plane, the normal to which would then be a kinematic axis b. This interpretation is consistent with the requirements of symmetry. But it neglects the possibility, indeed the probability, that the strain is nonplane and has a component of elongation normal to the symmetry plane of the fabric.

Kinematic Axes in Relation to Strain. The movement picture of affine laminar gliding involving a penetrative family of planar deformation discontinuities is commonly equated in geologic literature with simple shear. The difference between such a homogeneous movement picture and a strictly homogeneous simple shear lies in the necessary specification of a "glide" or "slip surface" for the movement picture; no such specification is part of the concept of simple shear. But, so long as there are no component displacements of particles other than those parallel to the glide surface, the mean strain of affine laminar gliding does correspond to simple shear with the glide plane (shear plane) parallel to a circular section of the deformation ellipsoid. This is true statistically not only for the gliding of a card deck on a family of pure displacement discontinuities, but for any plane movement picture with a laminar arrangement of shear domains—e.g., those pictured in Fig. 10-3d and e— on a scale where the local strain perturbations implicit in the movement picture can be neglected.

Natural deformation of rocks commonly forms families of planar discontinuities visible as imposed foliations or axial planes of folds; or in initially anisotropic rocks inherited s-surfaces may be active as discontinuities in deformation. Such visible structural discontinuities are usually chosen as an internal reference frame for a description of fabric properties (page 87).[50]

Reference axes are required also to specify the kinematic properties of a domain of homogeneous deformation. Where possible, the obvious axes to choose are the principal strain axes of the mean deformation, i.e., the A, B, and C axes of the strain ellipsoid. Only comparatively rarely, however, can the form of the strain ellipsoid be determined— notably where markers such as oolites or pebbles of known initial shape are present in the deformed body. In all other cases, i.e., in most tectonites, we must fall back upon some other frame of reference. Fortunately such is usually present in the form of visible structural surfaces

---

[50] Where the fabric properties are to be referred to an external frame of reference, geographic axes are chosen.

(*s*-planes), for these are known to contain the same material points at all stages of deformation. With this in mind, and taking into account the symmetry of the fabric, the geologist can safely select appropriate kinematic axes for active homotactic fabrics according to the following rules:[51]

1. *In an orthorhombic fabric* the symmetry planes of the fabric define the symmetry planes of the movement picture and of mean strain. Where, as is usually the case, a foliation and a lineation are present these completely define the axes of mean strain. It is not possible to identify the *A*, *B*, and *C* axes individually, except that it is likely, from the nature of the structure itself, that *C* is normal to the foliation. Obvious kinematic axes are the three symmetry axes labeled in some arbitrary fashion. If the axes are designated *a*, *b*, *c*, as has been done by some writers, these have totally different kinematic significance from similarly lettered axes of a laminar gliding deformation cited above. Movement paths for internally rotated passive planar and linear markers are those described by Flinn (cf. page 392).[52]

2. *In a monoclinic fabric*, the single plane of symmetry can be equated with a symmetry plane of the ellipsoid of mean strain, and the axis normal to this with an axis of rotation. Generally it is an axis of differential rotation in shear domains, but it can be also an axis of external rotation of the whole fabric. Any imposed foliation and lineation must lie normal to the symmetry plane of the fabric. For convenience the mean deformation can be resolved into two components referred to internal coordinates:

a. A plane mean strain corresponding to a simple shear. The movement picture is one of differential translation of particles with reference to a given plane (shear plane) which is a circular section of the strain ellipsoid for this component. Conveniently, an imposed foliation is selected as the plane of translation and the motion of all particles is referred to this plane as a stationary reference frame. The symmetry plane of the fabric becomes the deformation plane for this component of mean simple shear.

b. The remaining particle motions relative to this fixed plane can be expressed as a mean pure strain sharing a symmetry plane (that of the fabric) with the simple shear component. This mean pure strain is responsible for subsidiary elongations and shortenings of a nonrotational kind. Its symmetry cannot be lower than orthorhombic. Love[53] in his discussion of finite homogeneous strain expresses this component as

---

[51] The procedure is broadly analogous to that of the crystallographer who selects axes according to rules based on symmetry with a view to describing in the simplest possible way the configuration and properties of the crystal lattice.

[52] Flinn, *op. cit.*

[53] Love, *op. cit.*, p. 71, 1944.

ideally a simple extension or compression normal to the symmetry plane of the simple shear component.

The additional components of strain required for a complete specification of a particular strain are a uniform dilatation and a rigid-body rotation.[54] The dilatation has spherical symmetry $K_{\infty h}$ and affects all particles uniformly; the rotation is a rotation of the whole system relative to external coordinates. Both of these can be neglected, once the translation plane for the simple shear component is fixed as a reference frame, for neither leaves any imprint on the fabric.

In a monoclinic deformation the orientation of the two strain axes in the symmetry plane is unknown. These axes are therefore unsuitable as reference coordinates. Conventional procedure is to refer particle motion to an active foliation surface as a glide or slip surface, using the kinematic axes a, b, and c as defined above. Then b is normal to the plane of symmetry and a lies in the foliation normal to b. The movement paths for passive planar and linear markers for the corresponding simple shear component of mean deformation, referred to ab as the projection plane, are those given in Fig. 10-14. For a natural nonplane deformation, however, these movement paths are modified from their great-circle form by progressive deformation by the addition of the component of mean pure strain cited above.

3. *In a triclinic fabric* there is no indication of the orientation of principal axes of mean strain. Also, because the axis of the rotational component of mean strain is inclined obliquely to the strain axes, nothing is to be gained by defining reference axes related to simple shear components of mean deformation as has been done by Sander.[55]

Redefinition and Restriction of Kinematic Axes. On the basis of the above discussion we have now abandoned the broad use of kinematic axes previously advocated elsewhere.[56] For an orthorhombic movement picture there is no precise way of designating a, b, and c kinematic axes beyond the fact that each must be normal to a symmetry plane of the fabric. For triclinic movement pictures kinematic axes a, b, and c have no real meaning. So we restrict the use of kinematic axes a, b, and c to movement pictures—or components of movement pictures—having monoclinic symmetry and expressible in terms of gliding upon a prominent structural discontinuity (an s-surface). Other components of mean strain are generally present but are not included in the movement picture so described. The use of kinematic axes so defined is important particularly in discussing the locally heterogeneous movement pictures responsible for folding (cf. Chaps. 13, 14).

[54] *Ibid.*
[55] Sander, *op. cit.*, pp. 56–58, 1930.
[56] E.g., Turner, *op. cit.*, p. 198, 1948; Turner and Verhoogen, *op. cit.*, p. 628, 1960.

CHAPTER 11

INTERPRETATION OF MICROSCOPIC SUBFABRICS: PREFERRED ORIENTATION OF TECTONITE MINERALS

INTRODUCTION

Most published analyses of tectonite fabrics include at least some data regarding the state of preferred orientation (lattice orientation) of common easily measured tectonite minerals, notably quartz, micas, and calcite. The general prevalence of preferred orientation in all such minerals—first realized by Sander, Schmidt, and their coworkers—is itself an intriguing fact of petrography. But what is its significance? How can it be used to clarify the deformational history of a tectonite, by what means does a preferred orientation pattern evolve, and how may it ultimately disintegrate?

The student of microscopic fabrics of tectonites, confronted with the regularity and persistent recurrence of standard patterns of preferred orientation of quartz, mica, and other minerals (cf. pages 224 to 247, Figs. 6-19 to 6-25), cannot but attempt to find answers to these and related questions. But deformation and flow of a polycrystalline, multiphase aggregate in process of metamorphic recrystallization are a prolonged, variable, and complex process. And relevant experimental and thermodynamic data are far outweighed by the mass and variety of the petrographic phenomena whose significance is sought. Consequently the literature on fabric analysis has become encumbered and obscured with interpretive speculation and models of supposed orienting mechanisms lacking experimentally established foundation. Such interpretation is largely discarded in this book. Ever since the appearance of *Gefügekunde der Gesteine* in 1930 interpretation of fabric in general and of mineral orientation patterns in particular has been based mainly on homogeneity, symmetry, and detail of pattern such as maxima, minima, and girdles in the individual diagrams. With the passage of time detail of pattern has assumed less significance, but the importance of homogeneity and symmetry has been sustained.[1]

[1] For this gradual change in emphasis the English-speaking reader may compare opinions in the following: E. B. Knopf and E. Ingerson, Structural petrology, *Geol. Soc. America Mem. 6*, pp. 25, 26, 68–72, 140–147, 175, 1938; F. J. Turner, Mineralogical and structural evolution of the metamorphic rocks, *Geol. Soc. America Mem. 30*,

Before considering problems relating to individual minerals we raise and briefly discuss questions of a more general nature.

GENERAL INTERPRETATION

Interpretation in Terms of Stress. For over a hundred years attempts have been made to correlate patterns of preferred orientation—more particularly the parallel dimensional orientation of micas in foliated rocks —with simple regional stress visualized in terms of load as an external force. From the data of regional field geology vertical loading or lateral squeezing have been inferred as operating over very large tectonite bodies—geosynclines, orogens, and so on. Microscopic subfabrics, such as orientation patterns of quartz or mica, cannot be expected to yield information bearing on the general problem of such regional loading or compression. On the scale on which the microscopic subfabric is homogeneous (microscopic, mesoscopic, and the lower range of macroscopic) stress systems induced by regional external forces, although perhaps statistically homogeneous, are strictly localized. Any microscopic subfabric such as the preferred orientation pattern of mica or of quartz reflects the influence of the local stress system rather than that of regional forces. But it also reflects other influences such as that of initial anisotropy of fabric, and it may be impossible to isolate from these the influence of stress alone. The classic view that parallel alignment and accompanying lattice orientation of mica tables and other inequant mineral grains are due to recrystallization under compression with σ_1 normal to the plane of orientation[2] has little theoretical or experimental justification. Although consistent with the requirements of symmetry, this interpretation ignores all influences other than that of stress.

Thermodynamic correlation of homogeneous preferred orientation with homogeneous stress on a small scale is easy to visualize but difficult to apply. The common tectonite minerals are anisotropic with respect to mechanical properties such as compressibility. It follows that in a homogeneous field of stress the stability of a crystal varies according to its orientation with respect to the principal stresses σ_1, σ_2, and σ_3. Spontaneous internal adjustments within a stressed crystalline aggregate must tend to destroy the less stable and to favor the more stable of the mineral grains. Recrystallization is such a spontaneous process. On thermodynamic grounds an aggregate recrystallized under stress should

---

pp. 187–197, 1948; F. J. Turner and J. Verhoogen, *Igneous and Metamorphic Petrology*, 2d ed., pp. 627–631, McGraw-Hill, New York, 1960.

[2] E.g., F. Becke, Über Mineralabstand und Struktur der kristallinischen Schiefer, *Akad. Wiss. Wien Denkschr.*, vol. 75, pp. 37, 51, 1913; A. Harker, *Metamorphism*, p. 194, Methuen, London, 1932.

develop toward a state of preferred orientation of crystal lattices simply related to the stress field.   Such a stable pattern would be completely independent of the orienting process.[3]   But how likely is it that a thermodynamically stable orientation of tectonite minerals is ever achieved in nature?   The differences in free energy between stably and unstably oriented crystals are small, so that, at least within the lower range of metamorphic temperatures, rates of recrystallization may well be infinitely slow.   Moreover, there is still no agreement as to what orientations of quartz and calcite in relation to stress are the most stable.   Finally it must be borne in mind that the tectonite fabric is born of internal movement and flow.   The "stable" orientations so produced reflect a steady state in a mechanically unstable system rather than true thermodynamic stability.

In this dilemma we nevertheless may turn to the still limited fund of experimental experience relating to recrystallization of stressed minerals and rocks, notably calcite and marble.   The observations are empirical and imply nothing as to absolute stability of the recrystallized product. If calcite is typical of tectonite minerals it would seem that post-tectonic crystallization (annealing) at high temperature of cold-deformed rocks is likely to give rise to an almost randomly oriented aggregate.   Syntectonic recrystallization on the other hand may be a most effective orienting mechanism yielding patterns simply related to the stress system and almost uninfluenced by the initial fabric.   There is a close analogy here with the familiar "stable" orientation patterns developed in highly strained metallic aggregates.

Finally it has been found, in agreement with prediction, that where strain is not accompanied or followed by recrystallization—the condition that holds in most experiments to date—the strong orientation patterns that evolve may be correlated, on the basis of symmetry, with the combined influence of stress and initial fabric.   If the latter is unknown—a common situation with natural tectonites—the stress system cannot be fully reconstructed from fabric data.   The symmetry of the stress system may then be of the same or a higher order than that of the pattern of preferred orientation of the tectonite mineral; but stress and preferred orientation are likely to have some symmetry elements in common. Thus there is nothing inconsistent between a monoclinic preferred orientation pattern of mica with a north-south vertical symmetry plane ($\{001\}$-pole girdle), and a regional east-west horizontal compressive external force.   The two have a symmetry plane in common.   But it is logical to infer that the combination of factors (local stress system, initial fabric, and so on), which immediately influenced evolution of the observed

[3] Discussion of paper by W. Barclay Kamb, "The thermodynamic theory of non-hydrostatically stressed solids," *Jour. Geophys. Research*, vol. 66, pp. 2599 (G. F. J. MacDonald) and 2600 (A. Hoffer), 1961.

mica subfabric, itself had monoclinic or lower symmetry. The former is the more likely, but possibility of the latter cannot be discounted.

Interpretation in Terms of Strain. Orientation patterns of tectonite minerals commonly are symmetrically, and hence probably genetically, related to associated elements of the mesoscopic fabric—foliation, slaty cleavage, lineations, and so on. In classic literature these mesoscopic structures, and with them the associated mineral orientation patterns, have been correlated in various ways with the strain ellipsoid. Most readers will be familiar with the alternative views that planar schistosity and associated parallelism of {001} in mica are to be identified with the AB plane or alternatively with a circular section of the strain ellipsoid.[4] Some of these classic interpretations are based on assumed but unproved orienting mechanisms. The mutually incompatible processes of syntectonic recrystallization governed by "Riecke's principle," and passive rotation of rigid tabular crystals immersed in a flowing matrix, have both been invoked to explain orientation of mica crystals with {001} parallel to AB of the ellipsoid.[5] Neither mechanism has been proved experimentally to be capable of producing preferred orientation of the mica lattice under metamorphic conditions. Direct correlation of mineral orientation with strain on such a basis therefore remains speculative. More dubious still is the extension of such correlation to the same orientation patterns when these are unaccompanied by or asymmetrically related to foliation or lineation.

There is a limited amount of empirical experimental evidence as to relations between mineral orientation and strain. Thus in some experiments on marble, under conditions not permitting recrystallization, [0001] in calcite assumes a state of preferred orientation close to the C axis of the measured strain ellipsoid. It would be dangerous, however, to extrapolate this observation to cover all tectonite fabrics in which [0001] of calcite has strong axially symmetric preferred orientation. Likewise it cannot be inferred from individual tectonites where mica tables are aligned parallel to AB of the strain ellipsoid, as shown by associated deformed pisolites, concretions, and so on, that in the absence of direct evidence of strain the plane of alignment of mica flakes can be identified with AB of the ellipsoid.

Strain and fabric are twin products of the same combined influences—stress and initial fabric. The respective symmetries of strain and fabric are likely therefore to be related, but they need not be identical. Indeed the symmetry of homogeneous pure strain cannot be lower than ortho-

[4] E.g., C. K. Leith and W. J. Mead, *Metamorphic Geology*, pp. 177, 179, Holt, New York, 1915; W. J. Mead, Studies for students: folding, rock flowage and associated structures, *Jour. Geology*, vol. 48, p. 1010, 1940; G. Becker, Current theories of slaty cleavage, *Am. Jour. Sci.*, vol. 24, pp. 1–17, 1907.

[5] E.g., Harker, *op. cit.*, pp. 153–155, 1932.

rhombic if external rotation of the body is excluded (cf. page 275), and symmetry of homogeneous mineral orientation patterns is commonly monoclinic. The only safe inference regarding strain that can be drawn from mineral orientation patterns is that symmetry elements of the latter are likely to be shared in common with the strain ellipsoid.

Interpretation in Terms of the Movement Picture. In the sequence of correlated influences and phenomena concerned in the evolution of a tectonite fabric during flow of a stressed rock, the ultimate fabric is more closely related to the movement picture of flow than to the more remote phenomena of stress and strain. Consequently symmetry of fabric most closely reflects symmetry of the movement picture. The principal use of mineral orientation patterns in structural analysis is in clarifying the symmetry of the total tectonite fabric. In some cases the fabric as a whole is found to be homotactic: symmetry inherent in the mesoscopic subfabric is duplicated precisely in the patterns of preferred orientation of mica and of quartz. In other fabrics one or more of the mineral orientation patterns—more particularly that of quartz—is discordant with reference to foliations and lineation. Mesoscopic and microscopic fabrics, both perhaps monoclinic, combine to give overall triclinic symmetry; and the inferred movement picture must be of a more complex nature than that deduced from mesoscopic structures alone. In general, crystallization of a tectonite mineral can commonly be referred, on the basis of its orientation pattern, to one or other of the different phases of folding established on the basis of macroscopic analysis.

Mechanisms Responsible for Preferred Orientations. The tectonite fabric, and thus the patterns of mineral orientation in tectonites, are products of flow involving the whole gamut of componental movements— plastic strain, fracture and rotation of grains, diffusion of ions in the recrystallizing rock, and so on. The effectiveness of individual kinds of componental movement in producing preferred orientation of tectonite minerals has been investigated in a few cases only. We know something, for example, of how the grains in a calcite aggregate acquire a preferred orientation over a range of geologically possible temperatures and pressures by plastic strain and accompanying rotation, by syntectonic recrystallization and by annealing recrystallization (cf. pages 345 to 355). And the effects observed in calcite and marble are found to have much in common with the much more extensively investigated behavior of metals in process of strain. So it is possible to visualize in a very general manner the complexity of the mechanism by which any tectonite mineral acquires its observed state of preferred orientation. For brevity we shall refer to this as the *orienting mechanism* or *orienting process*.

To reconstruct in detail the orienting process as it applies to a particular pattern of a particular mineral—e.g., to any of the patterns illustrated in Figs. 6-21 and 6-22—is impossible in the absence of experimental data relating to similar patterns produced in the laboratory. Even what is known regarding calcite can be applied only with great caution to natural calcite subfabrics, for most of the laboratory experiments represent simple conditions uniformly sustained over a short time. Experience with marble and calcite has brought out the highly disconcerting fact that the experimentally revealed orienting process is at complete variance with that previously inferred from petrographic and orientation studies on naturally deformed marbles.

Discussion of orienting processes, inferred from the orientation pattern itself and invoking unduly simplified models, mostly overemphasizing direct componental movements, looms large in the literature on tectonite fabrics.[6] Most of this should be discarded as pure speculation. Some widely accepted concepts and inferences that fall in this category, and here are rejected until experimentally demonstrated, are listed below:

1. Translation gliding on crystal glide systems inferred purely from preferred orientation data, e.g., the frequently cited but unproved gliding on various prisms and rhombohedrons in quartz.

2. Translation gliding inferred from visible microscopic lamellae such as the well-known thin, sharp $\{01\bar{1}2\}$ lamellae in calcite, and $\{100\}$ lamellae in olivine.

3. Alignment of crystal glide planes in invisible "slip planes of the fabric." The concept of ubiquitous slip planes—visible or invisible—penetrating the fabric of a tectonite appears to owe its wide acceptance to (a) the proved existence of visible "slip planes"—actually thin domains of shear—in the form of strain-slip cleavage (e.g., Fig. 10-10c) in some tectonites; (b) possible overemphasis of laminar gliding as the main mechanism responsible for foliation in general; and (c) the uncritical use of simple models of simple and pure shear in discussion of the strain ellipsoid. Although one of us has employed this concept in previous interpretation of tectonite fabrics,[7] we now reject it as unsupported by the data of petrography and structural analysis and incompatible with the concept of the movement picture developed on pages 370 to 378. Even where it can be demonstrated that slip planes S are penetrative elements of a particular fabric on a given scale, there is no experimental justification for the widely prevalent idea that crystals rotate toward an ultimate stable orientation or steady state with their active glide planes aligned in S.

4. Models of purely mechanical deformation involving only direct componental movements (e.g., Schmidt's classic orienting mechanism for

---

[6] The present authors, in earlier publications, have contributed to such discussion or have accepted uncritically the orienting mechanisms proposed by others (e.g., Turner, op. cit., pp. 254–275).

[7] E.g., Ibid., pp. 164–176, 244–245.

quartz[8]) applied to tectonite fabrics which nevertheless have obviously been affected by syntectonic or post-tectonic recrystallization. Such recrystallization, and commonly accompanying appearance of new mineral phases, is characteristic of metamorphic rocks and probably overshadows direct componental movements in the orienting process.

5. Recrystallization determined by stress alone, in the absence of experimental data.

By contrast there are certain data and concepts that may be legitimately applied, with due exercise of caution, in constructing tentative models of orienting mechanisms:

1. Experimentally established glide mechanisms (e.g., on $\{10\bar{1}1\}$ and $\{01\bar{1}2\}$ in calcite; on $\{0001\}$ and $\{02\bar{2}1\}$ in dolomite) and accompanying effects of external rotation of the grains concerned. Such data can be applied only to tectonites that show no sign of recrystallization; the individual grains should show obvious strain effects such as elongated or lensoid outlines, undulatory extinction, and kink bands.

2. Syntectonic recrystallization; to be correlated with the movement picture on grounds of symmetry, and possibly (where experimental data are available) even with stress.

3. Mimetic crystallization (post-tectonic) whereby elongated or tabular crystals become aligned in planes or lines of maximum ease of growth provided by existing discrete discontinuities in the fabric (S-planes, lineations, joints).[9]

4. Annealing recrystallization of cold-worked material—essentially a deorienting process.

These mechanisms, of course, do not embrace all possible components of the orienting process. We visualize the latter as a long-sustained combination of alternating direct and indirect componental movements. Crystallization and grain deformation repeatedly alternate. The ultimate orientation pattern of a tectonite mineral may reflect several or only the last of these orienting processes.

PREFERRED ORIENTATION OF INDIVIDUAL MINERALS

General Statement.   Orientation patterns of individual minerals form an essential part of the total fabric of a tectonite viewed on the mesoscopic or the macroscopic scale. It is in this context that the broadest and most useful inferences may be drawn from mineral orientation (see

[8] W. Schmidt, *Tektonik und Verformungslehre*, pp. 189–191, Borntraeger, Berlin, 1932; Turner, *op. cit.*, pp. 256–259.

[9] B. Sander, *Gefügekunde der Gesteine*, pp. 156, 172, Springer, Berlin, Vienna, 1930; Turner and Verhoogen, *op. cit.*, pp. 647–649, 1960. Among the classic writers on schistosity and cleavage were some who regarded parallelism of mica flakes in foliated rocks as a mimetic effect purely incidental to foliation: D. Sharpe, On slaty cleavage, *Geol. Soc. London Quart. Jour.*, vol. 5, pp. 128–129, 1849; Becker, *op. cit.*, p. 7.

Chap. 13). But much has been written regarding the significance and evolution of mineral orientation in tectonites as an isolated phenomenon.[10] The classic views on this topic are diverse and speculative and now require critical revision in the light of what has subsequently emerged from experimental studies on the development of tectonite fabrics. In the brief critical discussion that follows, attention is focused mainly on the three minerals for which the most extensive fabric data are available— quartz, mica, and calcite. Because its behavior under stress has been more conclusively demonstrated than that of other minerals, the first of these to be considered is calcite.

Calcite. *Classic Interpretation Critically Reviewed.* Most recorded orientation data for calcite relate to c axes [0001] or to visible e lamellae $\{01\bar{1}2\}$. Only a few writers,[11] mainly of the Austrian school, have recorded adequately the basis on which particular sets of e lamellae have been selected for measurement, and related information on the relative strength of different sets of lamellae in each grain and on whether or not the lamellae are optically recognizable as broad twins. In other papers there are even instances where, through lack of confirmation of the characteristic angle c to $e = 26°$, e lamellae have been misidentified as r.

The classic interpretation of calcite orientation places strong emphasis on e gliding as an orienting mechanism, and correlates crystal gliding with the existence of imaginary "slip planes of the fabric"—actually visible or merely statistically defined s-surfaces—in which the active glide planes supposedly become aligned. Typical of the older views—though perhaps closing on a more cautious note than most—is the following:[12]

Secondary twinning, with e as the plane of gliding, and the edge $[r:r]$ as glide line, develops with great facility during laboratory deformation of single calcite crystals or of marble. On this account, and because of the almost universal occurrence of visible lamellae parallel to e in calcite of deformed rocks, twin gliding on e has generally been assumed to be the principal factor in the evolution of preferred orientation of calcite in tectonites. Certain calcite fabrics show patterns of preferred orientation that agree so well with the requirements of twin gliding, that this may safely be accepted as the essential orienting mechanism. Other patterns, however, are less readily explained on this basis. It is not improbable that in such cases the more obvious nature of the phenomena connected with twin gliding on e has caused equally or more effective mechanisms to be overlooked.

[10] For older views, most of which we must now modify or discard, the reader is referred to Sander, *op. cit.*, pp. 173–217; Knopf and Ingerson, *op. cit.*, pp. 163–178; Turner, *op. cit.*, pp. 254–275; H. W. Fairbairn, *Structural Petrology of Deformed Rocks*, pp. 117–149, Addison-Wesley, Reading, Mass., 1949.

[11] E.g., E. Felkel, Gefügestudien an Kalktektoniten, *Geol. Bundesanst. Wien (Austria) Jahrb.*, vol. 79, pp. 33–85, 1929; Sander, *op. cit.*, pp. 204–206, 293–294. These early studies give the most comprehensive and clearly specified orientation data today available for calcite of tectonites.

[12] Turner, *op. cit.*, p. 266.

Alternative mechanisms of gliding proposed by various writers include translation gliding on e—to account for the very common thin, not obviously twinned e lamellae[13]—and translation on $\{0001\}$ as in dolomite.[14] It is noteworthy that orienting of calcite—as also with quartz and mica—has been explained almost exclusively in terms of direct componental movement. This is largely because of the difficulty of constructing an orientation model based on the less completely predictable processes of diffusion and nucleation and growth of crystals.[15]

The classic model, as briefly outlined above, is here rejected for several reasons:

1. It has been shown experimentally that the principal glide mechanisms in calcite are twinning on e and translation on r and at high temperatures f. The possibility of e translation is disproved; and it has been found that translation on r and f leads to no visible manifestation of the active glide planes, even though it is the dominant glide mechanism for extensive strain.

2. If visible e lamellae are due solely to twinning, the total strain accompanying development of even a swarm of densely spaced thin e lamellae is relatively insignificant. The significance of e planes, microscopically conspicuous though they usually are, has been grossly over-emphasized in the classic concept of the orienting process. The e lamellae almost invariably are rationally oriented with respect to the calcite lattice, i.e., they show no indication of internal rotation. They generally reflect a late and insignificant fraction of the total strain, and can have nothing to do with the orienting mechanism.

3. Among the various kinds of visible s-surfaces in tectonites are some that are demonstrably and others that are probably surfaces of shear. But there is little basis for the classic view that the essence of the orienting process of tectonite minerals is rotation of grains to bring the active glide planes into stable alignment in slip planes of the fabric. There is no justification for interpreting a foliation as a slip surface merely because it is a plane of preferred orientation of visible e lamellae of calcite.

4. Recrystallization, either syntectonic or post-tectonic, has clearly played an essential role in the development of the fabrics of most calcite tectonites. It is highly probable that such recrystallization has affected the orientation pattern of calcite in such rocks much more profoundly than any combination of direct componental movements.[16]

[13] Sander, *op. cit.*, p. 202.

[14] H. W. Fairbairn and H. E. Hawkes, Dolomite orientation in deformed rocks, *Am. Jour. Sci.*, vol. 239, pp. 619, 630, 1941.

[15] Cf. Schmidt, *op. cit.*, pp. 170, 171, 1932.

[16] Post-tectonic recrystallization is not completely neglected in the classic interpretation of marble fabrics. For example, Felkel (*op. cit.*, p. 80) attributes the difference between the respective orientation patterns of large (relic) calcite grains and small grains of an enclosing matrix to post-tectonic recrystallization of the latter.

Revised Interpretation of Calcite Orientation. The interpretation of calcite orientation patterns proposed below is more generalized than that just criticized, and except for special cases that show obvious analogies with experimentally produced patterns, lacks the sharp detail of the classic hypothesis.

1. The pattern in most calcite tectonites is complex and is characterized by a c-axis girdle with monoclinic or less commonly orthorhombic or triclinic symmetry (cf. Figs. 6-25b to d; 11-1d; 11-2c and d). Most such patterns have not been produced experimentally and can be correlated with stress, strain, or movement only on the basis of symmetry. Petrographic evidence relating to form, size, and distortion of grains may show whether recrystallization or direct componental movements have played the dominant role in the orienting process.

2. Marbles composed of unstrained calcite grains, more or less equant in shape, uniform in size, and bounded by sharply defined interlocking surfaces are generally interpreted as products of recrystallization. There are two common cases which may be interpreted by analogy with experimentally recrystallized marble:

   $a.$ Random or weak orientation of c axes suggests post-tectonic recrystallization (annealing). Such is the explanation proposed by Felkel[17] for the matrix of small unstrained grains with weak preferred orientation that encloses large (relic) well-oriented crystals in a strongly foliated marble tectonite from Vennatal in the Tyrol (Fig. 11-1a and b).

   $b.$ A single strong c-axis maximum, especially if normal to a foliation marked by dimensional parallelism of slightly lensoid grains, is compatible with syntectonic recrystallization, the c axes being subparallel to the principal stress σ_1. This conclusion was reached long ago by Bain[18] from detailed correlation of preferred orientation patterns and field observations on folded American statuary marbles. Yule marble (Fig. 11-1c) can be interpreted thus. So, too, can a Dalradian marble from northeast Scotland (Fig. 11-1d) with the following petrographic characters:[19] ". . . a rather pure calcite marble, with graphite, quartz, and white mica as minor constituents. It has a single foliation defined by dimensional parallelism of lensoid grains of calcite [mean dimensions 0.6 mm $\times$ 0.45 mm $\times$ 0.25 mm]. The tabular habit is unrelated to crystallographic orientation. Grain outlines are sharp and approximately planar; internal strain and undulose extinction are almost absent." In general, marbles with a marked preferred orientation of

[17] *Ibid.*, pp. 43–49, figs. 40, 41.

[18] G. W. Bain, Geological, chemical and physical problems in the marble industry, *Am. Inst. Mining Metall. Engineers Tech. Pub. 1261*, pp. 11, 12, 1940.

[19] D. B. McIntyre and F. J. Turner, Petrofabric analysis of marbles from mid-Strathspey and Strathavon, *Geol. Mag.*, vol. 90, pp. 227, 228, 1953.

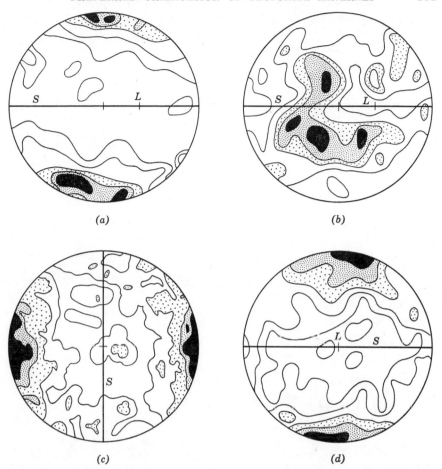

FIG. 11-1. Orientation diagrams for calcite in tectonites. S = foliation, L = lineation. (a) Vennatal, Tyrol.   (*After E. Felkel.*)   [0001] in 240 large strained grains.   Contours, 6%, 5%, 3%, 1%, 0.4%, per 1% area.   (b) Same rocks as *a*.   (*After E. Felkel.*) [0001] in 172 unstrained recrystallized grains.   Contours, 4%, 2%, 1%, 0.6%, per 1% area.   (c) Yule marble, Colorado.   (*After R. H. Dixon.*)   [0001] in 300 grains. Contours, 5%, 3%, 1%, 0.3%, per 1% area.   (d) Dalradian marble, Tomintoul, Scotland.   (*After D. B. McIntyre and F. J. Turner.*)   [0001] in 300 grains.   Contours, 5%, 3%, 2%, 1%, 0.3%, per 1% area.

c axes in a single direction are weather-resistant on surfaces cut normal to the mean trend of [0001].[20]

3. Calcite tectonites with markedly discoidal or highly elongated grains are likely to be products of strain without accompanying or subsequent recrystallization. It is likely, moreover, that such strain occurred in the lower range of metamorphic temperatures—otherwise

[20] Bain, *op. cit.*, pp. 3–8.

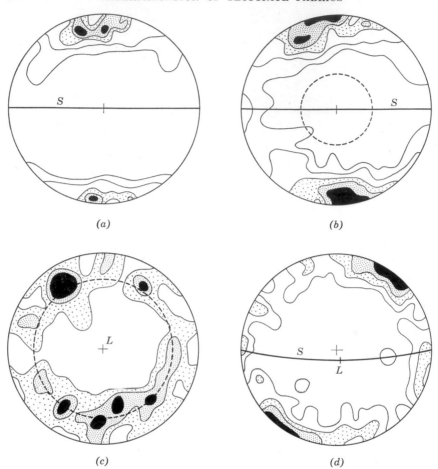

(a)   *(b)*

(c)   *(d)*

FIG. 11-2. Orientation diagrams for calcite in tectonites. S = foliation, L = lineation.
(a) Vennatal, Tyrol. (*After E. Felkel.*) [0001] in 246 large strained grains. Contours, 6%, 4.5%, 2%, 1%, 0.4%, per 1% area. (b) Same rock as a. (*After E. Felkel.*)
Poles of 336 prominent e lamellae in 246 large grains. Contours, 6%, 4.5%, 3%, 1%,
0.3%, per 1% area. Broken small circle encloses "blind spot." (c) Calc-phyllonite,
Brenner, Tyrol. (*After B. Sander.*) [0001] in 263 grains. Contours, 3%, 2%, 1%,
per 1% area. Broken small circle is drawn at 65° to lineation L. (d) Lineated marble,
Barstow, California. (*After L. E. Weiss.*) [0001] in 100 grains. Contours, 7%, 5%,
3%, 1%, per 1% area.

recrystallization would have occurred. In natural tectonites of this
kind several patterns have been recorded which are analogous or identical
with orientation patterns produced under experimental conditions. In
the absence of contrary evidence a similar origin may be inferred. Unfortunately, rotated lamellae $L_e{}^r$ and $L_e{}^e$ which record the mechanism of
strain in experimentally deformed marbles seldom survive in natural
tectonites. The interpretation outlined below is made in terms of stress.

It is assumed on the basis of experimental evidence (cf. pages 348 to 350) that the c axis concentrations are inclined at 20° to 30° to the axis of the principal compressive stress σ_1, and that elongation of grains and strongly developed late e lamellae are both aligned in the plane normal to σ_1.

a. Figure 11-2*a* and *b* shows c axes oriented in a small circle about the normal to a foliation S marked by parallelism of elongated grains, while prominent late e lamellae (one or two per grain) give a maximum coinciding with the pole of S. The calcite subfabric is consistent with flattening in S (AB of the strain ellipsoid) under axial compression normal to S.

b. A cleft-girdle pattern of c axes, with maxima on a small circle at 60° to 70° to the girdle axis (= direction of grain elongation) is consistent with axially symmetric extension parallel to the axis of minimal principal stress σ_3 (cf. Fig. 9-16*b*). This corresponds to what Sander has called *Einengung*—radial squeezing within what becomes the symmetry plane of the fabric, with extension normal to the symmetry plane, i.e., parallel to the principal stress σ_3. Poles of prominent late twin lamellae, if these are present, fall on a great-circle girdle whose axis coincides with that of the c-axis cleft girdle. This pattern has been recorded rather commonly in strongly lineated marbles and calc-schists[21] characterized by a homotactic monoclinic fabric whose symmetry plane is normal to the lineation (Fig. 11-2*c*). Indeed Sander[22] records a prevalent tendency for maxima in many c-axis diagrams for calcite to fall on small circles of wide angular radius (60° to 80°) rather than on the more familiar great-circle girdle such as is illustrated in Fig. 11-2*d*.

Interpretation of $\{01\bar{1}2\}$ *Lamellae.* Complete twinning of a calcite grain on $\{01\bar{1}2\}$ (= e) changes the orientation of the c axis through $52\frac{1}{2}°$. For this reason, and also because it was wrongly thought that calcite could glide by translation on e with a negative sense of shear, great importance was once attached to e gliding as a mechanism in the evolution of preferred orientation of calcite grains of tectonites. Many orientation diagrams for e lamellae therefore appear in the literature of structural petrology. Most of these, however, have no significance with regard to stress, strain, or movement picture of the principal phase of deformation recorded in the c-axis orientation pattern. For it is clear that the e lamellae are late structures superposed on grains that have already been oriented by some other means.[23] Analysis of the pattern of conspicuous

[21] E.g., J. Ladurner, Algemeine Kennzeichnung und regionale Stellung alpiner Dolomittektonite, *Geol. Bundesanst. Wien (Austria) Jahrb.*, vol. 96, p. 264, pl. 12, D7, 24, 1953; I. Schüller, Achsenverteilungsanalyse eines Glimmermarmors (Tauernhülle Glocknerstrasse), *Geol. Bundesanst. Wien (Austria) Jahrb.*, vol. 98, pp. 21–31, pl. 3, D6, 1955; R. P. Nickelsen and G. W. Gross, Petrofabric study of Conestoga limestone from Hanover, Pennsylvania, *Am. Jour. Sci.*, vol. 257, p. 280, fig. 3, 1959.

[22] Sander, *op. cit.*, pp. 295, 321, D112.

[23] F. J. Turner, Note on the tectonic significance of deformation lamellae in quartz and calcite, *Am. Geophys. Union Trans.*, vol. 29, pp. 565–569, 1948.

e lamellae in a calcite tectonite does indeed permit reconstruction of a movement picture and more particularly a stress system; but these refer only to the final phase of deformation usually involving strain of small magnitude.   Analysis of *e* lamellae becomes important especially for incipiently developed tectonite fabrics where the total strain itself is small.

In statistical analysis of *e* lamellae,[24] measurement is restricted to sets of lamellae that are especially prominent—either broad optically recognizable twins or swarms of linear lamellae with a spacing index (page 346) above some arbitrarily selected value.[25]   As described on page 242, for each such *e* axes of "compression" *C* and "tension" *T* are plotted at 45° to the pole of *e* on the great circle *ce* (Fig. 6-27).   The *C* and *T* axes of a calcite grain are not truly stress directions.   They are fabric elements defined by grain orientation and movement in a unique sense (*e* twin gliding).   Orientation diagrams for *C* and *T* axes commonly display a high degree of preferred orientation, and considered collectively may have monoclinic, orthorhombic, or even axial symmetry.   They have been interpreted dynamically as expressing a lately imposed homogeneous stress system in which the axes of principal stress σ_1 and σ_3 have been identified with single maxima in the *C* and *T* diagrams, respectively. This interpretation is justified only in particular cases—notably when the pattern of *c*-axis orientation is random or at least diffused.   In general the *C* and *T* diagrams reflect two equally effective influences: the pattern of lattice orientation as recorded in *c*-axis diagrams and the imposed stress system.   Fortunately one of these factors—the pattern of lattice orientation in the calcite aggregate—is always known.   To develop general procedure for evaluating the influence of stress alone, especially with regard to symmetry of the *C*- and *T*-axis pattern, we turn to consideration of experimentally deformed marble in which both the initial fabric and the stress system are known.[26]

Figures 11-3 to 11-5 show *C* and *T* diagrams constructed for experimentally deformed Yule marble in which conspicuous *e* lamellae reflect late strain of small magnitude.   From these data several generalizations emerge which may be applied to interpretation of *C* and *T* diagrams for naturally deformed calcite tectonites.

[24] F. J. Turner, Nature and dynamic interpretation of deformation lamellae in calcite of three marbles, *Am. Jour. Sci.*, vol. 251, pp. 276–298, 1953; McIntyre and Turner, *op. cit.*, pp. 225–240; L. E. Weiss, A study of tectonic style, *Univ. California Geol. Sci. Pub.*, vol. 30, no. 1, pp. 56, 57, 1954; P. Gilmour and M. F. Carman, Petrofabric analysis of the Loch Tay limestone from Strachur, Argyll, *Geol. Mag.*, vol. 91, pp. 49–60, 1954; R. H. Clark, A study of calcite twinning in the Strathavon marble, Banffshire, *Geol. Mag.*, vol. 91, pp. 121–128, 1954.

[25] Where the gains are lenticular, indicating notable postcrystalline strain, caution must be exercised in case *e* lamellae are relics from the initial lattice in a completely twinned host (cf. Turner, *op. cit.*, pp. 293–296, 1953).

[26] Measurements by F. J. Turner under National Science Foundation grant G16316.

1. As predicted from symmetry arguments (page 385), the symmetry of the combined C and T diagrams approximates closely the symmetry common to the initial fabric and the stress system (as determined by the external forces).

The perfect axial symmetry $D_{\infty h}$ of C and T patterns in Fig. 11-3b reflects coincidence of ∞-fold axes of stress and initial fabric. In Fig. 11-4a and b, the plane of projection has perfect symmetry; for in this plane lie the respective ∞-fold axes of stress and initial fabric. Planes m are planes of approximate symmetry. The total pattern is strictly mono-

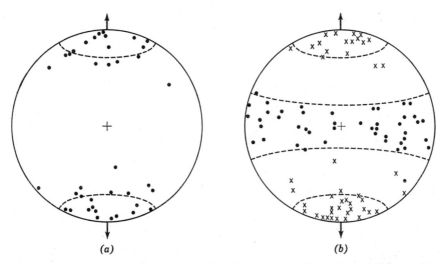

(a)   (b)

FIG. 11-3. Analysis of prominent e lamellae in experimentally deformed Yule marble: extension ($\epsilon = 7\%$) parallel to arrows, 20°C, 10,000 bars. Broken arcs at 30° and 70° to axis of extension. (a) [0001] in 39 grains with prominent e, in a sample of 50 grains. (b) C axes (dots) and T axes (crosses) for 46 prominent e in 39 grains.

clinic but almost orthorhombic. Figure 11-5b and c shows the C and T axis pattern where axially symmetric stress is superposed symmetrically on an initial orthorhombic fabric.[27] Symmetry argument demands that the symmetry of C and T axes must be orthorhombic. Actually there is a slight but consistent departure from this condition in that maxima on opposite sides of m_1 are not equally strong. Only m_2 normal to the ∞-fold axis of stress is a plane of strict symmetry. The discrepancy may be due to the small number of points in the sample. It may also be due to the fact that the c-axis diagram (Fig. 11-5a) does not precisely reflect the symmetry of calcite orientation; for there is also a tendency for pre-

[27] The "initial fabric" is itself the result of deformation under the same stress system as caused late development of conspicuous e twin lamellae (F. J. Turner, D. T. Griggs, R. H. Clark, and R. H. Dixon, Deformation of Yule marble, part VII, *Geol. Soc. America Bull.*, vol. 67, pp. 1272, 1276, 1290, 1956).

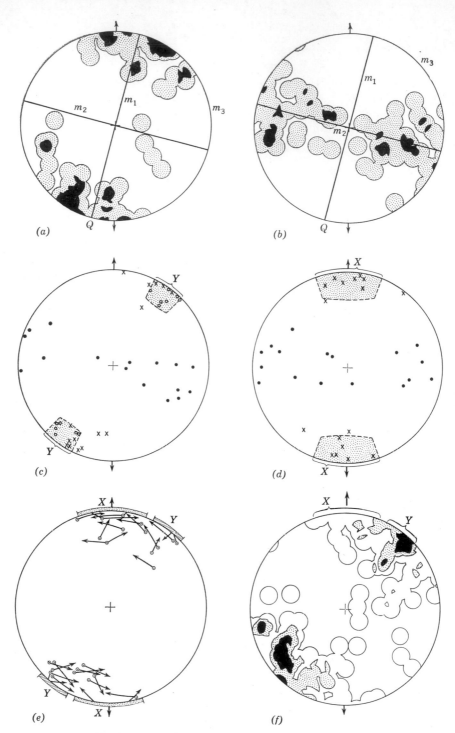

Fig. 11-4. For descriptive legend see opposite page.

ferred orientation of a axes of calcite, and this too would influence the pattern of C and T axes.

2. Since the symmetry of a homogeneous stress system cannot be lower than orthorhombic (page 262), certain properties of the stress system may be inferred from the initial fabric and the C and T diagrams—both of which are available for any naturally deformed marble:

a. Axial symmetry common to both the initial fabric and the C and T patterns (Fig. 11-3) implies identical axial symmetry in the stress system. C and T concentrations may be equated with σ_1 and σ_3, respectively. The same inference may be drawn from axial or orthorhombic symmetry of C and T combined with random orientation (spherical symmetry) of the initial fabric.

b. Where symmetry of C and T diagrams is orthorhombic or monoclinic (Figs. 11-4*a* and *b*; 5*b* and *c*) direct deductions are more limited. Any symmetry plane common to the initial fabric and the C-T pattern must be a principal plane of stress. This applies strictly to m_3 in Fig. 11-4 and to m_2 in Fig. 11-5. It may perhaps be applied also to the other m planes of near symmetry as a first approximation.

c. To clarify the picture of stress inferred as under *b* above, selective C and T diagrams for grains of limited orientation—direction groups in Sander's terminology (page 251)—are constructed. Consider, for example, Fig. 11-5. The three mutually perpendicular intersections of the three symmetry planes m_1, m_2, and m_3 in diagrams *b* and *c* are principal stress axes of a system with orthorhombic or axial symmetry. The problem is to identify σ_1, σ_2, and σ_3, and to determine whether σ_2 is equal to either σ_1 or σ_3. Figure 11-5*d* and *e* shows T and C patterns for two direction groups having c axes oriented in the vicinity of Y and of X, respectively. For these diagrams the "initial fabric" is the direction group in question (with axial symmetry). The geometry of construction requires that each T axis be inclined at 19° to [0001], each C axis at 71° to [0001]. The T concentrations of Fig. 11-5*d* and *e* must necessarily be close to the corresponding [0001] concentrations; but each is clearly displaced from the [0001] maximum toward the σ_3 axis of the stress system. The direction defined by intersection of m_1 and m_3 is thus identified as σ_3. It is not clear from the C and T diagrams whether σ_2 is equal to σ_1;

Fig. 11-4. Analysis of prominent e lamellae in experimentally deformed Yule marble: extension ($\epsilon = 7\%$) parallel to arrows, 20°C, 10,000 bars. (*a*) 58 T axes. Contours, 5%, 1.7%, per 1% area. Planes of approximate symmetry—m_1, m_2, m_3. (*b*) 58 C axes. Contours, 5%, 1.7%, per 1% area. Planes of approximate symmetry—m_1, m_2, m_3. (*c*) T axes (crosses) and C axes (dots) for grains with [0001] (open circles) in direction group Y (outlined in broken lines). (*d*) T axes (crosses) and C axes (dots) for grains with [0001] in direction group X (outlined in broken lines). (*e*) [0001] (circled dots) and T axes (arrowheads) for typical grains of direction groups X and Y. (*f*) 100 [0001] axes. Contours, 5%, 3%, 1%, per 1% area.

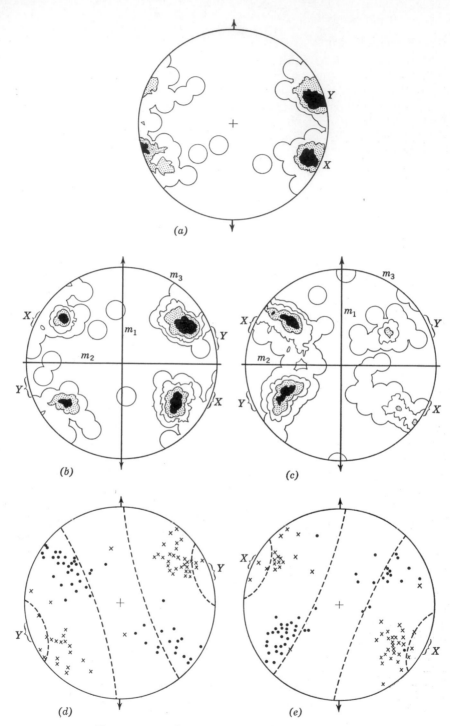

FIG. 11-5. For descriptive legend see opposite page.

418

ʼnor, if they are unequal, which should be equated with the respective intersections $[m_1:m_2]$ and $[m_2:m_3]$.

d. Figure 11-4c and d illustrates the same procedure for direction groups Y and X of Fig. 11-4f. The common axial symmetry of diagram d and of the [0001] pattern of direction group X identifies the stress system as axial, with σ_3 parallel to XX. The same inference may be drawn from Fig. 11-4e, in which arrows are drawn between [0001] and the T axis for representative crystals in the two direction groups. In group Y the arrows are directed counterclockwise toward σ_3 (XX); in group X six of the arrows are clockwise, seven are counterclockwise.[28]

3. As a test of the stress system deduced from the C- and T-axis diagrams the spacing index is measured and the coefficient of resolved shear stress S_o is calculated[29] for all three e planes in about 20 grains. Figure 11-6a is a plot of spacing index against S_o for the specimen of experimentally deformed Yule marble for which compression and tension data are given in Fig. 11-4. The value of S_o is given a positive sign when the sense of shear on e is positive (appropriate for twin gliding). This diagram, like all similar plots for experimentally deformed marble,[30] shows that in every grain e lamellae develop most profusely on that one of the three e planes for which S_o has the highest algebraic value. Where grains are oriented favorably for twinning (Fig. 11-6b, curve L) S_o for lamellae with a high spacing index has a value near $+0.5$. For grains unfavorably oriented (Fig. 11-6b, curve N), S_o for lamellae with a high spacing index has a low value and may be either positive or negative. The broken curves Q and R illustrate hypothetical relations between S_o and spacing index that would be inconsistent with the assumed stress system.

[28] The same property of the grain can be brought out (Turner, op. cit., p. 280, 1953) by drawing arrows connecting [0001] with the pole of e. These point in the reverse sense to those of fig. 11-4e.

[29] S_o may be determined rapidly by the graphic method described by J. W. Handin and D. T. Griggs (Deformation of Yule marble, part II, Geol. Soc. America Bull., vol. 62, pp. 867, 868, 1951).

[30] F. J. Turner and C. S. Ch'ih, Deformation of Yule marble, part III, Geol. Soc. America Bull., vol. 62, pp. 899, 900, 1951.

FIG. 11-5. Analysis of prominent (twinned) e in experimentally deformed Yule marble: extension ($\epsilon = 80$–120%) parallel to arrows, 500°C, 5,000 bars. (a) 100 [0001] axes. Contours, 10%, 5%, 1%, per 1% area. (b) 100 T axes in sample of 127 grains. Planes of approximate symmetry—m_1, m_2, m_3. (c) 100 C axes in sample of 127 grains. Planes of approximate symmetry—m_1, m_2, m_3. (d) C axes (dots) and T axes (crosses) for grains with [0001] in direction group centered at Y (cf. diagram a). Small circles at 20° and 70° to center of Y. (e) C axes (dots) and T axes (crosses) for grains with [0001] in direction group centered at X (cf. diagram a). Small circles at 20° and 70° to center of X.

Analysis of e twinning in a marble (Boyne limestone) from Moray Firth, Scotland,[31] gives diagrams shown in Fig. 11-7. The rock has bedding foliation S and consists of equant unstrained grains of calcite about one-third of which contain e lamellae broad enough to be recognized optically as twins. These grains have a restricted range of orientation (circled dots in Fig. 11-7a); and corresponding diagrams for C and T axes likewise show a high degree of preferred orientation (Fig. 11-7b). The

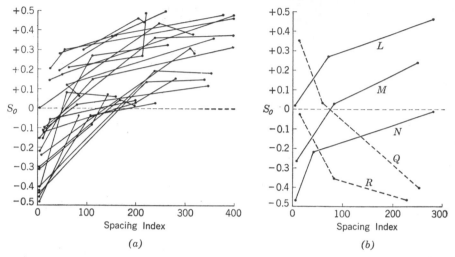

FIG. 11-6. Spacing index of e lamellae (three sets per grain, connected by straight lines) plotted against coefficient of resolved shear stress S_o. Sign of S_o indicates sense of shear on e (positive for twin gliding). (a) Experimentally deformed Yule marble; same specimen as Fig. 11-4. (After C. S. Ch'ih.) (b) Test of deduced stress system in natural deformation. L consistent with σ_3 parallel to [0001] maximum. M consistent with σ_3 inclined to [0001] maximum (cf. diagram a). N consistent with σ_3 normal to [0001] maximum. Q, R inconsistent with deduced stress system.

total calcite subfabric (Fig. 11-7a) is not sharply defined but has orthorhombic symmetry conforming to that of the foliation. The direction group comprising the twinned grains has axial symmetry, with the ∞-fold axis (P in Fig. 11-7a) inclined to the foliation. The inference is that the e twins represent a late strain unrelated to the foliation or to the deformation responsible for the total c-axis pattern. The stress system deduced from Fig. 11-7b is orthorhombic; σ_3 is identified with T, the center of concentration of T axes; and σ_1 is located near C, the center of concentration of the more dispersed C axes.[32] In Fig. 11-7c, arrows connecting [0001] of twinned grains (circles) with T axes in the same grains

[31] Turner, op. cit., pp. 277–283, 1953.

[32] This dynamic interpretation of the data is more conservative, and in our opinion more logical, than the more detailed interpretation previously made by Turner (ibid., p. 282).

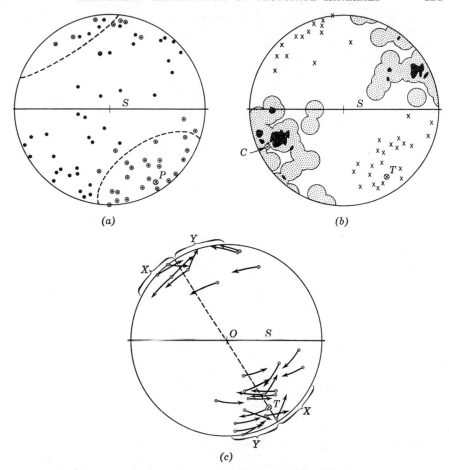

FIG. 11-7. Analysis of *e* twins in calcite of marble (Boyne limestone, Moray Firth, Scotland). *S* = foliation. (*a*) [0001] in 75 grains; circled points, 33 grains with prominent *e* twin lamellae. Broken arc is a small circle at 40° to *P*, the center of the circled points. (*b*) 40 *C* axes (contoured: 7.5%, 2.5%, per 1% area) and 40 *T* axes (crosses) for 33 grains with prominent *e* twins. *T* = center of *T*-axis concentration. *C* = center of *C*-axis concentration. (*c*) [0001] (circled dots) and *T* axes (arrowheads) for 25 representative grains with prominent *e* twins.

(arrowheads) show a regular trend consistent with observations on experimentally deformed marble (cf. Fig. 11-4*e*). For grains with [0001] in sector *X* the sense of the arrows is almost exclusively clockwise; in sector *Y* on the opposite side of *T* ($= \sigma_3$), the sense is counterclockwise.

Dolomite. The literature on preferred orientation of other rhombohedral carbonates than calcite[33] is chiefly concerned with dolomite, and

[33] Fairbairn and Hawkes, *op. cit.*, pp. 617–632; B. Sander, *Einführung in die Gefügekunde der Geologischen Körper*, Pt. II, pp. 350, 368, D76 (mislabeled "calcite"),

is largely descriptive. Orientation diagrams for [0001] commonly show a girdle pattern with the girdle axis parallel to the direction of elongation of dolomite grains. Cleft girdles, with maxima on a small circle inclined at 60° to 70° to the girdle axis (Figs. 6-30a and 11-8b) are commoner than peripheral girdles (Fig. 11-8a). Symmetry is typically monoclinic (Fig. 11-8b), but may be distinctly triclinic (Fig. 6-30a) or approximately orthorhombic (Fig. 11-8a). In the latter case the c axes tend to be concentrated at a high angle to the principal foliation if the fabric is homotactic.

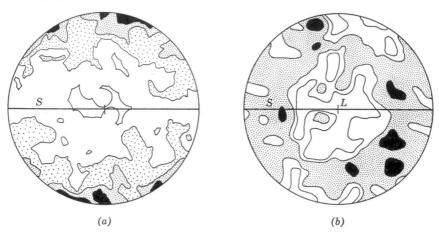

(a)   (b)

FIG. 11-8. Orientation diagrams for [0001] of dolomite in tectonites. (a) Dover Plains, New York. 500 axes. Contours, 3%, 2%, 1%, 0.2%, per 1% area. S = color banding (? bedding). (b) Pfelders, Austrian Tyrol. (After J. Ladurner.) 534 axes. Contours, 2%, 1%, 0.5%, per 1% area (maximum concentration 6%). S = foliation marked by parallel micas; L = lineation. Rock also contains calcite (30%).

Except that translation on {0001} parallel to any of the three a axes and (above about 300°C) twin gliding in a negative sense on {02$\bar{2}$1} presumably play the main role in plastic postcrystalline deformation, the mechanism of the orienting process in dolomite is unknown. Most described patterns of c axes refer to tectonites in which recrystallization has clearly played a significant part.

Twin lamellae in dolomite are late structures representing small strains imposed after the observed state of preferred orientation of [0001] was fully developed. Allowing for the negative sense of shear in dolomite twinning (cf. page 245), it is possible to construct compression axes C and tension axes T for strongly twinned grains of dolomite, just as for calcite.

Springer, Berlin, Vienna, 1950; Ladurner, op. cit., pp. 253–300; J. Ladurner, Zur Verhalten von Ankerit in geschlossenen Gefüge und als Einzelkorn, Tschermaks Mineralog. Petrog. Mitt., ser. 3, vol. 5, pp. 215–226, 1955; Über ein geregeltes Sideritgefüge, Geol. Bundesanst. Wien (Austria) Jahrb., vol. 98, pp. 15–20, 1955.

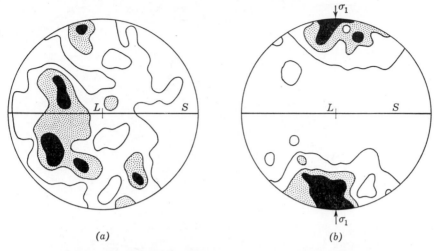

(a)   *(b)*

Fig. 11-9. Orientation diagrams for [0001] of dolomite, Hasmark formation, Montana. (*After H. W. Fairbairn and H. E. Hawkes.*) S = foliation; L = direction of elongation of dolomite grains.   (*a*) 117 axes of grains without f twins.   Contours, 6%, 4% 2%, per 1% area.   (*b*) 110 axes of grains with two sets of f twins.   Contours, 4%, 2%, 1%, per 1% area. σ_1 is stress axis inferred from distribution of twins.

The C axis lies at 45° to f and 17½° to [0001], the T axis at 45° to f and 72½° to [0001] (Fig. 11-10).   Indeed the negative sense of shear on f in twinning of dolomite was first demonstrated by Fairbairn and Hawkes[34] from the restricted range of c-axis orientation of doubly twinned grains compared with that of untwinned grains in dolomite tectonites (Fig. 11-9).

Figure 11-11 records data given by Christie[35] for a highly strained dolomite rock in the mylonite zone of the Moine Thrust, northwest Scotland.   Lamellae parallel to f are present in almost every grain; but

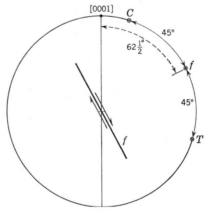

Fig. 11-10. Geometry of twin gliding on {02$\bar{2}$1} (f) in dolomite. C and T are compression and tension axes such that $S_o = 0.5$.

those having optically recognizable f twins have a sharply restricted range of orientation (compare Fig. 11-11*b* with *a*). C and T axes plotted for these twins have striking preferred orientation (Fig. 11-11*c*), the pattern

[34] *Op. cit.*

[35] J. M. Christie, Dynamic interpretation of the fabric of a dolomite from the Moine thrust-zone in north-west Scotland, *Am. Jour. Sci.*, vol. 256, pp. 159–170, 1958.

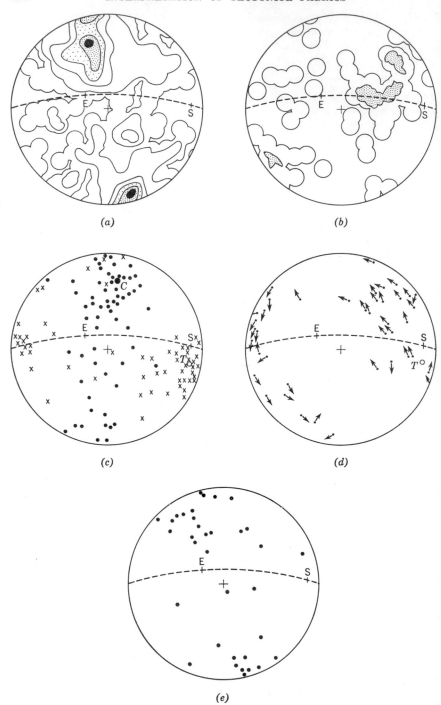

(a)

(b)

(c)

(d)

(e)

FIG. 11-11. For descriptive legend see opposite page.

of which has perfect orthorhombic symmetry. Its symmetry planes diverge slightly from those of the initial orthorhombic fabric (Fig. 11-11a); but the divergence almost certainly reflects the fact that twinning is restricted to a direction group within the dolomite fabric. The stress system inferred from Fig. 11-11c could have either axial or orthorhombic symmetry. Considering that the range of orientation of [0001] in the initial fabric is broad and the angle [0001] to T in any crystal is large (72½°), the concentration of T axes in Fig. 11-11c can be equated confidently with the axis of minimum principal stress σ_3. C, the center of concentration of C axes, is likely to be σ_1. The stress system so deduced is in harmony with independent data relating to internally rotated lamellae $L_f{}^c$ (cf. page 355). The sense of rotation of these is shown in Fig. 11-11d, and the orientation of [0001] in the same grains in Fig. 11-11e. Figure 11-12 gives in greater detail paths of rotation of f to $L_f{}^c$ consistent with Christie's data, together with the sense of gliding on each {0001} plane required by the stress system deduced from Fig. 11-11c. Christie's analysis is one of the few recorded instances in which a movement picture, a stress system, and even an estimate of minimal strain have been deduced in detail from preferred orientation of crystallographic elements of a tec-

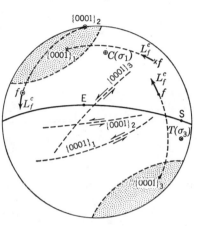

FIG. 11-12. Paths of rotation of three $L_f{}^c$ lamellae consistent with data of Fig. 11-11c and d. C and T = compression and tension axis maxima of Fig. 11-11c. Stippled sectors contain most of the [0001] axes of Fig. 11-11e.

tonite fabric. The strain deduced from the observed angles of internal rotation of $L_f{}^c$ (cf. page 338) is about 5% to 18% elongation parallel to T.

Quartz. *Classic Interpretation Critically Reviewed.* With regard to the nature and variety of preferred orientation patterns, more is known about quartz ([0001] orientation) than any other mineral of tectonites (Fig. 6-21, 22). Moreover, particular patterns tend to recur with constant relationships to standard combinations of foliation and lineation. Paradoxically virtually nothing is known—though much has been

---

FIG. 11-11. Dynamic interpretation of {02$\bar{2}$1} lamellae in strained dolomite rock, Loch Ailsh, Scotland. (*After J. M. Christie.*) (*a*) 310 [0001] axes of dolomite. Contours, 5%, 4%, 3%, 2%, 1%, 0.3%, per 1% area. Solid arc is the geographic horizontal; S = south, E = east. (*b*) Poles of 60 twinned {02$\bar{2}$1} lamellae. Contours, 5%, 1.7%, per 1% area. (*c*) T axes (crosses) and C axes (points) for 60 twinned {02$\bar{2}$1} lamellae. (*d*) Sense and degree of internal rotation of f (dots) to $L_f{}^c$ lamellae (arrowheads). T = T axis maximum of diagram c. (*e*) [0001] of grains with $L_f{}^c$ lamellae.

written—regarding the mechanics of the orienting process. And although much has been surmised as to possible states of preferred orientation of various prisms and rhombohedrons in quartz,[36] only in very rare instances has preferred orientation of any crystallographic line or plane other than [0001] been demonstrated.[37] The general problem, then, is to interpret preferred orientation of [0001] in relation to associated foliation and lineation. Certain notions in this connection are here rejected in the present state of our knowledge as unfounded speculation. Some are so firmly entrenched in the literature of structural analysis that they cannot be dismissed without brief categorical criticism:

1. One of the first and simplest patterns to be recognized is marked by parallel alignment of [0001] in the direction of displacement of slickenside films and mylonites (Fig. 11-13a). It has been argued by some geologists that the presence of the same pattern in any simply foliated rock (S-tectonite of Sander), with the quartz axes aligned in S and either normal or parallel to a lineation, implies penetrative displacement in S parallel to the trend of the quartz axes. Such, for example, would be the supposed significance of maximum X in Fig. 11-13b. All that can be said in support of this inference is that it does not contravene symmetry requirements. Completely unacceptable are the further inferences, which crop up repeatedly in the literature: (a) that the orienting mechanism involves prismatic gliding, and (b) that the hypothetical prismatic glide planes have aligned themselves in a "slip plane of the fabric," i.e., in S.

2. In many tectonites dominated by a planar foliation (S-tectonites) quartz-axis maxima are grouped symmetrically with regard to S and a pronounced lineation in S. The commonest situation is that shown in Fig. 11-13c. The fabric is homotactic and its symmetry almost perfectly orthorhombic; and that is all the information that can safely be used in a kinematic or dynamic interpretation. But currently in vogue are such divergent speculative views as the following: (a) each quartz-axis maximum represents a direction of displacement within a "slip plane of the fabric"; or (b) the foliation S is itself a "slip plane" in which have become aligned rhombohedral glide planes of the quartz lattice. Neither view is accepted here.

3. For half a century it has been known that in some tectonites—especially granulites and quartzites of high metamorphic grade—the

[36] E.g., W. Schmidt, *op. cit.*, pp. 176–178, 1932; A. Hietanen, *On the Petrology of Finnish Quartzites*, pp. 107–112, 1938; Turner, *op. cit.*, pp. 265–266, 1948; Sander, *op. cit.*, pp. 150, 151, 1950; G. Kojima and T. Suzuki, Rock structure and quartz fabric in a thrusting shear zone, *Hiroshima Univ. Jour. Sci.*, ser. C, vol. 2, pp. 192, 193, 1958.

[37] E.g., by X-ray diffraction technique D. V. Higgs, M. Friedman, and J. E. Gebhardt (in Rock deformation, *Geol. Soc. America Mem. 79*, pp. 284–287, 1960) demonstrated strong preferred orientation of a axes in a quartzite for which the [0001] pattern of quartz has a single sharp maximum.

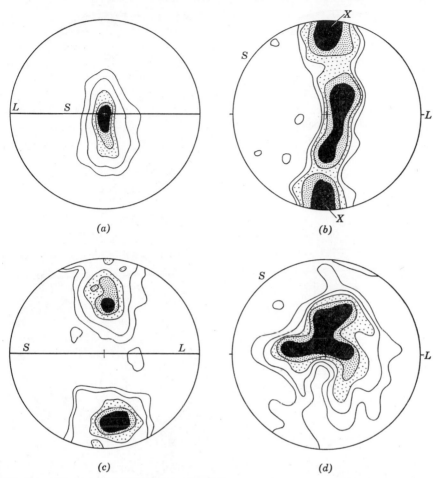

(a)   (b)

(c)   (d)

FIG. 11-13. Orientation diagrams for [0001] in quartz of tectonites with planar foliation
S and lineation L.   (a) Slickenside mylonite in granite, Melibokus, Odenwald.   138
axes.   Contours, 16%, 12%, 8%, 4%, 0.7%, per 1% area.   (After B. Sander, Gefügekunde der Gesteine, p. 306, D26, Springer, Berlin, Vienna, 1930.)   (b) Quartzite, Finland.   202 axes.   Contours, 4%, 2%, 1%, 0.5%, per 1% area.   (After A. Hietanen,
On the Petrology of the Finnish Quartzites, pl. 8, D.S. 40, Government Press, Helsinki,
1938.)   (c) Itacolumite, Brazil.   300 axes.   Contours, 8%, 6%, 4%, 2%, 1%, per
1% area.   (After D. Korn, Geol. Rundschau, Festschrift for Salomon-Calvi, p. 13, 1933.)
(d) Quartzite, Finland.   202 axes.   Contours, 4%, 3%, 2%, 1%, 0.5%, per 1% area.
(After A. Hietanen, On the Petrology of the Finnish Quartzites, pl. 8, D.S. 4b, Government
Press, Helsinki, 1938.)

quartz axes are concentrated in a single direction normal to a planar foliation S (Fig. 11-13d).   The quartz subfabric has axial or (if a partial
girdle is present) orthorhombic symmetry; the mesoscopic fabric is
orthorhombic; the superposed symmetry of total fabric is orthorhombic
or of a lower order—slightly triclinic in Fig. 11-13d.   This pattern,

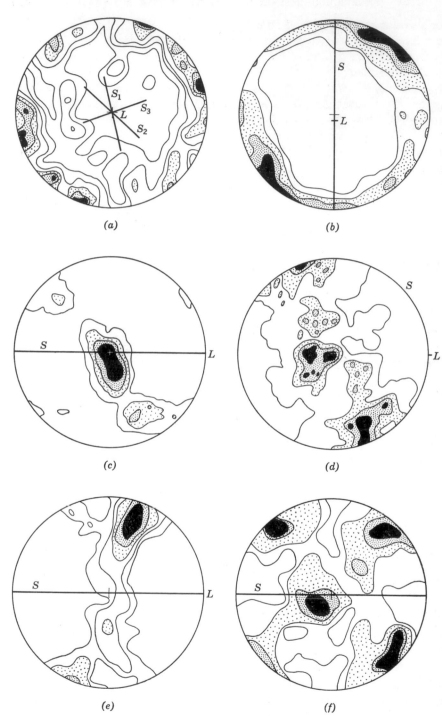

FIG. 11-14. For descriptive legend see opposite page.

because of the presence of Boehm lamellae subparallel to {0001} in the quartz and the existence of fine-grained bands of quartz parallel to S, has been attributed to alignment of supposed basal or near-basal glide planes of the quartz lattice in a "slip plane of the fabric" ($= S$). Actually there is no proof of displacement in S; and it is likely that recrystallization, rather than basal gliding, was the effective orienting mechanism (even though it is now known that quartz can glide on {0001}).

4. In some tectonites dominated by a lineation L coinciding with a B axis of mesoscopic folding (Sander's B-tectonites) there is a peripheral or a cleft girdle of quartz axes normal to the lineation; the fabric is homotactic and its overall symmetry monoclinic (Fig. 11-14a and b). Individual maxima in the quartz girdle have commonly been correlated with supposed "slip surfaces of the fabric"—visible or invisible. We now consider that such correlation is completely unjustified.[38] The essential feature of Fig. 11-14a is not the disposition of maxima, but the monoclinic symmetry of the superposed fabrics; also significant is the orthorhombic symmetry of the quartz subfabric considered alone.

5. A very common fabric pattern in folded rocks has a monoclinic or orthorhombic quartz-axis girdle obliquely inclined to the common symmetry plane of a monoclinic mesoscopic fabric and a mica girdle. The total fabric is triclinic (Fig. 11-14c and d). Rather similar is a triclinic (near-orthorhombic) quartz fabric associated with a monoclinic or triclinic mesoscopic fabric (Fig. 11-14e). It has been widely inferred that triclinic tectonite fabrics with these properties necessarily are products of repeated deformation, in the last phase of which the quartz—supposedly sensitive

---

[38] The shift in emphasis from individual maxima to overall symmetry as the significant property of the quartz-axis diagram can be seen by comparing different interpretations of the same fabric (Fig. 11-14a) by one writer at an interval of a dozen years (Turner, *op. cit.*, *Geol. Soc. America Mem. 30*, pp. 209–211, 1948; Turner and Verhoogen, *op. cit.*, pp. 639, 640, 1960).

FIG. 11-14. Orientation diagrams for [0001] in quartz of tectonites. S, S_1, etc., are visible s-surfaces; L = visible lineation. (*a*) Wissahickon schist, Pennsylvania. 200 axes. Contours, 5%, 4%, 3%, 2%, 1%, 0.5%, per 1% area. (*After A. Hietanen, Geol. Soc. America Spec. Paper 35, pl. 26, A15, 1941.*) (*b*) Quartzite, Barstow, California. 303 axes. Contours, 6%, 4%, 2%, 0.3%, per 1% area. (*c*) Quartzite, Dutchess County, New York. 300 axes. Contours, 10%, 5%, 3%, 1%, per 1% area. (*After R. Balk, Jour. Geology, vol. 60, p. 423, D29, 1952.*) (*d*) Quartz rod (mullion) elongated parallel to L, the lineation of the enclosing schist, eastern Otago, New Zealand. S is the dominant foliation of the enclosing schist. 300 axes. Contours, 4%, 3%, 2%, 0.3%, per 1% area. (*e*) Quartz-rich layer in schist, Besshi, Japan. 350 axes. Contours, 7%, 5%, 3%, 2%, 1%, per 1% area. (*After G. Kojima and K. Hide, Hiroshima Univ. Jour. Sci., ser. C, vol. 2, p. 213, fig. 9, 1958.*) (*f*) Plagioclase-bearing mica-free, granulite, Finland; with sharply defined S. 205 axes. Contours, 3%, 2%, 1%, 0.5% per 1% area. (*After T. G. Sahama, Comm. géol. Finlande Bull. 113, p. 36, D41, 1936.*)

to stress—has become completely reoriented.[39]   Certainly some of the rocks under discussion show in their mesoscopic fabrics the effects of more than one episode of folding—multiple lineations, curved lineations, small-scale homogeneity of S within heterogeneous larger domains, and so on. This is so for the Japanese schist whose quartz pattern is shown in Fig. 11-14*e*.   But there is no experimental evidence supporting the view that quartz is more sensitive to reorienting processes than is mica.   More-over, if the mica subfabric can be shown to portray passive elements in the fabric—bedding, for example—there is nothing incongruous in the simultaneous development of heterotactic mica and quartz subfabrics during one episode of strain under a stress system whose symmetry is closely reflected in the quartz subfabric alone.[40]

6. Orthorhombic quartz diagrams sometimes show two girdles—com-monly mutually perpendicular—symmetrically related to foliation and lineation (Fig. 11-14*f*).   These are the $B \wedge B'$- and $B \perp B'$-tectonites of Sander.   Some writers regard the two girdle axes as having properties of fold axes B, and attribute the $B \perp B'$ pattern to simultaneous or repeated folding about crossed B axes.   While this interpretation is consistent with symmetry requirements it is untenable on other grounds: penetrative folding about two inclined axes which maintain a constant trend throughout a domain is geometrically impossible (page 132).   We prefer to regard the crossed-girdle quartz diagrams simply as an expression of orthorhombic or near-tetragonal symmetry in a homogeneous subfabric; the girdle axes should not be designated B.

7. Experimental evidence bearing on the possible significance and mode of evolution of quartz subfabrics in tectonites is somewhat meager. When highly stressed under confining pressures corresponding to depths of the order of 20 or 30 km quartz ruptures into splinters whose long edges tend to be parallel to such simple crystallographic directions as $[0001]$ and the edge $\{10\bar{1}0\} : \{0001\}$.[41]   It has been suggested that passive rotation of splinters of this kind would ultimately align them in planes and directions of flow in the tectonite fabric; and by this means it has been possible to explain some of the well-known relationships between foliation and quartz patterns.   We tentatively reject this explanation for two reasons: First, there is no proof that the supposed slip planes of the fabric actually exist.   Secondly, some of the patterns so explained are exceedingly well developed in coarse-grained metacherts whose fabrics

[39] This is the interpretation once placed upon the fabric illustrated in fig. 11–14*d* (Turner, *op. cit.*, *Geol. Soc. America Mem. 30*, pp. 191–192, 1948).   It may ultimately become confirmed by other evidence; but it is also possible that the quartz and mica fabrics, though heterotactic, developed simultaneously.

[40] Cf. L. E. Weiss, Fabric analysis of a triclinic tectonite and its bearing on the geometry of flow in rocks, *Am. Jour. Sci.*, vol. 253, pp. 225–236, 1955.

[41] D. T. Griggs and J. F. Bell, Experiments bearing on the orientation of quartz in deformed rocks, *Geol. Soc. America Bull.*, vol. 49, pp. 1723–1746, 1938.

must have been influenced far more by recrystallization than by any kind of direct componental movement.   There is some experimental evidence, however, that bears more directly on the question of how preferred orientation of quartz develops in tectonites.[42]   Griggs found that syntectonic crystallization of quartz during intense shearing at 200° to 500°C may give one of two orientation patterns.   Most obvious is pronounced alignment of [0001] in the plane and normal to the direction of shear.   A secondary orientation parallel to the shear direction is not uncommon, and could be correlated with the fabric observed by Sander in certain slickenside mylonites (Fig. 11-13a).   A high degree of preferred orientation was also induced in quartz aggregates by syntectonic recrystallization under axial stress at temperatures upward of 500°C and confining pressures of 2,000 to 30,000 bars.

8. As may be inferred from the above comments, a persistent theme running through the literature on tectonite fabrics is the idea that an essential role in the orienting of quartz is played by crystal gliding. Prisms, the base, various rhombohedrons, and even irrational planes in the zone of $[m:r]$ have all been invoked, purely on petrofabric evidence, as possible planes of translation.   There is now some direct experimental evidence[43] that one of the effective glide mechanisms in quartz is translation on $\{0001\}$, and that Boehm lamellae nearly parallel to $\{0001\}$ and deformation bands parallel to [0001] are visible evidence of the process. Experience with calcite warns us of the futility of deducing supposed glide mechanisms from petrofabric data.   Moreover, there is no evidence that basal translation or any other glide mechanism plays an essential role in the evolution of preferred orientation patterns of quartz in tectonites.

Revised Interpretation of Preferred Orientation of [0001].   From the above discussion it follows that in the present state of our knowledge neither hypothetical orienting mechanisms nor detail of quartz-axis patterns can enter into our interpretation of preferred orientation of quartz in tectonites.   Strength and position of individual maxima in relation to schistosity and lineation are taken into account only to the extent that they define the symmetry of the quartz subfabric and of the tectonite fabric as a whole.   The significant property of a quartz pattern is its symmetry.   From the very fact that it is commonly discordant with respect to the symmetry of other subfabrics it follows that

[42] D. T. Griggs, F. J. Turner, and H. C. Heard, Deformation of rocks at 500° to 800°C., *Geol. Soc. America Mem. 79*, pp. 76, 102, 1960; N. L. Carter, J. M. Christie, and D. T. Griggs, Experimentally produced deformation lamellae and other structures in quartz sand, *Jour. Geophys. Research*, vol. 66, pp. 2518, 2519, 1961.

[43] J. M. Christie, N. L. Carter, and D. T. Griggs, Experimental evidence for the basal slip mechanism in quartz (abstract of paper presented to the National Academy of Sciences, Autumn meeting, October 1961), *Science*, vol. 3, p. 3, November, 1961.

analysis of preferred orientation in quartz is an important phase of structural analysis of tectonites, yielding data that cannot be obtained from other sources.

Also significant is the fact that the symmetry of quartz orientation patterns so commonly is approximately though seldom perfectly, orthorhombic. It is tentatively suggested—and this admittedly is speculation—that syntectonic recrystallization of quartz yields patterns whose symmetry approximates that of the stress system—orthorhombic in the most general case. Herein lie the orthorhombic affinities of most quartz patterns. Departure from perfect symmetry is attributed to the relatively feeble influence of some factor other than stress, in all probability the preexisting anisotropy of the parent rock. On the above interpretation the three mutually perpendicular directions of intersection of the planes of near-symmetry could be equated with the axes of principal stress σ_1, σ_2, and σ_3. One of these axes, the normal to the plane of the quartz girdle in patterns such as Figs. 11-14a, b, d, we believe to have special significance. In homotactic monoclinic fabrics it commonly coincides with the axis of mesoscopic folding and of microscopic elongation of mineral grains. In this particular combination of structures the girdle axis is surely incompatible with σ_1 but could well be equated with σ_2 or σ_3. We suggest, therefore, that one of the more likely possibilities to be considered in the dynamic analysis of any quartz subfabric with a pronounced girdle pattern, whether the fabric is homotactic or not, is that the σ_1 axis of the stress system lies somewhere in the plane of the girdle.

There are cases, too, where strong patterns of preferred orientation can be correlated with pronounced strain of individual grains, presumably the result of plastic flow. Such, for example, are (1) a sharply defined girdle normal to the direction of grain elongation (Fig. 11-14b), and (2) an orthorhombic crossed-girdle pattern in which two symmetry planes intersect in the direction of grain elongation (Fig. 11-14f). The mechanism of gliding in such cases is still unknown.

Rather rarely in tectonites with well-developed foliation, lineation, and mica subfabric, the quartz lattice shows very weak or even random preferred orientation.[44] The quartz grains in such rocks are clear and unstrained. Their lack of preferred orientation is attributed to post-tectonic recrystallization under essentially hydrostatic stress either by annealing or under the influence of pore fluids. There are other quartzites whose randomly oriented quartz subfabrics, combined with undis-

[44] E.g., J. B. Mackie, Petrofabric analyses of two quartz-mica-piedmontite schists from north-west Otago, *Royal Soc. New Zealand Trans.*, vol. 76, pt. 3, pp. 362–365, fig. 4, 1947; T. C. Phemister, The use of quartz as an index of movement in tectonites of metamorphic origin, *Internat. Geol. Cong., 19th, 1952, Algiers Comptes rendus*, sec. 3, pt. 3, pp. 113–116, 1953.

turbed sedimentary structures such as cross-bedding, bear witness to recrystallization under purely hydrostatic pressure without preliminary strain.[45]   These are not tectonites.

Interpretation of Deformation Lamellae.[46]   Apart from [0001] the only elements of the quartz subfabric to which much attention has been paid in structural analysis are deformation lamellae (Boehm lamellae). Although of widely variable and probably irrational crystallographic orientation, these are mostly inclined to [0001] at high angles, so that their pattern of preferred orientation is influenced by that of the quartz lattice.   The typical lamella pattern (page 237) is strongly defined and has orthorhombic symmetry (Figs. 6-23*b* and *f*, 11-15*c* and *f*) with paired maxima, subtending an angle of 60° to 80°, situated in some cases at least on a weakly defined small circle.

Deformation lamellae in quartz have been variously interpreted as visible translation lamellae (glide packets or deformation bands) due to gliding on basal, rhombohedral, prismatic, or other lattice planes,[47] as kink bands transverse to an active glide surface in the prism zone,[48] and as healed shear fractures.[49]   In experimentally deformed quartz they develop on planes of high resolved shear stress.   And contrary to a once-prevalent belief, they are of late origin, postdating a state of preferred orientation of the quartz lattice already achieved by some mechanism unknown.[50]   This explains why the symmetry of the quartz-lamella pattern may sometimes be discordant with regard to that of the quartz-axis pattern and commonly departs notably from that of the mesoscopic fabric.

The quartz-lamella pattern can be used, in somewhat the same way as the *e*-lamella pattern of calcite, to reconstruct the stress system for the final phase of deformation.   The perfect orthorhombic symmetry reflects that of the stress system.   Partly because in most tectonites there is a wide range of orientation of *c* axes, and partly because crystallographic

[45] H. W. Fairbairn, The stress-sensitivity of quartz in tectonites, *Tschermaks Mineralog. Petrog. Mitt.*, vol. 4, pp. 75–80, 1954.

[46] The nature of deformation lamellae in quartz and theories of their origin have been concisely reviewed by J. M. Christie and C. B. Raleigh (The origin of deformation lamellae in quartz, *Am. Jour. Sci.*, vol. 257, pp. 385–407, 1959).   See also N. A. Riley, Structural petrology of the Baraboo quartzite, *Jour. Geology*, vol. 55, pp. 453–475, 1947.

[47] E.g., Sander, *op. cit.*, pp. 177, 178, 1930; Hietanen, *op. cit.*, p. 35, 1938; H. W. Fairbairn, *op. cit.*, pp. 123–126, 1949; Christie, Carter, and Griggs, *op. cit.*

[48] Christie and Raleigh, *op. cit.*, p. 404.

[49] O. F. Tuttle, Structural petrology of planes of liquid inclusions, *Jour. Geology*, vol. 57, pp. 354–355, 1949; E. C. Hansen, I. Borg, and J. C. Maxwell, Dynamic significance of quartz lamellae, *Jour. Geophys. Research*, vol. 64, pp. 1104–1105, 1959.

[50] Turner, *op. cit.*, *Am. Geophys. Union Trans.*, 1948; Christie and Raleigh, *op. cit.*, p. 404; K. Naha, Time of formation and kinematic significance of deformation lamellae in quartz, *Jour. Geology*, vol. 67, pp. 120–124, 1959.

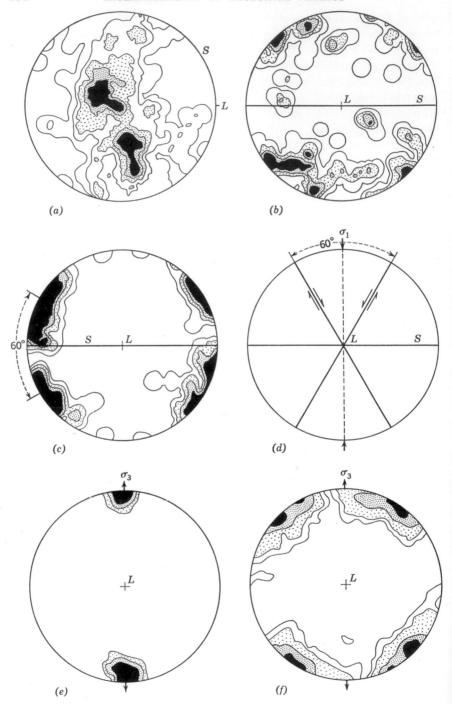

Fig. 11-15. For descriptive legend see opposite page.

control of lamellae in any crystal is not rigorous, the influence of the initial orientation pattern of quartz axes upon the lamella pattern is commonly negligible. The axes of intersection of the three symmetry planes of the lamella diagram may then be identified as the axes of principal stress σ_1, σ_2, and σ_3. Further inference depends upon the kinematic interpretation placed upon the lamellae—and here there is some difference of opinion. If, as maintained by some writers, the lamellae are healed shear fractures the stress axis σ_1 is likely to bisect the *obtuse* angle between the lamella-pole maxima (Fig. 11-15c and d); for in experimental deformation of rocks shear fractures on every scale are inclined at between 20° and 40° (commonly 30°) to the σ_1 axis (pages 292 to 295). Christie and Raleigh on the other hand identified σ_1 as the bisector of the *acute* angle between lamella-pole maxima and as the axis of the small circle of lamella poles which characterizes some of their diagrams. Later experimental data[51] caused Christie and his associates to revise their earlier views as to the nature of the lamellae (now believed to be parallel or subparallel to the crystal glide system), but confirmed the location of σ_1 as bisector of the acute angle between pole maxima. Possibly two microscopically similar structures are being confused: shear fractures whose acute angle of intersection is bisected by σ_1, and translation lamellae whose obtuse angle of intersection is bisected by σ_1.

Two studies have been made of lamellae in associated quartz and calcite. One of these concerns e lamellae in calcite cement and deformation lamellae in quartz grains of folded Oriskanay sandstone.[52] On the assumption that the quartz lamellae are shear surfaces a consistent stress picture emerges: σ_1, identified as the bisector of the obtuse angle between lamella-pole maxima, coincides with the mean "compression axis" deduced from e lamellae in calcite. This direction is normal, and

[51] Christie, Carter, and Griggs, *op. cit.*
[52] Hansen, Borg, and Maxwell, *op. cit.*

FIG. 11-15. Deformation lamellae in quartz of tectonites. (a–d) Quartz-piedmontite-muscovite schist, Otago, New Zealand. (*After J. B. Mackie, Royal Soc. New Zealand Trans., vol. 76, pt. 3, pl. 31, p. 366, 1947.*) S = single foliation emphasized by mineral lamination; L = lineation marked by alignment of long axes of piedmontite and of mica aggregates. (a) 250 [0001] axes of quartz. Contours, 4%, 3%, 2%, 1%, 0.4%, per 1% area. (b) [0001] of 100 quartz grains in which lamellae were measured. Contours, 4%, 3%, 2%, 1%, per 1% area. (c) 100 lamella poles measured in section normal to L. Contours, 4%, 2%, 1%, per 1% area; maximum concentration 14%. (d) Stress and movement inferred from diagram c, assuming that lamellae are shear fractures. (e) and (f) Quartz-garnet-mica schist, Singhbhum, India. (*After K. Naha.*) L = axis of mesoscopic folds and axis of [0001] girdle for quartz. (e) Poles of 54 tension fractures in 14 garnet grains. Contours, 20%, 10%, 5%, per 1% area. σ_3 = inferred direction of axis of minimal stress. (f) 158 quartz lamellae. Contours, 9%, 5%, 1.3%, 0.6%, per 1% area; maximum concentration 11%.

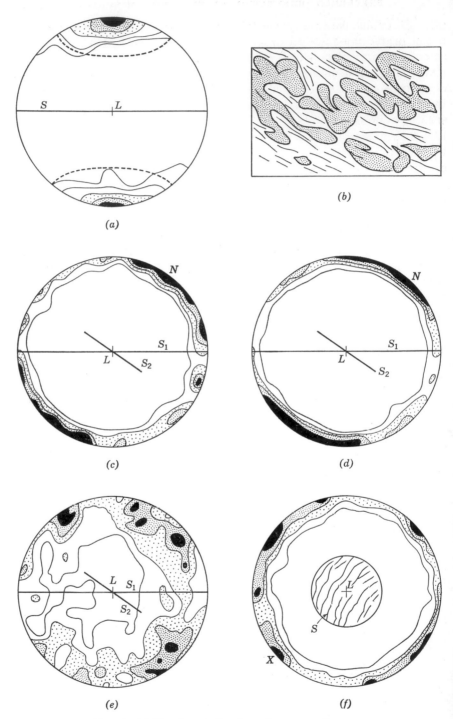

FIG. 11-16. For descriptive legend see opposite page.

the σ_2 direction parallel, to the fold axis. The second study deals with demonstrable shear fractures in quartz grains of experimentally deformed calcite-cemented sandstones.[53] Here too the stress pictures deduced respectively from shear fractures in quartz grains and e lamellae in cementing calcite are mutually consistent. They approximate closely the actual stress system induced by load. Further support for the shear-fracture hypothesis comes from Naha's[54] study of quartz lamellae in a folded garnetiferous mica schist. Extremely regular tension fractures in garnet—normal to σ_3 of the stress system—are symmetrically oriented with reference to quartz lamellae. The garnet-fracture maximum bisects the acute angle between the quartz-lamella maxima (Fig. 11-15e and f).

No satisfactory explanation has been put forward to account for what seems to be a characteristic feature of quartz lamellae:[55] Great-circle arcs drawn through the lamella pole and the c axis for individual grains have a constant direction and sense (Fig. 6-23d); if the lamella pole is marked with an arrowhead, the arrows point toward the center of the lamella-pole small circle.

Micas. *Orientation Patterns in Relation to s-Surfaces and Lineation.* A characteristic of schistosity or foliation as defined in classic literature[56] is a mesoscopically conspicuous tendency for platy crystals of mica to be aligned with $\{001\}$ parallel to prominent s-surfaces (schistosity) or linea-

---

[53] M. Friedman, Petrofabric analysis of experimentally deformed calcite-cemented sandstones, *Jour. Geology* (in press). We are indebted to Dr. Friedman for permission to use this unpublished material.

[54] Naha, *op. cit.*

[55] Riley, *op. cit.*; Christie and Raleigh, *op. cit.*

[56] E.g., H. C. Sorby, On the theory of slaty cleavage, *Philos. Mag.*, ser. 4, vol. 12, pp. 127–129, 1856; Becke, *op. cit.*, pp. 37, 51; U. Grubenmann, *Die Kristallinen Schiefer*, 2d ed., pp. 103–106, Borntraeger, Berlin, 1910; Harker, *op. cit.*, pp. 153–155, 1932.

FIG. 11-16. Orientation of $\{001\}$ in micas of tectonites. S, S_1, etc. = mesoscopic s-surfaces; L = lineation. (a) Biotite schist, Shuswap terrane, British Columbia. (*After J. Gilluly, Am. Jour. Sci., vol. 28, p. 193, 1934.*) 200 $\{001\}$ poles. Contours, 20%, 10%, 5%, 1%, 0.5%, per 1% area. (b–e) Quartz albite-muscovite-chlorite schist, Otago, New Zealand. Strong lineation L = axis of microfolding of quartz-rich layers S_1; axial-plane foliation of microfolds is S_2; gross mesoscopic trend of S_1 is horizontal. (b) Cross section of part of measured section; quartzose layers S_1 stippled; variable trend of S_2 indicated by lines in the intervening mica-rich domains. (c) 150 poles of $\{001\}$ in muscovite; small sharply crystallized flakes in quartzose layers. Contours, 6%, 4%, 2%, 0.7%, per 1% area. (d) 300 poles of $\{001\}$ in muscovite; larger crystals of micaceous layers. Contours, 6%, 4%, 2%, 0.3%, per 1% area. (e) 350 [0001] axes of quartz. Contours, 3%, 2%, 1%, 0.3%, per 1% area. (f) Quartz-albite layers in schist, Otago, New Zealand. L = lineation = axis of microfolding of foliation S. 200 poles of $\{001\}$ in muscovite. Contours, 6%, 4%, 2%, 0.5%, per 1% area.

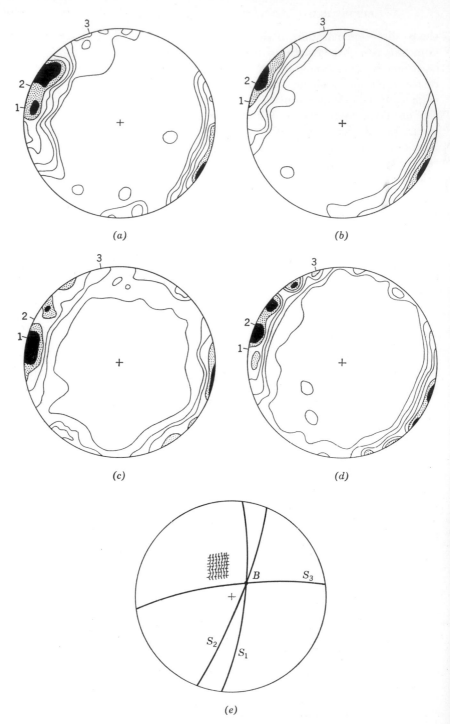

(a)

(b)

(c)

(d)

(e)

FIG. 11-17. For descriptive legend see opposite page.

tions.   Microscopic analysis of the mica subfabric confirms and elaborates this general relation between preferred orientation of mica and the elements of the mesoscopic fabric.   Such is illustrated in Figs. 11-16 and 11-17.   Allowing for the influence of tabular habit of the measured crystals and the central "blind spot" (pages 224 to 230), it is still obvious that maxima in the {001} diagrams for mica tend to coincide with poles of prominent mesoscopically visible s-surfaces.   Moreover, the {001} maxima commonly fall in a girdle whose axis coincides with a prominent lineation.

Figure 11-16a shows the common case where {001} of mica is subparallel to a single simple foliation S; as shown by the small circle drawn at 40° to the pole of S, there is only a slight tendency for the {001} maximum to spread into a partial girdle around the lineation L.   The symmetry is almost perfectly axial.

Figure 11-16b to e represents a more complex fabric typical of mica schists that have been intensely folded on a small scale.   In a quartz-albite-mica schist from New Zealand,[57] quartzose layers S_1 have been strongly folded about $B_{S_1}{}^{S_2}$ (= the strong lineation L), and alternating micaceous layers have been sheared along undulating s-surfaces S_2 approximating axial planes of the microfolds in S_1 (Fig. 11-16b).   The {001} diagrams for muscovite have strongly developed girdles concentric about L.   Both in the folded quartzose layers (Fig. 11-16c) and the sheared micaceous layers (Fig. 11-16d) sharply crystallized muscovites tend to be aligned in S_2 (maximum N) rather than in S_1.   While the mesoscopic fabric elements and the mica subfabrics are homotactic, the orientation pattern for quartz axes (Fig. 11-16e) is discordant—a common feature in rocks of this kind elsewhere.   In Fig. 11-16f, representing the muscovite subfabric of a coarse-grained low-grade schist from the same region, the mica maxima are more evenly distributed in a girdle around the axis of mesoscopic crenulation L.

Figure 11-17 shows a rather similar schist, though of much higher metamorphic grade, from the Wissahickon formation of Pennsylvania.[58]

[57] F. J. Turner, Structural petrology of the schists of eastern Otago, New Zealand, *Am. Jour. Sci.*, vol. 238, pp. 161–163, 1940.

[58] E. Cloos and A. Hietanen, Geology of the "Martic Overthrust," *Geol. Soc. America Spec. Paper 35*, pp. 161–164, pl. 26, A₁-A₈, 1941.

Fig. 11-17. Orientation of {001} in micas in a specimen of Wissahickon schist, Pennsylvania.   (*After A. Hietanen.*)   1, 2, and 3 are poles of S_1, S_2, S_3.   (a) 100 poles, large biotites.   Contours, 15%, 12%, 8%, 5%, 2%, 1%, per 1% area.   (b) 100 poles, large muscovites.   Contours, 15%, 9%, 6%, 3%, 2%, 1%, per 1% area.   (c) 200 poles, small muscovites.   Contours, 7%, 5%, 3%, 2%, ½%, per 1% area.   (d) 100 poles, bent muscovites.   Contours, 10%, 8%, 6%, 4%, 2%, 1%, per 1% area.   (e) Orientation of S_1 = bedding; S_2 = axial-plane cleavage of folds about $B_{S_1}{}^{S_2}$; S_3 = fracture cleavage. S_1, S_2, S_3 intersect in $B = B_{S_1}{}^{S_2} = B_{S_2}{}^{S_3}$.

Bedding foliation S_1, a conspicuous foliation ("flow cleavage") S_2, and a late fracture cleavage S_3 intersect in a common lineation L. This is the axis of the girdle that dominates the mica subfabric. Selective diagrams for large and small biotites and muscovites show some variation as to intensity and position of {001} maxima. The influence of S_1 is most obvious in the small muscovites (Fig. 11-17c). S_2 is expressed strongly in the diagram for large muscovites (Fig. 11-17b), less obviously in the other diagrams. Only the bent muscovites (Fig. 11-17d) obviously reflect the influence of the fracture cleavage S_3; and even here this is overshadowed by S_1. The quartz-axis diagram (not shown) is slightly discordant.

A completely different orientation pattern may be displayed in some tectonites by clear unstrained crystals of mica that have grown at a late stage in domains a few millimeters wide bounded on either side by surfaces of shear or other discrete s-planes. These are *cross micas*[59] and they tend to be oriented with {001} normal to s-surfaces that bound the domains within which they lie (maximum X in Fig. 11-16f).

Interpretation of Mica Orientation Patterns Critically Reviewed. For over a century geologists have speculated on the mechanism responsible for preferred orientation of mica in tectonites. Closely bound up with this question is further speculation regarding the dynamic significance of foliation, and correlation between foliation and strain (cf. pages 450 to 468). Among the processes that have been invoked we list the following:[60]

1. Orienting of seed crystals of sedimentary mica by sedimentary deposition and subsequent compaction under load during diagenesis.[61] Later recrystallization would give a bedding foliation emphasized by parallel micas. Such a fabric, if demonstrably of this origin, would not fall in the tectonite category.

2. Bodily rotation of small mica flakes into the plane normal to an axial compressive stress σ_1 during transformation of mudstone into slate.[62] The rheologic state of a mudstone impregnated with an intergranular film of aqueous fluid continuously generated during the first stages of metamorphism cannot be predicted. It is at least possible that in such a medium mica seeds might be reoriented into planes of flow inclined at very high angles to the axis of maximum compressive stress.

3. Bending of mica crystals so that the bent crystals (seeds for subsequent growth) become aligned nearly parallel to planes of strain-slip

[59] E.g., Sander, *op. cit.*, pp. 208, 212–213, D126, 1930.

[60] For a more detailed review see Turner, *op. cit.*, *Geol. Soc. America Mem. 30*, pp. 270–274, 1948. This summary, in conformity with ideas prevalent at that time, greatly overemphasizes the role of basal translation gliding in the orienting process.

[61] E.g., Grubenmann, *op. cit.*, pp. 103–104, 1910.

[62] E.g., Sorby, *op. cit.*; Harker, *op. cit.*, pp. 154–155, 1932.

cleavage. There is abundant direct petrographic evidence that this process is effective in fine-grained micaceous tectonites—slates, phyllites, and some mylonites.[63]

4. Translation gliding on {001} with rotation of the active glide planes into slip planes of the fabric.[64] Evidence for translation on {001} in mica was first recorded by Mügge, and this glide system has since been confirmed by modern experiments.[65] But most described examples of preferred orientation refer to unstrained recrystallized mica, rather than to crystals showing petrographic evidence of strain. Moreover (cf. page 406), we do not accept the classic doctrine that in rock deformation crystal glide planes ultimately become aligned in "slip planes of the fabric."

5. Syntectonic growth of mica crystals with their longest dimensions normal to the axis of maximum stress σ_1. This is the mechanism proposed by Becke[66] to account for horizontal "crystallization schistosity" which was attributed by him to vertically directed axial load. Lineation in rocks with crystallization schistosity was believed likewise to express a triaxial stress system with σ_1 (gravitational load) vertical, and σ_3 parallel to the lineation (a direction of "stretching"). Gravitational body forces undoubtedly play an important role in regional development of tectonites. But Becke's picture is too simple. Close examination of tectonites with horizontal or gently dipping foliation usually reveals evidence of complex deformation involving superposed folding. The axial symmetry of fabric (with a vertical ∞-fold axis) to be expected in products of load metamorphism is lacking. Instead the total fabric on the smaller scales is commonly monoclinic or triclinic, and on the macroscopic scale has symmetry no higher than orthorhombic.

6. Syntectonic and post-tectonic crystallization of mica in orientations controlled by existing visible s-surfaces and lineations. Here the markedly tabular habit of mica controls the state of preferred orientation of {001}. Sander[67] has assigned to this process a dominant role in the evolution of mica subfabrics in many tectonites; and our observations support his conclusion. Two orientation rules, the first much the more important, are recognized by Sander:

a. The crystals grow with their longest dimensions—the plane {001} parallel to the controlling s-surface or lineation. This is *mimetic crystal-*

[63] E.g., Harker, *op. cit.*, p. 158, fig. 68, 1932.

[64] E.g., Sander, *op. cit.*, p. 207, 1930; Turner, *op. cit.*, *Geol. Soc. America Mem. 30*, p. 271, 1948; Fairbairn, *op. cit.*, p. 141, 1949.

[65] O. Mügge, Ueber Translationen und verwandte Erscheinungen in Kristallen, *Neues Jahrb. Mineralogie, Geologie, u. Paläontologie*, vol. 1, p. 102, 1898; I. Borg, personal communication.

[66] Becke, *op. cit.*, pp. 37, 51.

[67] Sander, *op. cit.*, p. 207, 1930.

lization, whereby existing elements of the mesoscopic fabric are preserved or even emphasized by late crystallization of mica. The sharply bounded unstrained micas that faithfully follow the trend of *s*-surfaces on the microscopic scale in many tectonites exemplify this condition.[68] Micas of mica schists, moreover, are products of metamorphic reaction; and crystallization rather than direct componental movements presumably plays the major role in evolution of mica subfabrics.

b. Much less commonly mica crystals—cross micas—grow with {001} normal to a controlling *s*-surface.[69] Here it seems safe to assume that crystallization is post-tectonic.

Conclusion. Because mica of tectonites mostly crystallizes during or after deformation, and because of its markedly tabular crystal habit, preferred orientation of mica is controlled by crystal dimensions rather than by lattice structure. Preferred orientation patterns of mica for the most part reflect the presence and symmetry of *s*-surfaces and lineations that can be measured directly on the mesoscopic scale. To that extent the mica pattern adds little to the total picture of the mesoscopic fabric. Analysis of mica subfabrics, however, does give information relating to the time sequence in which the various mesoscopic elements have appeared in the fabric. It should be noted that control of mica orientation is by no means limited to active *s*-surfaces. In fact passive surfaces such as bedding and early segregation laminae commonly are the planes most conspicuously portrayed in the mica subfabric.

As yet unexploited is the possibility of utilizing preferred orientation of kink bands of mica crystals (cf. page 357) to reconstruct a pattern of late strain. For it has been found by experiment that kink bands tend to be oriented at high angles to the stress axis σ_1 in specimens deformed by axial compression.[70]

In micas with optic axial angles exceeding about 20°, it is possible to measure in near-basal sections the crystal axis [100]—i.e., the optic normal *Y*. This direction may show distinct preferred orientation, usually parallel or normal to the principal lineation,[71] and so defines the mica subfabric in greater detail. Orientation of [100] is difficult to reconcile with post-tectonic crystallization, and we offer no satisfactory explanation of its origin.[72]

---

[68] E.g., Harker, *op. cit.,* p. 246, fig, 119, 1932; H. Williams, F. J. Turner, and C. M. Gilbert, *Petrography,* p. 215, fig. 76C, Freeman, San Francisco.

[69] Sander, *op. cit.,* pp. 208, 212–213, D126, 1930.

[70] Griggs, Turner, and Heard, *op. cit.,* pp. 65, 66.

[71] Sander, *op. cit.,* p. 225, D137, 1930; F. J. Turner and C. O. Hutton, Some porphyroblastic albite schists from Waikouaiti River, Otago, *Royal Soc. New Zealand Trans.,* vol. 71, pt. 3, p. 232, 1941.

[72] Such patterns have been attributed elsewhere to the influence of translation on {001} parallel to [100].

Tectonite Minerals of Low Crystal Symmetry. Typically every essential mineral of a tectonite shows some degree of preferred orientation. This has been recorded for such minerals as amphiboles, feldspars, epidotes, and pyroxenes, though not in such detail as for quartz, carbonates, and micas.[73] To bring out the full pattern of preferred orientation of a mineral whose crystal symmetry is orthorhombic or lower, more than one lattice plane or optical direction must be recorded. One convenient way is to measure and record separately the three axes X, Y, and Z of the optical indicatrix. In hornblende, with its prismatic or acicular habit, it may be more convenient to record the axis of elongation [001] and the optic normal Y ($= [010]$). Measurement of cleavages or twin planes alone is not satisfactory, since the development of such structures in an individual crystal depends on accidents of growth or local stresses set up in preparation of the microsection.

Many biaxial minerals of tectonites habitually occur in idioblastic prismatic or tabular crystals. Their state of preferred orientation will be influenced or even completely controlled by dimensional characteristics; and just as with micas their orientation patterns very commonly conform to and emphasize mesoscopically visible s-surfaces and lineations. It may be impossible to be sure whether crystallization of a given mineral was syntectonic or post-tectonic, for the latter tends to portray mimetically the already existing mesoscopic elements of the tectonite fabric.

The symmetry of preferred orientation of a biaxial mineral is the common symmetry of the superposed measured crystallographic fabric elements whether these are X, Y, and Z of the indicatrix, or axes of the crystal lattice. The total pattern reflects in its symmetry two influences: that of the indicatrix or the crystal lattice, and that of the movement picture. The first is known, the second is what we wish to know. Several possibilities are illustrated in Fig. 11-18:

1. In the hornblende subfabric of Fig. 11-18a[74] the [001] pattern has axial symmetry $D_{\infty h}$, while the pattern for $\{100\}$ is orthorhombic. Their combined symmetry is orthorhombic; and this is also the symmetry of

[73] W. Schmidt, Zur Regelung zweiachsiger Mineralien in kristallinen Schiefern, *Neues Jahrb. Mineralogie, Geologie, u. Paläontologie*, Beilage-Bd., vol. 57, A, pp. 203–222, 1928; Sander, *op. cit.*, pp. 216, 217, 1930; E. Wenk, Zur Genese der Bandergneise von Ornö Huvud, *Upsala Univ. Geol. Inst. Bull.*, vol. 26, pp. 53–89, 1936; J. Ladurner, Deformation Wachstum und Regelung der Epidote als Gefügekorn und Einkristall, *Tschermaks mineralog. u. petrog. Mitt.*, vol. 82, pt. 3, pp. 317–412, 1951; K. Ishioka and K. Suwa, Fabric of hornblende in a schistose amphibolite from the Kurobe-gawa area, central Japan, *Nagoya Univ. Jour. Earth Sci.*, vol. 2, no. 2, pp. 191–199, 1954; G. Kojima and K. Hide, On new occurrence of aegirine-augite amphibole quartz schists, *Hiroshima Univ. Jour. Sci.*, ser. C, vol. 2, no. 1, pp. 1–20, 1957; G. Yoshino, Structural-petrologic studies of peridotite and associated rocks of Higashi-akaishi-yama district, *Hiroshima Univ. Jour. Sci.*, ser. C, vol. 3, pp. 343–402, 1961.

[74] Ishioka and Suwa, *op. cit.*, p. 197.

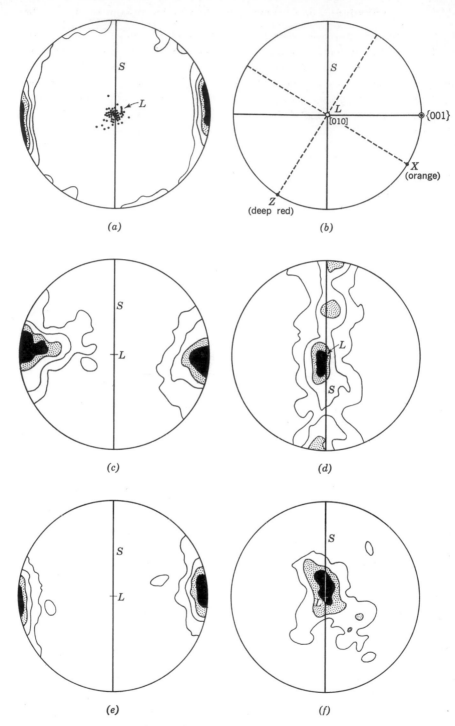

FIG. 11-18. For descriptive legend see opposite page.

444

the combination [001] + {100} in a single crystal. From this we conclude that the external factor influencing growth of the hornblende crystals had minimum symmetry that was orthorhombic. Neglecting the slight eccentricity of the {100} maximum—which probably reflects an error in orienting the thin section—the fabric as a whole is homotactic. Crystallization of hornblende could be syntectonic, the pattern reflecting directly the influence of the movement plan responsible for the foliation S and the lineation L. Alternatively the hornblende subfabric could conceivably be the product of post-tectonic mimetic crystallization. The sharp [001] maximum coinciding with L but showing no tendency to spread in S (contrast with Fig. 11-18d) favors syntectonic crystallization.

2. Figure 11-18c to f illustrates the patterns of preferred orientation of associated hornblende, biotite, and plagioclase in a banded gneiss.[75] Again the fabric as a whole is perfectly homotactic, and crystallization of hornblende could be either syntectonic or post-tectonic. The second alternative is favored by the strong girdle of [001] (the long axis of the prism) coinciding with the planar foliation S. This strongly suggests a rather even spread of crystals growing with their long axes in the plane of greatest ease of growth afforded by S, with a recognizable preference for the direction that coincides with the lineation L. Note that while three of the four individual diagrams for separate crystallographic fabric elements have axial or near-axial symmetry $D_{\infty h}$ the total fabric resulting from superposition of all four subfabrics is orthorhombic.

3. Piedmontite-quartz schists from New Zealand are metacherts with a strong foliation S (marked by parallel muscovites and by lamination) and conspicuous lineation L which in some rocks is an axis of microfolding. The long axes [010] of the piedmontite crystals are aligned parallel to L, the symmetry of their orientation being axial $D_{\infty h}$. Comparison of two sections cut parallel to L, the one parallel and the other normal to S, shows at a glance, however, that the symmetry of the piedmontite orientation pattern is not axial but orthorhombic or monoclinic. If the sections are viewed in polarized light with the long axes of the piedmontite prisms transverse to the vibration direction of the polarizer, most of the crystals

---

[75] E. Wenk, *op. cit.*, p. 76.

Fig. 11-18. Orientation diagrams for biaxial minerals. S = foliation, L = lineation. (a) Hornblende in amphibolite, Japan. (*After K. Ishikoa and K. Suwa.*) 100 c axes (scatter points around L) and 100 poles of {100}. Contours, 5%, 3%, 2%, 1%, per 1% area. (b) Probable orientation of piedmontite in piedmontite-quartz schist, New Zealand. (c–f) Banded gneiss, Sweden. (*After E. Wenk.*) (c) 123 {100} poles in hornblende. Contours, 7%, 5%, 3%, 0.8%, per 1% area. (d) 123 [001] axes in hornblende. Contours, 7%, 5%, 3%, 0.8%, per 1% area. (e) 170 {001} poles in biotite. Contours, 20%, 10%, 5%, 1%, per 1% area. (f) 35 [100] axes in plagioclase. Contours, 8%, 6%, 3%, per 1% area.

in the section parallel to S show the deep wine-red Z pleochroic tint; in the section normal to S most of the crystals are orange-yellow (X). This shows a preferred orientation with {001} close to S (Fig. 11-18b).[76]   Preferred orientation of amphiboles such as glaucophane, which have contrasted pleochroic tints for Y ($= [010]$) and X, can likewise be detected by comparing mutually perpendicular sections cut parallel to the direction of alignment of [001].

CONCLUSION

In structural analysis the chief value of preferred orientation patterns of quartz, carbonates, micas, and other tectonite minerals is that they amplify in detail the picture of fabric symmetry deduced from analysis of s-surfaces and lineations on the mesoscopic scale.   They also afford evidence as to time relations between crystallization of individual minerals and evolution of foliation and lineation.   Quartz and calcite occur in xenoblastic crystals lacking any obvious crystal habit; there is no consistent relation between grain elongation and any particular crystal direction.   The patterns of preferred orientation of quartz and of calcite therefore reflect the movement picture of deformation more directly and precisely than do patterns of micas, hornblende, and other minerals of pronounced crystal habit.   These latter commonly portray the movement picture indirectly in that post-tectonic crystallization tends to emphasize existing deformational and predeformational s-surfaces.

Little is known regarding orienting mechanisms, except that in most cases recrystallization under stress must play a significant role.   So the movement picture reflected in mineral orientation patterns more often than not must be dominated by indirect componental movements.   Symmetry remains the prime criterion for kinematic interpretation of mineral orientation.

Minor crystallographic fabric elements, notably twin lamellae in calcite and dolomite and deformation lamellae in quartz, are open to direct dynamic interpretation.   But the stress systems so deduced apply only to minor strain in the final phase of deformation that postdates tectonic events recorded in the patterns of lattice orientation of the same minerals. Lamellae are especially useful, then, in dynamic interpretation of incipient tectonite fabrics of slightly deformed rocks.

[76] C. O. Hutton, Piedmontite-bearing quartz schists from Black Peak, Northwest Otago, *New Zealand Jour. Sci. and Technology*, vol. 23, pp. 231B-232B, 1942.

CHAPTER 12

INTERPRETATION OF FOLIATION (SCHISTOSITY) AND LINEATION

THE GENERAL PROBLEM

Foliation (schistosity) and lineation are the most conspicuous meso-scopic structures of tectonites. For over a century they have been systematically mapped and their possible dynamic and kinematic significance has been debated. Among the divergent opinions to be found in classic literature on metamorphism are the following:

1. Foliation develops normal to the axis of principal compressive stress σ_1; lineation, where present, is parallel to the axis of intermediate or minimum stress.

2. Foliation ("flow cleavage") is parallel to the AB plane of the strain ellipsoid—which of course is not necessarily normal to σ_1 of the stress system.

3. Foliation is parallel to planes of minimum cohesion determined by slip on planes of high shear stress or of low resistance to shear.

4. Lineation is parallel to the direction of "slip," "flow," or "tectonic transport" in the flowing tectonite.

5. Lineation is transverse to the direction of "slip," "flow," or "tectonic transport."

6. The symmetry of combined foliation and lineation reflects the symmetry of the movement picture of deformation, and is geometrically related to though not necessarily identical with the symmetry of mean strain and of stress.

This last statement we believe to be universally applicable to all kinematically active foliations and lineations. Nothing in any of the five preceding generalizations contravenes, of itself, the symmetry principle. Some, however, are mutually contradictory and therefore must in any specific case be mutually exclusive—e.g., 2 and 3, 4 and 5. Clearly foliation and lineation are not simple structures uniquely oriented with reference to the strain ellipsoid, or to the axes of principal stress, or to any universally applicable movement picture. More than one interpretation of both structures is possible, but in any particular instance the only acceptable interpretations are those that conform to the criterion of symmetry.[1] Rejection or neglect of this criterion has contributed especially to the controversy that clouds the kinematic significance of lineation in tectonites—*a* lineation parallel to the direction of "movement," versus *b* lineation transverse to this direction.[2]

One of Sander's principal contributions through structural analysis was the realization that no one explanation of foliation and lineation is universally applicable. He recognized that some foliation is a slip phenomenon, some a product of compression or "flattening," some again the result of post-tectonic growth of mica tables parallel to preexisting planar anisotropies of diverse origins. Using fabric symmetry as the prime criterion, we shall now examine several widely prevalent combinations of foliation and lineation and review the various interpretations that have been placed upon them in classic literature. In every case it is necessary to take into account not only foliation and lineation but also associated structures and subfabrics—notably folds and patterns of preferred orientation of mica and quartz. Folds will be considered in much greater detail in the next chapter.

BROAD RELATIONS OF FOLIATION AND LINEATION TO MOVEMENT AND MEAN STRAIN

Foliation. With reference to a specific episode of deformation a given foliation may be either kinematically active or kinematically passive. An active foliation may be correlated directly with the movement picture of deformation, less directly with mean strain and stress. A passive foliation on the other hand acts merely as a marker recording something of the geometric properties of deformation, provided this is heterogeneous. Whereas the possible dynamic significance of foliation emerges only from analysis of the complete fabric, it may be possible from the character of the foliation itself (cf. pages 97 to 100) to make limited general inferences as to its role in movement and strain:

1. One of the commonest types of foliation (schistosity) is defined by parallel orientation of {001} in micas, and accompanying mineral lamination. These characters alone tell nothing of kinematic significance. Nor is it possible to say whether the foliation belongs to the active or to the passive class, except that the latter is a strong possibility if the

[1] Cf. F. J. Turner, Lineation, symmetry, and internal movements in monoclinic tectonite fabrics, *Geol. Soc. America Bull.*, vol. 68, pp. 1-18, 1957.

[2] In particular the symmetry criterion has been rejected outright in this connection by E. M. Anderson (On lineation and petrofabric structure and the shearing movement by which they have been produced, *Geol. Soc. London Quart. Jour.*, vol. 104, pp. 99–126, 1948) and by A. Kvale (Linear structures and their relation to movement in the Caledonides of Scandinavia and Scotland, *Geol. Soc. London Quart. Jour.*, vol. 109, pp. 51–73, 1953).

foliation in question can be shown to be earlier than other associated *s*-surfaces.

2. Slaty cleavage S_2 cutting bedding S_1, and axial-plane cleavage S_2 parallel to or symmetrically oriented with reference to axial planes of folds in S_1, are imposed and hence kinematically active structures.

3. Strain-slip foliation, and transposition foliation S_2 obviously displacing an earlier *s*-surface S_1, are kinematically active.

4. Another type of foliation may be defined by dimensional alignment of lensoid xenoblastic grains of minerals lacking any regular crystal habit —notably quartz and calcite. On the assumption that the grain shape is due to plastic deformation—not uncommon in calcite (Fig. 12-2)—or to crystallization under stress, the foliation may be correlated tentatively with AB of the strain ellipsoid. Parallel alignment of flattened pebbles, oolites, or lithic fragments has a similar but more definite significance.

Lineation. Lineation in tectonites is almost entirely a product of deformation, and therefore kinematically active. But where protracted deformation involves repeated folding, a lineation formed during an early stage may be kinematically passive during a later episode of deformation.

Lineation is very commonly the intersection of two or more *s*-surfaces, and its kinematic significance then depends upon that of the *s*-surfaces in question:

1. Bedding-cleavage intersections may be parallel to axes of folds in the bedding—a familiar situation with axial-plane cleavage. The significance of such lineation emerges from consideration of the various possible movement pictures of folding (pages 474 to 491). But symmetry alone precludes certain interpretations such as laminar flow parallel to the lineation.

2. Where one of the intersecting *s*-surfaces is demonstrably a surface of differential displacement of particles or shear domains, e.g., a strain-slip cleavage S_2, the direction of displacement in S_2 may be inclined at any angle to the lineation (cf. Fig. 10-14).

3. Curved lineation within the domain of a cylindrical fold in S_1 may be either (*a*) an early structure passively folded along with S_1 (Fig. 4-31) or (*b*) a late lineation developed where an active foliation S_2 cuts the passive *s*-surface S_1 (Fig. 4-30). Again the significance of the lineation is clarified by analysis of the whole folded structure (pages 185 to 187).

4. Where lineation is defined by intersection of several *s*-surfaces it is usually the dominant element of a monoclinic mesoscopic fabric. The corresponding movement picture must also be monoclinic, and this rules out interpretation of the lineation as a direction of gliding or flow.

There are other types of lineation that are defined by microscopic or mesoscopic fabric elements other than *s*-surface intersections:

1. Alignment of idioblastic prismatic crystals, e.g., of hornblende and epidote in amphibolites, gives no clue as to the properties of differential

movement and strain, except for limitations imposed by symmetry.   For example, symmetry of this subfabric is equally compatible with laminar flow parallel or normal to the lineation, and with other movement pictures as well.

2. Where long axes of xenoblastic crystals of minerals such as calcite and quartz are dimensionally aligned, the resulting lineation may be correlated tentatively with the A axis of the strain ellipsoid (cf. 4, page 447).

3. Mesoscopic lineation may be accompanied and emphasized by boudinage (page 104)[3]—the parallel alignment of elongated bodies of brittle rock enclosed in an incompetent foliated matrix.   The boudins are products of "necking" and possibly brittle fracture of relatively competent rock and may or may not be somewhat elongated as a result of minor internal flow preceding rupture.   The long axes of individual boudins need not represent a direction of elongation in the strained body; but to the extent that they have become separated and dimensionally aligned during flow of the enclosing matrix they can indicate components of elongation of the whole domain.

4. Lineation is commonly defined by parallel crenulations in a foliation. The form and kinematic significance of such lineation are the same as for cylindrical folds on a larger scale.

COMMON COMBINATIONS OF FOLIATION AND LINEATION: DETAILED DYNAMIC AND KINEMATIC INTERPRETATION

Style of Foliation and Lineation.   The above discussion reflects the view repeatedly expressed by Sander that foliation is of more than one kind and is not susceptible to any unique kinematic and dynamic interpretation.[4]   The opposite view, that foliation is a uniform structure originating in one way, dominates the classic writings of earlier workers such as Becke, Leith, and Becker,[5] and is still strongly upheld by some modern

[3] For discussion of the kinetic significance of boudinage see H. Ramberg, Natural and experimental boudinage and pinch-and-swell structures, *Jour. Geology*, vol. 63, pp. 512–526, 1955; N. Rast, The origin and significance of boudinage, *Geol. Mag.*, vol. 93, pp. 401–408, 1956; G. Wilson, The tectonic significance of small scale structures and their importance to the geologist in the field, *Soc. géol. Belgique Ann.*, vol. 84, pp. 496–503, 1961.   Experimental development of boudinage in rocks deformed at high temperature and pressure has been described by D. T. Griggs and J. Handin, *Geol. Soc. America Mem. 79*, pp. 355–358, 1960.

[4] Cf. also F. J. Turner, Mineralogical and structural evolution of the metamorphic rocks, *Geol. Soc. America Mem. 30*, pp. 276–281, 1948; F. J. Turner and J. Verhoogen, *Igneous and Metamorphic Petrology*, 2d ed., pp. 649–654, McGraw-Hill, New York, 1960.

[5] E.g., foliation normal to a compressive stress: F. Becke, Über Mineralabstand und Struktur der kristallinen Schiefer, *Akad. Wiss. Wien Denkschr.*, vol. 75, pp. 1–53, 1913; foliation parallel to AB plane of the strain ellipsoid: C. K. Leith and W. J. Mead, *Metamorphic Geology*, pp. 169–182, Holt, New York, 1915; foliation parallel to planes

students of the problem.[6]   Perhaps the divergence of opinion arises from the fact that style of foliation—like style of folding—though often consistent over large areas varies from one region to another.   The views of any writer tend to reflect his personal experience of a particular style of foliation.   In regions such as northern Wales, the slate belt of Pennsylvania,[7] and southern Victoria, Australia, there is one foliation—axial-plane cleavage (slaty cleavage) oriented symmetrically with regard to folded bedding.   Elsewhere, e.g., in the Rhine Massif of western Germany,[8] the style is complicated by widespread development of strain-slip cleavage which locally becomes the most conspicuous foliation.   These styles contrast sharply with that displayed in the schists of central Otago, New Zealand,[9] where uniformly oriented subhorizontal lineation is the dominant structure, foliations are mesoscopically contorted and disrupted but on a large scale are essentially horizontal, and bedding is unrecognizable.   Yet another style familiar in the Dalradian schists of Scotland, the Caledonian folds of Scandinavia, and many Archaean terranes[10] is characterized by superposed and repeatedly folded foliations of great complexity.

---

of high shear stress: G. Becker, Current theories of slaty cleavage, *Am. Jour. Sci.*, ser. 4, vol. 24, pp. 1–17, 1907.

[6] E.g., "The field and petrographic characters of schistosity in all kinds of terrain are so uniform, and their differences so gradational that it seems unwarranted to assume that it has different modes of formation. . . .   The term schistosity is used herein to comprise true schistosity, flow cleavage, axial-plane schistosity and slaty cleavage, terms which emphasize different aspects of the same phenomenon. . . . All true schistosity, as well as their associated overall fabrics, can be adequately explained by the normal mechanism of plastic deformation . . . the combined action of two slip planes corresponding to the planes of maximum shearing stress situated about 45° from the predominant force.   The net result . . . is flow perpendicular to the compressive force" (F. Gonzalez-Bonorino, The mechanical factor in the formation of schistosity, *21st Internat. Geol. Cong. Rept.* (1960), pt. 18, pp. 304, 309, 1960).

[7] E.g., C. H. Behre, Observations on structures in the slates of Northampton County, Pennsylvania, *Jour. Geology*, vol. 34, pp. 481–506, 1926; Slate in Pennsylvania, *Pennsylvania Geol Survey Bull. 16*, 1933.

[8] E.g., R. Hoeppener, Tektonik und Lagerstätten im Rheinischen Schiefergebirge, *Geol. Rundschau*, vol. 44, pp. 26–58, 1955; Zur Problem der Bruchbildung, Schieferung und Faltung, *Geol. Rundschau*, vol. 45, pp. 247–283, 1956.

[9] Turner, *op. cit.*, p. 211, 1948; "Gefügerelief" illustrated by "schist tor" topography in central Otago, New Zealand, *Am. Jour. Sci.*, vol. 250, pp. 802–807, 1952.

[10] R. Balk, Structural and petrogic studies in Dutchess County, New York, part I, *Geol. Soc. America Bull.*, vol. 47, pp. 685–774, 1936; A. E. J. Engel, Studies of cleavage in the metasedimentary rocks of the northwest Adirondack Mountains, New York, *Am. Geophys. Union Trans.*, vol. 30, pp. 767–784, 1949; L. E. Weiss and D. B. McIntyre, Structural geometry of Dalradian rocks at Loch Leven, Scottish Highlands, *Jour. Geology*, vol. 65, pp. 575–602, 1957; R. W. R. Rutland, Structural geology of the Sokumvatn area, north Norway, *Norsk geol. tidsskr.*, vol. 39, pp. 287–337, 1959; Wilson, *op. cit.*, pp. 519–526.

Style of foliation, like style of folding, reflects the rheologic state of the body at the time of deformation, and this is a function of physical conditions such as temperature and pressure as well as of the phases (minerals and intergranular fluid) of which the tectonite was composed. It is not surprising therefore to find that the style of foliation in slates and low-grade schists is commonly very different from that typical of granulites and amphibolites. In the discussion of common foliation-lineation combinations that now follows style is taken into account; but in drawing inferences as to possible dynamic and kinematic significance of the structure, emphasis is placed especially on the symmetry of the total fabric, including preferred orientation patterns of minerals such as mica and quartz.

Foliation and Lineation in Homotactic Orthorhombic Fabrics. *Simple Foliation.* Widely prevalent among tectonite fabrics is the simple orthorhombic combination of a plane foliation S with a lineation L. We shall consider the homotactic fabrics in which these structures are associated concordantly with orthorhombic patterns of preferred orientation of quartz, micas, or calcite. But first it is necessary to review briefly some classic opinions regarding the dynamic significance of plane foliation without reference to the symmetry of associated microscopic subfabrics.

Early British writers,[11] while not completely agreed as to the mechanism of origin, attributed plane foliation to a principal compressive stress σ_1 acting normal to S. This interpretation was elaborated by Becke,[12] who, invoking the influence of "Riecke's principle," correlated regionally horizontal "crystallization schistosity" with a vertically directed load—σ_1 of the stress system. Lineation, where present, was correlated with the axis of minimum stress σ_3 in an orthorhombic stress system.

Sander, who was the first to take into account the symmetry of the total fabric, also correlated certain types of plane foliation with "flattening" (*Plättung*) under compression normal to S. This interpretation he restricted to rocks in which the patterns of preferred orientation of quartz and mica have orthorhombic symmetry—in particular granulites and other quartzo-feldspathic tectonites where S is defined not only by parallel micas but also by parallel alignment of microscopic very flat lenses of coarsely crystalline quartz.[13] Such fabrics are widely prevalent among quartzo-feldspathic granulites (Fig. 12-1) and quartzites such as those of Saxony, Finland, northwest Scotland (the Moine Series), and

[11] E.g., D. Sharpe, On slaty cleavage, *Geol. Soc. London Quart. Jour.*, vol. 5, pp. 111–115, 1849; H. C. Sorby, On the theory of slaty cleavage, *Philos. Mag.*, ser. 4, vol. 12, pp. 127–129, 1856; A. Harker, *Metamorphism*, pp. 155–157, Methuen, London, 1932.

[12] Becke, *op. cit.*

[13] B. Sander, *Gefügekunde der Gesteine*, pp. 188, 219–220, Springer, Berlin, Vienna, 1930; *Einführung in die Gefügekunde der Geologischen Körper*, Pt. II, pp. 148–150, 263–264, Springer, Berlin, Vienna, 1950.

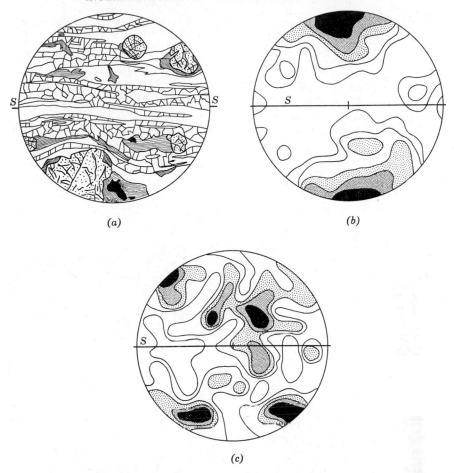

(a)   (b)

(c)

Fig. 12-1. Fabric of granulites, Finnish Lapland. (*After T. G. Sahama, Comm. géol. Finlande Bull. 113, pp. 29, 30, 1936.*) (*a*) Microdrawing (× 8) showing flat lenses of clear quartz, garnet porphyroblasts (stippled) and biotite (cross-shaded) in section normal to foliation S. (*b*) Orientation diagram for biotite; 200 poles of {001}. Contours, 5%, 3%, 2%, 1%, ½%, per 1% area. (*c*) Orientation diagram for quartz; 200 [0001] axes. Contours, 3%, 2%, 1½%, 1%, ½%, per 1% area.

elsewhere (cf. Fig. 11-13*b*, *c*, and *d*).[14] The orthorhombic fabric of marble in which a simple foliation S is defined by lenticular grains of calcite has also been attributed to compression with σ_1 normal to S; and

[14] E.g., Sander, *ibid.*, 1930, 1950; T. G. Sahama, Die Regelung von Quarz und Glimmer in den Gesteinen der Finnisch-Lappländichen Granulitformation, *Comm. géol. Finlande Bull. 113* (especially fig. 1, p. 29; D23, 24, 26, 29, 41), 1936; F. C. Phillips, A fabric study of some Moine schists and associated rocks, *Geol. Soc. London Quart. Jour.*, vol. 93, pl. 34, D1, 2, 18, 1937; A. Hietanen, On the petrology of the Finnish quartzites, pp. 45 (D Ka 1), 51 (D V 5), 53 (D V 4), Government Press, Helsinki, 1938; Turner and Verhoogen, *op. cit.*, pp. 635–639, 1960.

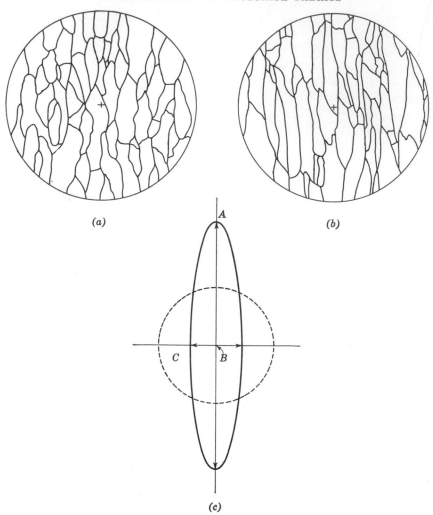

FIG. 12-2. Foliation defined by flattened grains of calcite in marble. (a) Marble, Tyrol. (*After B. Sander, Gefügekunde der Gesteine, p. 204, Springer, Berlin, Vienna, 1930.*) (b) Yule marble experimentally elongated at 500°C and 5,000 bars confining pressure. (c) Yule marble, same experiment as b. Strain ellipsoid constructed from dimensions of deformed cylinder. The B axis of the ellipsoid (normal to plane of diagram) equals the initial diameter of the unstrained sphere (broken circle).

such fabrics have been produced experimentally under just these conditions (Fig. 12-2).

Symmetry argument supports correlation of homotactic orthorhombic fabrics with geometrically concordant orthorhombic systems of pure strain and of stress. And, from the very nature of the foliation, as a preferred orientation of fabric domain boundaries, σ_1 is much more likely to be normal than parallel to S, so that S could also be identified as the

AB plane of the strain ellipsoid.   This correlation we accept, in partial agreement with the earlier writers cited, but with certain limiting reservations: First, the existence of lineation alone, without additional direct evidence of directions of elongation or shortening within S, is not a sufficient criterion on which to locate σ_2 and σ_3, beyond the fact that one must be parallel, the other normal to L.   Second, the existence of paired maxima and crossed girdles so characteristic of the quartz-axis patterns is no evidence of slip in planes symmetrically paired about S and L; we know nothing of the movement picture of deformation except that its symmetry must be orthorhombic.[15]   Finally we note that foliation attributable to compression commonly dips steeply.   Moreover, "regionally horizontal" foliation, once generally considered to be the product of vertical gravitational compression ("load metamorphism"), has been found, wherever investigated by structural analysis, to be a component of heterotactic monoclinic or triclinic fabrics, often including complexly folded s-surfaces and multiple lineations.   These cannot be correlated with simple loading normal to S; and subhorizontal attitudes of plane foliation can no longer be accepted as a criterion of "load metamorphism."[16]

Axial-plane Foliation.   Although on a mesoscopic scale the association of a folded early s-surface transected by a later axial-plane foliation is generally found only in fabrics with monoclinic or triclinic symmetry, on a larger scale where symmetric similar folds are of small size, the two structures can be associated in fabrics with orthorhombic symmetry. The most typical associations of this kind are bedding with slaty cleavage, or an early foliation (e.g., slaty cleavage) with a later transposition foliation (e.g., strain-slip cleavage).

On the evidence of distorted fossils and the form of folds in bedding, slaty cleavage symmetric to axial planes of folds has been attributed for more than a century to the effects of ". . . a compressive force acting at right angles to the planes of cleavage."[17]   This inference is consistent with bulk symmetry requirements in the special case where the total fabric is orthorhombic, regardless of the types of s-surfaces present.   It should be remembered, however, that axial-plane foliation is commonly fan-like in its large-scale arrangement and only its mean orientation would be symmetric to deforming forces.

---

[15] Contrast this opinion with views expressed earlier by Sander (*op. cit.*, p. 188, 1930), Hietanen (*op. cit.*, pp. 44–47, 52, 1938), Turner (*op. cit.*, p. 205, 1948), and others.

[16] E.g., J. Gilluly, Mineral orientation in some rocks of the Shuswap terrane as a clue to their metamorphism, *Am. Jour. Sci.*, vol. 28, pp. 182–201, 1934; F. F. Osborne and G. K. Lowther, Petrotectonics at Shawinigan Falls, Quebec, *Geol. Soc. America Bull.*, vol. 47, pp. 1343–1370 (especially p. 1355), 1936; G. A. Jones, Vernon map-area British Columbia, *Geol. Survey Canada Mem. 296*, pp. 54–127, 1959; Turner and Verhoogen, *op. cit.*, pp. 662–665, 1960.

[17] J. Tyndall, Comparative view of the cleavage of crystals and slate rocks, *Philos. Mag.*, ser. 4, vol. 12, p. 41, 1856; cf. also Sorby, *op. cit.*

Foliation and Lineation in Homotactic Monoclinic Fabrics. *General Character of the Fabric and Its Interpretation.* In some heterogeneous systems of cylindrical folds, the fabric is homogeneous and homotactic and on all scales has monoclinic symmetry. Thus in the high-grade schists of the Wissahickon formation of the Appalachian piedmont,[18] early mineral layering S_1, cleavage S_2, and late strain-slip cleavage S_3 intersect in a common axis which parallels the mesoscopic lineation L and the fold axes B_{S_1} and B_{S_2}. Diagrams for $\{001\}$ in mica and for $[0001]$ in quartz are essentially monoclinic in symmetry and show well-developed girdles normal to L (Figs. 11-14a, 11-17). S_2, described as "flow cleavage," in some places approximates axial planes of folds in S_1, but elsewhere is close to S_1 itself. S_3 is demonstrably a surface of laminar differential displacement normal to L and (as is invariably the case with strain-slip cleavage) is a late structure. From symmetry alone all that may be inferred is that the movement picture, the strain ellipsoid, and the stress system have a common symmetry plane normal to L ($= B_{S_1} = B_{S_2}$). It is not known whether S_1 was active or passive; but its folded form suggests that σ_1 must lie in the symmetry plane of the fabric. Axial elongation parallel to L is a possible component of strain, so that L might be either A or B of the regional strain ellipsoid. But symmetry rules out the possibility of any movement picture involving laminar flow in a constant sense parallel to L.

Slaty Cleavage. Slaty cleavage is a foliation characteristic of pelitic rocks in the lower grades of regional metamorphism. The rock (slate or phyllite) breaks with great regularity along foliation planes determined by dimensional parallelism of small crystals of mica and chlorite formed by recrystallization of the clay minerals of the parent sediment. The cleavage planes S_2 are independent of bedding S_1—which appears to have behaved at least in the later stages of deformation as a passive structure—and typically, though not invariably, are symmetrically oriented with reference to axial planes of folds in the bedding (Fig. 12-3). Slaty cleavage in fact is one of the most familiar types of axial-plane foliation. It is likely that axial-plane foliation in coarser-grained pelitic schists (mica schists) at a more advanced grade of metamorphism has developed from slaty cleavage with progressive metamorphism. The "grain" of slates—familiar to quarrymen—is a faintly defined lineation due to parallel alignment of long particles within the cleavage plane.[19]

[18] E. Cloos and A. Hietanen, Geology of the "Martic Overthrust" and the Glenarm series of Pennsylvania and Maryland, *Geol. Soc. America Spec. Paper 35*, pp. 18–26, 1941; A. Hietanen, Über einige Strukturzüge der Appalachen, *Geol. Rundschau*, vol. 32, pp. 672–692, 1941; C. Ch'ih, Structural petrology of the Wissahickon schist near Philadelphia, Pennsylvania, *Geol. Soc. America Bull.*, vol. 61, pp. 923–956, 1950.

[19] E.g., C. H. Behre, Geologic factors in the development of the eastern Pennsylvania slate belt, *Am. Inst. Mining Metall. Engineers, Tech. Pub. 66*, pp. 5, 6, 1928; *op. cit.*, pp. 31, 377, 1933.

There has been some disagreement as to whether development of cleavage accompanies and even causes folding of S_1 or is later than folding.[20] However, where, as is commonly so, the cleavage S_2 maintains a symmetric though fan-like attitude in relation to the axial planes of folds in

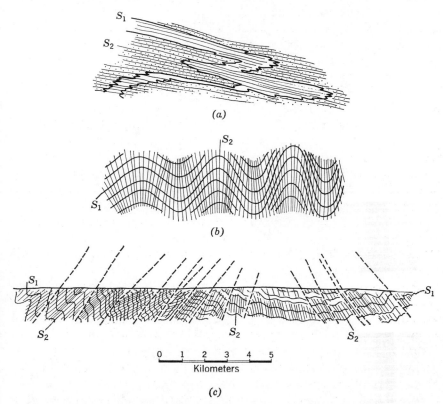

(a)

(b)

(c)

Fig. 12-3. Axial-plane slaty cleavage S_2 in relation to folded bedding S_1. (a) Fold in limestone layer in slate. (*After H. J. Zwart.*) (b) Schematic drawing of slaty cleavage fanned with respect to axial planes of associated folds. (*After L. U. De Sitter.*) (c) Section through part of the Rhine schist massif. (*After R. Hoeppener.*)

S_1 (Fig. 12-3*b*) and β_{S_2} coincides with $\beta_{S_1} = B_{S_1}{}^{S_2}$ (cf. pages 184 and 185), it can scarcely be doubted that cleavage and folding are genetically related. It seems likely that folding of S_1 normally proceeds to some critical stage before cleavage begins to form, after which the folds become more tightly appressed as cleavage intensifies.

[20] E.g., Behre, *op. cit.*, pp. 53–60, 1933; P. Fourmarier, Remarques au sujet de la schistosité, *Geologie en Mijnbouw*, no. 2 (new series), 18 Jaar., pp. 47–56, 1956, and subsequent discussion by M. G. Rutten (*ibid.*, pp. 57–58) and L. U. De Sitter (*ibid.*, pp. 58–59).

It has been widely held that slaty cleavage develops normal to a compressive force which is also responsible for the folded condition of associated bedding. This interpretation clearly conforms to symmetry requirements where the system of isoclinal folds itself has orthorhombic symmetry (page 159), and with the proviso that it is the mean attitude of the cleavage (the maximum in the S_2 diagram) that is correlated with the stress axis σ_1. The same cannot hold true for a macroscopic heterogeneous cylindrical fold system such as that of Fig. 12-3c. If this reflects deformation in response to regional compression, then the stress system must have varied throughout the section, or else some other interpretation of the cleavage must be invoked. Becker[21] advocated a completely different interpretation. He envisaged cleavage as a slip structure forming on planes of high shear stress inclined about equally to the principal stress axes σ_1 and σ_3, and he developed an ingenious explanation, based on rotational strain, to account for the fact that in most cases only one rather than two symmetrically inclined cleavages is present.[22] On symmetry grounds there is nothing incompatible between Becker's hypothesis and the general case of axial-plane cleavage in a monoclinic fold system, provided S_1 is regarded as a passive structure and the folds in S_1 are slip folds.

Against the background of these two rival hypotheses—compression versus slip (shear)—a clue to the dynamics and kinematics of the cleavage-forming process is provided by direct evidence of strain on the mesoscopic scale. Indeed the earliest interpretation of slaty cleavage as a compression phenomenon was founded largely on the observation that fossils in slates are flattened in the cleavage plane.[23] Outstanding among more recent contributions is the demonstration by Cloos[24] that, in deformed limestones interbedded with schists in the South Mountain fold of Maryland, strained oolites uniformly have their shortest axes normal to the axial-plane cleavage of a series of gently overturned folds; the mesoscopic fabric is everywhere monoclinic; the longest axes of the oolites lie normal to the fold axes and define a lineation in the plane of symmetry. Strain data such as these are consistent with compressive stress locally normal to the cleavage and are inconsistent with Becker's concept of cleavage as a surface of high shear stress.

[21] E.g., G. Becker, Experiments on schistosity and slaty cleavage, *U.S. Geol. Survey Bull.* 241, 1904; *op. cit.*, 1907.

[22] Much the same argument has been put forward by Hoeppener (*op. cit.*, pp. 29, 30) with regard to synchronous strain-slip cleavages having opposite senses of shear.

[23] E.g., Sharpe, *op cit.;* Sorby, *op. cit.;* S. Haughton, On slaty cleavage and the distortion of fossils, *Philos. Mag.*, vol. 12, p. 409, 1856; A. Harker, On slaty cleavage and allied rock structures, *British Assoc. Adv. Sci. Rept. 1885*, pp. 816–820, 1886.

[24] E. Cloos, Oolite deformation in the South Mountain fold, Maryland, *Geol. Soc. America Bull.*, vol. 58, pp. 843–918, 1947.

The conflict between the rival hypotheses can be resolved if we revise our notions of the rheologic state of slaty rocks under metamorphic conditions.   On stratigraphic grounds estimates of minimum depth for development of slaty cleavage range from about 7,000 to 22,000 ft[25] and 20,000 to 50,000 ft,[26] corresponding to confining pressures (load pressures) in the range 1,000 to 4,000 bars.   On mineralogic and geochemical grounds the greenschist facies has been assigned tentatively to the temperature range 300° to 500°C and load pressures of 3,000 to 8,000 bars.[27] Values appropriate to crystallization of slates and phyllites belong to the lower part of this range, perhaps 300° to 350°C and pressures exceeding 3,000 bars.   Metamorphism of shale to slate, phyllite, and ultimately schist involves progressive dehydration, so that water pressures equaling or exceeding load pressures are constantly maintained, and the pores of the recrystallizing rock are filled with an aqueous fluid that is slowly being expelled from the system as fast as it is generated.   Under such conditions, and given regional stress of long duration (favoring creep), the rheologic state of recrystallizing slate is perhaps akin to that of a viscous rather than a plastic body (cf. pages 278 to 280).   Such material could deform by laminar flow—involving indirect as much as direct componental movements—on planes of very low shear stress.   On this hypothesis the slaty cleavage would be a flow plane, the "grain" within it the direction of flow, and the folded S_1 surface would be kinematically passive. This view, put forward by a number of writers as a general explanation of most foliation,[28] is here tentatively accepted.   It has been applied by Billings[29] with specific reference to the deformed oolites of the South Mountain fold, as follows:

When stratified rocks are subjected to horizontal compression, they are deformed by flexure folding into anticlines and synclines with vertical axial planes and horizontal axes.   With further compression the rocks begin to flow upward and each particle [oolite] is elongated vertically and shortened at right angles to the compression.   Thus the a [long] and b [mean] axes of the oolites lie parallel to the cleavage, a relationship impossible to explain by any hypothesis of shear folding.

The dynamic significance of slaty cleavage envisaged as a flow structure becomes less important than correlation with strain; for in a strictly

---

[25] Behre, op. cit., pp. 53–60, 1933.

[26] A. Born, Ueber zonare Gliederung in höheren Bereich der Regionalmetamorphose, Geol. Rundschau, vol. 21, pp. 1–14, 1930; Fourmarier, op. cit.

[27] E.g., Turner and Verhoogen, op. cit., p. 534, 1960.

[28] E.g., W. Carey, The rheid concept in geotectonics, Geol. Soc. Australia Jour., vol. 1, pp. 91–98, 1953; L. U. De Sitter, Structural Geology, p. 101, McGraw-Hill, New York, 1956.

[29] M. P. Billings, Field and laboratory methods in the study of metamorphic rocks, New York Acad. Sci. Trans., ser. 2, vol. 13, p. 48, 1950.

viscous medium shearing stress is generated by the condition of flow, and flow itself is the response of the body to a pressure gradient rather than to a "compressive stress." So we find ourselves returning virtually to the classic interpretation of cleavage advocated at the turn of the century by geologists of the Wisconsin school,[30] namely, that slaty cleavage may generally or possibly invariably be correlated with the AB plane of the strain ellipsoid. The Wisconsin geologists, however, applied the term "flow cleavage" to other kinds of foliation originating through metamorphic recrystallization. Some of these are more likely to be s-surfaces of other origins—e.g., relic bedding or strain-slip cleavages—emphasized and preserved by post-tectonic crystallization. We restrict the flow interpretation to slaty cleavage, especially where this is also an axial-plane cleavage.

Foliation and Lineation in Triclinic Tectonites. *General Interpretation.* Triclinic symmetry in the overall fabric of a tectonite usually arises through noncoincidence of the symmetry planes of subfabrics having higher symmetry. For example, the monoclinic symmetry of a fabric in which the bedding-cleavage intersection $[S_1 : S_2]$ is normal to quartz and mica girdles is reduced to triclinic where a third s-surface S_3 is obliquely inclined to $[S_1 : S_2]$. Two alternative interpretations may be placed upon triclinic fabrics in general:

1. The fabric corresponds to a homogeneous movement picture and a homogeneous mean strain, both with triclinic symmetry. This implies that mean strain includes at least two components: pure strain having orthorhombic or axial symmetry, and rotation about an axis oblique to all symmetry planes of pure strain. A further implication is that the stress system is asymmetrically related to preexisting anisotropy of fabric, and that this initial fabric includes kinematically active elements.

2. The movement picture and strain both have orthorhombic or monoclinic symmetry. The initial fabric is composed of kinematically passive elements asymmetrically oriented with reference to subsequent strain. The ultimate fabric consists of two mutually discordant kinds of subfabric: (*a*) homotactic subfabrics having the same symmetry as the movement picture, and consisting of imposed active elements; (*b*) a subfabric composed of inherited passive elements (pages 382 to 384). The earliest fabric elements such as bedding foliation S_1 and lineation L_1 are likely to belong to this second category. This triclinicity implies asymmetric partial overprinting of a later upon an earlier fabric. This may or may not mean superposition of two strains; for the inherited fabric, whether active or passive, may be of either primary (e.g., sedimentary) or tectonic origin.

[30] E.g., C. R. Van Hise, Metamorphism of rocks and rock flowage, *Geol. Soc. America Bull.*, vol. 9, pp. 269–328, 1898; A treatise on metamorphism, *U.S. Geol. Survey Mon. 47*, pp. 748–761, 928, 1904; Leith and Mead, *op. cit.*, pp. 169–182, 1915.

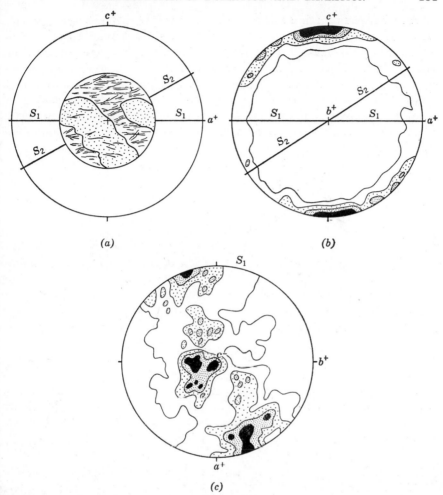

Fig. 12-4. Triclinic fabric of quartz-rich rods in quartz-albite-mica schist, eastern Otago, New Zealand. *a, b, c* are fabric axes; $b = L$, $ab = S_1$. (*a*) Diagrammatic section through quartz-rich rods (stippled) showing relation to S_1 and S_2 defined by micas. (*b*) Orientation diagram for muscovite. 160 poles of {001}. Contours, 10%, 7%, 4%, 0.6%, per 1% area. (*c*) Orientation diagram for quartz. 300 [0001] axes. Contours, 4%, 3%, 2%, 0.3%, per 1% area.

Lineation Oblique to the Quartz-axis Girdle. In one of the most familiar types of triclinic fabric a symmetry plane of an orthorhombic or mono-clinic [0001] axis subfabric of quartz is obliquely inclined to the principal lineation L. Figure 12-4 (cf. also Fig. 11-16*b* to *e*) represents the fabric of a quartz-albite-mica schist from eastern Otago, New Zealand.[31] An

[31] F. J. Turner, Structural petrology of the schists of eastern Otago, New Zealand, *Am. Jour. Sci.*, vol. 238, pp. 73–106, 153–191, 1940; *op. cit.*, pp. 187–189, 214, 1948.

early crenulated foliation S_1 intersects a later cleavage S_2 in a lineation L which is also the axis of microfolding B_{S_1}; the orientation pattern of {001} in mica is a girdle normal to L; but the girdle of the diagram for [0001] in quartz—which itself has monoclinic or near-orthorhombic symmetry—is oblique to L.   Again Fig. 12-5 shows the triclinic fabric of a quartz-mica schist from Anglesey,[32] in which there are two lineations in a single mesoscopic foliation, one normal to a mica girdle and the other approximately normal to a girdle of [0001] in quartz.   Oblique inclination of lineation to

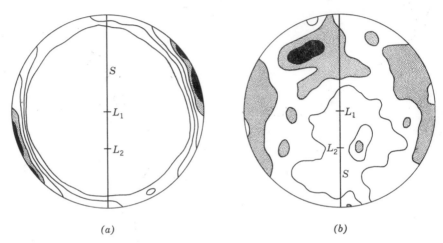

(a)   (b)

Fig. 12-5. Triclinic fabric of quartz-albite-mica schist, Anglesey, Wales. S = foliation (plane of mineral lamination); L_1 = strong lineation; L_2 = weak lineation. (a) Orientation diagram for muscovite and biotite.   761 poles of {001}.   Contours, 10%, 8%, 6%, 4%, 2%, per 1% area.   (b) Orientation diagram for quartz.   600 [0001] axes.   Contours, 3%, 2%, 1%, per 1% area.

the axis of the quartz girdle does not always give strongly triclinic symmetry.   Thus Balk[33] has described strongly lineated quartzites in which the axis of the quartz girdle and the lineation, although inclined mutually at angles of 30° to 50°, both lie close to a symmetry plane of the quartz subfabric (Fig. 12-6).   The symmetry of the total fabric is nearly monoclinic.

The situation just described has been variously interpreted—and indeed more than one explanation is possible.   Many writers have assumed two superposed deformations—an earlier principal phase recorded in the homotactic combination of foliation, lineation, and mica subfabric, followed by minor strain in which quartz (supposedly highly

[32] L. E. Weiss, Fabric analysis of a triclinic tectonite and its bearing on the geometry of flow in rocks, *Am. Jour. Sci.*, vol. 253, pp. 225–236, 1955.

[33] R. Balk, Fabrics of quartzites near thrust faults, *Jour. Geology*, vol. 60, pp. 415–435, figs. 13, 14, 21, 26, 29, 35, etc., 1952.

sensitive) alone has participated.[34]   The lineation would be normal to the symmetry plane of the movement picture of the earlier phase of deformation.   In the absence of any direct evidence that quartz acquires a preferred orientation more readily than mica, there is another possibility which may well have general application.[35]   The foliation, accentuated by post-tectonic mimetic crystallization of mica, may be an inherited passive structure, while the quartz pattern represents the movement

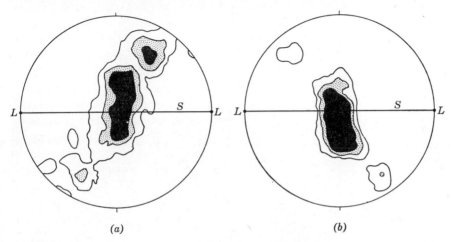

(a)   (b)

FIG. 12-6. Near-monoclinic fabrics with lineation L oblique to quartz-axis girdle; quartzites, Dutchess County, New York.   (*After R. Balk.*)   S = principal s-surface. Each diagram shows 300 [0001] axes; contours, 5%, 3%, 1%, per 1% area.   The plane of the page is a plane of near symmetry.

picture of deformation.   Balk advocated a completely different explanation for the monoclinic fabrics of Fig. 12-6.   He suggested intense shearing in the foliation S, parallel to the lineation L, somewhat analogous to rolling of sheet metal.[36]   This is an unorthodox interpretation of quartz-girdle patterns; but where, as in many of Balk's diagrams, the quartz pattern has a symmetry plane in common with the mesoscopic fabric, his movement picture does not conflict with the symmetry principle.[37]

Strain-slip (including Fracture) Cleavage.   Strain-slip cleavage, though not rare in monoclinic or even orthorhombic tectonites, is particularly common in fabrics with triclinic symmetry resulting from asymmetrically superposed deformations.   Like slaty cleavage it may take the form of

---

[34] E.g., Turner, *op. cit.*, 1940.

[35] Cf. Weiss, *op. cit.*

[36] Balk, *op. cit.*, pp. 430–433, 1952.

[37] In Balk's published diagrams there is some ambiguity as regards the relation of S and L (his *a* lineation) to the quartz pattern.   This led to an earlier misstatement that certain of the fabrics concerned are triclinic rather than monoclinic (Turner, *op. cit.*, p. 6, 1957).

an axial-plane cleavage S_2 cutting folded s-surfaces S_1. But it is invariably a late structure; and the folded S_1 surface to which it has the axial-plane relation may itself be a slaty cleavage of an earlier phase of deformation. We do not subscribe to Becker's view that slaty cleavage (or schistosity) and associated transverse strain-slip cleavage are broadly synchronous strain structures.[38] Rather it would seem that when a finely foliated, and hence mechanically anisotropic, rock such as slate or phyllite is stressed so that σ_1 is inclined at a high angle ($> 45°$ to $> 60°$) to the plane of foliation, failure is achieved by slip on surfaces cutting across the foliation (page 294).[39] The "surfaces" of slip, i.e., strain-slip cleavages, are not discrete fractures but rather laminar domains of intense strain. These domains may become foci of syntectonic or post-tectonic recrystallization of mica, so that ultimately the strain-slip structure evolves into a foliation (schistosity) whose role in the movement picture is no longer obvious.[40]

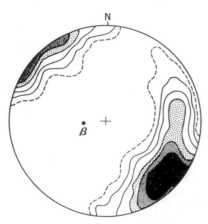

FIG. 12-7. Poles of late cleavage (700 measurements), Loch Leven, Scotland. (*After L. E. Weiss and D. B. McIntyre.*) Contours, 5%, 4%, 3%, 2%, 1%, ½%, per 1% area. β is the girdle axis.

Strain-slip cleavage is characteristic of fine-grained tectonites and may be irregular or absent in interbedded, more competent rocks such as quartzites. It tends to maintain a regular, though not necessarily constant, orientation throughout macroscopic domains even where these are markedly heterogeneous with respect to earlier folded s-surfaces. Thus throughout the Dalradian schists of Loch Leven[41] the poles of the latest s-surface (S')—a strain-slip cleavage—lie on a sharply defined girdle with a single maximum (Fig. 12-7), even though the tectonite body as a whole is markedly heterogeneous with respect to earlier s-surfaces (S) and early fold axes. This regularity strongly suggests some simple relation between cleavage and movement under regionally homogeneous stress in the final phase of deformation.

[38] Becker, *op. cit.*

[39] Cf. J. C. Jaeger, Shear failure of anisotropic rocks, *Geol. Mag.*, vol. 97, pp. 65–72, 1960; F. A. Donath, Experimental study of shear failure in anisotropic rocks, *Geol. Soc. America Bull.*, vol. 72, pp. 985–990, 1961.

[40] Cf. Cloos and Hietanen, *op. cit.*, p. 24; B. J. Collette, On the origin of schistosity, *Nederlandse Akad. Wetensch. Proc.*, ser. B, vol. 61, pp. 121–139, 1958; Gonzales-Bonorino, *op. cit.*, pp. 312–313.

[41] Weiss and McIntyre, *op. cit.*, pp. 581, 590.

The evolution of strain-slip cleavage is not a simple process and is still not fully understood. Detailed studies[42] suggest that in the incipient stage (Fig. 12-8a) it is a simple slip structure maintaining a constant sense of displacement at least through limited domains such as the limb of a fold in an earlier s-surface. But with progressive strain the laminar domains (microlithons) between adjacent strain-slip surfaces S_2 themselves become deformed by flattening; and this is shown by progressive

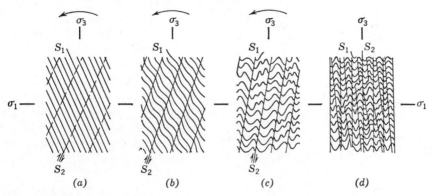

FIG. 12-8. Successive stages in evolution of strain-slip cleavages S_2 cutting an early foliation S_1. (*After R. Hoeppener.*)

folding of the early surfaces S_1 (Fig. 12-8b to d)—whether this is accomplished by buckling of S_1 or by slip within the microlithons upon systems of microscopic invisible s-surfaces inclined to both S_1 and S_2. By analogy with the behavior consistently observed in experimental deformation of specimens with constrained boundary surfaces (cf. pages 328 and 477), it seems likely that all active glide surfaces as well as passive domain boundaries become progressively rotated toward the normal to the principal compressive stress σ_1 (see page 337 for the geometry of the rotation process).[43] So in the final stage (Fig. 12-8d), in which the cleavages

---

[42] E.g., R. Hoeppener, *op. cit.*, pp. 272–279, 1955; Vorläufige Mitteilung über ein genetisches System tektonischer Gefügetypen, *Neues Jahrb. Geologie u. Paläontologie Monatsh.*, vol. 8, pp. 353–367, 1939; J. L. Knill, A classification of cleavages, *21st Internat. Geol. Cong. Rept.*, pt. 18, pp. 317–324, 1960; Wilson, *op. cit.*, pp. 480–483.

[43] In recent German literature (e.g., Hoeppener, *op. cit.*, p. 30, 1955; *op. cit.*, p. 252, 1956), following H. Cloos a distinction is drawn between synthetic and antithetic slip cleavages, according to whether the sense of slip is the same as or the reverse of the rotational component of strain for the domain as a whole. In metamorphic deformation, as opposed to simple laboratory experiments with clay and allied materials, the boundaries of every domain undergoing homogeneous deformation are constrained by adjacent domains. This situation is partially analogous to experimental deformation of minerals and rocks under high confining pressure, where the upper and lower surfaces of the specimen are constrained by the surfaces of the pistons with which they must maintain contact. Here external rotation (the rotational component of strain)

S_2 are closely spaced and the microfolds in S_1 in the intervening micro-lithons have become tightly appressed, the orientation of S_2 should be approximately normal to σ_1. This conclusion is consistent with observations in the Loch Leven schists. Here the cleavages whose orientation departs most from the maximum of Fig. 12-7 show characteristics of the incipient stages of Fig. 12-8; those whose poles lie in the maximum have the characteristics of the ultimate stage of evolution (Fig. 12-8d).

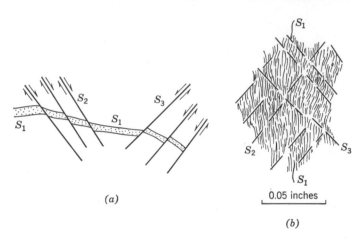

FIG. 12-9. Conjugate strain-slip cleavages S_2 and S_3, cutting older foliation S_1. (*a*) In separate small domains. (*After R. Hoeppener.*) (*b*) In a single domain. (*After M. J. Rickard, A note on cleavages in crenulated rocks, Geol. Mag., vol. 98, p. 330, 1961.*)

Conjugate strain-slip cleavages, believed to represent synchronous slip movements in response to the same stress system, have been described by several writers.[44] Where cleavage of each orientation is restricted to an individual small domain (Fig. 12-9*a*) there is no conflict with our generalization that the sense of internal slip within a domain is invariably opposite to that of external rotation of the domain with respect to its immediate neighbors. However, where the conjugate surfaces intersect each other within one domain (Fig. 12-9*b*) we must assume that the two

---

is invariably in the opposite sense to that of slip within the strained mass (cf. pp. 336–339); in other words the slip surfaces are antithetic. Possibly then under metamorphic conditions all strain slip is antithetic. The external coordinates with respect to which the rotation of any small domain is measured must be situated in the immediately adjacent material. The whole array of domains may rotate in either sense on the macroscopic scale (e.g., rotation of a large fold limb) without immediately affecting the rotation of a small domain with reference to its immediate neighbors.

[44] E.g., B. Sander, Typisierung von deformierten Tonschiefern mit optischen und rontgenoptischen Mitteln, *Zeitschr. Kristallographie*, vol. 89, A, pp. 97–124, 1934 (summarized by Turner, *op. cit.*, pp. 169–170, 1948); Knill, *op. cit.*, fig. 1.

were not strictly synchronous, although both might belong to a single broad phase of deformation.

In contrast to its common fanned or conjugate form, strain-slip cleavage can also show a strikingly regular planar arrangement with respect to axial planes of associated folds in older s-surfaces.   Excellent examples of such structures have been figured by Balk[45] and some are reproduced in

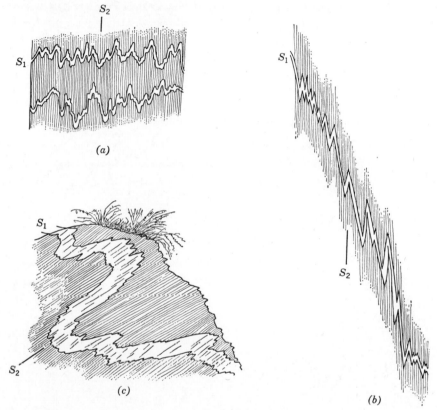

(a)

(c)

(b)

Fig. 12-10. Fracture cleavage S_2 parallel to the axial planes of associated folds in older s-surfaces S_1. (*After R. Balk.*) (*a*) Symmetric folds in siliceous layer in pelite. (*b*) Asymmetric folds in quartz vein in Mack pelitic schist (3 × 2 ft). (*c*) Fold in thick siliceous layer in pelite.

Fig. 12-10.   In some domains the folds are symmetric (Fig. 12-10*a*), in others asymmetric (Fig. 12-10*b*).   Any dynamic or kinetic interpretation of strain-slip cleavage must take these phenomena into account.

General Conclusions.   Some general conclusions emerging from the above discussion are as follows:

1. Foliations of different kinds may originate normal to the axis of principal compressive stress σ_1; or they may originate as surfaces of

[45] Balk, *op. cit.*, pp. 709–719, 1936.

differential laminar gliding or flow whose orientation in relation to stress depends upon the rheologic state of the rock undergoing deformation.

2. Slip foliations either are initially or tend ultimately to become oriented approximately normal to σ_1.

3. Lineation is commonly normal to the symmetry plane of a monoclinic fabric and movement picture (this is the b lineation of some writers). Lineations (a lineations of some writers) lying in the symmetry plane of a monoclinic fabric could on symmetry grounds be identified with directions of greatest differential displacement in the corresponding movement picture.

4. The kinematic significance of lineation normal to a symmetry plane in an orthorhombic homotactic fabric is ambiguous.

5. Lineations resulting from intersection of s-surfaces in triclinic fabrics commonly have no regular relation to the movement picture.

CHAPTER 13

FOLDING IN TECTONITES: INTERPRETATION OF FOLDS AS HETEROGENEOUS STRUCTURES

INTRODUCTION

The common tectonite folds whose geometric properties were described in Chaps. 4 and 5 will now be reexamined from the genetic standpoint. It is realized that present knowledge of the physical state of rocks under conditions of tectonic flow is inadequate for any rigorous treatment of the mechanics of rock folding. We therefore make no attempt to review the many theories relating to folding, nor can we frame any comprehensive theory in terms of the mechanics of polycrystalline solids. Rather we set out and examine some ideas consistent with the general philosophy of structural analysis and with available data on the properties of folds. Most of these ideas are tentative and open to future revision. They fall into three categories:

1. Theories of formation of individual folds in terms of kinematic models which specify the patterns of local displacements, strains, rotations, and so on, and the relations of these to the geometric features of the folds produced. Particular attention is focused on the kinematic role of the folded s-surface. Each model describes an ideal simple movement picture which is heterogeneous within the domain of a single fold or a small group of folds. Such models are familiar to geologists under the name of flexural-slip folding, slip or shear folding, glide folding, and flow folding.

2. Interpretations of a broadly homogeneous system of folds in terms of its geometric relations to homogeneous mean strains or movement pictures within a large tectonite body. In such treatments the kinematic properties of the individual fold are generally neglected. Familiar instances are correlation of the axial plane of a symmetric plane cylindrical system with the AB plane of the macroscopic strain ellipsoid, or identification of the fold axis in such a system with one of the axes of strain. Again the symmetry elements of the fold system may be correlated with symmetry elements of a large-scale movement picture.

3. Inferences regarding the influence of states of stress or systems of forces. Here the geometric properties of individual folds or systems of

folds are correlated with principal stresses (compressions or tensions), force couples, and so on.   To do this it is necessary to make assumptions regarding stress-strain relations, i.e., the rheologic state of the body undergoing folding.   The periodic deflections of an s-surface which are the essence of a fold system reflect local instability within the deformed body; but we can only speculate as to whether the instability was elastic or plastic in character, or perhaps even akin to the turbulence of a flowing viscous liquid.   A common assumption is that the instability arises from the presence of layers having rheologically different properties and that the folding process is one of buckling.   But other theories assume that the observed layering plays no part in the instability, which instead is determined only by properties of the flow pattern itself.   Because the rheologic state of a flowing tectonite is not known, such assumptions necessarily are insecurely founded.

This chapter deals with ideas in the first of the above categories.   The formation of the individual fold is treated in terms of several kinematic models—heterogeneous movement pictures—each appropriate to the observed features of particular kinds of fold.   In the next chapter homogeneous fold systems are interpreted on a larger scale in terms of homogeneous mean strains and movement pictures.   Here the geometric elements of individual folds constitute fabric elements of macroscopic fabrics.

HETEROGENEOUS DEFORMATION IN CONCENTRIC AND IN SIMILAR FOLDS

Patterns of Heterogeneity.   Regardless of the mechanism of formation, individual folds or groups of folds in initially planar s-surfaces are clearly products of heterogeneous deformation.   However, the nature of the heterogeneity is different in folds of different styles.   In an ideally concentric fold (Fig. 13-1a) the s-surface is not effectively planar even in small domains, so that even on a small scale deformation is heterogeneous. On the other hand an ideal similar fold with a hinge of limited extent (Fig. 13-1b)—the commonest type of fold in tectonites—can be divided into domains of homogeneous deformations with effectively planar s-surfaces (D_1, D_2, and D_3), separated by relatively narrow domains of heterogeneous deformation with curved s-surfaces (D_4 and D_5).   A kink or chevron fold (Fig. 13-1c) can likewise be divided into homogeneous shear domains (D_1, D_2, D_3) separated by discrete strain discontinuities (axial planes of the folds).

A further distinction between concentric and similar folding is that concentric folding is penetrative only to a limited degree with respect to a single hinge, because the curvature of individual surfaces and consequently the nature of the strain depends upon the level of the surface in the fold. Similar folding (including kinking), on the other hand, can be completely penetrative in tectonites and so represents a more regular type of deformation.

Although only a heterogeneous deformation can initiate a fold hinge, folds can exist in homogeneously deformed bodies as a result of intensification of a suitably oriented initial deflection in a set of kinematically passive s-surfaces.

Competence of Folded Layers. Concentric folding usually is shown by individual layers of finite—sometimes very great—thickness. The material forming such layers is said to be *competent*[1] as contrasted with the

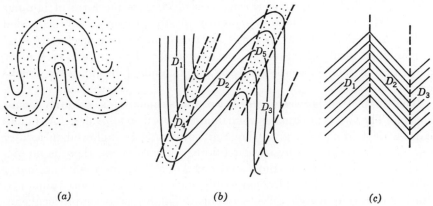

(a)   (b)   (c)

FIG. 13-1. Homogeneous domains (unstippled) in folds with different style. (a) Concentric fold with no homogeneous domains of significant size. (b) Similar folds with homogeneous limbs (D_1, D_2, and D_3) and heterogeneous hinges (D_4 and D_5). (c) Kink folds made up of homogeneous domains (D_1, D_2, D_3) linked by surfaces of strain discontinuity.

incompetent materials of similar folds. Since competence describes the behavior of a layer during folding, it also expresses the differential rheologic properties—and thus the stress-strain relations—in a heterogeneous layered body. Competence is not merely a property of a material under given physical conditions; it depends, too, on the physical properties (viscosity and so on) of adjacent layers. The model of concentric folding of competent layers involves buckling under a laterally transmitted compressive stress. Periodic local deflection of the layers resulting from elastic, plastic, or viscous instability leads to formation of fold hinges that grow in amplitude as lateral compression progresses.[2] Interstrati-

[1] E.g., M. P. Billings, *Structural Geology*, p. 88, Prentice-Hall, Englewood Cliffs, N.J., 1942; E. S. Hills, *Outlines of Structural Geology*, p. 82, Methuen, London, 1953.

[2] E.g., A. E. Scheidegger, *Principles of Geodynamics*, pp. 235–247, Springer, Berlin, 1958; H. Ramberg, Evolution of ptygmatic folding, *Norsk geol. tiddskr.*, vol. 39, pp. 99–151, 1959; M. A. Biot, Theory of folding of stratified viscoelastic media and its importance in tectonites and orogenesis, *Geol. Soc. America Bull.*, vol. 72, pp. 1595–1620, 1961.

fied incompetent layers accommodate themselves to the spaces between folded competent layers by flow of another kind.[3]

Many features of similar folds are difficult or impossible to explain by a mechanism of buckling. For example, similar folds tend to occur in rocks which lack layers of markedly different properties so that there is no substantial internal variation in the rheologic properties of the folded material. Again buckling cannot easily account for the remarkable persistence of individual hinges of similar folds for distances of hundreds or even thousands of feet normal to the fold axis, or for the commonly observed approach to periodicity in location of fold hinges. The mechanism of similar folding is generally conceived as some form of laminar flow or slip attributable to viscous or plastic properties of the folded material.[4] Or there may perhaps be a combination of mechanisms by which small local deflections of the s-surface, either initially present or generated by incipient early buckling, are magnified into folds by viscous or plastic flow.

The distinction between concentric and similar folds is by no means sharp. The two types appear in intimate relation on all scales. Although concentric folding of a given layered body may be followed in a later episode of deformation by similar folding, or vice versa, there is no evidence suggesting that the contrasted styles of folding represent two markedly different sets of physical conditions or geologic environments. Rather variation in style reflects a delicate balance between physical conditions and the rheologic properties of different materials in a heterogeneously layered body. In a single fold some layers may be competent while others are incompetent; in the first the folded s-surfaces tend to be active, in the second passive. So we tentatively suggest that all folds in tectonites are expressions of a single phenomenon—what has been termed local strain perturbation.[5] The homogeneous domains of folds are regarded as shear domains, and the folded s-surfaces and axial-plane foliation as strain and displacement discontinuities (cf. pages 367 to 370). To elaborate this view we now turn to purely kinematic aspects of individual folds, with emphasis on the widely accepted models of flexural-slip folding and slip or shear folding. Natural folding mechanisms are usually more complex than either of these simple ideal models, which, however, do represent in a general way two limiting types of behavior of the folded s-surface, namely, active (in flexural slip) and passive (in slip).

[3] E.g., E. Williams, The deformation of confined, incompetent layers in folding, Geol. Mag., vol. 98, pp. 317–323, 1961.

[4] E.g., S. W. Carey, The rheid concept in geotectonics, Geol. Soc. Australia Jour., vol. 1, pp. 91–98, 1953; L. U. De Sitter, Structural Geology, pp. 180–185, McGraw-Hill, New York, 1956.

[5] M. S. Paterson and L. E. Weiss, Symmetry concepts in the structural analysis of deformed rocks, Geol. Soc. America Bull., vol. 72, pp. 870–876, 1961.

FLEXURAL-SLIP FOLDING

General. In flexural-slip folding the folded s-surface is kinematically active. Two closely related broad types of folding may be distinguished:

1. Buckle or pure flexure folding of a single layer
2. Bend-glide or flexure-glide folding of a stack of parallel layers with slip (glide) upon the surfaces of adjacent layers, as in the bending of a deck of cards

Buckle Folding. The individual competent layer in a rheologically heterogeneous layered body undergoes flexure without significant change

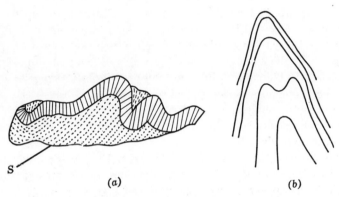

S

(a)   (b)

FIG. 13-2. Examples of flexure or flexural-slip folds. (*After B. Sander.*) (*a*) Folded quartz vein in phyllite with transposed foliation S. (*b*) Reverse folding of thin layer in arch of fold.

in thickness. Some characteristics of layers deformed by buckling have been enumerated by Sander[6] as follows:

1. The minor structures on the outer side of a hinge commonly differ from those on the inner side. Thus tension cracks on the outer side contrast with small-scale crumpling on the inner side; or again the grain-size of the dominant mineral is different on opposite sides.

2. Where early structures within the folded layer are preserved they maintain a constant angular relation to the local attitude of the folded s-surface:

a. In Fig. 13-2a the inherited prismatic structure of the buckled vein remains everywhere approximately normal to the folded s-surface. Unrolling of this restores approximately the original fabric of a planar quartz vein[7] with optic axes normal to the vein wall.

[6] B. Sander, *Gefügekunde der Gesteine*, pp. 243–251, Springer, Berlin, Vienna, 1930.
[7] Sander, *op. cit.*, p. 256, fig. 128.

b. In some folded layers a prefolding pattern of preferred orientation of one or more minerals has survived unchanged. Sander[8] has described how such fabrics may be "unrolled" (externally rotated about the fold axis) so as to restore the folded layer to a planar configuration, and its microscopic fabric to a pattern that is homogeneous throughout the layer. Herein is one of the diagnostic criteria of a flexure fold. But with mica subfabrics there is always the possibility that the preferred orientation pattern—with {001} everywhere parallel to the folded surface—is not inherited but is due to post-tectonic mimetic crystallization.

3. In a flexure fold there is a rough correlation between the thickness of the competent layers and the size of individual folds.[9] In any individual situation, however, the theoretically deduced relation depends on the assumed differential rheologic properties of interstratified layers.

4. Because flexure folds are concentric they are generally disharmonic from layer to layer. At the hinges thin layers may show reverse folding with respect to the overlying and underlying thicker layers (Fig. 13-2b) and localized décollement is not uncommon (Fig. 4-22a and b).

5. In the less competent material between flexed layers the structure indicates other mechanisms of deformation:

a. Finely laminated material may be crumpled—sometimes polyclinally—on a very small scale.

b. Discrete surfaces of discontinuity (Fig. 13-3a) or planar preferred orientation of micas (as in slaty cleavage, Fig. 13-3b) may give rise to a secondary foliation not present in the flexed layers.

c. In some ptygmatic folds the intervening layers appear to be structurally isotropic.

Whatever the mechanism of flow in the intervening layers, deformation is controlled by the form of the adjacent flexed layers. Incompetent material in all cases flows from the limbs into the hinges of the growing flexure folds.

Bend-glide or Flexure-glide Folding. Flexural-slip folding of a more penetrative kind is represented by bend gliding and kinking of single crystals,[10] and has been illustrated by bending a thick deck of very thin cards. Each card behaves as just described for flexure folding, so that its area is not significantly changed, and adjacent cards glide over one another. Either the sense of gliding is reversed in opposite limbs—in

[8] *Ibid.*, pp. 255–260. See also J. Ladurner, Beitrage zur Typisierung von Quartzfalten, *Tchermaks Mineralog. Petrog. Mitt.*, ser. 3, vol. 2, pp. 47–66, 1954; I. Shäffler-Zozman, Gefügeanalysen und Quartzfalten, *Neues Jahrb. Mineralogie*, vol. 87, pp. 321–350, 1955.

[9] Sander, *op. cit.*, p. 247; H. Ramberg, The relation between length of arc and thickness of ptygmatically folded veins, *Am. Jour. Sci.*, vol. 28, pp. 36–46, 1960.

[10] E.g., M. J. Buerger, Translation gliding in crystals, *Am. Mineralogist*, vol. 15, pp. 45–64, 1930; A. H. Cottrell, *Dislocations and Plastic Flow in Crystals*, p. 165, Oxford, Fair Lawn, N.J., 1953.

nature this may even be indicated by rotated porphyroblasts (Fig. 13-4c)[11] —or gliding is confined to one set of limbs, the other remaining undeformed. If no spaces develop between adjacent cards in the hinges the folding is nonpenetrative (Fig. 13-4a). But as the extent of the hinge area decreases with respect to the thickness of the folded body, the strongly deformed sector along the hinge narrows to a discrete surface of strain discontinuity separating planar limbs (Fig. 13-4b). In the

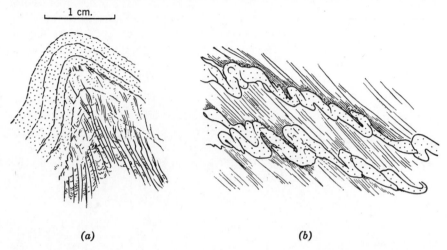

1 cm.

(a)   (b)

Fig. 13-3. Combination of flexure folding in competent layers with appearance of axial-plane foliation in incompetent layers. (*After L. U. De Sitter.*)

ultimate kink or chevron fold so formed (cf. page 114) folding is completely penetrative. Such folding in thinly laminated rocks[12] is clearly due to laminar gliding on the folded s-surfaces. Kinematically the folds are closely analogous to kink bands that develop more or less transversely to crystal glide planes during experimental deformation of a crystal,[13] and may be approximately similar in form.

Experimental confirmation for this model of folding in platy rocks has recently been obtained.[14] Cylindrical specimens of phyllite and mica schist with planar foliation were deformed axially at room temperature under confining pressure of 5,000 bars while constrained in thick brass or copper jackets. Total strains corresponding to relative length changes

[11] H. J. Zwart, Relations between folding and metamorphism in the central Pyrenees, *Geologie en Mijnbouw* (n.w. ser.), 22 Jaar., p. 179, fig. 15, 1960.

[12] J. L. Knill, Joint-drags in mid-Argyllshire, *Geologists' Assoc. Proc.*, vol. 72, p. 14, fig. 1, 1961.

[13] E.g., C. S. Barrett, *Structure of Metals*, 2d ed., pp. 375, 376, McGraw-Hill, New York, 1952; F. J. Turner, D. T. Griggs, and H. C. Heard, Experimental deformation of calcite crystals, *Geol. Soc. America Bull.*, vol. 65, p. 896, 1954.

[14] M. S. Paterson and L. E. Weiss, Experimental folding in rocks, preliminary report in *Nature*, vol. 195, no. 4846, pp. 1046–1048, 1962.

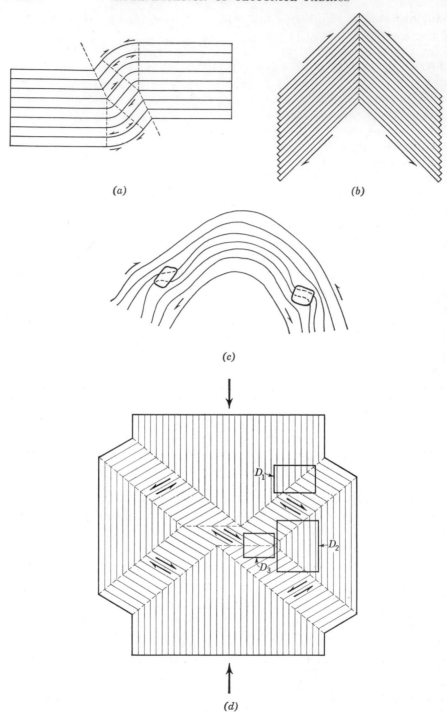

FIG. 13-4. For descriptive legend see opposite page.

ranging from 5 to 80 per cent were achieved.   Following are some specific observations on the results:

1. Except in the most highly strained specimens, there is no substantial dimensional change in the cross-sectional direction parallel to the foliation.   Therefore, since the behavior remains elastic in this direction while large permanent length changes occur in other directions, the rock is markedly anisotropic mechanically.   This anisotropy is a reflection of the dominant role of gliding or slip on the foliation as the mechanism of deformation.

2. At small strains, narrow bands of kink folding appear at approximately 50° to the direction of shortening.   In the specimens compressed parallel to the foliation, the kink bands are in symmetrically oriented conjugate sets and where the foliation crosses successively two conjugate kink bands it forms a conjugate fold (Fig. 13-4d).   In the other specimens the kink bands are asymmetrically developed and in specimens compressed at 25° and 45° to the foliation only one set of kink bands generally appears.   For all orientations, the kink bands grow in number and width as the strain increases, almost filling the whole specimen when 30 to 40 per cent shortening is reached.

3. In the domains where kink bands intersect, folds appear in the foliation which are distinctly different in style and orientation from the folds forming the kink bands.   Whereas the kink folds are asymmetric and open, with axial planes inclined to the specimen axis, these folds are commonly symmetric in form and tightly appressed, with axial planes perpendicular to the specimen axis and thus to the compression axis; they closely resemble the similar folds so widespread in strongly deformed rocks (Fig. 13-4d).   The more highly strained specimens in which the coalescence of intersecting kink bands is nearly complete tend to contain only folds of this kind.   With further strain, these folds become more tightly appressed.

4. In specimens compressed at 25° and 45° to the foliation in which only one set of kink bands develops, such a second generation of folds does not appear at larger strains.   Instead further deformation is by uniform gliding on the foliation accompanied by external rotation of the glide plane, similar to that observed in single crystals deformed by gliding.

Clearly therefore the constraint offered by the thick brass or copper jackets strongly influences the structures produced by preventing the development of major inhomogeneity or arbitrary change of shape such as is observed in speci-

---

Fig. 13-4. Flexural-slip folding.   (a) Bend gliding leading to kinking.   (After A. H. Cottrell.)   (b) Kink folding.   (c) Rotation of porphyroblasts on limbs of flexural-slip fold.   (After H. J. Zwart.)   (d) Experimental flexural slip folding in phyllite (diagrammatic).   Compression (heavy arrows) parallel to foliation.   Kink folding with axial plane inclined to compression in domain D_1; conjugate folding in domain D_2; similar folding with axial plane perpendicular to compression in domain D_3. (After M. S. Paterson and L. E. Weiss.)

mens jacketed only in rubber. That is, the role of the thick brass or copper jacket is to prescribe the gross strain in the specimen, which can only be realized by small scale kinking and folding because the strong planar anisotropy restricts gliding to the foliation plane. In this prescription of the gross strain, the experiments go some way to simulate natural situations in which a given part of a body of rock undergoing deformation is not free to change its shape arbitrarily but must conform with the deformation of neighbouring parts of the same body. It is presumably mainly for this reason that the structural features produced are similar to many occurring naturally in such rocks. Otherwise it must be emphasized that the present combination of physical conditions (short duration, room temperature, confining pressure equivalent to that at about 15 kilometers depth) may not be representative of the natural conditions under which such types of folding are produced. However, it is believed that the observations in these experiments are of considerable value in aiding the geometrical understanding of the development of similar folding by flexural slip in foliated rocks, including such aspects as the orientation of kink bands and of axial planes of later folds relative to the mean strain ellipsoid and the close connection between the generation of the similar folds and the intersection of kink bands.[15]

Kinematic Properties of Flexural-slip Folding. In the monoclinic movement picture of the flexed card deck all particles move by relative translation in a plane (deformation plane) normal to the fold axis. For the fold as a whole, deformation corresponds to laminar gliding and clearly is heterogeneous. The kinematic axes of the movement picture (cf. pages 395 to 400) are defined as follows: ab = glide surface; b = glide axis and axis of bend gliding = fold axis B; a = glide direction. The b axis is constant but a and c vary from one part of the fold to another.

Figure 13-5a illustrates the geometry of cylindrical flexural-slip folding of a surface S_1 about an axis B. The poles of S_1 and the different positions of a and c for different segments of the fold all lie on the great circle normal to b (= B). The configuration of S_1 in relation to B is the same as in any other kind of cylindrical fold. But the presence of inherited initial structures other than S_1 may give rise to geometric features peculiar to and hence diagnostic of flexural-slip folds:

1. Any passive rectilinear lineation L_1 must maintain a constant angular relation to B on any planar segment of the folded surface. (This is because there is no significant change in the area of any such segment of S_1.) Thus in Fig. 13-5b, representing the projection of planar segments within a symmetric fold whose axial plane is S_2, the lineation L_1 appears as points on a small circle about B. This corresponds to one of the ideal patterns described earlier (page 128, Fig. 4-31a). Sander's technique of "unrolling" folded lineations[16] is based on this property, which, however, is peculiar to flexural-slip folds.

[15] *Ibid.*, p. 1048.

[16] B. Sander, *Einführung in die Gefügekunde der Geologischen Körper*, Pt. I, pp. 170–184, Springer, Berlin, Vienna, 1948; L. E. Weiss, Geometry of superposed folding, *Geol. Soc. America Bull.*, vol. 70, pp. 98–100, fig. 7a, 1959.

2. A passive planar s-surface S' is rotated, as a result of gliding on S_1, about its intersection (L) with S_1 (cf. pages 391 to 395). But as S_1 becomes folded, L also becomes curved within the domain of the fold, so that on the projection plane its impingement points are distributed through a small circle about B. So $B_{S'}$, the axis of rotation of S', varies

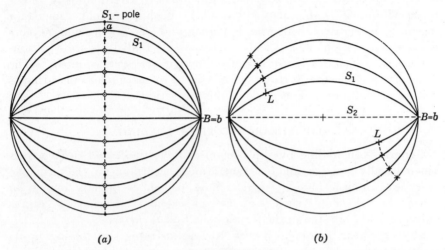

(a)   (b)

FIG. 13-5. Kinematic properties of flexural-slip folds: a and b are kinematic axes; B is fold axis; S_1 is the folded surface; S_2 is the axial plane of the fold in S_1; L is an older lineation lying in S_1. Arcs are planar segments of S_1, with solid dots as corresponding poles. Circled points are local a axes in segments of S_1. Crosses are folded lineation L.

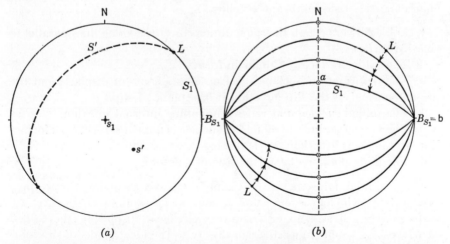

(a)   (b)

FIG. 13-6. Schematic representation of folding of a passive surface S' by flexural-slip folding on surface S_1 intersecting S' in L. (a) Condition before deformation (S_1 parallel to plane of projection). (b) After cylindrical folding of S_1 about $B_{S_1} = b$. The folding of S' in the whole body is nonplane noncylindrical and is not represented in the diagram. Circled dots are a axes in segments of S_1.

from point to point within the fold (along the small circle of L), and at the same time the angle through which S' is rotated likewise varies. This complex folding of S', which accompanies plane cylindrical folding of S_1, is illustrated diagrammatically in Fig. 13-6. (Diagram a shows an initially horizontal S_1 intersected in L by S' striking N45°E and dipping 35°NW; diagram b shows six planar segments of S_1 after folding, with the new position of $L = B_{S'}$ marked in each.) Within any fold segment for which S_1 is planar, S' likewise is planar and passes through the corresponding position of L. Clearly the passively folded surface S' is noncylindrical, except for the special case where it intersects S_1 in B_{S_1}. The poles of representative segments of S' will be on a complex curve that is neither a small nor a great circle of the projection.

SLIP, SHEAR, AND FLOW FOLDING

General. In folding by slip (shear) or flow, the folded surface S_1 is kinematically passive and is transformed according to the principle described on page 393. The movement picture is directly related to other fabric elements[17] such as families of secondary s-surfaces S_2, and is only partially reflected in the form of the folded surface S_1.

Slip or Shear Folding. Figure 13-7a illustrates slip folding in its simplest form. The passive surface S_1 becomes folded by laminar gliding on discrete periodically repeated displacement discontinuities S_2. On a scale which is large compared with the spacing of S_2 surfaces, deformation approximates the continuous geometric transformation and internal rotation shown in Fig. 13-7b (cf. pages 391 to 395). Geometric features characteristic of slip folds are as follows:

1. Folded layers retain the same dimensions only along lines parallel to the slip surfaces.
2. The folds are ideally similar in form.
3. The deformation is plane since no components of displacement are present normal to the slip direction in the plane of slip.
4. The folded surface undergoes a nonaffine internal rotation.
5. The area of an individual folded surface is not conserved. Deformation on hinges is less than on the limbs.
6. The glide plane is the axial plane of the fold.

Many similar folds in tectonites have marked secondary axial-plane foliations S_2 which in some cases appear to be families of discrete slip surfaces (e.g., strain-slip or fracture cleavages) displacing the folded s-surfaces S_1. Some folds conform closely to the ideal model of slip folding. But in most, slip on discrete surfaces S_2 is not the only component of deformation; for, between the individual visible S_2 surfaces, the

[17] Sander, *op. cit.*, pp. 260–262, 1930; *op. cit.*, pp. 47–59, 1948.

broadly folded S_1 surface commonly is crumpled on a small scale; or again dimensional markers (oolites, pebbles, and so on) may be elongated in directions incompatible with the simple model of slip.

Flow Folding. Folding of passive s-surfaces, usually somewhat irregular in pattern, without development of visible discrete slip surfaces has

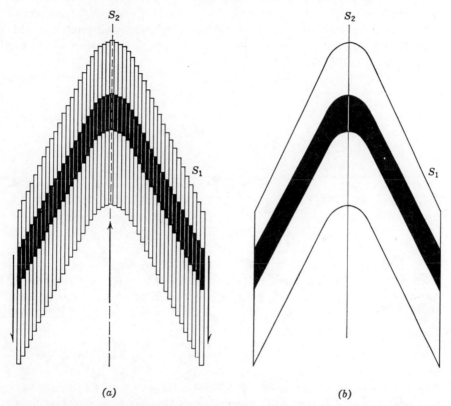

(a)   *(b)*

Fig. 13-7. Slip folding of S_1 with axial plane S_2. (a) By slip on discrete displacement discontinuities parallel to S_2. (b) By a continuous nonaffine transformation.

been termed *flow folding*. In flow folds there may even be no obvious secondary foliation of any kind. The most general model is a nonaffine continuous transformation of passive s-surfaces without specification of a movement picture. Clearly, however, in any particular flow-fold system a movement picture must exist, and some of its properties (local displacements and discontinuities) will be reflected in the detailed structure. Whereas slip folding is a plane deformation related for convenience to specified slip surfaces, flow folding need not be plane and is not referred to any particular system of slip. In general the resultant fold is nonplane noncylindrical (Fig. 13-8). The limiting case where flow folding is a plane deformation is best considered as slip folding with slip on planes that are infinitely closely spaced.

Kinematic Properties of Slip Folding. *General.* In its simplest form slip folding may be discussed in terms of the card-deck model, as a non-affine transformation with kinematic axes a, b, and c as defined on page 396. This differs from the model of flexural-slip folding only in that b is not an axis of bending. For folding of S_1 to occur by slip on S_2, deformation and accompanying internal rotation of S_1 (cf. page 391) must be nonaffine. The resulting fold in an initially planar surface S_1 must be plane cylindrical, and the axial plane is S_2.

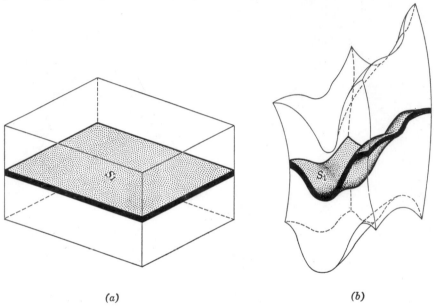

(a)   *(b)*

Fig. 13-8. Schematic illustration of flow folding (general case). (*a*) Undeformed body with passive s-plane S_1. (*b*) After inhomogeneous transformation (nonplane deformation) not related to any specific flow plane.

In Figs. 13-9 to 13-11 let S_1 be an initially planar passive s-surface containing a passive lineation L_1; and let S_2 be the glide plane, intersecting S_1 in a lineation L_2; and let a and b be kinematic axes. Three cases may be distinguished:[18]

Case 1 (Fig. 13-9). L_2 is parallel to b. Slip upon S_2 gives rise to plane cylindrical slip folds—either symmetric or asymmetric—with S_2 as axial plane and L_2 ($= b = B_{S_1}{}^{S_2}$) as fold axis. The plane (m in Fig. 13-9d) normal to $B_{S_1}{}^{S_2}$ is a plane of symmetry in the fold and in the movement picture. During the affine transformation in any planar segment of the fold the passive lineation L_1 rotates in a unique plane toward the kine-

[18] Weiss, *op. cit.*, p. 92.

matic axis a.   All measured attitudes of L_1 within the fold therefore fall
on the corresponding unique great circle through a.

Case 2 (Fig. 13-10). L_2 is parallel to a. S_1 is not folded but must
remain planar.   The symmetry plane of the movement picture, being

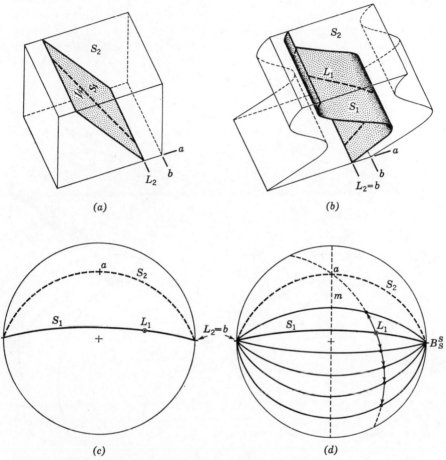

(a)   (b)

(c)   (d)

Fɪɢ. 13-9. Slip folding of passive s-plane S_1 (containing a passive lineation L_1) by slip
on S_2 in a direction a normal to the intersection (L_2) of S_1 and S_2.   (a) and (c) Before
folding.   (b) and (d) After folding.   In projections (c) and (d), S_1, or planar segments of S_1, are shown as full lines; dots are attitudes of rotated L_1.

normal to b and to S_2, generally is inclined obliquely to S_1 (cf. Fig.
13-10d).   The passive lineation L_1 assumes a curved form described by
the great circle through its initial impingement point and the a axis.
This combination of structures—a curved early lineation in an early
planar s-surface—has been recorded in some tectonites.[19]

[19] J. G. Ramsay, The deformation of early linear structures in areas of repeated
folding, *Jour. Geology*, vol. 68, pp. 75–93, 1960.

Case 3 (Fig. 13-11). L_2 is inclined to both a and b—the general case for slip folding. Plane cylindrical folds form in S_1. The fold axis L_2 is not the kinematic axis b, so that the plane of symmetry (m) of the movement picture is inclined to that of the fold (m').

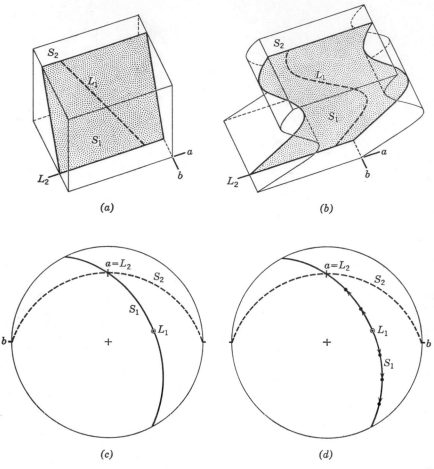

(a)   *(b)*

(c)   *(d)*

FIG. 13-10. Slip folding of passive lineation L_1 within a passive s-plane S_1 (stippled) by slip on S_2 in a direction a parallel to the intersection (L_2) of S_1 and S_2. (*a*) and (*c*) Before folding. (*b*) and (*d*) After folding. Solid dots in d are attitudes of rotated L_1.

Passive Rotation of a Lineation. In Figs. 13-9 to 13-11 the initial orientation of the passive lineation L_1 is the same in all diagrams though the attitude of S_1 in which it lies varies. The path of rotation of L_1—the great circle through L_1 and a—is the same in all three cases. Now consider the possible relations of L_1 to the kinematic axes a and b.

1. Where L_1 is parallel to a it is not rotated.

2. Where L_1 is normal to b but not parallel to a, it is rotated along a great circle normal to b (Fig. 13-12a). The fold axis $B_{S_1}{}^{S_2}$ does not coincide with b. The symmetry plane (m) of the movement picture coincides with the great circle that describes all attitudes of L_1.

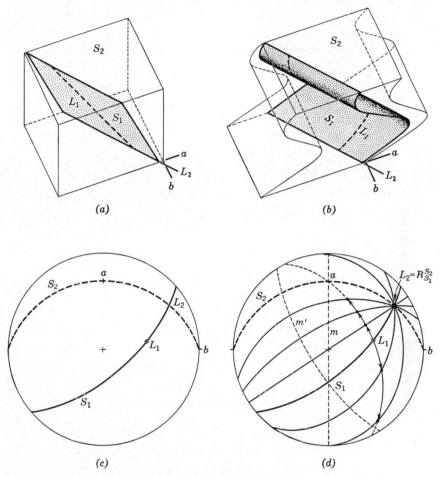

(a)   (b)

(c)   (d)

FIG. 13-11. Slip folding of passive s-plane S_1 (containing a passive lineation L_1) by slip on S_2 in a direction a oblique to the intersection (L_2) of S_1 and S_2. (a) and (c) Before folding. (b) and (d) After folding. Solid dots in d are attitudes of rotated L_1.

3. In the general case where L_1 is inclined to both a and b (Fig. 13-12b), L_1 rotates on a great circle through a but oblique to b and to the symmetry plane of the movement picture.

Summary. From the kinematic properties of slip folding there follow certain conclusions applicable to some types of folds described in Chap. 4 (page 129):

1. The axis of a slip fold has no unique kinematic significance. It is

generally inclined to both the a and the b kinematic axes, and coincides with b only in the special case where the intersection of the folded surface and the slip surface is normal to a.   Sander,[20] realizing this fact, designated such fold axes "pseudo-B axes."   We use the symbol B for these as for all axes of cylindrical folds.

2. Diagnostic of slip folds is the configuration of passively rotated lineations of any origin: within a single fold in S_1 the local attitudes of the lineation are coplanar and so fall on a great circle of the projection. This intersects the axial plane (the slip plane S_2) in a.   The b kinematic

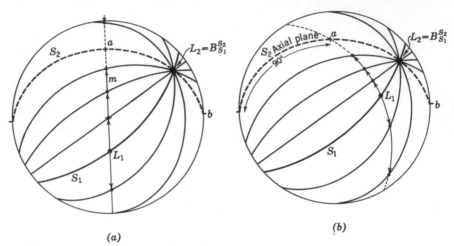

(a)   (b)

FIG. 13-12. Internal rotation of passive linear structure L_1 in a passive surface S_1. (a) Where L_1 is initially normal to b.   (b) Where L_1 is initially oblique to b.

axis lies normal to a in S_2, so that the kinematic axes of the movement picture are completely defined.

3. Pure slip folding of an initially planar s-surface S_1 gives rise to plane cylindrical folds in S_1.

4. Pure slip folding of an initially curved or folded s-surface S_1 generally gives rise to plane noncylindrical folds.   An exception is the special case where the initial configuration of S_1 is a cylindrical fold whose axis B_{S_1} is also the intersection of the slip surface S_2 with S_1 and so becomes $B_{S_1}{}^{S_2}$, the axis of the later slip folding (cf. page 496).

5. Bend gliding on S_2—as contrasted with our simple model of plane gliding—generally yields nonplane noncylindrical slip folds.

GENERALIZED KINEMATIC MODELS OF FOLDING IN TECTONITES

Departure of Folds from Ideal Models.   Most folds in tectonites show features not strictly compatible with either of the card-deck models of ideal flexural slip or slip.

[20] Sander, *op. cit.*, p. 139, 1948.

1. In "flexural-slip folds" the folded layers are not separated by discrete displacement discontinuities. Commonly the layer boundaries are merely arrays of local deformation discontinuities (boundaries of grains or other small domains). In heterogeneously layered folds the most conspicuous boundary surfaces tend to be those separating competent flexed layers from interstratified layers deformed by flow of some other kind.

2. Similar folds in S_1 with marked axial-plane foliation S_2 have been widely attributed to slip folding. Where S_2 is a slaty cleavage there are no recognizable discrete slip surfaces and it cannot be assumed that laminar gliding parallel to S_2 was not accompanied by strain normal to S_2. Where S_2 is a strain-slip cleavage, discrete displacement discontinuities may indeed be present and departure from the card-deck model is perhaps less obvious. But very commonly the cleavage "surfaces" are periodically spaced thin domains of intense strain, and the intervening laminae (the microlithons of De Sitter[21]) show evidence of pronounced internal strain in the form of crenulated relic S_1 foliation (page 465, Fig. 12-8d).[22] Also, folds approximating the similar in form have now been made experimentally by flexural slip (pages 475 to 478).

3. Deformed oolites, fossils, or pebbles may supply evidence of effectively homogeneous strain that is incompatible with one or another of the card-deck models. Such for example is elongation parallel to the axes of "flexural-slip folds" and elongation or shortening in the axial planes of "slip folds."[23]

4. Whereas passively rotated lineations not uncommonly approximate the small circle[24] or great circle patterns[25] respectively demanded by flexural-slip folding and by slip folding, in other cases they conform to neither pattern.[26]

Resolution of Strain in Natural Folds. *General.* With such discrepancies in mind as well as obvious analogies between natural folds and the card-deck models of plane deformation, we may resolve the strain of a folded tectonite into two components:

1. A heterogeneous plane strain reflected in the folded configuration

[21] De Sitter, *op. cit.*, p. 97, 1956.

[22] T. Hoeppener, Zur Problem der Bruchbildung, Schieferung und Faltung, *Geol. Rundschau*, vol. 45, p. 278, fig. 28, 1956.

[23] E. Cloos, Oölite deformation in the South Mountain fold, Maryland, *Geol. Soc. America Bull.*, vol. 58, p. 883, 1947; A. Kvale, Petrologic and structural studies in the Bergsdalen quadrangle (part II), *Bergens Mus. Årb. Natur.*, no. 1, p. 28, 1946–47; R. Lyon, Studies in the Geology of the central Sierra Nevada, unpublished doctoral dissertation, Univ. California, p. 22, 1954; R. D. Elwell, The lithology and structure of a boulder bed in the Dalradian of Mayo, Ireland, *Geol. Soc. London Quart. Jour.*, vol. 111, pp. 71–81, 1955.

[24] J. P. Schaer, Géologie de la partie septentrionale de L'Eventail de Bagnes, Thesis, Univ. Neuchâtel, pp. 546–547, 1960.

[25] A. Baird, Superposed deformations in the Central Sierra Nevada Foothills east of the Mother Lode, *Univ. California Geol. Sci. Pub.*, vol. 42, pp. 40–44, 1962.

[26] Ramsay, *op. cit.*, pp. 90–92, 1960.

of initially planar layers[27] and defined precisely by passively folded lineations.

2. A broadly homogeneous component that may be expressed as a pure strain uniformly affecting all parts of the fold.   This component is responsible for the anomalous overall elongations and shortenings recorded in oolites, fossils, and so on.

The two components may be considered separately or together.   Each can be expressed in terms of a movement picture with its own symmetry.

Heterogeneous Component of Folding.   The models of flexural-slip folding and slip folding redefined below are adequate ideal movement pictures for the heterogeneous component of strain:

1. In flexural-slip folding the folded *s*-surfaces are sites of some or all deformation discontinuities.

2. In slip folding deformation discontinuities are geometrically tied, not to the folded *s*-surfaces, but to a planar or curviplanar family of "glide" surfaces parallel to the axial planes or axial surfaces of the folds. Flow folding can be viewed as a special case of slip folding in which the array of deformation discontinuities has no simple geometric relation to the folds.

In neither model need the "glide surfaces" be discrete slip surfaces, separating undeformed laminae.   In the first the folded surface is some kind of geometric image of the movement picture, and the two share symmetry elements in common.   In the second the movement picture and the folded surface, except in special cases, are not symmetrically related.

The concept outlined above does not assume that the "glide surfaces" are discrete surfaces of true slip.   It is analogous rather to the picture of translation gliding as a mechanism of strain in an individual crystal. This is a highly complex process involving generation and migration of lattice imperfections (dislocations); but the geometric effects of strain can be defined completely in terms of laminar gliding of lattice layers parallel to a specified glide plane and glide direction.[28]   So, too, the strain recorded in a fold can be described in terms of simple gliding regardless of the precise nature of the componental movements—indirect as well as direct—on a very small scale.

Some inkling of the nature of a particular fold (flexural-slip versus slip) may be gained from preferred orientation patterns of constituent minerals.   Folds have been described as homoaxial or heteroaxial according

---

[27] There is also the possibility that the fold expresses homogeneous plane strain of a body in which the passive *s*-surfaces initially were not strictly planar.   A small initial deflection may then become exaggerated into a fold.   Such an origin is unlikely, however, for a fold system of uniform style.

[28] E.g., Barrett, *op. cit.*, pp. 393–396, 1952.

to whether the symmetry of mineral orientation conforms or does not conform to that of the fold.[29]   A homoaxial fold in which the mineral orientation pattern can be "unrolled" about B (page 474), i.e., in which it varies from one domain to another and is homogeneous only within domains where the s-surface is planar, is likely to be a flexural-slip fold. Heteroaxial folds in which the microscopic fabric is homogeneous or heterogeneous are likely to be slip folds; and the symmetry of preferred orientation of minerals such as quartz and calcite with xenoblastic habit

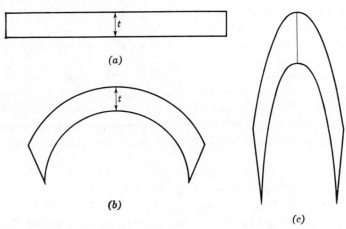

FIG. 13-13. Flexure folding plus a homogeneous component of pure strain.   (*After J. G. Ramsay.*)   (*a*) Undeformed layer of thickness t.   (*b*) Flexed layer assuming conservation of thickness.   (*c*) Addition of a homogeneous pure plane strain with 50 per cent shortening normal to axial plane.

is likely to reflect that of the movement picture.   These generalizations assume that development of mineral orientation and folding were synchronous, and that the passively folded s-surface has not influenced the preferred orientation of the crystallizing minerals.

Homogeneous Component of Flexural-slip Folding.   Visible effects of the homogeneous component of strain in plane cylindrical folds whose properties otherwise suggest flexural slip are as follows:

1. Deformed dimensional markers (pebbles, oolites, etc.) indicate bulk homogeneous elongation along the fold axis or in the axial plane normal to the fold axis and bulk homogeneous shortening normal to the axial plane.

2. Thickening of individual layers, regardless of the mechanism concerned, can be expressed in terms of homogeneous strain superposed on

[29] E.g., E. B. Knopf and E. Ingerson, Structural petrology, *Geol. Soc. America Mem. 6*, p. 61, 1938.

buckling (Fig. 13-13).[30] Concentric flexure gliding (cf. Fig. 13-11b) transforms the layer of diagram a in Fig. 13-13 to the folded configuration of diagram b (a circular arc). The result of an additional plane homogeneous strain—50 per cent shortening normal to the axial plane—is shown in diagram c, where thickening in the hinge is reminiscent of similar folding.

3. Flexural-slip folding deforms a passive lineation L so that it conforms to a small circle (around B) on the projection. Addition of a general homogeneous strain changes the angle $L \wedge B$ to different values in different parts of the fold, so that the locus of L on the projection is now intermediate between the small circle characteristic of flexural-slip and the great circle diagnostic of slip folding. Superposition of slip upon flexural-slip folding would produce the same effect.[31]

Homogeneous Component of Slip Folding. The presence of a homogeneous component of strain in no way affects the principal geometric property of slip folds—namely, the fact that at all stages they are similar folds. The only obvious effect of the homogeneous component is shortening and elongation of dimensional markers in directions within the axial plane, which in a pure slip fold is a plane of no distortion.

Diagrammatic examples are illustrated in Fig. 13-14. The passive s-plane S_1 of diagram a is shown in diagram b as a slip fold resulting from slip in S_2 parallel to the a kinematic axis. The other two diagrams show the same fold combined with a homogeneous strain: elongation parallel to a and shortening normal to ab in Fig. 13-14c, elongation parallel to b and shortening normal to ab in Fig. 13-14d. The geometric effects correspond to a pure affine transformation (pages 391 to 395) as follows:

1. Internal rotation of S_1 causes the folds to become more appressed; but they remain plane cylindrical.

2. The fold axis, like any other linear marker, rotates toward the axis of extension.

3. The plane containing various attitudes of any bent passive lineation L rotates toward the AB section of the strain ellipsoid.[32] This plane still contains the a kinematic axis, but no longer contains the original attitude of L prior to folding. As seen in a projection upon the axial plane of the fold the plotted attitudes of L therefore fall on a great circle passing through a.[33]

---

[30] J. G. Ramsay, The effects of folding upon the orientation of sedimentary structures, *Jour. Geology*, vol. 69, p. 96, fig. 14, 1961. See also Carey, *op cit.*, p. 91, fig. 15; L. U. De Sitter, Boudins and parasitic folds in relation to cleavage and folding, *Geologie en Mijnbouw*, 20 Jaar., pp. 282–285, 1958.

[31] Ramsay, *op. cit.*, pp. 91–92, 1960.

[32] Weiss, *op. cit.*, pp. 104, 105.

[33] Flinn has recently expressed a different view and has criticized Ramsay's account (*op. cit.*, pp. 86–91, 1960) of rotation of lineation during similar folding. Ramsay's

Symmetry of Movement in Plane Cylindrical Folding. The movement picture of folding can be regarded as compounded of a heterogeneous and a homogeneous movement picture corresponding to the heterogeneous and homogeneous components of strain. The symmetry of the heterogeneous movement picture of simple folding may be either orthorhombic C_{2v} (for symmetric folding) or monoclinic C_{1h} (for asymmetric folding).[34] That of the homogeneous component cannot be lower than orthorhombic D_{2h}.

The symmetry of flexural-slip folding is not affected by addition of the homogeneous component of deformation, provided the latter is symmetrically oriented with reference to the fold. This is the situation that appears to be reflected in the fabric (including mineral orientation patterns) of homoaxial flexural-slip folds. If the symmetry planes of the homogeneous component of strain are inclined to those of the fold the symmetry of both the movement picture and the fabric becomes triclinic, and the folds heteroaxial.

Except for a special case ($B = b$, Fig. 13-9), the respective symmetry elements of the movement picture and the folded s-surface of a slip fold do not coincide. Slip folds, then, are generally heteroaxial. Since a slip fold reflects completely passive behavior of the folded s-surface, the initial body must commonly approximate a mechanically isotropic state. It is then likely that the homogeneous and inhomogeneous components of the movement picture—and hence all imposed elements of the fabric—share symmetry elements in common. It is these imposed elements of the fabric—the axial plane and the mineral orientation patterns—rather than the more conspicuous inherited elements (notably the folded s-surface), that yield information regarding symmetry of the movement picture.

In the above treatment of movements in folding there is nothing to distinguish strictly synchronous operation of both components of movement from the case in which one component succeeds the other under the influence of a single stress system. In some flexural-slip folds there is evidence suggesting that the heterogeneous component of pure folding was followed by symmetrically related homogeneous strain in the later stages of deformation. This could account for the uniform homogeneous

---

views are much as expressed above. Flinn's conclusions cannot be applied to a slip fold by reason of two of his premises: (1) his model is one of buckle folding in a rheologically heterogeneous layered body, whereas our conclusions apply to slip folding in a rheologically homogeneous body; (2) Flinn's plane of projection is the AB plane of the ellipsoid of mean strain in a homogeneous system of folds, whereas the movement paths described above are plotted on the plane of no distortion (the axial plane) common to a series of differently oriented strain ellipsoids in a heterogeneous body— a single fold.

[34] The individual fold lacks a center of symmetry.

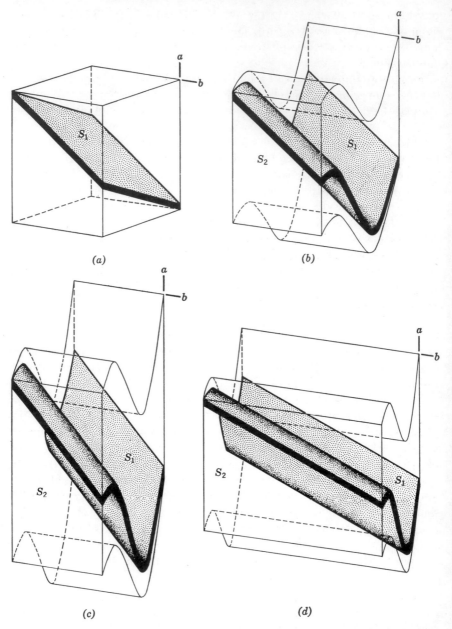

Fig. 13-14. Internal rotation of fold axes by homogeneous component of folding. (a) Undeformed body with passive surface S_1. (b) Slip folding of S_1 with S_2 as glide surface for the general case B oblique to b. (c) Addition of a plane homogeneous pure strain consisting of elongation in a and shortening normal to ab. Fold axis rotates toward a. (d) Addition of a plane homogeneous pure strain consisting of elongation in b and shortening normal to ab. Fold axis rotates toward b.

preferred orientation of quartz or calcite commonly observed in all domains of a homoaxial flexural-slip fold.[35] The mineral subfabric would then reflect recrystallization during the late phase of homogeneous deformation.[36]

Structural Indicators of the Folding Mechanism. *Axial-plane Foliation.* Some general kinematic inferences regarding the mechanism of folding of s-surfaces S_1 may be drawn from axial-plane foliation S_2.

1. The presence of axial-plane foliation precludes simple flexural-slip folding as the sole mechanism. It seems probable, however, that the folds are commonly located in the first instance by flexural slip on S_1 and that the folded surfaces have remained kinematically active during later development of S_2 by flow or slip. There is also the possibility that many folds with axial-plane cleavage are slip or flow folds in which S_1 has been passive throughout deformation.

2. Because axial-plane foliation is an imposed structure it generally reflects the properties of deformation more directly than does the folded surface itself. This is particularly true of slip folds. Here although the fold axis has little kinematic significance the axial plane is directly related to the symmetry of the movement picture.

3. "Refraction" of axial-plane foliation S_2 across the boundaries of lithologically distinct folded layers S_1 reflects differential rheologic properties of the rocks concerned. Where the texture and hence properties change gradationally within a layer, the attitude of S_2 may be correspondingly curved rather than sharply deflected.

4. Where axial-plane cleavages are acutely intersecting conjugate surfaces, or are dispersed in a fan rather than strictly parallel to the axial plane, the structure generally has the same point-group symmetry as that of the fold in S_1. This emphasizes the genetic relation between cleavage and folding.

Lineation.[37] The relation of inherited passive lineations to folding has already been discussed (pages 478 to 486). Most folds also have imposed lineations that are active elements in the tectonite fabric, and so reflect properties of the movement picture and of the geometry of strain.

1. Crenulation lineation is a very common structure, especially in micaceous rocks and phyllonites. It is defined by minute folding of an early s-surface S_1 and simultaneous development of an axial-plane folia-

[35] Sander (*op. cit.*, pp. 258–262, 1930) classes these, along with slip folds, as "non-unrollable folds," because unrolling of the layers into a plane does not restore a homogeneous microscopic fabric.

[36] E.g., J. M. Christie and C. B. Raleigh, The origin of deformation lamellae in quartz, *Am. Jour. Sci.*, vol. 257, pp. 398, 399, 1959.

[37] For details of the relations observed between lineations and folds in the metamorphic rocks of the Scottish Highlands, see P. Clifford, M. S. Fleuty, J. G. Ramsay, J. Sutton, and J. Watson, The development of lineation in complex fold systems, *Geol. Mag.*, vol. 94, pp. 1–24, 1957.

tion S_2. So the crenulation lineation has the properties of a microfold axis $B_{S_1}{}^{S_2}$. All stages are possible, from crenulation of S_1 with incipient development of S_2, to complete transposition of S_1 into S_2 which is then the dominant foliation. Kinematically crenulation has been interpreted in two different ways corresponding to distinct and perhaps equally common movement pictures. In the one, flexural slip on S_1 is accompanied and outlasted by slip on S_2, which becomes increasingly prominent until S_1 ultimately survives merely as hinges of minute folds in the laminae (microlithons) between adjacent S_2 transposition surfaces.[38] The lineation here defines the b kinematic axis of a monoclinic deformation. The second movement picture involves slip on discrete S_2 surfaces with synchronous progressive crenulation of S_1 in the intervening microlithons (pages 465 to 467).[39] Here the kinematic significance of the lineation is ambiguous, for the mechanism of crenulation is not known. Where crenulation lineation maintains a constant attitude over areas of many square miles and is even the dominant element of a monoclinic tectonite fabric, as in parts of southern New Zealand,[40] it may be identified with confidence as the b kinematic axis.

2. Lineation defined by intersecting s-surfaces has varied kinematic implications. Where both s-surfaces are active, as where an axial-plane foliation intersects an earlier s-surface folded by flexural slip, the lineation is kinematically significant: e.g., it is commonly normal to a symmetry plane of an orthorhombic or a monoclinic fabric, and in the latter case defines the b axis of the movement picture. Where the folded s-surface is passive, as in bedding-cleavage intersections in many slates, the lineation is not certainly related to the symmetry of the movement picture.

3. Lineations defined by elongated or stretched markers or by dimensional alignment of xenoblastic mineral grains (notably of quartz) commonly present evidence of strain incompatible with simple models of plane deformation by flexural-slip folding or by slip folding.

SUPERPOSED FOLDING

General. Nonplane and noncylindrical folds can form either as a result of a single completely heterogeneous deformation, or by superposition of later folding upon the s-surfaces of an earlier plane cylindrical fold. With regard to the first possibility the buckling and flexural-glide

[38] B. Sander, Über Zusammenhänge zwischen Teilbewegung und Gefüge in Gesteinen, *Tschermaks Mineralog. Petrog. Mitt.*, vol. 33, pp. 305–307, 1911; Knopf and Ingerson, *op. cit.*, pp. 189–191.

[39] R. Hoeppener, *op. cit.*, pp. 272–279, 1956; De Sitter, *op. cit.*, p. 217, 1956.

[40] E.g., F. J. Turner, "Gefügerelief" illustrated by "schist tor" topography in Central Otago, New Zealand, *Am. Jour. Sci.*, vol. 250, pp. 802–807 (especially pl. 1), 1952.

components of flexural-slip folding can be nonplane, and the resulting fold will then also be nonplane. Again if the rate of flow of individual laminae varies from place to place in slip folding of a passive s-plane, the result will be a noncylindrical fold. Irregular folds can form, too, in a single deformation by flow ("rheid") folding,[41] conjugate folding,[42] or en échelon folding.[43]

With this reservation in mind we turn to the second possibility—superposed folding. Indeed the various kinds of natural complex folds whose ideal geometric properties were described in Chap. 4 may be explained in terms of different simple models of superposed flexural-slip folding and slip folding. From this fact and from demonstrable differences in age and symmetry of associated fold elements it cannot be doubted that many of the less regular folds found in tectonites are products of superposed folding.

In the discussion of superposed folding and accompanying ideal projections (Figs. 13-15 to 13-17) let the structural elements of the superposed folds be as follows:

S_1: folded surface.

S_2: axial surface of the first generation of folds in S_1, assumed to be marked by a visible foliation. In slip folding S_2 is the glide surface.

S_3: axial surface of the second generation of folds.

$B_{S_1}{}^{S_2}$: axis of the first generation of folds in S_1.

$B_{S_1}{}^{S_3}$: axis of the second generation of folds in S_1.

$B_{S_2}{}^{S_3}$: axis of second-generation folds in S_2.

L_1: lineation in S_1 prior to first folding.

L_2: lineation parallel to $B_{S_1}{}^{S_2}$.

a', b', c': kinematic axes of first folding.

a'', b'', c'': kinematic axes of second folding.

Folding by Flexural Slip in the Second Generation. *General.* Since in flexural-slip folding the b kinematic axis (fold axis) must lie in the folded surface, a rectilinear axis of bend gliding $B_{S_1}{}^{S_3}$ in the second deformation can develop only in a planar segment, e.g., a limb, of the first fold.[44] Consequently within the domain of a single early fold the various local attitudes of the glide direction a (normal to b in S_1) cannot, except in special cases, be coplanar, so that in general the second fold is necessarily nonplane. Departure from the plane condition is minimized, and the second-generation folds in consequence are effectively plane

---

[41] Carey, *op. cit.*, pp. 91–98.

[42] E.g., M. R. W. Johnson, Conjugate fold systems in the Moine thrust zone in the Loch Carron and Coulin Forest areas of Wester Ross, *Geol. Mag.*, vol. 93, pp. 345–350, 1956; R. Hoeppener, Vorläufige Mitteilung über ein genetisches System tektonischer Gefügetypen, *Neues Jahrb. Paläontologie Monatsh.*, vol. 8, p. 354, fig. 1, 1959.

[43] J. D. Campbell, En échelon folding, *Econ. Geology*, vol. 53, pp. 448–472, 1958.

[44] Weiss, *op. cit.*, p. 98.

noncylindrical, where the local attitudes of $B_{S_1}{}^{S_3}$ are approximately coplanar.

Case 1: Flexural-slip Followed by Flexural-slip Folding. The general geometric properties of superposed folding involving buckling and flexural slip in both generations are still imperfectly defined. To analyze the process it is necessary to make simplifying assumptions which both prediction and experiment suggest to be by no means universally valid.[45] It is necessary, too, to ignore local heterogeneities that must appear in hinges of folds of both generations. However, such analysis of simplified or special cases is valuable, not for presenting a comprehensive true picture of superposed folding in tectonites, but because it shows the limitations of the kinematic inferences that may be drawn from the observed geometric properties of superposed folds. In particular it eliminates naïve interpretation of such structures in terms of mutually perpendicular rectilinear "axes," and shows what geometric operations are permissible in the "unrolling" of structures such as lineations distorted by repeated flexural-slip folding.

The simplifying assumption on which the following discussion is based is that the second-generation folds are plane noncylindrical. This permits comparison with Case 3 in which flexural-slip folding is followed by slip folding.

A special and perhaps important case is that of coaxially refolded folds (Fig. 13-15).[46] Here the fold axes of both generations, $B_{S_1}{}^{S_2}$ and $B_{S_1}{}^{S_3}$, and the corresponding kinematic axes b' and b'' all coincide. Diagrams a and b in Fig. 13-15 show attitudes of S_1, S_2, and L and local kinematic axes a' and a'' after the first and the second deformation, respectively. S_2 is affected by the second folding, so that within the figured domain as a whole the fold remains cylindrical but is nonplane (Fig. 13-15c). The early lineation L_1, bent on a small circle around $B_{S_1}{}^{S_2}$ in the first episode, is further dispersed on the same small circle by the second folding.

In the more general case (Fig. 13-16) the late fold axes $B_{S_1}{}^{S_3}$ (thus the local kinematic axes b'') are distributed in the axial plane S_3 of late folding.[47] Figure 13-16a shows the attitudes of the earliest structures S_1 and L_1 in a single fold of the first generation. Also shown are S_3 and local attitudes of b'' as they will appear during the second folding. In the

[45] Cf. Ramberg, *op. cit.*, pp. 124–127, 1959.

[46] E.g., Sander, *op. cit.*, p. 146, fig. 49, 1948; Clifford, Fleuty, Ramsay, Sutton, and Watson, *op. cit.*, pp. 8–11; R. R. Reid, Reconnaissance geology of the Elk City region, Idaho, *Idaho Bur. Mines and Geology Pamph. 120*, pp. 40–41, 1959.

[47] This is a geometric stipulation without any dynamic implications of the kind put forward by L. E. Weiss and D. B. McIntyre (Structural geometry of Dalradian rocks at Loch Leven, Scottish Highlands, *Jour. Geology*, vol. 65, p. 597, 1957) and criticized by Flinn (unpublished manuscript; abstract in *Geol. Soc. London Circ. 94*, November, 1961).

complexly folded structure resulting from the second folding, three local domains of cylindrical folding of S_1, respectively designated I, II, and III, have been selected for individual analysis.   Figure 13-16b, c, and d illustrates the transformations of S_1, L_1, and L_2 ($= B_{S_1}{}^{S_2}$) in the three domains.   In each, S_1 becomes cylindrically folded about the local b''

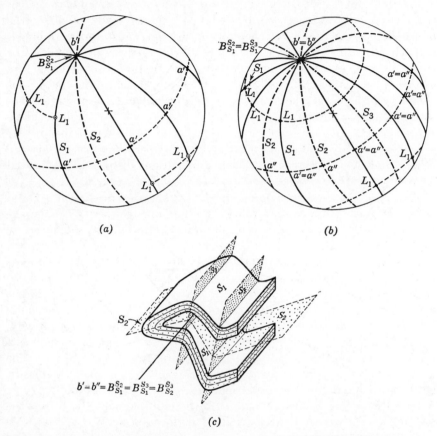

(a)   (b)

(c)

Fig. 13-15. Coaxial superposition of flexural-slip folds (explanation in text).   Segments of S_1 shown in projection as full arcs.   (a) First-generation folding of S_1 and rotation of lineation L_1.   (b) and (c) Second-generation folding of S_1 and S_2.

axis.   Both S_1 and S_2 cannot be simultaneously folded by flexural slip: S_2 is folded by some other mechanism (see, for example, Fig. 13-6).   The linear markers L_1 and L_2 (initial positions shown by double-circled points) come to lie on small circles of the projection centered on the local b'' axis.

A synoptic diagram for S_1 (Fig. 13-16e) shows that for the body as a whole S_1 is no longer cylindrically folded (cf. Fig. 4-37).   And in the synoptic diagram for L_1 and L_2 (Fig. 13-16f), L_1 (crosses) is scattered irregularly because in each domain a local rotation axis is coupled with

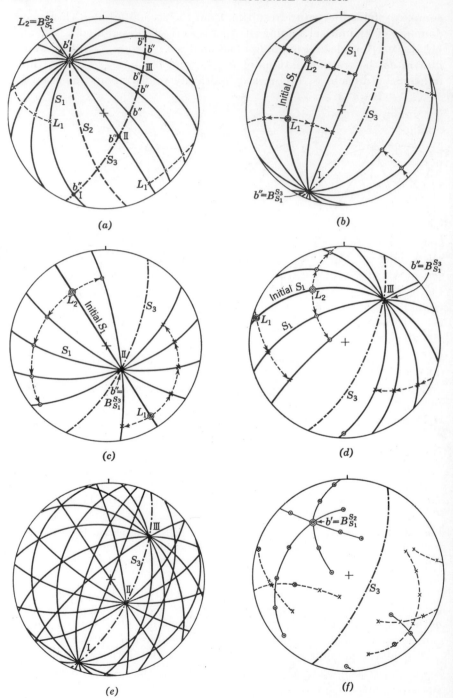

Fig. 13-16. General case of superposed flexural-slip folds (explanation in text). Segments of S_1 shown as full arcs.

a unique initial orientation of L_1 (circled cross). On the other hand, L_2 (circled dots) lies on a series of small circle girdles that have a common intersection (double circle) representing the constant preferred orientation of L_2 prior to the second folding $(B_{S_1}{}^{S_2})$. Implications regarding "unrolling" of flexural slip folds are discussed later (pages 516 to 520).

Where second-generation folds are on such a small scale as to constitute a crenulation lineation L_3 $(= B_{S_1}{}^{S_3})$, this still falls on a great circle S_3 oblique to the axis of early major folding $B_{S_1}{}^{S_2}$ (cf. Fig. 4-30). But the cylindrical gross form of the first-generation fold and hence its axis $B_{S_1}{}^{S_2}$ is still clearly preserved.

Case 2: Slip Folding Followed by Flexural-slip Folding. Once a set of s-surfaces S_1 has behaved passively in early slip folding it is unlikely to assume an active role in subsequent folding. Case 2 therefore has no practical significance. However, the axial-plane foliation S_2 of the first generation of folds commonly becomes folded by later flexural slip—necessarily on S_2 (cf. Fig. 13-6). The resulting plane cylindrical folds in S_2 are accompanied by nonplane noncylindrical folds in the passive S_1 (see also Fig. 5-30).

Folding by Slip in the Second Generation. *General.* The ideal conditions assumed in the following discussion are (1) that the s-surfaces S_1 already folded about $B_{S_1}{}^{S_2}$ behave passively in the second folding about $B_{S_1}{}^{S_3}$; (2) that the glide plane S_3 is strictly planar and uniformly oriented throughout the domain of a single fold of the first generation. It follows that in such a domain, although the folds of the second generation have variously oriented axes $B_{S_1}{}^{S_3}$, the axial plane (glide plane) and the kinematic axes a, b, and c maintain constant orientations. Folds of the second generation are plane noncylindrical.

Case 3: Flexural-slip Followed by Slip Folding. Figure 13-17 illustrates the general case where S_3 is oblique to the axis $B_{S_1}{}^{S_2}$ of the first generation of folds. To contrast the effects of slip with those of flexural slip in the second episode, the form of the initial fold and the angle $B_{S_1}{}^{S_2} \wedge S_3$ (Fig. 13-17a) are the same as in the previous case (Fig. 13-16a). In any three selected domains, I, II, and III, for which S_1 is planar in the first fold, the respective axes $B_{S_1}{}^{S_3}$ of the second folding are the intersections of S_3 with the local plane of S_1. Figure 13-17b, c, and d shows the following effects of slip folding about $B_{S_1}{}^{S_3}$ in each of these domains:

1. Except for special orientations of S_1 (cf. Figs. 13-9 and 13-10), S_1 becomes cylindrically folded about an axis $B_{S_1}{}^{S_3}$ oblique to the kinematic axis b''.

2. S_2 likewise becomes cylindrically folded about an axis $B_{S_2}{}^{S_3}$ oblique to both $B_{S_1}{}^{S_3}$ and b'' and uniformly oriented throughout the whole body.

3. L_1 (shown as crosses) is bent to lie in a plane containing its initial orientation (double-circled cross) and the kinematic axis a'' (cf. Fig. 13-12b). L_2 (circled dots) likewise is bent along a great circle from its initial orientation (double-circled dot) toward a''.

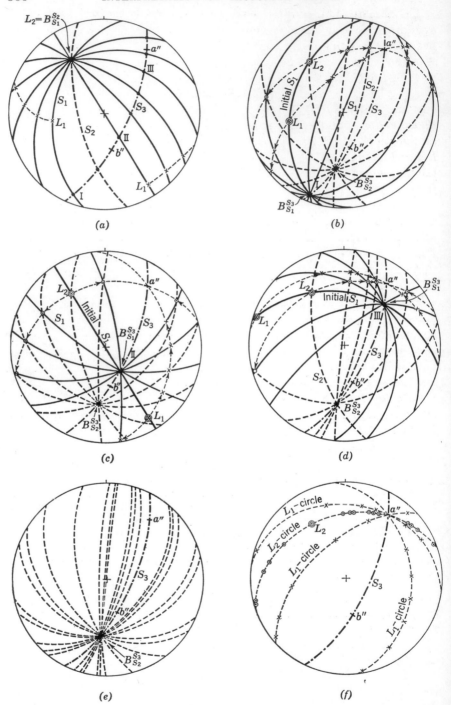

FIG. 13-17. General case of superposition of slip folds on flexural-slip folds (explanation in text).   Segments of S_1 shown as full arcs.

The domains I, II, and III have been selected so that the form of the cylindrical fold in each is identical with that formed by superposed flexural-slip folding in the corresponding domain of Fig. 13-16b, c, and d. A synoptic diagram for S_1, combining Fig. 13-17b, c, and d, would therefore be identical with Fig. 13-16e. However, the character of the synoptic diagram for S_2 (Fig. 13-17e) is peculiar to slip folding: throughout the domain of the complete first-generation fold S_2 is cylindrically folded about a unique $B_{S_2}{}^{S_3}$ axis. In the synoptic diagram for L_1 and L_2, all lineations lie on great circles passing through a'' (Fig. 13-17f). The L_2 circle is unique,[48] but there is a separate L_1 circle for each domain of the first-generation fold. The b'' axis is a unique direction located at 90° from a'' within the axial plane S_3 of second-generation folds.

In many complexly folded tectonites lineations have been found to approximate great-circle girdles corresponding to the ideal examples figured in Figs. 4-31, 4-32, and 4-37, and kinematically explained in Fig. 13-17. Other structural features, too, accord well with interpretation of these tectonites in terms of slip folding in the final episode of deformation.[49]

The linear structures L_1 and L_2 could be axes of early formed small folds or even, on a very small scale, β axes. Survival of such structures depends on the relative sizes of the earlier and the later folds.[50] In the geometric analysis of superposed folds in Figs. 4-36, 4-37, and 5-23 to 5-25, it was assumed that in certain domains within the twice-folded body remnants of cylindrical folds of the first generation survive.

Case 4: Slip Folding Followed by Slip Folding. This differs from Case 3 only with regard to the orientation of L_1 after the first episode of folding. L_1 would then be dispersed in a great circle through a'—instead of in a small circle around $B_{S_1}{}^{S_2}$ as in Fig. 13-17a.

---

[48] Weiss, *op. cit.*, pp. 100–102.

[49] E.g., Ramsay, *op. cit.*, pp. 92–93, 1960; A. Baird, *op. cit.*, pp. 40–44. M. Best, Petrology and structural analysis of metamorphic rocks in the Southwestern Sierra Nevada Foothills, *Univ. California Geol. Sci. Pub.* (in press).

[50] Weiss (*op. cit.*, p. 98) in an analysis of internal rotation of old linear structures refers specifically to "rotation of early formed B structures (in particular lineations and small folds)." Included here are small-scale β axes; but excluded are β axes of early folds that are large compared with superposed slip folds. It is these large early folds that become noncylindrical by late slip folding of their limbs with consequent dispersion of their β axes (*ibid.*, pp. 100–102). These views have been misunderstood in a subsequent paper by M. Lindström (On the significance of β intersections in superposed deformation fabrics, *Geol. Mag.*, vol. 98, pp. 33–40, 1961).

CHAPTER 14

FOLDING IN TECTONITES: INTERPRETATION
OF FOLD SYSTEMS

THE GENERAL PROBLEM

For practical purposes a fold system need be defined only for a large body folded on a relatively small scale. In terms of folding such macroscopic tectonite bodies are of two kinds (cf. pages 147 to 151):

1. Heterogeneous bodies in which the patterns of preferred orientation of geometric elements of mesoscopic folds in all representative samples are not identical. Most arbitrarily outlined tectonite bodies are of this kind, because the number of large macroscopic folds is small. On the limbs of such large folds there are generally domains in which the structure is homogeneous.

2. Homogeneous bodies in which the patterns of preferred orientation of geometric elements of mesoscopic folds in all representative samples are the same. Bodies and domains of this kind possess macroscopic fabrics some of the elements of which are the geometric elements of the small folds.

In this chapter fold systems of both kinds are considered in terms of the correlated movement picture and bulk strain. The mechanism of folding, and hence the details of the movement picture of a fold system, are likely to be complex. In a given system it commonly varies from one domain to another (e.g., buckling in some layers, slip in others), and also from time to time in a single deformation (e.g., buckling in the early stages followed by later slip or flow). Many fold systems, moreover, are products of superposed episodes of folding. In spite of the variability of the folding mechanism, however, some idea of the local strains and discontinuities that make up the movement picture may be inferred from the nature of the geometric transformation of the s-surfaces into their present configuration from an initial attitude assumed to be planar and, in the case of bedding, horizontal.

KINEMATIC PROPERTIES OF FOLD SYSTEMS

Plane Cylindrical Fold Systems. *General Properties.* Figure 14-1 illustrates the general properties of homogeneous plane cylindrical fold

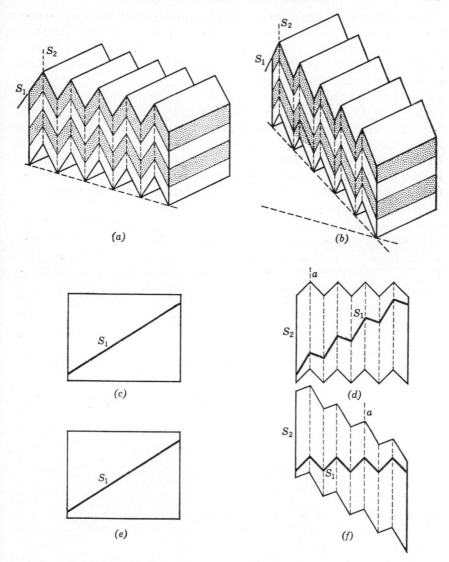

FIG. 14-1. Shear domains in idealized plane cylindrical folds. (a) Symmetric folds. (b) Asymmetric folds. (c) and (d) Asymmetric folds in passive surface S_1 formed by symmetric movement picture. (e) and (f) Symmetric folds in passive surface formed by asymmetric movement picture.

systems (in S_1) of two ideal kinds—symmetric and asymmetric. Both consist of two sets of periodically alternating shear domains bounded by parallel planes S_2. In symmetric folds (Fig. 14-1a) alternating domains are mirror images of each other, whereas in asymmetric folds (Fig. 14-1b) they differ in their strain properties (cf. Fig. 10-3e).

In a system of flexural-slip folds this symmetry or asymmetry reflects symmetry of the movement picture—orthorhombic D_{2h} for Fig. 14-1a, monoclinic C_{2h} for Fig. 14-1b. This is not true however for a system of slip folds (cf. pages 482 to 486). For example Fig. 14-1c and d shows asymmetric folding of a passive marker S_1 by a transformation (gliding on S_2 parallel to a) for which the movement picture has orthorhombic symmetry. Conversely in Fig. 14-1e and f, the fold system is symmetric, but the corresponding movement picture (gliding on S_2 parallel to a) has monoclinic symmetry. In slip folds, moreover, the glide axis b can be inclined to the fold axis B (cf. Fig. 13-11). The symmetry of slip folding can be inferred only from that of synchronously developed preferred orientation patterns of minerals such as quartz (page 489).

Illustrative Examples. In the Turoka area of Kenya,[1] gneisses, quartzites, and marbles have a common foliation S_1 mesoscopically folded in gently plunging reclined plane cylindrical folds with appressed limbs. These folds are dominantly though not universally symmetric (Fig. 14-2a). Their plane cylindrical character throughout a domain of 40 square miles is demonstrated by collective diagrams for poles of S_1 (Fig. 14-2b) and for small fold axes and lineations (Fig. 14-2c). The three planes of symmetry (m) shared by both diagrams are present also in a collective diagram for 2,800 [0001] axes of quartz grains measured in 12 widely scattered specimens (Fig. 14-2d). The domain is thus homogeneous and homotactic and has orthorhombic symmetry. This agreement between all measured subfabrics indicates that folding was dominantly by flexural slip, so that the symmetry of the fabric reflects that of the movement picture.

Later investigation of a much larger area[2] shows that the Turoka area is a locally homogeneous domain within a much larger totally heterogeneous body of tectonites. The symmetric reclined folds of Turoka appear to be superposed upon planar (either homoclinal or isoclinal) limbs of larger earlier folds[3]—a situation common in metamorphic terranes with long and complicated tectonic histories.

Another instance of a homogeneous domain of plane cylindrical folds within a larger heterogeneous body was described by McIntyre from Tomintoul in the Scottish Highlands.[4] The mesoscopic features of the area closely resemble those of Turoka, except that on this scale the folds appear to be consistently asymmetric as shown by a constant orientation

[1] L. E. Weiss, Structural analysis of the basement system at Turoka, Kenya, *Overseas Geology and Mineral Resources*, vol. 7, nos. 1, 2, pp. 3–35, 123–153, 1959.

[2] E. P. Saggerson, P. Joubert, G. H. H. McCall, and L. A. J. Williams, Cross-folding and refolding in the Basement System of Kenya Colony, *21st Internat. Geol. Cong. Rept.* (1960), pt. 18, pp. 335–346, 1960.

[3] *Ibid.*, p. 344.

[4] D. B. McIntyre, The tectonics of the area between Grantown and Tomintoul (mid-Strathspey), *Geol. Soc. London Quart. Jour.*, vol. 107, pp. 1–22, 1951.

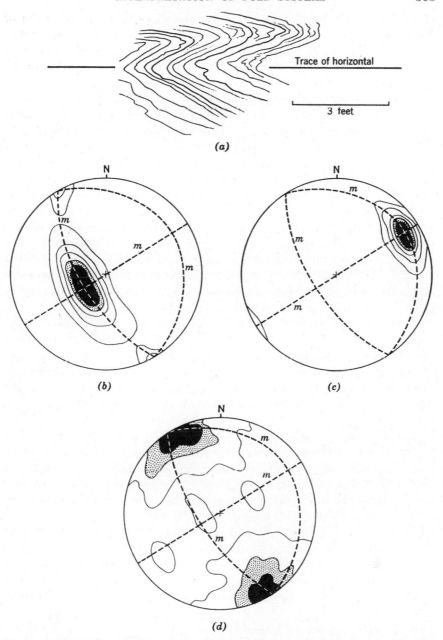

Fig. 14-2. Structural data from Turoka in Kenya. (*After L. E. Weiss.*) (*a*) Profile of gently plunging reclined fold. (*b–d*) Projections on geographic horizontal plane (*N* = north). Planes of symmetry, *m*. (*b*) 1,000 poles to foliation S_1. Contours, 9%, 7%, 5%, 3%, 1%, per 1% area. (*c*) 800 lineations and axes of small folds. Contours, 20%, 15%, 10%, 5%, 1%, per 1% area. (*d*) 2,800 [0001] of quartz (synoptic). Contours, 9%, 6%, 3%, per 1% area.

of axial planes oblique to the enveloping surface.[5] The mechanism of folding cannot certainly be inferred from the published data, so that the true nature of the movement picture is in doubt. However, it is probably homogeneous, and the axial plane of the fold system must be kinematically significant.

Nonplane Cylindrical Fold Systems. *General Properties.* Systems of nonplane cylindrical folds can form either as a result of a single deformation or by superposed folding. In both cases the poles of the axial planes fall close to a great-circle girdle, the normal to which is the fold axis of the system.

Folding in a Single Deformation. Some systems of convolute folds have a whorled but axially symmetric form suggesting a movement picture characterized by "turbulence" or eddy-like differential rolling motion about a constant symmetry axis. The movement picture has been compared to the rolling of dough and has been widely invoked on a smaller scale to explain monoclinic orientation patterns of quartz and other minerals, and the presence of rolled porphyroblasts with a common rotation axis and rotation sense. Within a large domain the movement picture of folding is homogeneous if the distribution of local "eddies" is statistically homogeneous and the "eddy axes" maintain a statistically constant attitude. The state of flow in the tectonite on a large scale then has analogies with shearing flow of a liquid on a smaller scale. The symmetry of movement is monoclinic. There is a single plane of symmetry normal to the axis of rolling (fold axis), even though—as in the familiar example of rolled dough—this is also an axis of elongation.

In other systems of nonplane cylindrical folds there is no evidence of a uniform sense of overall rotation. Such are the polyclinal folds of Fig. 4-23b. They have been correlated with strain involving elongation parallel to the fold axis and shortening in all directions normal to it. Sander[6] has termed this process *Einengung* and the resulting fold structures *Schlingen*. The movement picture has axial symmetry tending to monoclinic, the principal symmetry plane being normal to the fold axis.

There is yet a third pattern, in which the mesoscopic folds are conjugate[7] or else are plane cylindrical folds whose axial planes maintain a fan-like pattern within a large domain. Penetrative conjugate folding can represent a movement picture of high symmetry. Orientation diagrams for the folded S_1, the axial planes S_2, and the fold axes $B_{S_1}{}^{S_2}$ can be

[5] *Ibid.*, pp. 6, 7, figs. 4, 5.

[6] B. Sander, *Einführung in die Gefügekunde der Geologischen Körper*, I, p. 68, Springer, Berlin, Vienna, 1948; L. E. Weiss, A study in tectonic style, *Univ. California Geol. Sci. Pub.*, vol. 30, pp. 39–43, 1954.

[7] M. R. W. Johnson, Conjugate fold systems in the Moine Thrust zone in the Loch Carron and Coulin Forest area of Wester Ross, *Geol. Mag.*, vol. 93, pp. 345–350, 1956; R. Hoeppener, Vorläufige Mitteilung über ein genetisches System tektonischer Gefügetypen, *Neues Jahrb. Paläontologie Monatsh.*, vol. 8, pp. 353–361, 1959.

identical with those for a totally different type of fold system resulting from coaxial superposed folding of S_1 (cf. Fig. 14-3).

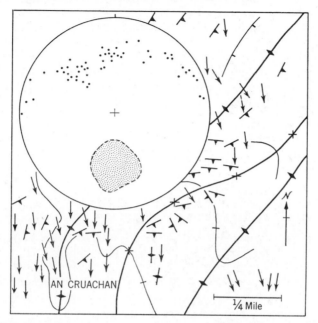

FIG. 14-3. Cylindrical folding of axial planes and axial-plane foliation of small folds in the Scottish Highlands. (*After J. G. Ramsay.*) Short lines, axial planes of minor folds and axial-plane foliation; arrows, axes of minor folds; thin lines, generalized strike lines; heavy lines, traces of axial surfaces at large folds. Inset is projection of poles to axial-plane structures (dots) and area (stippled) in which associated linear structures fall.

Superposed Folding. Systems of nonplane cylindrical folds resulting from coaxial refolding have been described from the Scottish Highlands. Thus in the Loch Fannich area,[8]

The formation of involutions due to the continuation of folding on the original axis directions after the first formed structures had become more or less isoclinal, is to be seen on a small scale in several localities. The same process, acting on a larger scale, has led in some places (for example, in the ground south of the eastern end of Loch Fannich) to the flexing of the axial plane of a major fold, and in others (for example, south-west of Loch Monar) to a dispersion of the strikes of minor axial plane structures. Since the refolding takes place about the original axes, the lineation-patterns may remain quite simple and may, therefore, be inadequate as guides to the major structures.

An example from the same publication is reproduced in Fig. 14-3. On the sketch map the strikes of axial planes of small folds and accompanying

[8] P. Clifford, M. J. Fleuty, J. G. Ramsay, J. Sutton, and J. Watson, The development of lineation in complex fold systems, *Geol. Mag.*, vol. 94, pp. 8–10, 1957.

axial-plane foliations vary over a small area.   But on a projection (inset) the poles to axial-plane foliation lie in a great-circle girdle centered on the common fold axis.

Many such nonplane cylindrical folds can be treated as products of coaxial repeated folding: a plane cylindrical system is superposed upon a nonplane (initially plane) cylindrical system with the fold axis in common (cf. Fig. 13-15).   Where folding in both phases is by flexural slip the symmetry of the movement picture is monoclinic, with a plane of symmetry normal to the fold axis.   If the system is homogeneous in all respects the symmetry is C_{2h}; if it is heterogeneous the symmetry remains monoclinic but becomes C_{1h}.   This is the most likely natural situation, because an initially active surface is likely to remain an active anisotropy during a second deformation and so to guide the form of the folds.   If, however, the second deformation is by slip folding the movement picture will generally be more independent of the form of the folded surface.

Noncylindrical Fold Systems.   *Folding in a Single Deformation.*   In many geologic bodies noncylindrical (both plane and nonplane) fold systems seem to have formed in a single complex deformation.   Such systems are usually composed of individual folds of canoe or basin shape— therefore of limited axial extent.   The arrangement may be apparently patternless, indicating a very low degree of correlation between movement pictures in different parts of a body; or there may be a well-defined systematic arrangement such as a broad arc (as in the Jura mountains) or an angular curve such as a *syntaxis* or a *virgation*.[9]   The folds of a system may be arranged en échelon and may be spatially related to, and hence probably genetically connected with, other structures such as larger folds,[10] major movement horizons, or strike-slip faults.   Segments of the individual folds commonly are conical in form.[11]

The movement picture may be heterogeneous on all scales, as in the examples mentioned above.   Or alternatively the movement picture may be homogeneous but nonplane.   Some idea of the nature of a homogeneous movement picture of noncylindrical folding may be obtained by considering an ideal example in which interfering homogeneous fold systems develop simultaneously in a single domain.   Figure 14-4 illustrates simultaneous formation of two systems of plane folds by tangential shortening of layers in two mutually perpendicular directions.   The mechanism of folding is not specified.   In Fig. 14-4*a* the two systems differ with regard

---

[9] E.g., D. N. Wadia, The syntaxis of the north-western Himalaya: its rocks, tectonics and orogeny, *Geol. Survey India Recs.*, pt. 2, pp. 190–220, 1931; S. W. Carey, The orocline concept in geotectonics, part I, *Royal Soc. Tasmania Papers and Proc.*, vol. 89, pp. 255–288, 1955.

[10] J. D. Campbell, En échelon folding, *Econ. Geology*, vol. 53, pp. 448–472, 1958.

[11] E.g., P. J. Hamann, Manual of stereographic projection for a geometric and kinematic analysis of folds and faults, *West Canadian Research Pubs.*, pp. 32–36, 1961.

to the size of the individual folds but share common symmetry planes (*m*). Ideally the system consists of homogeneous shear domains separated by planar strain discontinuities. The symmetry of their arrangement is orthorhombic and this is a possible symmetry, too, for the movement picture. In Fig. 14-4*b* the size of folds in the two systems is approximately the same. Because the arrangement of shear domains is periodic the symmetry of the fabric is thereby increased toward tetragonal symmetry (cf. pages 376 to 378; Fig. 4-33*a* and *b*).

A natural fold system in the Dalradian schists of Argyllshire[12] has obvious affinities with the hypothetical examples illustrated in Fig. 14-4. It is a plane noncylindrical system with very high (nearly tetragonal) symmetry, and can be resolved into two plane noncylindrical systems with mutually perpendicular axial planes. Roberts[13] attributed the structure to single deformation in a tetragonal stress field. However, since no homogeneous stress state (denoted by a tensor) can have tetragonal symmetry, a more likely condition, and one equally compatible with symmetry argument (cf. page 386), is a state of axially symmetric stress.

Other geologists have interpreted complex systems of folds as products of simultaneous folding and cross-folding.[14] Flinn[15] attributes simultaneous buckling and cross-buckling and related axes of shortening to a critical orientation of the deformed layer with reference to the principal axes of bulk mean strain.

Superposed Folding. The commonest cause of noncylindrical systems of mesoscopic folds in tectonites may prove to be the oblique superposition of a second generation of folds on an earlier system as a result of repeated deformation. The existence of such systems has been conclusively demonstrated in widely scattered parts of the earth's crust, but the genetic relation between the component systems is not always clear. Some examples must represent the combined effects of two or more deformations widely separated in time; in others the later episode appears to have followed closely upon the first. In a few instances the earlier of two generations of structures in one part of a tectonite body seems to correlate with the later generation elsewhere.

A system of noncylindrical folds formed by repeated folding is seldom homogeneous on a large scale. But it is usually possible to outline

[12] J. L. Roberts, Fold structures in the Dalradian rocks of Knapadale, Argyllshire, *Geol. Mag.*, vol. 96, pp. 221–229, 1959.

[13] *Ibid.*, p. 228.

[14] Of historic interest are references given by Lord Avebury (*The Scenery of England and Wales*, pp. 183–186, Macmillan, New York, 1902) to opinions of classic writers such as Charles Darwin, Bertrand, de Lapparent, and Lapworth regarding the phenomena of complex folding.

[15] D. Flinn, On folding during three-dimensional progressive strain, *Geol. Soc. London Quart. Jour.* (in press), abstract *Geol. Soc. London Circ. 94*, November, 1961; cited with kind permission of the author.

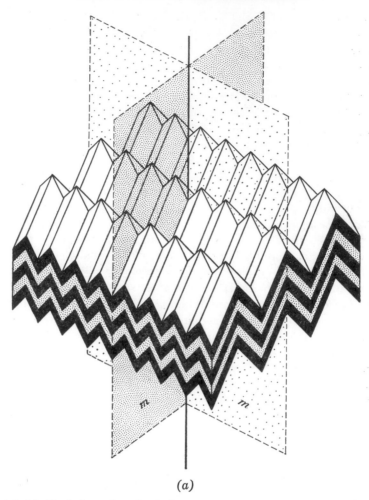

(a)

FIG. 14-4. Idealized shear domains in homogeneous fold systems. (*a*) Superposed plane systems with both axial planes (*m*) as symmetry planes. (*b*) Approach to tetragonal symmetry where folds are of the same size.

smaller homogeneous domains containing folds of both generations. For the general case the symmetry of such a domain is triclinic. However, Sander[16] has pointed out that oblique homogeneous superposition of a fold system with vertical axial planes on an initial fold system with vertical axial planes can give rise to a fabric with a vertical diad axis of symmetry which he terms a "digyre."

The following general properties characterize superposed folds of the kind under discussion (cf. pages 494 to 501):

[16] Sander, *op. cit.*, pp. 180–181.

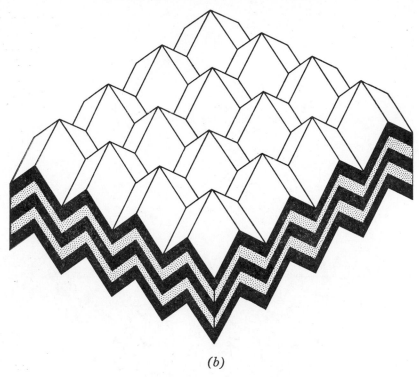

(b)

FIG. 14-4. *(Continued)*

1. The folds of the first generation are nonplane noncylindrical, with cylindrically folded axial surfaces.

2. The folds of the second generation are plane noncylindrical or nonplane noncylindrical.

3. The movement picture of the second folding depends on the fold mechanism. Thus if the second folding involves buckling or flexural slip each cylindrical segment of a second fold corresponds to a local regular but heterogeneous deformation; even for a domain of homogeneous superposition the symmetry of the total movement picture is then triclinic. Where the second deformation is by slip folding the kinematic axes can be constantly oriented within a given domain so that higher symmetry of movement is possible.

KINEMATIC SIGNIFICANCE OF PATTERNS OF PREFOLDING LINEATIONS

General.   Lineation syngenetic with cylindrical folding is generally parallel to the fold axes (e.g., Fig. 14-2c).   An earlier lineation that predates folding, on the other hand, is usually distorted in individual folds and throughout the fold system as a whole.   Its statistically established

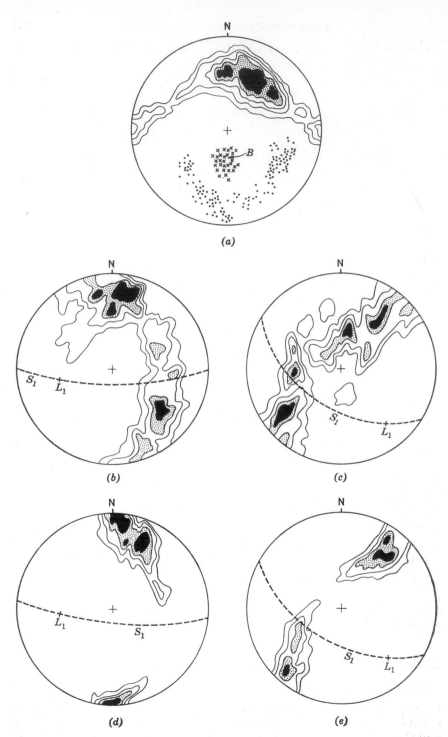

FIG. 14-5. For descriptive legend see opposite page.

pattern within a large domain is then a valuable guide to the mechanism of folding within the system. The technique can be applied to any domain of plane cylindrical folding, whether homogeneous in all respects or not.

Illustrative Examples. *In Systems of Flexural-slip Folds.* Figure 14-5 shows structural data for a restricted domain about a mile wide within a body of Moinian and Lewisian rocks in the vicinity of Loch Luichart, northern Scotland.[17]   In Fig. 14-5a poles of a foliation S_1 fall on the contoured great-circle girdle whose axis coincides with the center of concentration of late lineations (crosses) and so defines a B axis of late cylindrical folding.   An early lineation L_1 (dots) is dispersed in a small circle about B as required by a model of late flexural-slip folding (page 478). The data are equally consistent with a homogeneous domain of small mesoscopic folds or with a heterogeneous domain of one or two large folds.   Orientation diagrams for [0001] of quartz and {001} poles of mica in representative specimens (Fig. 14-5b to e) show that on the scale of a hand specimen the fabric is homotactic.   The axes of the quartz and mica girdles coincide with the local early lineation L_1.   This condition also is consistent with flexure folding of S_1 and simultaneous external rotation of the quartz and mica subfabrics about B without substantial change of the mineral orientation patterns.   Here is an instance where "unrolling" about B to bring S_1 and L_1 of both diagrams into coincidence would restore the initial preferred orientation pattern of quartz with respect to internal coordinates.

In Systems of Slip Folds.   Data consistent with regional slip folding recorded by Best[18] for phyllites of the western foothills of the Sierra Nevada, California, are presented in Fig. 14-6.   The whole body is a system of noncylindrical folds in a foliation S, resulting from superposition of two episodes of folding.   Within it are smaller domains of plane cylindrical folds of the second generation.   Data for one such domain are reproduced in Fig. 14-6a and b.   Diagram a shows an old lineation L_1 (lying in the folded S_1) dispersed in a great-circle pattern consistent with deformation by slip folding.   Assuming this mechanism, the a kinematic

---

[17] P. Clifford, The geological structure of the Loch Luichart area, Ross-shire, *Geol. Soc. London Quart. Jour.*, vol. 115, p. 377, fig. 9-D9, 1960.

[18] M. Best, Petrology and structural analysis of metamorphic rocks in the Southwest Sierra Nevada Foothills, California, *Univ. California Geol. Sci. Pub.* (in press).

FIG. 14-5. Structural data from domain of cylindrical folding, Loch Luichart, Ross-shire, Scotland.   (*After P. Clifford.*)   (a) Poles to foliation S_1 (contoured), early lineations L_1 within S_1 (dots), late lineations synchronous with folding (crosses), mean axis of late folding (B).   (b) and (c) 200 [0001] axes of quartz in each of two representative rocks.   Contours, 4%, 3%, 2%, 1%, per 1% area.   (d) and (e) 100 poles of {001} of mica in same specimens as b and c.   Contours, 8%, 4%, 2%, 1%, per 1% area.

axis is given by the intersection of the great circle of best fit on the lineation diagram (broken arc, Fig. 14-6b) and the statistically defined axial
plane of folds in S_1 (full arc).   The b axis lies in the axial plane normal to
a.   Unfortunately the folded rocks are unsuitable for analysis of a quartz

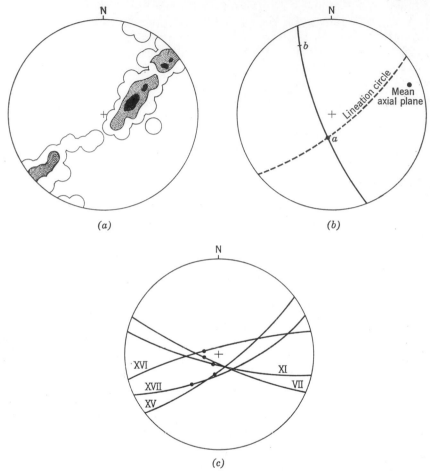

FIG. 14-6. Structural data for complexly folded phyllites, Mariposa area, Sierra
Nevada foothills, California. (*After M. Best.*) (*a*) 50 early lineations L_1 bent by
late plane cylindrical folding in a small domain. Contours, 12%, 8%, 2%, per 1%
area. (*b*) Graphic location of a and b kinematic axes from the data of diagram a,
assuming slip folding. (*c*) Great circles of best fit for early lineations L_1, drawn for
each of five adjacent domains (numbered in Roman numerals). Solid circles are
a kinematic axes constructed as in diagram b.

subfabric whose symmetry would confirm or disprove the folding mechanism.   Other domains show similar but differently oriented great-circle
patterns for L_1.   Figure 14-6c shows the great circle of best fit for L_1 in
each of five adjacent domains, together with the geometrically con-

structed a kinematic axis for each. The five a axes are closely clustered in an area where the five L_1 circles also intersect. Best concludes that the pattern of L_1 and the system of second-generation folds reflect a regionally

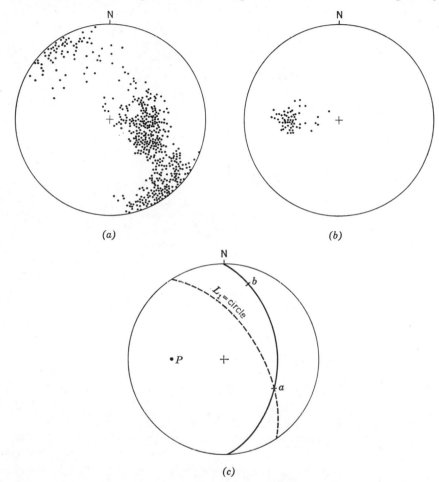

(a)

(b)

(c)

Fig. 14-7. Structural data for domains of repeated folding, north of Loch Hourn, Scottish Highlands. (*After J. G. Ramsay.*) (a) Early lineations L_1 in a domain of late folding of S_1. (b) Poles of axial planes S_2 from same domain. (c) Kinematic axes located from the same data assuming a dominant mechanism of slip folding. P = pole of mean axial plane.

homogeneous movement picture the a axis of which is uniformly oriented throughout the five domains considered.

In an area of repeated folding of high-grade metamorphic rocks near Loch Hourn, Scottish Highlands,[19] the latest folding of the foliation S_1

[19] J. G. Ramsay, The deformation of early linear structures in areas of repeated folding, *Jour. Geology*, vol. 68, pp. 81–88, 1960.

has dispersed an old lineation L_1 in a great-circle pattern (Fig. 14-7a). The folds so formed show strong preferred orientation of axial planes S_2 (Fig. 14-7b). If a mechanism of slip folding is assumed for the heterogeneous component of the final deformation, the a kinematic axis of the regional movement picture is given as before by the intersection of the great circle of best fit for L_1 and the great circle corresponding to the mean attitude of S_2 (Fig. 14-7c). The b kinematic axis lies normal to a in S_2. A test of the assumed mechanism of folding could be provided by orientation patterns for [0001] in quartz—unfortunately not available. A collective diagram should show a symmetry plane normal to the deduced b axis of movement.

UNROLLING OF COMPLEX FOLDS BY GRAPHIC CONSTRUCTION

The General Problem. The aim of one kind of kinematic analysis (page 9) is to restore the deformed body to its initial shape and orientation, and thereby to analyze in reverse the displacements and strain that constitute the deformation. This approach is possible—at least theoretically—where the deformed body contains folded s-surfaces with correspondingly distorted lineations. Sander and coworkers of the Innsbruck school have developed graphic techniques collectively termed "constructive unrolling" (*Konstruktive Rückformungen*), and have applied these in attempts to decipher the kinematic history of folded tectonites.[20]

The techniques of unrolling are based upon several assumptions:

1. The folded set of s-surfaces was planar at the time of formation. If they are bedding surfaces they were initially horizontal with recognizable top and bottom.

2. Distorted lineations were rectilinear at the time of formation. It is also commonly assumed that they were horizontal.

3. Upon folding of a set of s-surfaces containing a lineation about an axis oblique to the lineation, the lineation moves on a small circle of the projection.

Sander clearly states that he is considering only folding arising by flexural slip. Shear folds (in which the paths followed by distorted lineations are not small circles of the projection) are considered by him to be "nonunrollable."

Ideal Hypothetical Examples. The potentialities and limitations of the unrolling technique may be illustrated by hypothetical examples

---

[20] Sander, *op. cit.*, pp. 170–184. For applications to specific problems see also A. Fuchs, Untersuchen am tektonischen Gefüge der Tiroler Alpen II (Kalkalpen Achensee Kaisergebirge), *Neues Jahrb. Mineralogie*, vol. 88, pp. 337–373, 1944; F. Karl, Analytisch-Tektonische Studien an Gesteinen des Gerlostales, *Neues Jahrb. Geologie u. Paläontologie Monatsh.*, vol. 1, pp. 5–24, 1952; M. Lindström, Tectonics of the area between Mt. Keron and Lake Allesjaure in the Caledonides of Swedish Lapland, *Lunds Univ. Årsskr.*, N.F., avd. 2, vol. 53, pp. 3–33, 1957.

without regard to scale. They are applicable alike to fold systems and to single folds.

Example 1. Let S be a set of s-surfaces, with recognizable top and bottom (denoted by arrow), containing an early lineation L_1 and folded cylindrically about a horizontal axis B_2. All attitudes of S may be

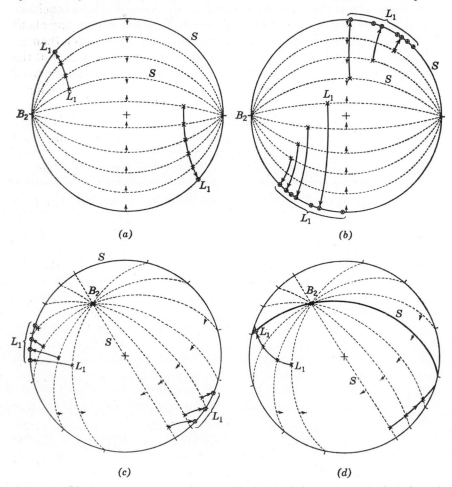

(a)   (b)

(c)   (d)

Fig. 14-8. Ideal examples of graphic unrolling of folded s-surfaces S (dotted arcs) containing early lineations L_1 (crosses). The axis of unrolling is the fold axis B_2 of folds in S. Circled crosses are unrolled L_1. All projections on the geographic horizontal plane. For further explanation, see text.

returned to the horizontal plane by rotation about B_2; and at the same time the corresponding L_1 lineations are brought to coincidence at a unique point on the primitive circle of the projection (circled cross in Fig. 14-8a). If the direction of top and bottom in each segment of S were not known, the sense of unrolling about B_2 would be uncertain;

however, trial and error would show that rotation of one group of s-surfaces in one sense and the other group in the opposite sense would bring L_2 lineations into coincidence.

Sander considers (and we agree) that the above-described behavior of L_1 on rotation—which depends on the original small-circle pattern of L_1 around B_2—shows that L_1 is older than B_2. Conversely Sander concludes that if L_1 does not lie on a small circle about B_2 (so that unrolling about B_2 fails to bring L_1 lineations into coincidence), L_1 is younger than B_2 (cf. Fig. 14-8b). This is certainly one possibility (cf. Fig. 4-30). But the same pattern also is possible for an old L_1 lineation that has been dispersed by some mechanism of folding about B_2 other than flexural-slip folding—a common situation in tectonites. In fold systems where data are treated statistically, especially where the amplitude of folds is small and the L_1 girdle correspondingly incomplete, it may be difficult to decide whether or not the L_1 girdle is a small circle of the projection.

Example 2. Let the fold in S be a cylindrical fold with a plunging axis B_2 (Fig. 14-8c and d). To bring S and L_1 horizontal it is necessary to make an arbitrary choice between several alternative compound unrolling procedures.

a. B_2 is first rotated into a horizontal attitude, and then both S and L_1 are unrolled into the horizontal plane about B_2 as in Fig. 14-8a or b. But in the first step B_2 can be rotated about any axis normal to it, so that the orientation of the fold at the end of the first step is subject to wide variation. One may ask what, if any, tectonic significance can be attached to the initial leveling of B_2?

b. Each plane segment of S is brought to the horizontal by rotation about its strike (Fig. 14-8c). This is an artificial geometric procedure. It does not retrace in reverse a possible path of deformation, nor does it bring the L_2 lineations (circled crosses) into coincidence on the primitive circle of the projection.

c. S segments are rotated about B_2 into a common plane (heavy arc of Fig. 14-8d) and this is then brought to the horizontal by rotation about the strike. Whereas this procedure could retrace in reverse a *possible* deformation path, there is no certainty that the *actual* deformation path has been retraced.

The difficulties and uncertainties inherent in unrolling procedures have been emphasized by Sander.[21] Even a method of trial and error resulting in the closest grouping of L_1 attitudes around a mean horizontal trend cannot lead to a satisfactory unique solution. We prefer to apply the technique of unrolling only to cases, as described below, where it is not necessary to make arbitrary assumptions as to the axis of unrolling.

Unrolling about Uniquely Determined Rotation Axes. Consider the unrolling of the complex superposed folds illustrated in Fig. 13-16. Fig-

[21] Sander, *op. cit.*, pp. 170–179.

ure 14-9a shows plotted structures in the folded body: planar segments of S_1 (full arcs) from three cylindrical domains (I, II, and III, Fig. 13-16e), and two lineations contained in S—an older L_1 (crosses) and a later L_2 (circled dots). The L_2 points of each domain lie in a small circle; and the three small circles for the three domains intersect in a point O. For each domain S_1, L_1, and L_2 are unrolled about the axis of the appropriate L_2 small circle (respectively R_I to R_{III}), thus bringing L_2 to O; at the same time the S_1 segments of each domain become coplanar, and the L_1 lineations of each domain are brought to coincidence. Figure 14-9b shows the result of unrolling—the form of the fold about $B_{S_1}{}^{S_2}$ prior to superposition of the last generation of folds. Further unrolling of this

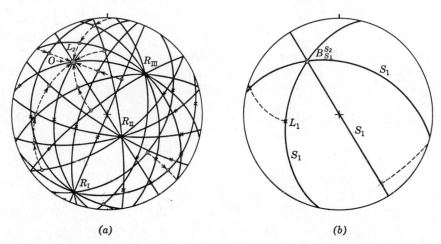

(a)   (b)

Fig. 14-9. Graphic unrolling of (a) complex fold—cf. Fig. 13-16—to give (b) the form of the fold prior to the last episode of folding. For explanation, see text.

fold is impossible without making arbitrary assumptions as to the initial orientation of S_1 and L_1, and will yield no certain information regarding the movement picture of the first episode of folding.

Reconstruction of Pre-tectonite Structures. Unrolling techniques have been used to establish the orientation of inherited nontectonite structures such as sedimentary lineations and paleomagnetic directions in initially horizontal strata prior to folding. These procedures are attended by the possibility of significant error:

1. Tilted beds of uniform dip are commonly unrolled into the horizontal position by rotation about the strike. This is completely satisfactory only where the tilted bed is part of a simple fold system with a horizontal fold axis. For beds that are tilted but not folded the axis of rotation may be any line in the planes P_2 and P_3 of Fig. 3-6b (where L_1 is vertical and L_2 is the pole of the tilted bed). The restored position of a linear marker in the unrolled bed depends on the selected axis of unrolling.

2. If, as in all metamorphic tectonites, the original folding is accompanied by penetrative movement within the tilted body, the position of the lineation with respect to coordinates within the layer (e.g., the strike) will change during deformation.[22]   Simple unrolling takes no account of this, even for simply tilted beds.

3. Beds folded about plunging axes are subject to the same restrictions as those discussed with respect to unrolling of lineations (page 518).   It is necessary to assume arbitrary axes of rotation so that no unique solution to the problem is possible.

HOMOGENEOUS FOLD SYSTEMS AND MEAN STRAINS

On any given scale a homogeneous fold system is the result of deformation that also is statistically homogeneous.   But, particularly in systems of slip folds, there need be no simple relation between the principal axes of mean strain and the geometric elements of the fold system.   The following general conclusions are based on symmetry argument:

1. A homoaxial homogeneous system of folds with orthorhombic symmetry of total fabric has three symmetry planes in common with the pure-strain component of mean deformation—the AB, BC, and AC planes of the mean strain ellipsoid.   Identification of individual planes of the fold system with particular planes of strain is possible only on the basis of criteria other than symmetry.   It is likely, for example, that the axial plane of the folds can be equated with AB of the ellipsoid.   On symmetry grounds it is probable that there is no rotational component of strain.

2. Homoaxial homogeneous fold systems with monoclinic total fabrics have a single symmetry plane (normal to the fold axis) which is also a symmetry plane of the pure-strain component of deformation.   The orientation of the remaining two symmetry planes (assuming a triaxial ellipsoid of mean strain) and the relative magnitude of the principal strains cannot be deduced on grounds of symmetry.   If the mean strain includes a rotational component the axis of rotation is most likely to be normal to the single plane of symmetry of the structure.

3. Heteroaxial homogeneous fold systems with triclinic total fabrics (e.g., plane cylindrical systems with discordant subfabrics, or nonplane and noncylindrical systems) provide no indication of the orientation of the symmetry planes of the pure-strain component of mean deformation. Likewise, the orientation of the axis of the rotational component that is generally present is unknown.

Bodies with low symmetry, therefore, even where homogeneous, cannot generally be interpreted directly in terms of strain on the basis of symmetry arguments.   Other criteria must be used in strain analysis; and

[22] J. G. Ramsay, The effects of folding upon the orientation of sedimentation structures, *Jour. Geol.*, vol. 69, pp. 84–100, 1961.

of these by far the most important is the distortion of passive dimensional or angular markers such as oolites, pebbles, or fossils. Many such studies have been published.[23]

RHEOLOGIC ASPECTS OF FOLDING IN TECTONITES

General. The stress-strain relations existing in folding processes, as in all natural deformations, depend upon the physical or rheologic state of the body during deformation. No direct observations can be made on the actual physical condition of rocks during the formation of natural folds. The geologist is therefore forced to attack the problem indirectly in one or more of the following ways:

1. Ideal rheologic properties and combinations of such properties are assumed, and by use of mathematical models the theoretical form of resulting folds is predicted. Comparison of features of theoretically deduced folds with natural structures may show whether the model is realistic.

2. Scale-model experiments are made in which materials with suitably scaled-down rheologic properties are arranged in layers and experimentally deformed to produce folds. Where the resulting structures resemble natural fold systems it may be permissible to extrapolate from the dynamic and kinetic conditions of experiment to those of folding in a natural environment.

3. Some rocks can be folded under laboratory conditions.[24] But there is no guarantee that natural conditions are being duplicated. The mechanism of flow (crystal gliding versus recrystallization), the magnitude of stress, and the rate of strain are likely to differ greatly in natural as compared with experimental deformation.

4. Some aspects of the state of stress in homogeneously stressed bodies may be deduced from symmetry argument.

[23] Among the more recent are the following: J. Ladurner, Zur Kenntnis des Gefüges "gestreckter" Belemniten, *Tschermaks mineralog. petrog. Mitt.*, vol. 44, pp. 479–494, 1933; H. Cloos, Oölite deformation in the South Mountain fold, Maryland, *Geol. Soc. America Bull.*, vol. 58, pp. 843–918, 1947; C. Oftedahl, Deformation of quartz conglomerates in Central Norway, *Jour. Geology*, vol. 56, pp. 476–487, 1948; D. Flinn, On the deformation of the Funzie conglomerate, Fetlar, Shetland, *Jour. Geology*, vol. 64, pp. 480–505, 1956; G. Voll, New work on petrofabrics, *Liverpool and Manchester Geol. Jour.*, vol. 2, pp. 536–544, 1960; W. F. Brace, Analysis of large two dimensional strain in deformed rocks, *21st Internat. Geol. Cong. Rept.* (1960), pt. 18, pp. 261–269, 1960; H. J. Koark, Zur deformation des Venna-Konglomerates in Trondheim-Gebiete, Norwegen, *Upsala Univ. Geol. Inst. Bull.*, vol. 40, pp. 139–161, 1961; W. F. Brace, Mohr construction in the analysis of large geologic strain, *Geol. Soc. America Bull.*, vol. 72, pp. 1059–1080, 1961.

[24] E.g., M. S. Paterson and L. E. Weiss, Experimental folding in rocks, preliminary report in *Nature*, vol. 195, No. 4846, pp. 1046–1048, 1962.

A detailed treatment of folding as a rheologic phenomenon is beyond the scope of this book. Instead we review briefly such conclusions regarding forces and stresses in relation to folding of tectonites as are consistent with currently available data.

Some Conclusions Based on the Analytic Approach. The problem has been approached analytically by a number of writers.[25] In particular Flinn has predicted the attitudes in which fold axes will develop in a surface of any general orientation within a body undergoing homogeneous pure strain. His analysis relates the orientation of fold axes to the principal axes of the strain ellipsoid, as follows:

Any planar layer cuts the mean strain ellipsoid in a section whose outline, in the general case, is elliptical. Its principal axes are termed the principal directions of the section. One of these is a direction of compression (shortening of the whole body) or of extension (elongation). On the assumption that different layers have different rheologic properties—i.e., that they vary in competence—it is predicted (1) that folding by buckling can occur parallel to a principal direction of a section whose other principal direction is one of compression; (2) that parting giving rise to boudinage can occur parallel to a principal direction of a section whose other direction is one of extension.

Some Results from Model Experiments. The theory of scale-model experiments in geology has been discussed by Hubbert.[26] In scale-model experiments related to problems of folding,[27] the initial body consists of parallel planar layers having different or in some cases similar rheologic properties. Some general conclusions with regard to folding seem warranted:

[25] H. Ramberg, Evolution of ptygmatic folding, *Norsk geol. tidsskr.*, vol. 39, pp. 99–151, 1959; Relationship between length of arc and thickness in ptygmatically folded veins, *Am. Jour. Sci.*, vol. 258, pp. 36–46, 1960; M. A. Biot, Theory of folding of stratified viscoelastic media and its implications in tectonics and orogenesis, *Geol. Soc. America Bull.*, vol. 72, pp. 1595–1620, 1961; Flinn, *op. cit.*, 1961 (cited by kind permission of the author).

[26] M. K. Hubbert, Theory of scale models as applied to the study of geologic structures, *Geol. Soc. America Bull.*, vol. 48, pp. 1459–1520, 1937.

[27] Selected references are as follows: H. M. Cadell, Experimental researches in mountain building, *Royal Soc. Edinburgh Trans.*, vol. 35, pp. 337–357, 1888; R. T. Chamberlin and F. P. Shephard, Some experiments in folding, *Jour. Geology*, vol. 31, pp. 490–512, 1923; P. H. Kuenen and L. U. De Sitter, Experimental investigation into the mechanism of folding, *Leidche geol. Medd.*, 10, pp. 217–239, 1938; W. H. Bucher, Role of gravity in orogenesis, *Geol. Soc. America Bull.*, vol. 67, pp. 1295–1318, 1956; S. Bhattacherji, Theoretical and experimental investigation on cross folding, *Jour. Geology*, vol. 66, pp. 625–667, 1958; Ramberg, *op. cit.*, pp. 99–151; A. R. McBirney and M. Best, Experimental deformation of viscous layers in oblique stress fields, *Geol. Soc. America Bull.*, vol. 72, pp. 495–498, 1961; M. A. Biot, H. Odé, W. L. Roever, Experimental verification of the theory of folding of stratified viscoelastic media, *Geol. Soc. America Bull.*, vol. 72, pp. 1621–1632, 1961.

1. Where thin layers of high viscosity are enclosed in a matrix of low viscosity, deformation tends to form folds in the more viscous layers.

a. Ramberg[28] enclosed plasticine strips or sheets in putty with a lower viscosity. A rectangular body with this structure was constrained between wooden boards. Tangential tractions were then applied to the upper and lower surfaces by sideways motion of the boards in opposite senses to give what is termed a "simple-shear" type of deformation. Results for strips of three different initial orientations (1, 1′, and 1″) are illustrated in Fig. 14-10 in terms of four successive stages of deformation numbered 2 to 5. The nature and degree of folding are seen to depend upon the orientation of the layers with reference to the mean strain axes and the stress axes. Some layers at certain stages (e.g., 4′) develop asymmetric folds, others at the same stage (e.g., 4) develop symmetric

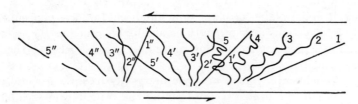

FIG. 14-10. Deformation of plastic strips enclosed in putty constrained between boards (above and below) undergoing translational movement. (*After H. Ramberg.*) Initial configurations of three strips are 1, 1′, and 1″.

folds (cf. Fig. 14-1). Some layers, folded at an early stage, later assume a more nearly planar configuration (e.g., 3′ → 5′). Some layers are scarcely folded at all and even develop boudinage as a result of extension and fracture (e.g., 1″ → 5″)—much in accordance with Flinn's subsequent analysis (page 522). In another experiment[29] layers of different initial orientation simultaneously develop folds and boudinage respectively. An important conclusion drawn from photographs of Ramberg's material[30] is that axial planes of buckle folds, initially at least, develop subparallel to the *AB* plane of the ellipsoid of mean strain.

b. McBirney and Best[31] found an approximate correlation, as predicted by Ramberg,[32] between the amplitude of folds and (1) the thickness of the more viscous layers and (2) the ratio of the viscosities of the two materials. They found too that at very slow rates of deformation the surfaces of separation of the two media are almost passive in their behavior so that folding is minor or fails to develop.

[28] Ramberg, *op. cit.*, pp. 124–126, fig. 125.
[29] *Ibid.*, p. 130.
[30] *Ibid.*, pls. 1–6.
[31] McBirney and Best, *op. cit.*, p. 497.
[32] Ramberg, *op. cit.*, pp. 131–151.

2. Folds analogous to slip folds in passive s-surfaces may develop in color-banded material of uniform rheologic properties.[33] Folding reflects instability in flow rather than buckling of layers.

3. Plane folds can develop with axial planes approximately normal to a direction of compression and maximum shortening. McBirney and Best[34] applied oblique compression to a previously folded body and were able to impose a system of secondary plane noncylindrical folds and accompanying axial linear structures upon the earlier folds. They conclude as follows: "The orientation of linear features and fold axes produced by deformation of viscous materials is determined by the intersection of the layered surface and a plane normal to the direction of maximum shortening and is independent of the orientation of the minimum and intermediate bulk strain axes. Large components of strain are possible in the direction of fold axes." If this conclusion is justified in general, the axial planes of plane noncylindrical fold systems superposed on early fold systems may prove to be a valuable guide to the orientation of the axis of greatest mean shortening and possibly also to the axis of greatest principal stress σ_1.

Some Conclusions Based on Symmetry Argument. Several general conclusions may be drawn from applying the principles of symmetry to tectonic situations involving folding:

1. Homogeneous homoaxial fold systems with orthorhombic total fabrics are symmetric to the axes of principal stress, i.e., one principal stress axis is normal to each of the planes of symmetry of the fabric. For example, the axes of the three principal stresses must lie normal to the axial plane, parallel to the fold axis B, and normal to B within the axial plane, in any symmetric system of plane cylindrical homoaxial folds. The relative magnitudes of the principal stresses respectively correlated with each of these fabric directions can be determined only from criteria other than symmetry. Probably σ_1 is always normal to the axial plane.

2. In a homogeneous homoaxial fold system with monoclinic total fabric, one axis of principal stress is normal to the symmetry plane of the fabric. The directions of the other two stress axes are indeterminate.

3. On the basis of symmetry alone it is not possible to correlate the fabric of a fold system having triclinic total symmetry with the axes of principal stress.

Any such correlation as the above carries the implication of elastico-viscous behavior in which stresses are supported and transmitted by flowing rocks and can in certain cases give rise to buckling and even necking leading ultimately to fracture. There is, however, the possibility that under some metamorphic conditions the rheologic behavior of the deformed body may be more truly viscous. Such a state has been invoked, for example, to explain similar folds in tectonites. Indeed such

[33] Bucher, *op. cit.*, p. 1303, pl. 4, fig. 2.
[34] McBirney and Best, *op. cit.*, p. 496. See also Ramberg, *op. cit.*, pp. 126–127.

behavior in the upper part of the earth's mantle and the deeper levels of the crust is required by the theory of isostasy.

The flow is laminar with the flow lines essentially vertical. The only strain during flow is the viscous shear strain between successive laminae. There is no flow across the flow laminae. The angle of shear is constant throughout the vertical length of any lamina so long as the boundaries of the lamina are parallel, but the angle of shear will diminish as they diverge, and vice versa. The constancy of volume demands that the width of any bed measured in the direction of the flow laminae remains constant so long as the flow laminae are parallel (the area of a parallelogram between parallel lines is constant) but the thickness in this direction is reduced or increased as the flow laminae diverge or converge. . . . A . . . factor which may contribute to changes in thickness of beds is differential rheidity. If one bed has a lower rheidity than the others, it will flow with a greater velocity under the same stress difference. It will therefore tend to become diapiric towards the others even though they are also flowing into rheid folds.[35]

In this quotation, which refers specifically to upward flow in salt domes, we recognize many of the geometric properties observed in similar folds of tectonites. Carey believes that rheid flow, essentially viscous in nature, involves transport of material along a pressure gradient—from a region of high to a region of lower pressure, e.g., from deeper to higher levels in the earth's crust. Geometrically there is a close analogy between "rheid folds" as described by Carey and our models of slip folding.

In conclusion we cite an additional recent statement with regard to essentially viscous behavior of rocks under metamorphic conditions.

Within a lower stress range rocks are elastic for fast deformations and tend to behave approximately like a viscous medium for slow deformations. Results of the theory indicate that the viscous behavior predominates in tectonic folding. This leads to large deformations without fracture, and the dependence of fracture on deformation rates. . . .

If one assumes that rocks behave as a purely viscous solid, significant folding may appear under relatively low tectonic stresses. However, in such a case the influence of gravity becomes important near the surface and may be sufficient to prevent folding. Even deep folds may be blocked by the presence of a stabilizing density gradient.[36]

So uncertainty as to rheologic behavior of rocks undergoing metamorphism clouds the dynamic interpretation of fold systems just as it obscures the dynamic significance of foliation, lineation, and all other elements in the tectonite fabric. The ground on which we stand is firmer when our interpretation of folds and fold systems is framed in terms of strain and the movement picture of deformation.

[35] W. Carey, The rheid concept in geotectonics, *Geol. Soc. Australia Jour.*, vol. 1, p. 92, 1953.
[36] Biot, *op. cit.*

POSTSCRIPT

CHAPTER 15

TREND OF STRUCTURAL ANALYSIS

The broadly statistical geometric procedure of structural analysis was first applied to microscopic subfabrics, more particularly to elucidation of patterns of preferred orientation of minerals in tectonites. But it is a mistake to think of structural analysis as a technique restricted or even principally appropriate to the microscopic scale. Sander first developed his procedure to investigate microscopically the fabric of rocks already studied in great detail in the field. In later years he brought it to bear upon mesoscopic and macroscopic structures, especially upon folds, fold systems, and the varied patterns of s-surfaces and lineations associated with these structures. This, too, has been the principal objective of structural analysis during the past decade in Britain.

On the descriptive side the data of structural analysis relate principally to (1) preferred orientation of tectonite minerals and (2) the geometric properties of folded s-surfaces and lineations. To date our knowledge of the former—however imperfect our interpretation—is reasonably complete; but much still remains to be found out with regard to the geometric complexities of folding, for in most tectonites there is evidence of repeated deformation and corresponding superposition of one fold system upon another. The geometry and significance of folding as set out in this book are based on only the simplest of models and do not fully portray the complexities of folds to be expected in nature. Moreover, all too little is known about the relation of preferred orientation of individual minerals to folding. Future studies embracing analysis of both mesoscopic structure (especially folded s-surfaces and lineations) and patterns of mineral orientation on the microscopic scale cannot but prove fruitful. Likewise much important information is to be obtained by more intense study of relations between mineral phases crystallized during successive periods of deformation.

Experimental deformation of minerals and rocks under geologically possible conditions has already yielded valuable data on the nature and significance of preferred orientation of minerals and the possible rheologic states to be expected in the materials from which tectonites evolve in nature. Within the next decade we can confidently expect further information regarding other minerals—notably quartz and mica—whose behavior to date has been only imperfectly explored.   Particularly to be desired are data relating to creep—i.e., to the all-important factor of time in natural deformation—and to the role of recrystallization in the evolution of the tectonite fabric and the generation of structures such as folds and foliations.   A start has already been made in all of these directions.

With this general picture in mind we may expect that the content of Parts I and II of this book will soon need to be extended in scope and modified in some detail.   That of Part III will undoubtedly need drastic revision as well as extension.   But in spite of inevitable extension, modification, and revision of the kind just envisaged, the basic foundation of structural analysis can be expected to survive—just as it has in the decades immediately past—the test of future observation and experiment. In particular we emphasize three facets of this foundation, all initiated and developed by Sander: The material appropriate for structural analysis will continue to be defined and limited by the subtle concept of the statistically homogeneous tectonite fabric.   Interpretation of tectonites to the fullest possible degree will still be framed in terms of the movement picture.   And the prime criterion by means of which a tectonite fabric can be correlated with movement, strain, or stress will continue to be its symmetry.

INDEX